P9-CJH-787

INSTRUCTOR'S MANUAL FOR

GENETICS
THE CONTINUITY OF LIFE

W. RALPH ANDERSEN

DANIEL J. FAIRBANKS

Brigham Young University

Brooks/Cole
Thomson Learning

Pacific Grove • Albany • Belmont • Boston • Cincinnati • Johannesburg • London • Madrid • Melbourne
Mexico City • New York • Scottsdale • Singapore • Tokyo • Toronto

COPYRIGHT© 1999 by Brooks/Cole
A division of Thomson Learning
The Thomson Learning logo is a trademark used herein under license.

For more information, contact:

BROOKS/COLE PUBLISHING COMPANY
511 Forest Lodge Road
Pacific Grove, CA 93950
USA
www.brookscole.com

All rights reserved. Instructors of classes using Fairbanks/Andersen's *Genetics: The Continuity of Life* as a textbook may reproduce material from this publication for classroom use. Otherwise, the text of this publication may not be reproduced, stored in a retrieval system, or transcribed, in any form or by any means—electronic, mechanical, photocopying, recording, or otherwise—without the prior written permission of the publisher, Brooks/Cole Publishing Company, Pacific Grove, California 93950.

Printed in the United States of America.

5   4   3   2   1

ISBN 0-534-25276-1

Contents

Contents

Introduction

Genetics: The Continuity of Life is a groundbreaking textbook with a novel organization that proceeds logically from molecules to cells to organisms to populations. It establishes a molecular foundation early so that all aspects of genetics can be taught in a modern molecular context. It also has a strong focus on genetic analysis, relying on analysis of real data from published sources in the worked examples and end-of-chapter problems to teach students how genetics is practiced in the real world.

The molecular-first approach and the focus on analysis of real data provide distinct advantages to students as they learn genetics. They learn transmission genetics in a modern molecular context, rather than as a historical part of genetics whose time has passed. They can forge connections between Mendelian and molecular genetics easily. From the first day of class, professors can teach their students the way most geneticists think when tackling real genetic research.

However, these approaches also provide some unique challenges to professors. Many professors have taught for years using the standard Mendel-first approach and the change to a molecular-first approach is not always easy. It also is not easy for students to analyze real data, although the analysis of real data prepares students to think as scientists do much better than the fabricated data in the end-of-chapter problems of most textbooks. When students work with real data, they are often challenged with ambiguities, sampling error, alternative interpretations, and tentative conclusions, just as professional researchers are. Professors must show students teach students how to avoid some the pitfalls that are inherent when working with real data.

This manual is intended to help professors deal with these challenges and gain the greatest advantages when using *Genetics: The Continuity of Life*. The first section provides a conversion guide with a set of suggestions on how to change from a Mendel-first to a molecular-first approach. The second section contains a course organization guide with a set of suggested syllabi and hints on how to organize different types of genetics courses. The third section consists of individual chapter reviews with key concepts, key terms, chapter topics, and chapter outlines to assist professors as they organize their lectures. The fourth section focuses on how to use the end-of-chapter problems to teach genetic analysis. It rates each problem by its level of difficulty and includes detailed solutions to all end-of-chapter questions and problems. The solutions are the same as those in the student solutions manual, *Student Companion to Genetics: The Continuity of Life*.

We hope that you find *Genetics: The Continuity of Life* to be a valuable resource for your genetics course. For additional aids in teaching the course, consult our website at http://www.brookscole.com/biology. You may also contact Daniel Fairbanks (the senior author) directly at the following e-mail address which is specifically designated for questions and comments related to the textbook: fairbanks_genetics@byu.edu.

Section 1
Conversion Guide: How to Move from a Mendel-First to a Molecular-First Approach

As transmission and population genetics have become firmly grounded in molecular biology, many professors have reorganized their genetics courses to teach with a molecular-first approach. *Genetics: The Continuity of Life* is designed for the increasing number of professors who choose this approach. This section describes the resources available for course organization and presentation, and provides hints on how to move from a Mendel-first to a molecular-first approach.

Resources for Course Organization and Presentation

The most demanding aspect of switching to a molecular-first approach is the need for professors to reorganize their course syllabi and lecture materials. We have assembled set of resources to simplify the transition and to help professors coordinate their lectures with the book. Section 2 of this manual provides a course organization guide with samples of course syllabi. Section 3 provides chapter outlines for professors to use in lecture preparation and presentation. Refer to our website for additional information: http://www.brookscole.com/biology.

GeneLink is a CD-ROM electronic presentation tool that contains most images from the book for use in classroom presentation. (The only images from the book that are not included on GeneLink are those with copyright restrictions that prohibit their use in electronic format.) GeneLink includes presentation software with features, such as a chalk tool for highligting parts of the images during a presentation. Standard presentation software applications can also access the images for presentation for professors who prefer to use their own software. Over 100 color acetate transparencies of images in the book are also available for overhead projection.

Several supplemental resources are available to assist professors with course organization and presentation. *The Student Companion to Genetics: The Continuity of Life* contains detailed solutions to all end-of-chapter questions and problems. Our website (http://www.brookscole.com/biology) includes *Hypercontents*, a set of updated links to supplemental information coordinated with each section in the book; *Flashcards*, a set of electronic flashcards with hundreds of glossary terms from the book with definitions to assist students as they learn the vocabulary of genetics; *Tutorial Quizzes*, a set of quizzes to assist students as they study for examinations; *Updates and Corrections*, a section that updates material in the book and corrects errors; and a variety of other resources for professors and students. *InfoTrac College Edition* delivers online access to full-length articles from over 700 periodicals. *GeneticUpdates* is an online genetics newsletter with essays on current topics and issues in genetics. *Current Perspectives in Genetics*, by Shelley Cummings, features over 50 selected articles in genetics as a complement to a genetics course. *Genetics on the Web*, by Daniel J. Kurland, gives students exercises to become proficient with the Internet as they study genetics.

Hints on How to Move from a Mendel-First Approach to a Molecular-First Approach

Emphasize the material in Chapter 1 at the beginning of the course to help students learn to relate molecular genetics to other areas of genetics. Students learn molecular genetics best if they have in mind how molecular genetics is related to other areas of genetics. For this reason, it is important for students to carefully read Chapter 1 as they begin the course. Perhaps the most important sections of Chapter 1 are the final two sections, Section 1.5 The Concept of the Gene, and Section 1.6. Genetic Analysis. In these two sections, students learn to view the gene as a common thread that connects the genetics of molecules, cells, organisms, and populations, and to understand the importance of genetic analysis in the study of genetics. Section 1.6 uses Mendel's experiments as an example of genetic analysis and relates Mendel's results to the molecular basis of inheritance. This exercise helps students make the connection between observable patterns of inheritance and the molecular basis for those patterns.

Help students to make the connection between genotype and phenotype. The connection between genotype and phenotype is introduced in Chapter 1. Chapters 2–5 focus on a concrete, rather than abstract, concept of genotype. With a molecular-first approach, students perceive *genotype* as the nucleotide sequence in DNA, rather than as an abstract underlying genetic constitution. Chapter 6 is an important summary chapter that integrates the material in the previous five chapters and helps students to understand the relationship between the sequence of nucleotides in a gene with the outward phenotype.

Avoid frequent reference to homozygosity and heterozygosity until Chapter 12. Most students already understand the concepts of homozygosity and heterozygosity from their introductory biology course. However, they often do not understand the underlying molecular basis of those concepts. We remind students of homozygosity and heterozygosity in Chapter 1 but refrain from an extensive discussion of those topics until Chapter 12 where we explain their molecular basis. Chapters 2–11 focus on the effects of individual genes and the methods used to study genes at the molecular level. When students reach Chapter 12, they are well prepared to learn disomic inheritance at the molecular, cellular, and organismal levels.

Help students to understand the fundamentals of molecular biology at the beginning of the course. The level of presentation in our book presumes that students have completed an introductory biology course that includes basic principles of biochemistry, such as the fundamentals of atomic theory and bonding, including ionic, covalent, and hydrogen bonding, an understanding of acids, bases, and pH, and an introduction to enzyme function. Some students have weak preparation in these areas. A molecular-first approach allows a professor to address such deficiencies at the beginning of the course, rather than part way through it. It is sometimes worthwhile to provide students with a brief review of the fundamental principles of biochemistry during the first week of classes.

Integrate molecular biology into discussions of transmission genetics. The molecular-first approach becomes especially beneficial about a third of the way through the course when students confront transmission genetics. As students learn important genetic concepts such as dominance, partial dominance, codominance, epistasis, pleiotropy, penetrance, expressivity, sex determination, loss-of-function mutations, and gain-of-function mutations, they learn them in a molecular context. In so doing, they understand these concepts in a concrete rather than abstract way, and the concepts make sense to them.

Section 2
Course Organization Guide

Genetics: The Continuity of Life is organized for those professors who prefer to teach with a molecular-first approach, which leaves available a wide range of possible course organizations. This section explains the prerequisites for each chapter and shows how to organize several different types of courses with *Genetics: The Continuity of Life*. It also includes a detailed sample syllabus patterned after the authors' genetics course. We invite you to submit your own syllabi for inclusion on our website. Please contact the senior author, Daniel J. Fairbanks at fairbanks_genetics@byu.edu if you would like to add your syllabus or any other material to the website.

Prerequisite Material for Each Chapter

In any course organization, it is important to know which chapters have prerequisite material in previous chapters. A professor may not need to assign an entire chapter but may need to include particular sections of chapters as prerequisite material. We recommend that professors assign all of Chapters 1–6 at the beginning of the course to provide a firm molecular foundation for the chapters that follow. Below is a list of each chapter and the prerequisite material from previous chapters.

Chapter	Prerequisite Information From Previous Chapters
1. Introduction	There are no prerequisites for this chapter other than the preparation that students have from an introductory biology course. This is an important chapter because sets the stage for a genetics course and the rest of the book. Among the most important sections in it is Section 1.5, The Concept of the Gene, which describes the gene as a common thread that ties molecular, transmission, and population genetics together. Having read this section, students will have in mind the overall picture of genetics as they confront the more specialized chapters that follow.
2. DNA Structure and Replication	Chapter 1 and material from an introductory biology course.
3. Transcription and RNA Processing	Sections 2.2, 2.3, and 2.4 help students understand the basics of nucleic acid structure and DNA replication and prepare them to study transcription.
4. Translation and Protein Function	Sections 2.2, 2.3, and 2.4 and all of Chapter 3 are essential for students to understand the details of translation.
5. Mutation	Sections 2.2, 2.3, and 2.4 and all of Chapters 3 and 4 provide the background that students need to understand how mutations affect proteins.

6. An Integrated View of Gene Expression	Chapter 6 ties together the concepts taught in the previous four chapters. Its prerequisites are Sections 2.2, 2.3, and 2.4, Chapters 3 and 4, and sections 5.1, 5.2, and 5.3.
7. Bacterial Genetics	Students must have a good background in DNA replication, transcription, and translation from Chapters 2–4 to understand this chapter. In particular, Section 2.5 provides information on replication of circular genomes which is essential for this chapter. Section 5.1 provides information on mutations that is helpful for this chapter.
8. Regulation of Gene Expression	All of Chapters 2–6 are helpful. Sections 7.1 and 7.2 provide background information that students will need to understand operon regulation in Sections 8.1–8.3. Section 7.6 is a prerequisite for students to understand regulation of lysis and lysogeny presented in Section 8.4.
9. Recombinant DNA and Molecular Analysis	All of Chapters 2–4 are important. Sections 7.1, 7.2, and 7.6 discuss bacterial culture, plasmids, and phage life cycles, information that is essential for students to understand plasmid and phage cloning vectors in Sections 9.2 and 9.3. The material on the *lac* operon in Section 8.1 is good background for students to understand blue-white screening of recombinant plasmid and phage vectors described in Sections 9.2–9.5.
10. Eukaryotic Genome Organization	Chapters 2–4 provide prerequisite information on DNA structure and gene organization for this chapter.
11. Mitosis, Meiosis, and Cell Cycles	Chapters 2–4 are the essential prerequisites for this chapter. The information on eukaryotic chromosome organization from Chapter 10 is also helpful.
12. Mendelian Genetics	Because of its discussion on the molecular and cellular bases of inheritance, this chapter requires background information from Chapters 2–6 and 11. The material on biochemical pathways from Section 6.3 and the information on meiosis from Section 11.2 are especially important.
13. Variations on Mendel's Theme	All of Chapter 12 and its prerequisites are required for this chapter. Chapter 13 discusses DNA markers and requires information on restriction endonuclease digestion, electrophoresis, blotting, probes, and PCR from sections 9.7 and 9.8.
14. Sex Determination and Sex-Related Inheritance	Chapters 12, 13, and their prerequisites are required for this chapter.
15. Chromosome Mapping	Chapters 12–14 and their prerequisites are

required for this chapter.

16. Genetic Fine Structure	Chapters 12–15 and their prerequisites are required for this chapter.
17. Alterations in Chromosome Number and Structure	Chapters 12–15 and their prerequisites are required for this chapter. The information on meiosis from Section 11.2 is especially important.
18. Extranuclear Inheritance	Chapters 12–14 and their prerequisites are required for this chapter.
19. Population Genetics	Chapters 12–14 and their prerequisites are required for this chapter.
20. Quantitative Genetics	Chapters 12–14, 19, and their prerequisites are required for this chapter.
21. Evolutionary Genetics	Chapters 12–14, 19, and their prerequisites are required for this chapter.
22. Transposable Elements	The information on mutation from Section 5.1 and the introduction to transposable elements in Section 10.1 provide important background information for this chapter.
23. Developmental Genetics	The molecular information in Chapters 2–4 is essential for students to understand this chapter. Sections 8.5 and 8.6 provide information on eukaryotic gene regulation that is helpful for this chapter. This chapter also discusses the use of transposable elements as vectors for the study of gene regulation in *Drosophila*. The discussion of transposable elements in Sections 22.1 and 22.4 provides helpful background information.
24. Genes and Cancer	The molecular information in Chapters 2–4 is essential for students to understand this chapter. A good understanding of eukaryotic gene regulation from Sections 8.5 and 8.6 is useful for students who study this chapter.
25. Genes and Immunity	The molecular information in Chapters 2–4 is essential for students to understand this chapter. A good understanding of eukaryotic gene regulation from Sections 8.5 and 8.6 is useful for students who study this chapter.
26. Genetics in Medicine and Forensics	Chapter 9 and its prerequisites are helpful for students who study this chapter.
27. Genetics in Agriculture and Industry	Chapters 9, 20, and their prerequisites are helpful for students who study this chapter.

28. Legal and Ethical Issues in Genetics

Most of the material in this chapter stands on its own without essential prerequisites. This chapter is best taught toward the end of the course when students have a firm grasp of the principles and applications of genetics.

Sample Syllabi

Below are six sample syllabi that suggest possible alternatives for course organization. The lecture periods are assumed to be 45–50 minute sessions. More intensive courses are assumed to have 56 lecture periods (a 4-credit course in a semester system or a 5-credit course in a quarter system) and less intensive courses are assumed to have 42 lecture periods (a 3-credit course in a semester system or a 4 credit course in a quarter system). In each case, we have set aside several lecture periods to accommodate differences in number of lecture periods, exams, review sessions, and lectures on special topics.

1. An intensive general genetics course with balanced representation of molecular, transmission, and population genetics. (56 lectures)

This type of course is intended for students who are majors in the biological sciences and have taken a majors-level introductory biology course.

Chapter 1. Introduction (1 lecture)
Chapter 2. DNA Structure and Replication (2 lectures)
Chapter 3. Transcription and RNA Processing (3 lectures)
Chapter 4. Translation and Protein Function (2 lectures)
Chapter 5. Mutation (2 lectures)
Chapter 6. An Integrated View of Gene Expression (1 lectures)
Chapter 7. Bacterial Genetics (2 lectures)
Chapter 8. Regulation of Gene Expression (2 lectures)
Chapter 9. Recombinant DNA and Molecular Analysis (3 lectures)
Chapter 10. Eukaryotic Genome Organization (1 lecture)
Chapter 11. Mitosis, Meiosis, and Life Cycles (1 lecture)
Chapter 12. Mendelian Genetics (3 lectures)
Chapter 13. Variations on Mendel's Theme (3 lectures)
Chapter 14. Sex Determination and Sex-Related Inheritance (2 lectures)
Chapter 15. Chromosome Mapping (3 lectures)
Chapter 16. Genetic Fine Structure (3 lectures)
Chapter 17. Alterations in Chromosome Number and Structure (3 lectures)
Chapter 18. Extranuclear Inheritance (1 lecture)
Chapter 19. Population Genetics (3 lectures)
Chapter 20. Quantitative Genetics (2 lectures)
Chapter 21. Evolutionary Genetics (2 lectures)
Chapter 26. Genetics in Medicine and Forensics (1 lecture)
Chapter 27. Genetics in Agriculture and Industry (1 lecture)
Chapter 28. Legal and Ethical Issues in Genetics (1 lecture)
Review, exams, and special topics lectures (8 lectures)

2. A course focused on molecular genetics (56 lectures).

This type of course focuses on molecular aspects of genetics for students whose major focuses on molecular biology and biochemistry.

Chapter 1. Introduction (1 lecture)
Chapter 2. DNA Structure and Replication (2 lectures)
Chapter 3. Transcription and RNA Processing (3 lectures)
Chapter 4. Translation and Protein Function (2 lectures)
Chapter 5. Mutation (2 lectures)
Chapter 6. An Integrated View of Gene Expression (1 lecture)
Chapter 7. Bacterial Genetics (2 lectures)
Chapter 8. Regulation of Gene Expression (2 lectures)
Chapter 9. Recombinant DNA and Molecular Analysis (3 lectures)
Chapter 10. Eukaryotic Genome Organization (1 lecture)
Chapter 11. Mitosis, Meiosis, and Life Cycles (1 lecture)
Chapter 12. Mendelian Genetics (2 lectures)
Chapter 13. Variations on Mendel's Theme (3 lectures)
Chapter 14. Sex Determination and Sex-Related Inheritance (2 lectures)
Chapter 15. Chromosome Mapping (3 lectures)
Chapter 16. Genetic Fine Structure (3 lectures)
Chapter 17. Alterations in Chromosome Number and Structure (3 lectures)
Chapter 18. Extranuclear Inheritance (1 lecture)
Chapter 22. Transposable Elements (2 lectures)
Chapter 23. Developmental Genetics (2 lectures)
Chapter 24. Genes and Cancer (2 lectures)
Chapter 25. Genes and Immunity (2 lectures)
Chapter 26. Genetics in Medicine and Forensics (1 lecture)
Chapter 28. Legal and Ethical Issues in Genetics (1 lecture)
Review, exams, and special topics lectures (9 lectures)

3. A simplified general genetics course that provides an introduction to essential concepts of genetics (42 lectures).

This type of course is intended for students who are not majors in the biological sciences or who are majors in applied biological sciences and need a brief introduction to genetics.

Chapter 1. Introduction (1 lecture)
Chapter 2. DNA Structure and Replication (2 lectures)
Chapter 3. Transcription and RNA Processing (3 lectures)
Chapter 4. Translation and Protein Function (2 lectures)
Sections 5.1–5.3 of Chapter 5. Mutation (1 lecture)
Chapter 6. An Integrated View of Gene Expression (1 lecture)
Sections 7.1–7.3, and 7.6 of Chapter 7. Bacterial Genetics (1 lecture)
Section 8.1 of Chapter 8. Regulation of Gene Expression (1 lecture)
Sections 9.1, 9.2, 9.4, and 9.6–9.9 of Chapter 9. Recombinant DNA and Molecular Analysis
        (2 lectures)
Chapter 11. Mitosis, Meiosis, and Life Cycles (1 lecture)

Chapter 12. Mendelian Genetics (2 lectures)
Chapter 13. Variations on Mendel's Theme (3 lectures)
Chapter 14. Sex Determination and Sex-Related Inheritance (2 lectures)
Chapter 15. Chromosome Mapping (3 lectures)
Chapter 17. Alterations in Chromosome Number and Structure (3 lectures)
Chapter 19. Population Genetics (3 lectures)
Chapter 21. Evolutionary Genetics (2 lectures)
Chapter 26. Genetics in Medicine and Forensics (1 lecture)
Chapter 27. Genetics in Agriculture and Industry (1 lecture)
Chapter 28. Legal and Ethical Issues in Genetics (1 lecture)
Review, exams, and special topics lectures (6 lectures)

4. A course focused on human genetics and medicine (42 lectures).

This type of course is for students who have an interest in human genetics. It is also for students whose major is in the allied health sciences and may be used as a course for premedical or predental students whose majors are not in the biological sciences.

Chapter 1. Introduction (1 lecture)
Chapter 2. DNA Structure and Replication (2 lectures)
Chapter 3. Transcription and RNA Processing (3 lectures)
Chapter 4. Translation and Protein Function (2 lectures)
Chapter 5. Mutation (2 lectures)
Chapter 6. An Integrated View of Gene Expression (1 lecture)
Sections 7.1–7.3, and 7.6 of Chapter 7. Bacterial Genetics (1 lecture)
Chapter 8. Regulation of Gene Expression (2 lectures)
Chapter 9. Recombinant DNA and Molecular Analysis (3 lectures)
Chapter 10. Eukaryotic Genome Organization (1 lecture)
Chapter 11. Mitosis, Meiosis, and Life Cycles (1 lecture)
Chapter 12. Mendelian Genetics (2 lectures)
Chapter 13. Variations on Mendel's Theme (3 lectures)
Chapter 14. Sex Determination and Sex-Related Inheritance (2 lectures)
Chapter 17. Alterations in Chromosome Number and Structure (3 lectures)
Chapter 18. Extranuclear Inheritance (1 lecture)
Chapter 23. Developmental Genetics (2 lectures)
Chapter 24. Genes and Cancer (2 lectures)
Chapter 25. Genes and Immunity (2 lectures)
Chapter 26. Genetics in Medicine and Forensics (1 lecture)
Chapter 28. Legal and Ethical Issues in Genetics (1 lecture)
Review, exams, and special topics lectures (4 lectures)

5. A course focused on transmission and population genetics (42 lectures).

This type of course is for students whose major is focused on organismal or conservation biology. It provides sufficient molecular background for students to understand transmission and population genetics in a modern context.

Chapter 1. Introduction (1 lecture)
Chapter 2. DNA Structure and Replication (2 lectures)
Chapter 3. Transcription and RNA Processing (3 lectures)
Chapter 4. Translation and Protein Function (2 lectures)
Sections 5.1–5.3 of Chapter 5. Mutation (1 lecture)
Chapter 6. An Integrated View of Gene Expression (1 lecture)
Sections 7.1–7.3, and 7.6 of Chapter 7. Bacterial Genetics (1 lecture)
Section 8.1 of Chapter 8. Regulation of Gene Expression (1 lecture)
Sections 9.1, 9.2, 9.4, and 9.6–9.9 of Chapter 9. Recombinant DNA and Molecular Analysis
    (2 lectures)
Chapter 11. Mitosis, Meiosis, and Life Cycles (1 lecture)
Chapter 12. Mendelian Genetics (2 lectures)
Chapter 13. Variations on Mendel's Theme (3 lectures)
Chapter 14. Sex Determination and Sex-Related Inheritance (2 lectures)
Chapter 15. Chromosome Mapping (3 lectures)
Chapter 17. Alterations in Chromosome Number and Structure (3 lectures)
Chapter 18. Extranuclear Inheritance (1 lecture)
Chapter 19. Population Genetics (3 lectures)
Chapter 20. Quantitative Genetics (2 lectures)
Chapter 21. Evolutionary Genetics (2 lectures)
Chapter 27. Genetics in Agriculture and Industry (1 lecture)
Chapter 28. Legal and Ethical Issues in Genetics (1 lecture)
Review, exams, and special topics lectures (4 lectures)

6. A course focused on concepts and application of agricultural genetics (42 lectures).

This type of course is for students whose major is in the agricultural sciences. It provides sufficient molecular background for students to understand transmission and population genetics and how they are related to agricultural research and production.

Chapter 1. Introduction (1 lecture)
Chapter 2. DNA Structure and Replication (2 lectures)
Chapter 3. Transcription and RNA Processing (3 lectures)
Chapter 4. Translation and Protein Function (2 lectures)
Sections 5.1–5.3 of Chapter 5. Mutation (1 lecture)
Chapter 6. An Integrated View of Gene Expression (1 lecture)
Sections 7.1–7.3, and 7.6 of Chapter 7. Bacterial Genetics (1 lecture)
Section 8.1 of Chapter 8. Regulation of Gene Expression (1 lecture)
Sections 9.1, 9.2, 9.4, and 9.6–9.9 of Chapter 9. Recombinant DNA and Molecular Analysis
    (2 lectures)
Chapter 11. Mitosis, Meiosis, and Life Cycles (1 lecture)
Chapter 12. Mendelian Genetics (2 lectures)
Chapter 13. Variations on Mendel's Theme (3 lectures)
Chapter 14. Sex Determination and Sex-Related Inheritance (2 lectures)
Chapter 15. Chromosome Mapping (3 lectures)
Chapter 17. Alterations in Chromosome Number and Structure (3 lectures)
Chapter 18. Extranuclear Inheritance (1 lecture)
Chapter 19. Population Genetics (3 lectures)

Chapter 20. Quantitative Genetics (2 lectures)
Chapter 21. Evolutionary Genetics (2 lectures)
Chapter 22. Transposable Elements (2 lectures)
Chapter 27. Genetics in Agriculture and Industry (1 lecture)
Chapter 28. Legal and Ethical Issues in Genetics (1 lecture)
Review, exams, and special topics lectures (2 lectures)

Detailed sample syllabus

The following detailed course syllabus is an example derived from the syllabus used by the authors. It is for a junior–senior level, four-credit genetics course taught during a single semester. The example given here is for a fall semester class that meets for two consecutive 50-minute periods twice per week for a total of four lectures per week. Some topics that are often taught in a genetics course are omitted because they are taught in the cell biology course that accompanies this genetics course.

Genetics

This course is an intensive course in genetics and molecular biology. It is a required course for students majoring in all areas of biology and is an excellent choice as a genetics course for students who intend to apply for admission to graduate, medical, or dental school. It is a pivotal course providing a foundation for several of the courses many of you will take in the future. For that reason, it is essential that you be adequately prepared for this class and that you allot sufficient time for study during the course of the semester. This is a challenging and difficult course, but it is fascinating as well. You should plan to work long and hard in it, but you should also be able to catch a glimpse of the beauty and logic of genetics in the process. Many students feel that this was among the most difficult yet most fascinating courses of their college careers.

Class schedule

The class is scheduled to meet Tuesdays and Thursdays from 2:00-3:50. There will be a 10 minute break from 2:50-3:00. Three help sections will be scheduled during the week. The help section schedule will be provided for you during the second week of class.

Prerequisites

Completion of the prerequisite classes is essential. Learning genetics and conducting genetic analysis require constant reference to principles of basic biology, chemistry, and mathematics. If you lack the necessary training from previous courses, you will probably not be able to follow lectures, understand the textbook, or complete the homework assignments. I will not spend the time during the lecture periods explaining basic principles of biology, chemistry, or math that you should already have from previous classes. If you have not completed the prerequisites, you should drop this class today and enroll in the prerequisite courses.

The required prerequisite courses are

Mathematics: College-level algebra. You should know how to work with exponential and logarithmic functions and how to setup and solve algebraic problems.

Biology: Introductory biology. You should understand the fundamentals of chemistry and biochemistry as presented at the beginning of your biology course; basic life cycles of animals, plants, fungi, and bacteria; cellular structure and function including the structures and functions of all major organelles; cell cycle, mitosis, cytokinesis, and meiosis; Mendelian and X-linked inheritance; structure and replication of DNA; transcription and translation.

I expect you to understand the above topics at the level they are covered in the prerequisite courses. Most of the topics will be covered at greater depth in this class, so a basic understanding of these topics is essential.

Textbooks

There are two required textbooks for this class:

Fairbanks, D.J. and W.R. Andersen. 1999. *Genetics: The Continuity of Life.* Pacific Grove, CA: Brooks/Cole and Wadsworth Publishing Companies.

Andersen, W.R. and D.J. Fairbanks. 1999. *Student Companion to Genetics: The Continuity of Life.* Pacific Grove, CA: Brooks/Cole and Wadsworth Publishing Companies.

The first textbook is the main textbook for the course. The second is a manual that gives solutions to all of the questions and problems in your homework assignments. Both are available in the university bookstore. Because exams for this class are open book, you must have your own copy of the textbook. It also is wise for you to keep your copy after the class is finished. Genetics occupies a central role in biology and you will find yourself referring back to this class and your book often in the years ahead.

Homework

There is assigned homework for this class. The homework is for your benefit and will not be graded. Analysis and problem solving are particularly important in genetics. To do well in this class, most students need to practice problem solving over and over. You should do your homework on time and not wait until quiz or exam time to cram. This is a class for which cramming is likely to cause undue stress and a poor grade.

Evaluation and grading

There will be six quizzes, three midcourse examinations, and one final examination. The examinations and their point values are:

6 Quizzes (20 points each)	100 points	(lowest quiz score is dropped)
3 Examinations	300 points	
Final examination	100 points	
Total	500 points	

Each quiz is worth 20 points. The score of the lowest quiz will be dropped. There are no make-up quizzes and no examination scores will be dropped. There are no extra credit opportunities. The class will not be graded on a curve, so you will not be competing with any other students for a grade. If no students reach 100% on an exam, or if a large number of students miss a particular question on an exam, I may adjust all exam scores upward. Typically, at least four or five students have perfect scores on examinations, so adjustment is usually not necessary. Your final grade will be calculated on a point basis as follows:

Range	Cutoff	Grade
465-500	93%	A
450-464	90%	A-
435-449	87%	B+
415-434	83%	B
400-414	80%	B-
385-399	77%	C+
365-384	73%	C
350-366	70%	C-
335-349	67%	D+
315-334	63%	D
300-314	60%	D-
0-299		E

Important Dates:

Quiz 1:	10-11 Sep (Wednesday-Thursday) in the Testing Center
Quiz 2:	17-18 Sep (Wednesday-Thursday) in the Testing Center
Exam 1:	25-29 Sep (Thursday-Monday) in the Testing Center
Quiz 3:	8-9 Oct (Wednesday-Thursday) in the Testing Center
Quiz 4:	15-16 Oct (Wednesday-Thursday) in the Testing Center
Exam 2:	23-27 Oct (Thursday-Monday) in the Testing Center
Quiz 5:	5-6 Nov (Wednesday-Thursday) in the Testing Center
Quiz 6:	12-13 Nov (Wednesday-Thursday) in the Testing Center
Exam 3:	21-25 Nov (Thursday - Monday) in the Testing Center

Final examination time: Dec 13-18 in testing center. You may go at any time within the testing center's hours during finals week.

(Note to professors: We adminster our quizzes and exams in a testing center to allow students flexibility in choosing the time to take a quiz or exam. We permit students to use their notes and books during quizzes and exams. The quizzes and exams consist of problems that are similar to the end-of-chapter problems in the textbook. None of the problems are multiple choice; students must show not only the answer, but how they derived it for each problem. To detect cheating, we provide different versions of each quiz and exam to the testing center but do not inform students of the differences. Answers that match a different version are evidence of cheating.)

THE ABOVE DATES ARE FIRM. For exams and quizzes, that means you must take the quiz or exam on the dates scheduled above in the testing center. Because one quiz will be dropped, *there will be no late or makeup quizzes.*

Late Examinations. If you miss an examination for any reason, you have one week to take an alternative examination late. You must schedule an appointment with the instructor to take a late examination. Late examinations are not given in the testing center. All late examinations are a different version than the regular examinations *and are more difficult.* The regular examination will be available only during the scheduled days. If you miss it, regardless of the reason, you must take the alternative version.

Final grades will be available on the grade report available over the telephone system and on the grade report sent to you by the University. In accordance with College policy, grades will not be posted and your professor will not give grades over the telephone.

An incomplete "I" grade will be given only under very rare circumstances and only after the twelfth week of class. That means you must have completed all work through November 22 including the first and second exams and all quizzes in order to be eligible for an incomplete grade. Otherwise, if you must drop the course after the drop deadline (October 6), you will need to petition for a nonacademic withdrawal from the university.

Help sessions

Help sessions with a teaching assistant present are scheduled at several hours throughout the week. A schedule of help sessions and the office hours for teaching assistants will be provided during the second week of class. You would be well advised to attend help sessions regularly. These give you chances to work through your homework assignments with other members of the class and to ask questions. Although help sessions are optional, those who attend help sessions tend to perform better in the class.

Individual help

Teaching assistants and professors have scheduled office hours where we can meet with you individually. Unfortunately this is a large class. Your professor and the teaching assistants have numerous responsibilities and university assignments. As a result we cannot give you unlimited access to us. Office hours are scheduled to provide you with a designated time to ask questions or deal with problems. If you must meet with the professors or teaching assistants at a time other than office hours, please schedule an appointment. Please do not consider us rude if we cannot meet with you at a time other than office hours. With a class this large it is impossible to accommodate everyone's schedule. *Also, please do not call us at home.* You may call your instructor at his office at any time and leave a message on phone mail. Also, any questions about your grade must be directed only to the instructor. The teaching assistants cannot look up your current grade nor can they make any grade changes. Test grades and final grades will not be given over the telephone. Because exams in this class are not machine graded, it takes some time to grade the final exam and submit final grades. Please be patient. Final grades will not be posted, but will be available over the telephone and web systems as soon as they have been submitted.

Honor Code

Honor and integrity are among the most aspects of a person's character. While few, if any, of you may be inclined to be dishonest, a reminder of what it means to be honest is important for everyone. All of us have agreed to abide by the University Honor Code which includes maintaining academic integrity. In addition to the stated items in the University Honor Code, the items listed below must be followed for you to be fully honest in your work for this class:

1. Your quizzes and examinations must represent your own work and not the work of another.

2. Do not discuss the content of exams or quizzes with anyone until the exam or quiz has been handed back. You should not discuss the content of an exam or quiz with another individual even if she or he has already taken the exam or quiz.

3. Taking a graded exam that belongs to another student or attempting to find out another student's grade are dishonest acts and are considered serious violations of the Honor Code.

Academic dishonesty is very rare. Most of us are deterred from it by conscience and respect for integrity. Unfortunately, a very small number of students seem to value an undeserved grade above their personal integrity and the commitments they have made. Confirmed violations of any aspect of the Honor Code involving academic integrity will result in a failing grade for this course and will be reported in writing to the Honor Code Office. Cases of theft (such as taking another student's examination or entering a professor's office without permission and taking materials) will be reported to University Police and may result in legal as well as academic penalties.

Reading Assignments and Lecture Schedule

We will follow the sequence of topics listed below in class. Certain topics that are in your textbook, such as gene regulation, developmental genetics, and the genetics of cancer will be covered in your cell biology course. The lecture schedule below is approximate. The class presentations may move more or less quickly than outlined below. There may be some supplementary reading assignments in addition to those listed and certain parts of some chapters may not be as important as others. In order to keep up on your readings and homework properly, you should attend class regularly. You are responsible for all announcements made in class, even if you are not there. If you miss a class or come late after announcements have been made, you are responsible to find out what announcements were made. The topics that will be covered on each exam will be announced in class prior to each examination.

Topic	Reading	Lecture Schedule (approximate)
Introduction	Chapter 1	2 Sep
DNA Structure and Replication	Chapter 2	2, 4 Sep
Transcription	Chapter 3	9, 11 Sep
Translation	Chapter 4	16, 18 Sep
Mutation	Chapter 5	23 Sep
Gene Expression	Chapter 6	25 Sep
Bacterial Genetics	Chapter 7	30 Sep
Recombinant DNA	Section 8.1 Chapter 9	3, 9 Oct
Mitosis, and Meiosis	Chapter 11	7 Oct
Mendelian Genetics and Probability	Chapter 12	9, 14 Oct
Extensions of Mendelian Genetics	Chapter 13	16 Oct
Sex Determination	Chapter 14	21 Oct
Linkage and Chromosome Mapping	Chapter 15	23 Oct
Cytogenetics	Chapter 17	28, 30 Oct
Extranuclear inheritance	Chapter 18	4 Nov
Population genetics	Chapter 19	11, 13 Nov
Quantitative genetics	Chapter 20	18 Nov
Evolutionary genetics	Chapter 21	20 Nov
Transposable Elements	Chapter 22	25 Nov
Genetics in Medicine	Chapter 26	2 Dec
Genetics in Agriculture	Chapter 27	4 Dec
Legal and Ethical Issues	Chapter 28	9 Dec

Please note: The above schedule and procedures are subject to change in extenuating circumstances.

Section 3
Chapter Outlines

The following chapter outlines provide key concepts and key terms for each chapter, chapter topics, and a detailed outlines of the material covered in each chapter for use in lecture and syllabus preparation.

Chapter 1
Introduction

KEY CONCEPTS
- Genetics, one of the most rapidly progressing branches of biology, has applications that affect all of humanity.
- Many of the principles of genetics are universal among the vast diversity of species on earth, making it possible to apply concepts discovered in one species to other species.
- The concept of the gene is central to the study of genetics.
- Genetics, an analytical science, is best understood through a study of how genetic experiments are conducted and their results interpreted.

KEY TERMS

genetics
gene
model organism
molecular genetics
transmission genetics
population genetics
quantitative genetics
evolutionary genetics

CHAPTER TOPICS

1.1 GENETICS IN HUMAN SOCIETY
1.2 THE UNIVERSALITY OF GENETIC PRINCIPLES
1.3 MODEL ORGANISMS
1.4 ORGANIZING THE STUDY OF GENETICS
1.5 THE CONCEPT OF THE GENE
1.6 GENETIC ANALYSIS

CHAPTER OUTLINE

Introduction

Genetics: organization of genetic information, expression, and transmission
    Heredity has existed for at least 2 billion years on earth
    A central theme of modern biology
    A rapidly progressing science with powerful tools
A science of hopes and fears

1.1 GENETICS IN HUMAN SOCIETY

Central idea:
- Genetics has played a significant role in shaping human society both historically and in modern times. Modern application of genetics has been particularly important in medicine, agriculture, industry, and forensics.

Important events
    1865: Principle laws of heredity described by Mendel
    1900: Three botanists rediscover Mendel's principles
    1905: William Bateson coins the term "genetics"
    Ancient recognition of "like begets like" and crop and breed development (Figure 1.1)
    Role of genetics in shaping human history
        Ancient civilizations and development of cultivated crops
        Effects of modern breeding on crop yields in 20th century
        Modern genetic principles and medicine
        Genetics and industrial development
        Genetics and land reclamation
        Genetics, DNA fingerprinting and law
            Parentage analysis
            Criminal assault cases
            Plant and animal patents
Modern genetic analysis has revolutionized almost all areas of biological research

1.2 THE UNIVERSALITY OF GENETICS PRINCIPLES

Central idea:
- Underlying the discussions in the chapters that follow are two major principles: (1) DNA is the inherited material, and (2) its inheritance is manifest as traits that appear in consistent patterns in parents and offspring. Throughout our study of genetics, we will repeatedly encounter discoveries made in one organism that are widely—even universally—applicable throughout life.

Universality of genetic principles a constant theme of life
        DNA is hereditary material of all cellular organisms
        Some viruses use RNA but general principles apply
        Same code is used to specify primary structure of proteins
        Gene structures are remarkably similar
Recognition of universality of genetic principles came gradually
        Mendel unwilling to assume his laws applied to all organisms
        Apparent exceptions when finally understood proved the rule

1.3 MODEL ORGANISMS

Central idea:
- Model organisms are species selected for genetic study because they possess characteristics that allow important research questions to be addressed efficiently. Information learned from model organisms may be applied to humans or other species of economic or social importance that cannot be so efficiently studied. Recent DNA analysis has made humans

one of the best genetically characterized species.

Model organism: species preeminently suited to the study at hand
    Species with efficient analysis characteristics
        Short generation times
        Large numbers of progeny per mating
        Cheaply cultured and maintained
        Genetic diversity available for study
        Relevant background information
        (e.g. *Drosophila melanogaster*)
    Other model organisms
        E. coli
        Neurospora crassa
        Saccharomyces cerevisiae
        Zea mays
        Arabidopsis thaliana
        Mus musculus domesticus
    (See Example 1.1 The laboratory mouse, *Mus musculus domesticus*, as a model organism.)
    Modern DNA technology and choice of modern model organisms
        Humans have become one of the most extensively studied species genetically

1.4 ORGANIZING THE STUDY OF GENETICS

Central idea:
* A foundation in molecular genetics serves as the basis for understanding transmission genetics, which, in turn, underlies the genetics of populations.

Genetics a logical and integrated branch of biology
    Molecular genetics: study of principle molecules of heredity DNA, RNA and proteins
        Most fundamental level of genetics
        Organization and interactions of DNA, RNA and proteins
        How genes determine a trait
    Transmission genetics: the study of transmission of traits and genetic material
        Often called "classical genetics"
        Mendelian genetics (basic laws of heredity)
        Population genetics
        Quantitative genetics

1.5 THE CONCEPT OF THE GENE

Linear segment of nucleotides in DNA
Gene is transcribed into RNA
    Linear sequence in RNA transcribed into linear sequence of amino acids in polypeptide
    Polypeptide processed into protein (usually an enzyme)
Gene may mutate and change genetic code or a polypeptide
Genes are found in chromosomes in cell nuclei, mitochondria and chloroplasts, in bacteria and viruses
Single genes may determine phenotype of discontinuous traits
Continuously variable hereditary traits are determined by many genes acting together

(See Example 1.2 Purple and white flowers on Mendel's pea plants: An example of discontinuous genetic variation and its relationship to genes, Figure 1.9)

1.6 GENETIC ANALYSIS

The process of discovery in an analytical science
  Example: Mendel's analysis of tall × dwarf pea experiments
    Mathematical analysis revealed underlying cause of genetic variation
    Tall × dwarf pea varieties:
    Hybrid offspring: all tall
    Second generation: 787 tall, 277 dwarf (close to 3 tall:1 dwarf)
    Mendel's interpretation:
    Concluded hybrid carried factor for tall and factor for dwarf
    Tall and dwarf hereditary factors separated from each other in the formation of the gametes (1:1 ratio)
    Half the gametes carried the tall factor half carried dwarf factor
    Combining pollen and egg gametes at random produced 1/4 *TT*:2/4 *Tt*:1/4 *tt* ratio
    Mendel studied inheritance of seven pairs of contrasting traits in pea (Figure 1.10)
  (See Example 1.3 Applying further analysis to Mendel's results: Developing a model to explain dominance, Figure 1.11)

Chapter 2
DNA Structure and Replication

KEY CONCEPTS

- In DNA, four different nucleotide subunits connect to each other in a linear fashion to form a long strand of nucleotides. Two strands wind around each other in a double helix in the typical DNA molecule.
- Nucleotides pair with each other according to strict pairing rules determined by the chemical properties of the nucleotides.
- The strict pairing of nucleotides allows the DNA molecule to replicate: first the double helix splits into single strands, and then the old strands serve as templates to which new nucleotides are added according to the pairing rules, forming new strands.

KEY TERMS

deoxyribonucleic acid (DNA)
nucleic acid
ribonucleic acid (RNA)
nucleotide
pyrimidine
thymine
cytosine
purine
adenine
guanine
uracil
phosphodiester bond
antiparallel strands
major groove
minor groove
B form (B-DNA)
A-DNA
DNA-RNA hybrid
Z-DNA
H-DNA
replication fork
semiconservative replication
template
conservative replication
dispersive replication
supercoil
RNA polymerase
primase
primer
leading strand
lagging strand
Okazaki fragment
semidiscontinuous replication

DNA polymerase
DNA ligase
proofreading
unidirectional replication
bidrectional replication
θ-mode replication
σ-mode (rolling circle) replication
D-loop (displacement-loop) replication

CHAPTER TOPICS

2.1 THE GENETIC MATERIAL
      Discovery of DNA
      The transforming principle
      DNA as the transforming principle
      The genetic material in bacteria and viruses
2.2 NUCLEIC ACID STRUCTURE
      The DNA molecule
      Nucleotide structure
      The RNA molecule
      Base pairing models for double-stranded DNA
      Base pairing rules
      The double helix
      Alternative forms of DNA
2.3 SEMICONSERVATIVE DNA REPLICATION
2.4 THE PROCESS OF DNA REPLICATION
      Separating and stabilizing DNA strands
      Synthesizing new DNA strands
      Semidiscontinuous DNA replication
      Simultaneous synthesis of leading and lagging strands
      Proofreading newly synthesized DNA
      Replication of eukaryotic DNA
2.5 REPLICATION OF ENTIRE DNA MOLECULES
      Origins of replication
      Bidirectional DNA replication
      Strategies for replicating circular DNA
      Strategies for replicating linear DNA

CHAPTER OUTLINE

Introduction
      The hereditary material is DNA
      DNA structure provides means of replication, information transmission, mutation

2.1 THE GENETIC MATERIAL

Central ideas:
- DNA is the universal genetic material, with the exception of some viruses.
- Several key experiments demonstrated that DNA is the substance of heredity.

Discovery of DNA

    1860s: Friedrich Miescher discoverer of DNA (Figure 2.1)

        Large quantities of viscous substance isolated from puss cell nuclei

            Proposed as phosphate reservoir for cell

            Later called deoxyribonucleic acid (DNA)

            DNA staining: DNA identified with chromosomes

    Late 1800s: E. B. Wilson proposed DNA important in heredity

The transforming principle

    1928: transformation reported in bacteria by Griffith (Figure 2.2)

        Live virulent strain kills mice

        Mice insensitive to avirulent strain

        Heat-killed virulent cells, plus live avirulent cells, kill mice

        Heat-stable substance transform avirulent cells

    The heat-stable substance is the transforming principle

DNA as the transforming principle

    1944: transforming principle is DNA as demonstrated by the experiments of Avery, MacLeod, McCarty (Figure 2.3)

        Protein, DNA, RNA and carbohydrate tested as transforming principle

        Only DNA from virulent strain of bacteria transformed avirulent strain

        Cautious conclusion by workers: DNA is the transforming principle

        (See Example 2.1 Chemical composition of the transforming principle.)

The genetic material in bacterial viruses (Figure 2.4)

    1952: genetic material in T2 bacteriophage is DNA (Hershey and Chase)

        T2 phage particles inject ^{32}P labeled DNA into host bacteria

        ^{35}S labeled protein remains outside host cells

        Conclusion: DNA is the genetic material of T2 phage

    Reasons for delay in recognition of DNA

        Varying intensity of DNA stains during cell cycle

        DNA structure seemed too simple to be genetic message

        Protein complexity suggested protein as genetic material

    Doubts about DNA short-lived

    1953: correct model of DNA molecule discovered (Watson and Crick)

        DNA structure key to understanding genetic message and replictation

2.2 NUCLEIC ACID STRUCTURE

Central ideas:

- DNA is composed of four different deoxyribonucleotide subunits, generally referred to by the names of the bases attached to them: thymine (T), cytosine (C), adenine (A), and guanine (G). The nucleotides T and C consist of a single six-membered ring in the nitrogenous base and are both referred to as pyrimidines. The other two nucleotides, A and G, each contain a nitrogenous base composed of two rings and are referred to as purines.
- The nucleotide subunits of DNA are attached to each other with phosphodiester bonds linking the 3' carbon of one nucleotide to the 5' carbon of the adjacent nucleotide. This 3'→ 5' linkage is repeated forming a sugar-phosphate backbone. The DNA molecule is formed of two strands wound into a double helix with the nitrogenous bases pointing toward the center of the helix. The sugar phosphate backbone of one strand is antiparallel to the other, meaning that the 5' carbons of one strand face in the opposite direction of the 5' carbons in

the other strand. The two strands are held together by hydrogen bonding between specific base pairs. Thymine pairs with adenine, and cytosine pairs with guanine.

- DNA may exist in several forms. The most common form of DNA in living cells is a right-handed helix called the B-form (or B-DNA). A-DNA apparently does not exist in living cells, but double-stranded DNA-RNA hybrids and double-stranded RNA assume a conformation similar to A-DNA in living cells. Z-DNA consists of a helix wound in a left-handed conformation where the sugar phosphate backbones of Z-DNA form a zig-zag pattern instead of a smooth helix. Z-DNA may be present in certain locations within DNA molecules in the cell. H-DNA occurs when a short region of a double-helical molecule rearranges itself to form a triple helix.

The DNA molecule
> DNA and RNA are nucleic acids
> Length of DNA molecule measured in millimeters
> Width of DNA measured in nanometers
> Total length of 46 DNA molecules in human cell: over 2 meters
> Over six billion nucleotide pairs in human DNA
> Double-stranded helix

Nucleotide structure (DNA) (Figure 2.6)
> Five carbon atoms of deoxyribose sugar named 1′, 2′, 3′, 4′, 5′
> Phosphate group bonded to 5′ carbon
> Nitrogen base bonded to 1′ carbon
> Four deoxyribonucleotides: T, C, A and G
> Purines (bases with two rings): A and G
> Pyrimidines (bases with one ring): T and C

The RNA molecule (Figure 2.7)
> Ribonucleotides differ only slightly
>> The five-carbon sugar is ribose in RNA
>>> Ribose has hydroxyl on 2′ carbon
>>> Deoxyribose has hydrogen on 2′ carbon
>> RNA has A, C, and G and Uracil (U) instead of T
> RNA and DNA long chain polymers of nucleotides
> Nucleotides linked with 5′ to 3′ phosphodiester bonds
> RNA usually single-stranded

Base pairing and models of double-stranded DNA
> 1930: A, T, C, and G were present in DNA (Phoebus Levine)
>> Proposed A, T, C, and G formed simple repeating tetramer
>> DNA not serious candidate for genetic material
> DNA not composed of repeating tetramers of A, T, C, and G
>> 1940s to 50s: Chargaff calculated A, T, C, and G ratios in DNAs
>> Rules for DNAs purified from different species:
>>> A + G = T + C;
>>> A = T and C = G;
>>> (A + T) ≠ (C + G);
>>> A ≠ G, T ≠ G;
>>> ratio (A +T)/(C + G) varied with species
> 1953: James Watson and Francis Crick construct model for DNA molecule
>> Confident DNA genetic is material
>> Guided by X-ray diffraction images of crystalline DNA (Figure 2.8)

Followed Erwin Chargaff's rules for base ratios in DNA

(See Example 2.2 Chargaff's data on nucleotide composition from eleven different sources.)

Calculated chemical bond angles and bond distances in the nucleotides

Constructed and described correct molecular model of DNA double helix

Base pairing rules

Nucleotide sequence on one strand determines nucleotide sequence on paired strand (Figure 2.10)

Partial negative and positive charges align bases

A hydrogen bonded to a nitrogen: slight positive charge δ+

An oxygen bonded to a carbon: slight negative charge δ–

A nitrogen bonded to carbons: slight negative charge δ–

A=T base pairs: two aligned H bonds

C≡G base pairs: three aligned H bonds (Figure 2.11)

(See Example 2.3 Restrictions on base pairing in DNA.)

The double helix

Anti parallel strands of double helix

One strand 5′→3′; complementary strand 3′→5′

A=T, C≡G hydrogen bonds hold DNA strands together

B-form: a regular repeating pattern

Right handed double spiral

Paired bases stacked almost flat

Each base pair rotates ca. 36°

One turn of the helix: ten bases 360°

Two spiral grooves

Major groove 22A wide

Minor groove 12A wide (Figure 2.12)

Other DNA molecule forms (Figure 2.13)

DNA-RNA hybrids and double-stranded RNA form A-type helix

Helix wound less tightly ; bases tilted more steeply than B-DNA

A-helix forms right handed coil

Z-DNA wound in left handed double coil

Structure is compact

Z-DNA-specific antibodies bind to a few regions of cell DNA

H-DNA has triple helix form

May be present in living cells

May be associated with gene expression

2.3 SEMICONSERVATIVE DNA REPLICATION

Central idea:

- DNA replicates in a semiconservative fashion, meaning that the two original strands are conserved, each serving as a template for the formation of a new strand. The two daughter molecules will each contain an original parental strand and one newly synthesized strand.

Models for DNA replication (Figures 2.14, 2.15)

DNA structure suggested modes of replication

Conservative replication

Original double helix conserved

Both strands of new double helix are new

Semiconservative replication
    Each daughter double helix has parent strand and new strand
Dispersive replication
    New strands have fragments from original parent strands
1958: DNA replicates in semiconservative mode (Meselson and Stahl, Figure 2.16)

2.4 THE PROCESS OF DNA REPLICATION

Central ideas:

- DNA is replicated by a group of enzymes collectively referred to as a replisome. The helix is unwound by enzymes called helicases, and the tension built up by unwinding is relieved by transient single strand breaks in the molecule that allow it to rotate ahead of the replication fork, a process catalyzed by topoisomerases. The resulting single stranded segments of DNA are stabilized by single stranded binding proteins (SSBs) that prevent the strands from reattaching. Nucleotides may then be added to the single stranded DNA by enzymes referred to collectively as DNA polymerases.

- All known DNA polymerases must add nucleotides to the 3' end of a nucleotide already present and therefore cannot initiate replication. Initiation of replication requires an RNA primer, a short segment of RNA synthesized on the DNA template strand from which DNA polymerases can extend the chain with DNA. The primer is later removed and the space it occupied filled with the appropriate deoxyribonucleotides.

- DNA replication is semidiscontinuous. Since the DNA strands are anti parallel and DNA may be synthesized only in the 5' → 3' direction, only one strand may be synthesized continuously in the direction that the replication fork is moving. That strand is referred to as the leading strand. The other strand, the lagging strand, must be synthesized discontinuously as a series of fragments synthesized in the opposite direction that the replication fork is moving. These fragments, known as Okazaki fragments, each require a separate initiation event.

- Errors in DNA replication are corrected by a proofreading mechanism. About once every 1000 nucleotides, an incorrect nucleotide is added. Prokaryotic DNA polymerases have a 3' → 5' exonuclease activity that removes the incorrect nucleotide and then the polymerase continues DNA synthesis, adding the correct nucleotide where it removed the incorrect one.

Separating and stabilizing DNA strands
    Replication fork: strands separate and unwind
        Helicases unwind DNA
        Topoisomerases relieve tension (Figure 2.17)
    Single strands stabilized at replication fork
        SSBs bind single stranded DNA
        Cooperative binding more SSBs
    Stabilized single DNA strands are templates
Synthesizing new DNA strands (Figures 2.18, 2.19, 2.20)
    Strict requirements of DNA polymerases
        Require small primer RNA on template strand
        New nucleotide added to 3'-0H of primer
        New strand: synthesized in 5' → 3' direction
    Primase: RNA polymerase makes primer to initiated DNA synthesis
    Source of energy for phosphodiester bonds between nucleotides
        Precursor nucleotides are triphosphates
        Hydrolysis of two phosphates

Semi-discontinuous DNA replication (Figure 2.22)

    Lagging strand and leading strand synthesis at replication fork

        DNA strands are anti parallel

            $3' \rightarrow 5'$ template used for leading strand synthesis

            $5' \rightarrow 3'$ template used for lagging strand synthesis

        Leading strand: strand of DNA synthesized continuously $5' \rightarrow 3'$

        Lagging strand: strand of DNA synthesized discontinuously $5' \rightarrow 3'$

            Okazaki fragments: formed $5' \rightarrow 3'$ on the lagging strand

            Okazaki fragments: primase initiates each fragment

            RNA primers: synthesized by primase

    E. coli DNA polymerase III synthesizes lagging and leading strands

    E. coli DNA polymerase I:

        RNA primers removed $5' \rightarrow 3'$ direction;

        adds DNA nucleotide in the $5' \rightarrow 3'$ direction

    (See example 2.4 Accumulation of Okazaki fragments in ligase-deficient *E. coli.*.)

Simultaneous synthesis of leading and lagging strands

    Replisome: all enzymes for DNA synthesis

        Synthesizes leading, lagging strand simultaneously

        DNA polymerase III α subunits replicate DNA

        α subunit replicates leading strand

        α subunit replicates lagging strand

    The β subunits guide DNA templates

Proofreading newly-synthesized DNA (figure 2.23)

    Mismatches occur about 1 per 1000 nucleotides

    E. coli RNA polymerase III: (Table 2.1)

        recognizes mismatch;

        $3' \rightarrow 5'$ exonuclease activity removes mismatch;

        Continues $5' \rightarrow 3'$ synthesis

    DNA Polymerase II can repair mismatches and damaged DNA

Replication of Eukaryotic DNA

    Five DNA polymerases known in mammals (Table 2.2, Figure 2.25)

    Five mammalian enzymes are α, β, δ, ε, γ

        α: responsible for lagging strand synthesis and functions as primase

            48 and 58 kD subunits: act as primase combined with holoenzyme or alone

            180 and 70 kD subunits: function in DNA replication (Okazaki fragments)

        δ: responsible for leading strand synthesis (no primase activity)

        ε and β: repair of damaged DNA in association with exonucleases

        γ: synthesis of mitochondrial DNA (D-loop synthesis)

    $3' \rightarrow 5'$ exonuclease activities of d, e and g suggest role in proofreading

        Model suggests a and d associate in single complex

2.5 REPLICATION OF ENTIRE DNA MOLECULES

Central idea:

- DNA molecules range in size from a few thousand nucleotide pairs in viruses to more than a hundred million nucleotide pairs in eukaryotic chromosomes. Several different strategies are employed for DNA replication depending upon the size of the DNA molecule. DNA replication is bidirectional in most cases. This means that replication forks proceed from an initiation site in both directions along the DNA strand. Circular prokaryotic DNAs generally have a single initiation site from which bidirectional replication proceeds around the circle until the two replication forks meet. Large eukaryotic DNAs are linear and typically have many initiation sites along the molecule from which bidirectional replication proceeds. Initiation sites appear to be fixed sites in the DNA that are rich in A-T base pairs. Small linear molecules can be replicated by strand displacement. Large linear molecules require telomerase to finish synthesis at the ends of the molecule.

Origins of DNA replication (Figure 2.27)
    Points of initiation of DNA replication called "origins of replication"
        Origins are rich in A-T base pairs
        Large molecules (i.e., eukaryotic chromosome DNA):many origins
        One origin (*oriC*) in *E. coli*: (Figures 2.28, 2.29)
            245 nucleotide pairs;
            13-mer segments are rich in A-T pairs;
            9-mer segments direct binding of DnaA protein
        DnaA catalyzes strand separation at the 13-mers
Bidirectional DNA replication
    DNA replication: unidirectional in viruses and bacterial plasmids
        One replication fork is formed
        Replication proceeds in one direction
    DNA replication: bidirectional in large circular molecules and linear DNAs
        E. coli : one origin of replication site
            Two replication forks formed at origin
            Replication in both directions from replication fork
        Long linear molecules of DNA molecules in eukaryotes have many origin sites
            Replication: bidirectional from each origin
            Approaching replication forks meet
    (See Example 2.5 DNA replication in *Bacillus subtilis*.)
Strategies for replicating circular DNA
    θ-mode: bidirectional from point of origin (Figure 2.29)
    σ-mode: called the "rolling-circle" mode has a σ-shape (Figure 2.30)
        One strand at the origin of replication is nicked
        5′ end separates; leading-strand replication begins at exposed 3′ end
        5′ strand is replicated discontinuously
    D-loop replication: mitochondrial DNA (Figure 2.31)
        Unbroken strands are separated at origin
        Continuous synthesis displaces other strand (D-loop)
        Continuous synthesis on displaced strand follows
Strategies for replicating linear DNA (Figures 2.32, 2.33)
    Each 5′ DNA end not finished;
    Primer removal leaves 3′ end overhang
    Linear virus DNAs circularize before replication
    Eukaryotic chromosomes use telomerase
        Telomerase carries RNA template sequence for extension of 3′ overhang
        Telomerase template sequence complementary to telomere
        The 3′ overhang is extended
        RNA primer made on extended 3′ end
        DNA polymerase fills gap, primer removed, overhangs trimmed

Chapter 3
Transcription and RNA Processing

KEY CONCEPTS

- A gene is a segment of DNA that is transcribed into an RNA molecule.
- The central dogma of molecular genetics is the idea that the information in a gene is transcribed into RNA. The information in RNA is then translated into protein.
- Transcription proceeds through three steps, initiation, elongation, and termination.
- To become functional, most RNA molecules must be modified after transcription.

KEY TERMS

gene
central dogma
transcription
translation
polypeptide
protein
mRNA
tRNA
rRNA
snRNA
pre—mRNA
RNA polymerase
RNA polymerase I, II, III
promoter
sense strand
antisense strand
template strand
upstream/downstream
$5' \rightarrow 3'$ direction
transcription start point
conserved sequences
consensus sequences
Pribnow box
Hogness box
CAAT box
holoenzyme
core enzyme
sigma factor
enhancer
rho-dependent termination
intrinsic termination
hairpin structure
potential terminators
AAUAAA
NOR
5' capping

3' polyadenylation
intron/exon
intron removal
GT–AG rule
spliceosome

CHAPTER TOPICS

CHAPTER OUTLINE

Introduction

Concept of gene is central to genetics
Word "gene" coined by Wilhelm Johannsen 1909
The gene can be studied at the molecular level

3.1 THE CENTRAL DOGMA

Central ideas:
- A gene may be defined as a segment of a DNA molecule that is transcribed into an RNA molecule.
- The genetic information in the DNA of a gene is transcribed into RNA which is then translated into a polypeptide and the polypeptide is processed into a protein. This is the central

dogma of molecular genetics.

Defining gene function
> Refining definition of gene
>> 1909: "gene" coined by Wilhelm Johannsen: "the fundamental unit of heredity"
>> 1953-present: Gene at the molecular level "segment of DNA transcribed into RNA"
> Gene expression and the central dogma
>> Winter of 1952: Watson's sign above desk "DNA → RNA → protein"
>>> Arrows meant "transfer of genetic information"
>>> DNA and proteins: both linear chains of subunits
>>> Nucleotide sequence in DNA: information for amino acid sequence in proteins
>>> RNA chains copied from DNA: possible "templates" for protein synthesis
>> Late 1950s: acceptance of RNA as intermediate information carrier between DNA and protein synthesis
>> Central dogma of molecular genetics formalized
> Central dogma: two important processes of gene function
>> Transcription: DNA information template for RNA synthesis
>>> Many genes encode proteins
>>> Some genes encode tRNAs, rRNAs, snRNAs, ribozymes
>> Translation: Information in RNAs translated into amino acid sequences of proteins
>>> Enzymes: control of chemical reactions
>>> Protein hormones: chemical messengers of cell metabolism
>>> Structural proteins: structures of cells and tissues
>>> Carrier molecules: blood, substance transport
>>> Storage proteins: energy and nutrient storage
>>> Antibodies: protection from invaders

3.2 OVERVIEW OF TRANSCRIPTION AND RNA PROCESSING IN PROKARYOTES AND EUKARYOTES

Central ideas:

- Transcription and translation are coupled in prokaryotes. In eukaryotes, transcription is compartmentalized within the nucleus. The RNA transcripts are exported from the nucleus to the cytoplasm where they are translated.

- There are three general classes of RNA molecules: messenger RNA (mRNA), ribosomal RNA (rRNA), and transfer RNA (tRNA). Messenger RNA contains the information that will be translated into proteins. Ribosomal RNA is a structural component of ribosomes making up about one–half of the intact ribosome. The other half is made of protein. Transfer RNAs are small RNA molecules that carry amino acids to the ribosome for translation.

- Transcription of RNA in prokaryotes is accomplished by a single RNA polymerase. However, in eukaryotes there are three RNA polymerases. RNA polymerase I transcribes the larger rRNA genes. RNA polymerase II transcribes genes that code for mRNA. RNA polymerase III transcribes tRNA genes and genes for other small RNAs including the small rRNAs.

- During transcription, RNA polymerase adds one ribonucleotide to the previous ribonucleotide in the 5' → 3' direction, the same as in DNA synthesis. One DNA strand serves as the template to determine the nucleotide sequence of the RNA using essentially the same base pairing rules as in DNA replication, with one exception. Whenever RNA polymerase encounters A in the DNA strand, it incorporates U instead of T in the RNA strand.

Transcription: similar to DNA replication
>DNA template strand used by RNA polymerases
>RNA synthesis: 5' → 3'
Steps of transcription: initiation, elongation, termination
>Initiation: binding of RNA polymerase to DNA template
>Elongation: RNA chain elongation 5' → 3'
>Termination: removal of RNA polymerase from DNA template
Major classes of RNA molecules: mRNA, rRNA, tRNA
>mRNAs: information for amino acid sequences of proteins
>rRNAs: structural components of ribosomes
>tRNAs: carriers of amino acid anticodons and amino acids to ribosomes on mRNAs
Major kinds of RNA polymerases
>Eukaryotes:
>>RNA polymerase I: most rRNA genes
>>RNA polymerase II: all mRNAs
>>RNA polymerase III: small RNAs such as tRNA and small rRNA
>Prokaryotes: one RNA polymerase for all genes
Transcription and translation: coupled in prokaryotes
>Ribosomes translate mRNAs during transcription
>mRNAs not processed before translation
Transcription and translation: compartmentalized in eukaryotes
>Pre—mRNAs processed to mRNAs in nucleoplasm
>mRNAs translated in cytoplasm

3.3 INITIATION OF TRANSCRIPTION

Central idea:
- Transcription is initiated at a promoter, a specific sequence of nucleotides in the DNA that determines where the RNA polymerase should begin transcribing.
- Only one DNA strand is used as a template for transcription of RNA. Since it contains the complementary or antisense nucleotide sequence as the RNA, it is called the antisense strand. The DNA strand not used as a template has the same nucleotide sequence or same sense as the RNA, and is called the sense strand. Coding strand and nontemplate strand are synonymous with sense strand. Anticoding strand and template strand are synonymous with antisense strand.
- Promoters contain conserved sequences that serve as signals for RNA polymerase to initiate transcription. The sequences and positions of conserved sequences differ in prokaryotes and eukaryotes.

The gene promoter and transcription
Promoter: signal in DNA for RNA polymerase binding and transcription initiation
>Identifies beginning of a gene
>Directs point of binding of RNA polymerase to DNA
>Assists helix opening after RNA polymerase binding
>Determines template strand for RNA synthesis
>Identifies transcription initiation point in gene
The DNA strands and initiation
>Sense strand

Same nucleotide sequence as RNA (except T instead of U);
Nontemplate strand
Antisense strand
Complementary nucleotide sequence to RNA;
Template strand

Conserved sequences in promoters
Identification of similar sequences among promoters
Conserved sequences: similar nucleotide sequence regions among promoters
Consensus sequence: most representative sequence among conserved sequences
David Pribnow: first promoter consensus sequence −10 nucleotides upstream
Conserved sequences in prokaryotic promoters
Point of reference for gene: transcription start point (nucleotide 0)
Transcription start point for most *E. coli* genes
Determined by matching 5′ end of RNA with DNA sequence;
Usually an "A" in *E. coli* genes
Other consensus sequences
Minus 10 sequence TATAAT (Pribnow box)
T and A pairs facilitate strand separation
Site of initial DNA strand separation
Minus 35 sequence TTGACA: initial binding RNA polymerase to promoter

Prokaryotic polymerase
Single RNA polymerase in bacteria
Five subunits in holoenzyme
Core enzyme: two α subunits and β and β′ subunits
Fifth subunit: σ factor
Holoenzyme binds to promoter
Initiates transcription
σ factor releases from core enzyme during transcription

Conserved sequences in eukaryotic promoters
Conserved sequences in mRNA promoters
Transcription start point: PyAPy
5′ end mRNA: usually "A"
Minus 25 to −30: TATA box or Hogness box (consensus TATAAAA)
Minus 75 to −80: CAAT box (consensus GGCCAATCT)
Additional consensus sequences: CACC box and GC box(some mRNA promoters)

Transcription factors and the basal eukaryotic transcription complex
Transcription factors assist eukaryotic RNA polymerase
TFIID, TFIIA, TFIIE, TFIIJ, TFIIH assist binding and initiation
TFIIH is helicase
After initiation polymerase proceeds alone

Enhancers
Location: usually upstream from promoter (some downstream)
Function: increase transcription of some genes

3.4 ELONGATION

RNA synthesis: 5′ → 3′ direction with antisense DNA strand as template
Energy source for phosphodiester bonds: ribonucleotide triphosphates A, U, C, and G
DNA−RNA hybrid rapidly separates during elongation

Features of rate of elongation
        E. coli RNA polymerase elongates by bursts and pauses
        NusA protein bound to *E. coli* polymerase (replaces σ) paces transcription with translation
        TFIIS in eukaryotes starts stalled RNA polymerase II

3.5 TERMINATION

Central ideas:
- Two modes of termination of transcription are known in prokaryotes. The first is intrinsic termination which requires a conserved sequence at the end of the gene that causes a hairpin structure in the mRNA. The second is rho-dependent termination which requires a protein known as rho factor.
- Termination of transcription in eukaryotes differs, depending on the RNA polymerase that transcribes the gene. RNA polymerase I terminates transcription at a conserved sequence that binds a transcription factor. However, the rRNA precursor is cleaved prior to termination. RNA molecules transcribed by RNA polymerase II are also usually cleaved before the RNA polymerase reaches the termination site. Cleavage is determined by conserved sequences.

Prokaryotic termination: intrinsic termination; rho-dependent termination
    Intrinsic termination
        Conserved terminator sequence in RNA: UUUUUUA
        Hairpin located upstream from terminator sequence
        Hairpin plus UUUUUUA sequence terminates transcription of RNA polymerase
    Rho—dependent termination
        Rho and RNA polymerase at rho-dependent terminator site terminates transcription
        Rho—dependent terminator site downstream from translation termination site
            Presence of ribosomes prevent chain termination at "potential terminators"
            Ribosomes close behind RNA polymerase (speed regulated by NusA)
            Absence of ribosomes allows termination

Eukaryotic termination
    RNA polymerase I termination
        Requires consensus sequence: AGGTCGACCAG(A/T)NTG
        Termination requires interaction with termination factor TTFI
        Large precursor RNA cleaved 18 nucleotides upstream from termination sequence
    RNA polymerase II termination
        Pre-mRNA cleaved 11—30 nucleotides downstream of consensus AAUAAA
        RNA polymerase II continues transcribing after RNA cleavage
        Termination not understood
    RNA polymerase III termination
        Termination site present in DNAs transcribed by RNA polymerase III
        Little is known about termination sites

3.6 TRANSCRIPTION OF rRNAs and tRNAs

    Three rRNAs in *E. coli*
        5S, 16S and 23S
        Three rRNAs transcribed as large precursor RNA (5600 nucleotides)

Post—transcriptional processing: precursor RNA cleaved to three rRNAs
Number of copies or rRNA precursor gene in *E. coli*: seven
rRNAs in eukaryotes transcribed by RNA polymerase I
    5S, 16S, 28S, plus 5.8S in some eukaryotes (5S by RNA polymerase III in larger eukaryotes)
    (2S and 7.8S rRNA in some species)
    RNA polymerase I transcribes large precursor RNA
    Post—transcriptional processing: large precursor yields 5.8S, 16S, 28S rRNAs
    Many copies large precursor gene located in nucleolus organizer region
    Nucleolus: site for
        RNA polymerase I transcription
        rRNA precursor processing;
        ribosome assembly
5S rRNA and tRNAs transcribed by RNA polymerase III (most eukaryotes)

3.7 mRNA PROCESSING

Central idea:
- Eukaryotic mRNAs begin as a pre-mRNA that is processed to become the mature mRNA. A 5′ cap, consisting of a methylated guanine nucleotide, is added to the 5′ end of the molecule. A poly (A) tail is added to the 3′ end of the molecule. Introns are removed from the transcript, yielding the mature mRNA.

Processing of eukaryotic pre-mRNA
    Addition of 5′ cap
        5′ carbon 7-methyl guanine attached to triphosphate on 5′ end of RNA
        Attachment is 5′— 5′
        Protects 5′ end from degradation enzymes
    Polyadenylation 3′ end
        Cleaved Pre-mRNA polyadenylated by poly A polymerase
        No template for poly A synthesis
    Intron removal from pre-mRNA guided by consensus sequences
        GT—AG rule: GU on 5′ end AG on 3′ end of intron
        Conserved sequences with **GU—AG**: **GU**AAGU and 6PyNC**AG**
        Additional conserved sequence 18—40 nucleotides from 3′ end:
            PyNPyPuAPy (A is invariant)
        Spliceosome: made of small ribonucleoproteins (snRNPs) removes introns
            snRNP U1 binds to GUAAGU
            snRNP U2 binds to PyNPyPyPu conserved sequence
            U1 binds to U2 forming intron loop
            snRNPs U4, U5, U6 join with complex
            Intron cut at 5′ G at 5′ intron/exon junction
            5′ G end of intron forms 5′–2′ bond with A in PyNPyPuAPy
        Intron cut 3′ end of G at intron-exon junction (6PyNC**AG**)
        Remaining snRNPs join exons

3.8 PROCESSING OF rRNAs AND tRNAs

Central idea:
- The large precursor RNA in eukaryotes is cleaved in a stepwise fashion to form the final rRNA products. Nucleotides may also be modified, typically by methylation. Many of the nucleotides in tRNAs are also modified.

rRNA processing
    Processing large rRNA precursor molecule in prokaryotes
        Seven precursor genes are transcribed
        All seven include 5S, 16S, 23S and several tRNAs
        Each differ in kind of tRNAs
        Ribonuclease III cleaves precursor forming mature rRNAs and tRNAs
    Processing large rRNA precursor molecule in eukaryotes
        Large precursor cleaved stepwise to yield mature rRNAs
        Mature rRNAs incorporated into ribosome subunits with ribosome proteins
        Some rRNAs methylated before ribosome assembly

tRNA processing
    Cleaving large tRNA precursors in prokaryotes to form mature tRNAs
        Some tRNAs cleaved from large rRNA precursor RNAs
        Others cleaved from transcribed precursor cluster of tRNAs
    Eukaryote tRNAs transcribed individually from gene clusters
    All tRNAs extensively modified after transcription
        All have CCA on 3' ends
            Some added after transcription
            Some transcribe with tRNA
        Many nucleotides in tRNA modified
        Modifications in anticodon aid wobble effect

Chapter 4
Translation and Protein Function

KEY CONCEPTS

- Proteins, the ultimate product of most genes, consist of amino acids that are connected together with peptide bonds during translation. The linear sequence of amino acids corresponds to the linear sequence of nucleotides in RNA which corresponds to the linear sequence of nucleotides in the DNA of a gene. Thus, proteins and the genes that code for them are colinear.
- The sequence of nucleotides in an mRNA corresponds with the sequence of amino acids in a polypeptide. The genetic code of triplet codons defines the relationship between nucleotide sequence and amino acid sequence.
- During translation, mRNA, tRNA, and ribosomes interact to form a linear chain of amino acids.
- Translation proceeds through the steps of initiation, elongation, and termination.

KEY TERMS

amino acids
R-groups
codon
termination codon
stop codon
initiation codon
start codon
reading frame
large ribosome subunit
small ribosome subunit
polysome
acceptor arm
amino acid attachment site
anticodon arm
D arm
TΨC arm
charged tRNA
tRNA synthetase
cognate tRNAs
wobble hypothesis
Shine-Dalgarno sequence
$tRNA_f^{met}$
N-formyl methionine
N-formyl-methionyl-tRNA (fMet-tRNA$_f$
ribosome A site
ribosome P site
Met-tRNA$_i$
scanning
peptidyl transferase
protein primary structure
protein secondary structure
α helix

β strand
β-pleated sheet
random coil
β turn
protein tertiary structure
disulfide bond
quaternary structure
enzyme active site

CHAPTER TOPICS

4.1 AMINO ACIDS AND POLYPEPTIDES
4.2 THE GENETIC CODE
     From nucleotides to amino acids
     The reading frame for translation
4.3 RIBOSOMES, THE SITES OF TRANSLATION
4.4 THE ROLE OF tRNA
     tRNA structure
     Amino acid specificity of tRNAs
     Degeneracy and the wobble hypothesis
4.5 DECIPHERING THE GENETIC CODE
     Demonstration of nonoverlapping codons
     Indirect approaches
     Exceptions to the genetic code
4.6 INITIATION OF TRANSLATION
     Prokaryotic initiation
     Eukaryotic initiation
4.7 ELONGATION
4.8 TERMINATION
4.9 PROTEIN STRUCTURE AND FUNCTION
     Protein modification and processing
     Protein function
     Enzymes

CHAPTER OUTLINE

Introduction
     The second part of central dogma (mRNA → protein)
          Translation
          Protein processing
     All proteins are specified by genes (with perhaps one exception)

4.1 AMINO ACIDS AND POLYPEPTIDES

Central ideas:
- A polypeptide is a linear chain of amino acids connected to one another by peptide bonds. There are 20 different amino acids utilized in protein synthesis. The amino acids differ in the R-group portion of the molecule.
- The nucleic acid sequence of a gene is colinear with the amino acid sequence of the

polypeptide encoded by the gene. Each amino acid in a polypeptide is specified by a three-nucleotide codon in the mRNA.

Proteins have many functions and are the most diverse class of biological molecules
    The sole function of most genes is to specify the primary structure of the proteins
    Many proteins are enzymes
    Some function in membrane transport
    Some are stored for energy and food in bird eggs and seeds
    Some are structural such as muscle fiber proteins
    Some are poisons such as snake or spider venom
Regardless of function each protein is encoded by a gene
Translation: conversion of genetic code to amino acid sequences of proteins
    All amino acids have a common structure and a unique structure
        Common structure in amino acids
            Central carbon with carboxyl attached
            Amino and hydrogen also attached to central carbon
        Unique structure attached to central carbon: the R group
    Twenty kinds of amino acids based on R group differences
    Properties of R groups vary tremendously
    Hydrophilic, hydrophobic, acidic, basic, polar, nonpolar R groups
    Function of protein: determined by chemical properties of R groups
Translation: mRNA codons used to link amino acids by peptide bonds
    Peptide bond: carboxyl group of one amino acid covalently bonded to amino group of next
        amino acid in the chain
    Peptide bonds created by enzyme in ribosome during translation
Twenty kinds of amino acids linked together form the great diversity of proteins

4.2 THE GENETIC CODE

Central ideas:
- The genetic code contains 64 codons, 61 of which code for amino acids. The remaining three codons specify termination of translation.
- Codons are read according to a fixed reading frame that is non-overlapping and uninterrupted. Translation begins at a specific AUG codon called the initiation codon. The codons are then read in frame from the initiation codon according to the genetic code. Translation continues until the ribosome encounters a termination codon.

Codons in mRNA colinear with amino acid sequence in protein
    mRNA codons translated in $5' \rightarrow 3'$ direction
    Amino acid chain: carboxy terminal $\rightarrow \rightarrow \rightarrow$ amino terminal
    1964: Yanofsky: genetic codon sequence and amino acid sequence colinear
Genetic code structure
    Sixty-four combinations of triplet code
    Codons nonoverlapping
    Three stop (termination) codons: UAA, UAG, UGA
    Sixty-one codons code 20 amino acids
    Genetic code nearly universal
    Same code in humans and bacteria
        Human insulin gene translated by bacteria

Bacterial human insulin native insulin identical in amino acid sequence

From nucleotides to amino acids

First major question about the genetic code

Number of nucleotides per codon: two, three, four

Two nucleotides: $4^2 = 16$ (not enough)

Three nucleotides: $4^3 = 64$ (more than enough)

Genetic code is three per codon

Three termination codons

Sixty one codons specify the 20 amino acids (Table 4.4)

(See Example 4.1 Colinearity of gene and its protein.)

The reading frame for translation

Translation means reading genetic code

Ribosomes bind to 5′ end of mRNA at a recognition site

Initiation codon is AUG downstream from 5′ end

Translation of initiation codon AUG

Prokaryotes: N-formyl methionine

Eukaryotes: methionine

Genetic code is nonoverlapping

AUG first codon

Next triplet is next codon

Last codon is triplet before termination codon

(See Example 4.2 Determining the amino acid sequence of a polypeptide from the nucleotide sequence, Figure 4.7)

4.3 RIBOSOMES: THE SITES OF TRANSLATION

Central idea:

- Ribosomes are composed of a small and a large subunit that assemble on the mRNA for translation. Prokaryotic and eukaryotic ribosomes are similar in structure, although eukaryotic ribosomes are larger.

Ribosome RNA and proteins

Prokaryotic ribosomes are 70S

50S large subunit

23S and 5S rRNAs

Thirty-one proteins

30S small subunit

16S rRNA

Twenty-one proteins

Subunits interlock

Mammalian ribosomes are 80S

60S large subunit

28S, 5.8S, and 5S rRNAs

Forty-five to 50 proteins

40S small subunit

18S rRNA

Thirty to 35 proteins

4.4 THE ROLE OF tRNA

Central ideas:
- Transfer RNA carries amino acids to the ribosome. The tRNA molecule folds back on itself forming base pairs in a cloverleaf structure containing an acceptor arm, an anticodon arm, a D arm, TΨC arm, and a small extra arm.
- The amino acid is attached to the acceptor arm of a tRNA by an aminoacyl tRNA synthetase. Once the amino acid is attached, the tRNA is said to be charged. The charged tRNA enters the ribosome where its anticodon pairs with the codon in the mRNA.

tRNA structure
- Similar in all organisms
- Seventy four to 95 nucleotides
- All tRNAs processed after transcription
- Four-armed clover leaf (two dimensional view)
    - Acceptor arm: both ends of single strand
        - Base-paired stem and three unpaired nucleotides
        - CCA unpaired nucleotides on 3' end
        - A of CCA: amino acid attachment site
        - 2' or 3' carbon of A hold amino acid
    - Anticodon arm: opposite acceptor arm
        - Base-paired stem plus loop of seven unpaired nucleotides
        - Anticodon middle three nucleotides of loop
        - tRNA anticodon $3' \rightarrow 5'$ pairs with mRNA codon $5' \rightarrow 3'$
        - Three other arms: **D arm, TΨC arm,** and **extra arm**
    - Base-paired stems and loops with modified nucleotides
        - **T:** transcribed U modified to T
        - **Ψ:** U modified to pseudouridine
        - **D:** U modified to dihydrouridine after transcription
        - **Extra arm:** between **D** and **TΨC arms**
            - Variable unpaired nucleotides
            - A distinguishing feature among many tRNAs
    - 3-D structure: folded L-shape in the cell

Amino acid specificity of tRNAs
- Anticodon determines amino acid specificity
- Amino acid attachment site (CCA) uniform among tRNAs
- Two forms of tRNA
    - Free tRNA
    - Activated tRNA
        - Amino acid attached by aminoacyl high energy bond
        - Attachment site: 2' or 3' carbon of A nucleotide of ACC-tRNA attachment site
        - Enzyme: aminoacyl tRNA synthetase
- (See Example 4.3 Nucleotide sequence and secondary structure of tRNA.)

Codon degeneracy and the wobble hypothesis
- Number of anticodons (tRNAs) needed
    - Codon-anticodon pairing precise for first two nucleotides of codon
    - Base-pairing rules at third codon position:
        - U pairs with A or G (third codon position)
        - C pairs with G

A pairs with U
G pairs with U or C
I pairs with U, C, or A
Less anticodons needed to complement 62 codons

4.5 DECIPHERING THE GENETIC CODE

Central ideas:
- The genetic code is degenerate, meaning that some amino acids are encoded by more than one codon. Although there are 61 codons, there are less than 61 tRNAs, due to the fact that some anticodons may pair with more than one codon, according to the wobble hypothesis.
- The genetic code was deciphered through a series of experiments based primarily on the use of synthetic mRNAs in cell-free translation systems. With rare exceptions, the genetic code is universal among all species on earth.

Demonstration of nonoverlapping triplet code
Sydney Brenner 1957: overlapping code required at least 70 codons to account for known amino acid sequences in proteins (triplet code only 64 codons possible)
Single nucleotide mutations changed only one amino acid in protein
(See Example 4.4 Testing the overlapping codon hypothesis.)

Indirect approaches to solving the genetic code
Synthetic mRNA templates and crude cell-free extracts
    Poly U coded for phenylalanine
    Poly C coded for proline
Synthetic mRNAs with two nucleotides
    Code degeneracy evident
    Leucine has several codons
Isolated tRNAs and code in synthetic mRNA
    Anticodons identified
    Specific charged tRNAs identified using 3-nucleotide RNA bound to ribosome
        Amino acid on identified charged tRNA identified with ribosome-bound codon
        Nirenberg and Leder identified, confirmed, 50 of 64 codons with ribosome binding test
Khorana and coworkers: di-, tri- and tetra- nucleotide synthetic mRNAs
    Over 50 codons were confirmed
    Filling in remaining gaps in codon dictionary

Exceptions to genetic code
Nucleotide sequence and amino acid sequence
    Mycoplasma capricolum (UGA read as "tryptophan)
    Protozoans (UAA and UAG read as "glutamine")
    Minor differences in Mitochondrial systems
"Exceptions" to the code that were not exceptions
    mRNA editing after transcription

4.6 INITIATION OF TRANSLATION

Central idea:
- Translation proceeds through the stages of initiation, elongation, and termination.

Prokaryotic initiation

    Steps of initiation

    30S subunit binds to IF-3

        Complex binds to Shine-Dalgarno sequence 5' end mRNA

            Recognition sequence near 3' end 16S rRNA: 3' UCCUCC5'

            Complementary Shine-Dalgarno sequence: AGGAGG

            AGGAGG and downstream AUG codon covered by complex

        N-formyl-methionyl-tRNA plus IF-2 enter complex at AUG codon

    50S subunit assembles with complex

        GTP hydrolysis provides energy

        IF-2 and IF-3 released

    Two tRNA holding sites in complete ribosome

        A site: aminoacyl (or entry) site

        P site: peptidyl (amino acid donor) site

    At initiation:

        P site covers AUG codon;

        P site holds N-formyl-methionyl-tRNA;

        A site covers 2nd codon in mRNA sequence

    Second activated tRNA enters A site

Eukaryotic initiation

    Steps of initiation:

        Met-tRNA$_i$ bind to eIF-2 and GTP (small subunit complex);

        Met-tRNA$_i$-eIF-2-GTP bind small ribosome subunit complex;

        Small subunit complex with IF-4A and CBP bind to 5' cap mRNA

            Small subunit complex scans to initiation codon AUG

            Anticodon Met-tRNA$_i$ binds at AUG

        Large subunit binds to small subunit

            eIF-2 released

            GTP hydrolyzed

        Second activated tRNA enters A site

4.7 ELONGATION

    Elongation in prokaryotes

        Charged tRNA binds to EF-Tu and GTP

        Charged tRNA-EF-tu -GTP enters A site

            EF-Tu released

            GTP hydrolyzed

        Ribosome peptidyl transferase forms peptide bond between adjacent amino acids

    Ribosome translocates to next codon

        tRNA with peptide in A site moves to P site

        Next charged tRNA-EF-Tu-GTP enters A site

        Translocation requires ribosome complexed with EFG and GTP

            EFG-GTP released from ribosome

            GTP hydrolyzed

    Elongation in eukaryotes analogous to prokaryotes

4.8 TERMINATION

    Elongation stops at termination codon in A site

Termination codons are UAA, UAG, or UGG

No tRNA for termination codons

Release factors join ribosomes

Aminoacyl bond cleaved and polypeptide chain released

4.9 PROTEIN STRUCTURE AND FUNCTION

Central ideas:

- Following translation, polypeptides are processed to form proteins. Processing includes removal of amino acid segments, folding of the polypeptides, and attachment of external groups to the protein.
- Protein structure is hierarchical. The primary structure is the linear chain of amino acids in a polypeptide. The secondary structure may consist of several structural features, including a helices, b strands, b pleated sheets, random coils, and b turns. The secondary structures attach to one another through interactions among the R groups, forming the tertiary structure. Two or more protein subunits may associate to form the quaternary structure.
- A protein's amino acid composition and its structure determine its function. There are many different classes of proteins. Enzymes are among the most important in genetics. An enzyme is catalyst that contains an active site where the reaction takes place.

Protein modification and processing

Post-translational modification

Signal peptide and insertion into membrane

Nonpolar and hydrophobic amino acids

Signal peptide cleavage

Folding of polypeptide (amino acid interactions)

Secondary structure

α helix

β strand

β turn

random coil

β pleated sheet

Tertiary structure

R group interactions cause folding

Disulfide bonds between R groups

Combining of several polypeptides

Quaternary structure

Several units of same polypeptide

Different polypeptides

Structure depends on amino acid sequence

Protein function

Positions of amino acids determine protein chemical properties

Chemical properties of R groups

Positions of R groups in tertiary, quaternary structure

Physical conformation of protein and amino acid R-group position

Enormous diversity of function

Enzymes

Structure, active site, and catalytic function of enzyme

Substrate and product

Chapter 5
Mutation

KEY CONCEPTS:

- Mutation is the only original source of genetic variation.
- Mutations in the same gene may have different effects depending on the type and location of the mutation.
- Errors in DNA replication may mutate genes.
- Mutagenic agents may damage DNA causing mutations.
- Cells have DNA repair mechanisms that restore the original sequence to damaged DNA.

KEY TERMS

point mutation
transposable elements
chromosome aberrations
same-sense mutation
silent mutation
missense mutation
nonsense mutation
transition
transversion
deletion
insertion
frameshift
fragile X premutation
fragile X full mutation
Huntington disease
loss-of-function mutation
gain-of-function mutations
forward mutation
reversion
suppressor mutation
spontaneous mutation
induced mutation
mutation hot spots
lesion
damaged DNA
depyrimidination
apurinic site
apyrimidinic site
AP site
cytosine deamination
ionizing radiation
free radical
nonionizing radiation
pyrimidine dimer
intercalating agent

deaminating agent
hydroxylating agent
aflotoxin B_1
alkylating agent
carcinogen
photoreactivation
AP endonucleases
DNA glycosylase
mismatch repair
SOS response
induced state
error-prone synthesis
transcription-repair coupling
xeroderma pigmentosum
Cockayne syndrome

CHAPTER TOPICS

5.1 TYPES OF MUTATIONS
    Substitution, deletion, and insertion mutations
    Trinucleotide repeat expansions
    Mutation and protein function
    Mutations outside of the transcribed region of a gene
    Forward mutations and reversions
5.2 SPONTANEOUS MUTATION
    Tautomeric shifts
    Mutations in repeated DNA segments
    Spontaneous lesions
5.3 INDUCED MUTATIONS
    Radiation
    Chemical mutagens
5.4 DNA REPAIR MECHANISMS
    Mechanisms that prevent DNA damage
    Mechanisms that repair damaged DNA
    Excision repair mechanisms
    Postreplication repair
    SOS response and mutagenesis
    Transcription-repair coupling

CHAPTER OUTLINE

Introduction
Mutation creates new genetic variation
    Mutation alters nucleotide sequence in DNA in some way
    Change in DNA may alter amino acid sequence in a protein
Changes in proteins can affect the phenotype

5.1 TYPES OF MUTATIONS

Central ideas:
- Substitution mutations may or may not have an effect on the gene product depending on where they are located. If a mutation does not change the amino acid sequence of the polypeptide, the mutation is a same-sense mutation, which is also silent. Missense mutations cause a change in the amino acid sequence of the polypeptide. Nonsense mutations create a premature termination codon, causing the polypeptide to be shorter than usual. Insertion and deletion mutations may be frameshift mutations.
- Trinucleotide repeat expansions are responsible for several genetic disorders in humans, including fragile X syndrome and Huntington disease.

Mutations create new genetic variation
> Heritable change in DNA
> Point mutation: change in one to few adjacent nucleotides
> Transposable elements can alter gene by insertion or removal of element
> Chromosome aberrations can alter many genes

Substitution, deletion, and insertion mutations
> Substitution mutation: most common (point mutations, Figure 5.1)
>> One nucleotide substituted for another (Figure 5.2)
>> Substitutions written: G → A
>> G → A implies C → T in complementary strand
>> Same-sense mutations (silent mutations)
>>> Changes codon, amino acid sequence unchanged
>>> GUG → GUA (same-sense) both encode valine
>> Missense mutation: amino acid sequence changed
>> Nonsense mutation: creates termination codon
> Transition mutation: purine → purine, pyrimidine → pyrimidine
> Transversion mutation: purine → pyrimidine, pyrimidine → purine
> Deletion mutation: one or more nucleotides deleted from DNA
> Insertion mutation: one or more nucleotides inserted in DNA
> Frameshift mutation: reading frame shifted by insertion or deletion mutation
>> Many deletion or insertion mutations shift reading frame
>> Frameshift mutations may change many amino acids

Trinucleotide repeat expansions (Table 5.1)
> DNA repeats can increase or decrease by errors in replication or crossing over (Figure 5.3)
> Fragile X syndrome: CGG repeat in 5′ untranslated region *FRM1* gene
>> Normal repeat number: 6 to 50 repeats
>> 50 to 230 repeats: fragile X premutation
>> Descendants of females with fragile X premutation
>>> Increase risk of syndrome in offspring
>>> Fragile X syndrome individuals: 700 to >1000 repeats
>> Missense mutation within *FRM1* can cause syndrome
> Huntington disease: CAG repeat in coding region of *IT15* gene
>> CAG codes for glutamine
>> Unaffected persons: 10–35 repeats in reading frame
>> Affected persons: 36–121 repeats in reading frame
> (See Example 5.1 Trinucleotide repeat expansion and fragile X syndrome.)

Mutations and protein function

Effects depend on several factors
        Which amino acids exchanged
        Number of amino acids altered
        Specific changes in amino acid sequence
Loss-of-function mutations
        Reduce or eliminate function of protein
        Most genetic disorders of humans
Gain-of-function mutations
        Usually occur in regulatory regions
        More rare than loss-of-function mutations
        Cancers often due to gain-of-function mutations
Mutations out of the transcribed region of a gene
        Affect depends on location
                Can affect amount of protein produced
                May affect place or timing of protein production
        May reduce or rarely enhance RNA polymerase binding
Forward and reversion mutations
        Forward mutation
                Changes common gene to mutant form
                Changes common DNA sequence to mutant sequence
        Reversion mutation
                Mutant gene reverts to functional form of gene
                        Mutation restores original DNA sequence
                        Mutation compensates for forward mutation (Figure 5.4)
                Reversion mutations order of magnitude less frequent
                        Changes in many locations alter function of protein
                        Only changes in specific locations restore function of protein
        Suppressor mutations
                Mutation in another gene compensates for loss of function
                Example: tRNA mutant compensates for stop codon mutation

5.2 SPONTANEOUS MUTATION

Central ideas:
- The nucleotides of DNA generally exist in stable forms, but may occasionally undergo tautomeric shifts to a less stable form. When a nucleotide in the template strand during DNA synthesis happens to be in the less stable form due to a tautomeric shift, its base pairing properties are altered, and an incorrect nucleotide may be added opposite the unstable nucleotide during DNA replication.
- Tautomeric shifts, as well as many other alterations in DNA, cause transitions during DNA replication. A transition is the substitution of the wrong purine for the correct purine or the substitution of the wrong pyrimidine for the correct pyrimidine during DNA replication.
- Transitions are the most common form of substitution mutations. Less frequent are transversions where a purine is substituted in the place of a pyrimidine or vice-versa.
- Short repeated nucleotide sequences tend to be "hotspots" for insertion and deletion mutations. During DNA replication, either the template strand or the newly synthesized strand may slip at a repeated sequence causing too few or too many nucleotides to be added as DNA replication continues.
- Depurination and depyrimidization leave a deoxyribose sugar in the DNA backbone with

no base attached to it. Such a lesion is called an AP site.
- Cytosine deamination changes C into U. Because U pairs with A instead of G, a transition takes place during DNA replication.

Tautomeric shifts (Figure 5.5)
   Shifts in molecular structure alter pairing properties of nucleotides
         T and G shift to enol form
         C and A shift to imino form
   Shifts in template strands may cause transition mutations
Mutations in repeated DNA segments (Figure 5.6)
   Mutation hot spots are short repeats
   Repeats misread at replication fork
   Insertions and deletions caused by strand slippage at repeats
   Slippage at repeats most often occurs during lagging strand synthesis
   (See Example 5.2 A mutation hot spot in T2 bacteriophage.)
Spontaneous lesions (natural chemical alterations of bases)
   Hydrolysis of purine or pyrimidine base bonded to deoxyribose
         Depurination lesion: loss of purine base from deoxyribose
         Depyrimidization: loss of pyrimidine base (less frequent)
         Apurinic site: depurinized site
         Apyrimidinic site: depyrimidinized site
         Apurinic and apyrimidinic sites are identical AP sites (Figure 5.7)
   Cytosine deamination
         Converts C to U
         If unprepared U in template pairs with A (C → T transition)
         U in DNA recognized by repair mechanism
   Methylation is common modification bases in DNA
         Cytosine → 5-methyl cytosine (Figure 5.8)
         Deamination of 5-methyl cytosine → T (C → T transition)

5.3 INDUCED MUTATIONS

Central ideas:
- Ionizing radiation (X-rays, α, β, and γ rays) deeply penetrates biological tissues. The radiation creates free radicals which, in turn, react chemically with the DNA altering it. Ionizing radiation frequently causes breaks in the sugar-phosphate backbone of DNA.
- Non-ionizing radiation consists primarily of ultraviolet light in sunlight. It penetrates only the surface layers of tissues and causes electrons to temporarily assume higher energy levels. Pyrimidines in DNA are particularly sensitive to non-ionizing radiation and may form pyrimidine hydrates or pyrimidine dimers.
- Base analogs are nitrogenous bases that are similar to the bases in DNA and may be incorporated in place of their usual counterparts during DNA replication. Two of the more common base analogs are 5-bromouracil (5-BU) and 2-aminopurine (2-AP). These base analogs tend to undergo tautomeric shifts more readily than their usual counterparts, causing transitions during DNA replication.
- Intercalating agents, such as ethidium bromide, acridine dyes, and ICR compounds, insert themselves within the stacked bases of the DNA molecule making a kink in the DNA molecule that may cause insertion or deletion mutations during DNA replication.
- Deaminating agents, such as bisulfate compounds and nitrous acid, may remove amino

groups from the nitrogenous bases. Alkylating agents add alkyl (usually methyl or ethyl) groups to the nitrogenous bases of DNA. Hydroxylating agents add hydroxyl groups to the nitrogenous bases. All of these lesions may cause mutations during DNA replication.

- Aflatoxin B_1 removes guanine bases from the DNA molecule leaving AP site halting DNA replication until lesion repaired.

Mutagens: agents that enter cell and cause mutations (Table 5.3)

Radiation

    Ionizing radiation creates free radicals

        Include: proton, neutron, X-rays, alpha, beta and gamma rays

        Indirect damage by free radical formation

            Free radicals highly reactive with DNA (Figure 5.9)

            Can break phosphodiester bonds in both strands

                One-strand break can be repaired

                Two-strand break difficult to repair

        Mutagenic effects are cumulative

        Workers must be protected from ionizing radiation

    UV Non-ionizing radiation excites electrons

        UV affects single cells and surface cell layers

        DNA absorbs UV at 254 nm Figures 5.10, 5.11)

            Pyrimidine hydrates

            Pyrimidine dimers

            Thymine dimers

Chemical mutagens

    Base analogs: similar to bases of DNA (Figure 5.12)

    Incorporated into DNA during synthesis

        5-bromouracil (5-BU) analog of thymine

            Frequent keto-enol tautomeric shifts

            Causes frequent transition mutations (Figure 5.13)

        2-amino purine (2-AP) analog of adenine

            Frequent keto-enol tautomeric shifts

            Causes frequent transition mutations

    Intercalating agents (Figure 5.14)

        Agents insert between DNA bases

        Cause single base insertion or deletion mutations

        Single base insertions or deletions cause frameshift mutations

            Acridine dyes

            Proflavin

            Ethidium bromide

            ICR compounds

    Deaminating agents (Figure 5.15)

        Causes frequent transition mutations

        Bisulfite ions deaminate C to U

        Nitrous acid deaminates C to U

    Hydroxylating agents (Figure 5.16)

        Converts C to hydroxyaminocytosine (pairs like T)

        Causes A to G transitions

    Aflatoxin B_1

        Removes guanine leaving AP site

DNA polymerase inserts A across from AP site

Causes Transversion mutation

Alkylating agents

Add methyl and ethyl groups on all DNA bases

Most mutations are transition mutations

Some transversion mutations

(See Example 5.3 Carcinogens in tobacco smoke and transversions.)

5.4 DNA REPAIR MECHANISMS

Central idea:
- There are three levels of DNA protection mechanisms that prevent or eliminate many mutations. The first is preventative, the second is direct DNA repair, and the third is post-replication repair.

DNA repair mechanisms greatly reduce mutation rate

Repair mechanisms similar in prokaryotes and eukaryotes

Repair mechanisms repair lesion not mutation

Three levels of repair

Mechanisms that prevent DNA damage (Table 5.4)

Detoxification of free radicals

Super oxide dismutase

Converts superoxide to hydrogen peroxide

Catalase

Converts hydrogen peroxide to water

Mechanisms that repair damaged DNA

Alkyltransferase: removes alkyl groups from bases

Photoreactivation: corrects UV damage

Enzyme PRE cleaves pyrimidine dimers

Requires blue light for activation

PRE is absent from placental animals

Excision repair mechanisms (Requires double-stranded DNA)

Variety of DNA lesions recognized and excised

Damaged sites excised by excinuclease

AP endonucleases excise AP sites

DNA glycosylase hydrolyzes sugar-base bond leaving AP site

DNA polymerase fills in excision gaps

Post-replication repair

Recombination repair (Figure 5.20)

Damaged strand repaired by recombination

Homologous segment replaces damaged segment

DNA polymerase fills in both gaps

Mismatch repair

Repairs mismatches in new strand that escaped proofreading

New strand identified by temporary lack of methylation

SOS response and mutagenesis (Figure 5.21)

Delay of DNA synthesis for DNA repair

Several repair mechanisms are activated

Permits error-prone repair mechanisms normally suppressed (Figure

5.22)

RNA polymerase III permitted to insert nucleotides opposite lesions

Transcription repair coupling (Figures 5.23, 5.24)

RNA polymerase stalls at lesion

TRCF removes stalled RNA polymerase

Excision repair: repairs lesion at TRCF binding site

Mutations in genes that encode repair system enzymes

Xeroderma pigmentosum: high skin cancer rate

Mutations cause failure in excision repair system

XP-variant probably encodes post-replication repair enzyme

Cockayne syndrome: failure of transcription-repair coupling

Chapter 6
An Integrated View of Gene Expression

KEY CONCEPTS

- Genes encode proteins and protein functions affect the phenotype.
- Mutations in the nucleotide sequence of genes may alter protein functions, which alter the phenotype.
- Variation in the nucleotide sequences of genes is expressed as phenotypic variation.

KEY TERMS

phenotypic variation
phenotype
genotype
gene expression
hemoglobin
β-globin gene
heme group
heme pocket
sickle-cell anemia
Hb A
Hb S
thalassemia
splice site
cryptic splice site
biochemical pathway
pathway substrate
pathway intermediate
end product
alkaptonuria
homogentisic acid
homogentisic acid oxidase
imaginal disks
minimal medium
auxotrophic mutant
one gene-one enzyme
one gene-one polypeptide

CHAPTER TOPICS

6.1 THE ANATOMY OF A GENE AND ITS EXPRESSION: THE HUMAN
    β-GLOBIN GENE
        DNA sequence and organization of the human β-globin gene
6.2 MUTATIONS IN THE β-GLOBIN GENE
        Sickle-cell anemia
        β thalassemia
6.3 ENZYMES, BIOCHEMICAL PATHWAYS, AND MUTATION
        Biochemical pathways

Mutations and biochemical pathways
The one gene-one polypeptide hypothesis and biochemical pathways

CHAPTER OUTLINE

Introduction

Genetic basis of phenotypic variation among individuals (Figure 6.1)
    Amounts and types of melanins vary from person to person
    Variation in melanins due to variations in genetic coding
    Melanins not coded by genes
Genes encode protein enzymes
    Enzyme-controlled pathways synthesize and regulate all cell compounds such as
        melanins
    Differences in hair color due to differences in encoded enzymes
Differences of coding sequences among individuals
    Differences in coding sequences produce altered enzymes
    Altered enzyme can cause observed differences in melanin phenotype

6.1 THE ANATOMY OF A GENE AND ITS EXPRESSION: THE HUMAN β-GLOBIN GENE

Central ideas:
- Gene expression is the process through which the nucleotide sequence of a gene is manifest in the phenotype of an organism.
- The human β globin gene is an excellent example of how the sequence of nucleotides in a gene are eventually expressed as a functional protein. Mutations in the DNA may alter the protein function which may cause an altered phenotype.

Hemoglobin; two β globin and two α globin proteins complexed with heme group
    Location: erythrocytes
    Function: oxygen and carbon dioxide transport
Mutations that alter hemoglobin function can cause wide-spread tissue damage
DNA sequence and organization of the human β globin gene
    Size including promoter: 1700 nucleotide-pairs (Figure 6.1)
    Two introns: 60% of gene
    Two CACCC boxes −90, −106
    CCAAT box −75
    TATA box −29 (CATAAAA)
pre-mRNA structure
    Introns adhere to GT-AG rule
    One intron structure
        5′ splice site: GTTGGT
        3′ splice site: CCACCCTTAG
        CACTGAC upstream 3′ splice site (consensus: PyNPyPyPuAPy)
    Other intron structure
        5′ splice site: GTGAGT
        3′ splice site: CCTCCCACAG
        TGCTAAT upstream 3′ splice site (consensus: PyNPyPyPuAPy)
    Reading frame start at first AUG in ACAGACACCAUGG

In-frame stop codon UAA (148 codons after AUG codon)

Cleavage of pre-mRNA transcript 18 nucleotides beyond AAUAAA sequence

β-globin protein: 146 amino acids (amino-end methionine is cleaved)

Complexes with heme group, two α globins, another β globin (Figure 6.3)

Heme pocket composed of hydrophilic amino acid residues

Each α and β subunit carries a heme pocket

02 carried in heme pockets: hydrophobic amino acids

C02 carried on arginines near carboxy-terminal ends

Hydrophilic amino acids on hemoglobin outer surface

Binding one gas prevents binding other gas (an allosteric heme-protein)

Sickle-cell anemia (mutation in 6th amino acid encoded by β-globin gene)

Codon: GAG → glutamic acid

Glutamic acid: acidic and hydrophilic

A → T transition mutation GAG (codes glutamic acid) → GUG (codes valine)

Valine: nonpolar and hydrophobic

Hemoglobin S forms chain fiber

Carboxy terminal end β globin S

With hydrophobic valine

Inserts into hydrophobic heme pocket

Several Hb S molecules link to form fiber protein chains (Figures 6.4, 6.5)

Reduced oxygen affinity

Hb S erythrocytes form sickle-shape

Sickle erythrocytes clog capillaries (Figure 6.6)

Tissues starve for nutrients and oxygen

Enlarged spleen etc.

β thalassemia

Reduction in β-globin synthesis

Reduced hemoglobin

Iron overloading and liver damage

Increase in bone-marrow mass

Brittle bones

Skeletal deformities

Nearly half of 30 known thalassemia mutations disrupt intron removal

Mutations involve splice sites

Mutant introns removed at cryptic splice sites

Result: codon deletions and frame shift mutations

(See Example 6.1 A mutation that causes β+ thalassemia.)

6.3 ENZYMES, BIOCHEMICAL PATHWAYS, AND MUTATION

Central ideas:
- Many compounds in cells are synthesized through biochemical pathways. A biochemical pathway begins with a substrate which is converted through a series of intermediates into the end product of the pathway.
- Mutations in genes that encode enzymes may block a biochemical pathway causing an intermediate to accumulate.
- The phenotypic effects of mutations that block biochemical pathways can be overcome by supplying the end product of the pathway or an intermediate of the pathway that appears farther along the pathway than the enzyme affected by the mutation.

- Mutations in the genes that encode enzymes in the same biochemical pathway can be used to identify the relative orders of intermediates and enzymes in the pathway.
- A mutation in any gene that encodes an enzyme in a biochemical pathway may block the pathway, cause the intermediate just before the block to accumulate, and prevent synthesis of the end product of the pathway.

Mutations in several genes can have similar phenotypes
  α thalassemia and β thalassemia: similar phenotypes
  Mutations that reduce hemoglobin amount have similar phenotypes

Biochemical pathways
  Pathway components (Figure 6.8)
    Pathway step (enzyme catalyzed reaction of pathway)
    Pathway substrate
    Pathway intermediate
    End product
  Melanin pathway and dietary phenylalanine
    Phenylalanine: pathway substrate
    PAH enzyme: phenylalanine $\rightarrow$ tyrosine (first intermediate)
    Tyrosinase: tyrosine $\rightarrow$ DOPA $\rightarrow$ dopaquinone
    Dopaquinone $\rightarrow \rightarrow \rightarrow \rightarrow$ (enzyme steps) melanins
  Genetic variations in genes for enzymes cause variations in pigmentation phenotype

Mutations and biochemical pathways (Figure 6.9)
  Mutant block: buildup of pathway intermediate
  Alkaptonuria
  Buildup of homogentisic acid ("alkapton" early 1900s) in body tissues
  Mutant block: gene for homogentisic acid oxidase
  (See Example 6.2 Beadle and Ephrussi's experiments with eye color mutations vermilion and cinnabar in *Drosophila melanogaster*.)

One gene-one polypeptide hypothesis and biochemical pathways
  Research of Beadle and Tatum
    Neurospora: wild type growth on minimal medium
    Supplemented medium: mutant growth
    Supplemented substance allowed mutants to grow
  Beadle and Tatum propose genes specify structure of enzymes
    Formulated: one gene one enzyme hypothesis
    Two or more genes encode multimeric enzymes
    Modified gene-enzyme hypothesis: one gene one polypeptide
  Neurospora mutants auxotrophic for arginine
    Nonallelic arginine auxotrophic mutations
    Different mutants require different pathway intermediates
  Auxotrophic mutants used to identify steps of biochemical pathway
    Reveal which intermediates in pathway
    Reveal relative order of pathways steps (enzymes)
  (See Example 6.3 Using auxotrophic mutants to determine the steps in the biochemical pathway for arginine synthesis in *Neurospora*.)

Chapter 7
Bacterial Genetics

KEY CONCEPTS

- Many important genetic concepts were discovered first in bacteria. Bacteria also serve as tools for practical applications of genetics.
- Most bacterial genes are found on a circular DNA molecule called the bacterial chromosome.
- DNA may be transferred from one bacterial cell to another where transferred DNA recombines with the chromosomal DNA.
- DNA transfer and recombination are used to map bacterial genes.
- Determination of complete DNA sequences in bacterial species is the first step toward understanding the complete biology of those species.

KEY TERMS

minimal medium
selective medium
nonselective medium
auxotrophy
prototrophy
allele
wild-type allele
mutant allele
phenotype
genotype
carbon source mutation
antibiotic resistant
temperature sensitive mutants
replica plating
bacterial chromosome
plasmid
episome
binary fission
recombination
heteroduplex DNA
homology
D-loop
Holliday junction
transformation
competent cells
gene mapping
cotransformation
F factor
conjugation bridge
Hfr
exogenote
endogenote
leading gene

interrupted mating
time-of-entry gene mapping
F′ factor
sexduction
F-duction
merozygote
partial diploid
complementation analysis
bacteriophage
phage
capsid
phage particle
lytic cycle
lawn
plaque
prophage
lysogeny
induction
virulent phage
temperate phage
turbid plaque
transduction
generalized transduction
specialized transduction

CHAPTER TOPICS

CHAPTER OUTLINE

Introduction
    Biochemical and industrial significance
        Tools to better understand eukaryotic genetics
        Uses in health care and medicine
        Used in gene transfers between widely different species
    Understanding the genetic systems of bacteria has shed light on genetic systems of all other organisms

7.1 BACTERIAL CULTURE

Central ideas:
- Bacteria are usually studied in laboratory cultures. They are grown on a liquid or agar-solidified medium that contains all the nutrients needed for the bacterial cells to grow. Minimal medium contains only those substances needed for growth.
- Bacteria that are prototrophic for a substance are capable of growing on medium that does not contain that substance. Bacteria that are auxotrophic for a substance are unable to grow unless the medium is supplemented with that substance.
- Mutant types of bacteria are typically identified by differences in their ability to grow and divide on selective media.
- Genetic variation used in bacterial genetics research includes auxotrophic mutations, carbon-source mutations, antibiotic-sensitive or resistant genes, and temperature-sensitive mutations.
- Each unique mutation within a single gene creates a new allele of that gene. Wild-type alleles are the versions of a gene found most often in nature. In most cases, wild-type alleles produce a functional protein product. Mutant alleles arise by mutation of a wild-type allele and usually fail to encode functional products.
- The observed characteristics of a bacterial culture is called the phenotype. The underlying genetic constitution that confers a phenotype is called the genotype.
- Medium can be selective or nonselective. A mutant bacterial strain can be distinguished from a nonmutant strain on selective medium. Both mutant and nonmutant strains grow equally well on nonselective medium.

    Bacterial genetic studies yield broadly applicable tools and information
        Used as genetic research tools in science and industry
        Studies aid in control of bacterial diseases
        Serve as producers of eukaryotic gene products
        Production of valuable pharmaceutical products
        Used in gene transfer between wide taxonomic groups

Bacterial growth media (Figure 7.1)
    Liquid
    Semi-solid gels
    Minimal media
    Selective media
    Nonselective media
    Sterilization: heat, filtration
    Isolation of culture media

Bacterial growth media and detection of mutations

Minimal medium: minimum substances needed for growth
  Water
  Inorganic salts
  Carbon source (usually glucose)
Auxotrophic mutants
  Require medium supplement(s)
  Example: arginine auxotrophy requires arginine
Prototrophic strains
  Do not require special substance(s) for growth
  Example: cultures prototrophic for arginine grow without arginine
Allele (in bacterial context)
  A particular nucleotide version of a gene
  A different allele: at least one nucleotide difference
Wild-type alleles
  Most are functional forms of a gene
  Usually the most abundant allele in natural population
  Mutant allele
    A mutation of a wild-type allele
    A mutation of a mutant allele
    Several different alleles can produce mutant phenotype
Phenotype
  Outward measurable or visible characteristics
  Phenotypes in normal letters, first letter capitalized
    Met+: prototroph does not require methionine
    Met− : auxotroph requires methionine
  Genotype: genetic constitution that causes phenotype
    met+: genotype for methionine prototrophy
    met− : genotype for methionine auxotrophy
  Antibiotic resistant strains
    Tet^r: resistant to tetracycline
    Tet^s: susceptible to tetracycline
    tet^r: tetracycline resistant genotype
    tet^s: tetracycline susceptible phenotype
  Temperature-sensitive mutants
    Usual culture temperature 37°C
    Growth prevented at higher or lower temperature
  Selective or nonselective medium (Figure 7.2)
    Selective medium: distinguishes mutant and wild-type
    Nonselective medium: cannot distinguish mutant and wild-type
      Lac+, Lac− not distinguished on medium with glucose (nonselective medium)
      Lac+, Lac− distinguished on medium with lactose as sole σ−carbon source (selective medium)
  Replica plating (Figure 7.4)
    Master plate: nonselective solid medium
    Colonies blotted from master plate to selective solid media

7.2 STRUCTURE OF BACTERIAL CHROMOSOMES

Central idea:
- The DNA molecule of the prokaryotic chromosome is circular and is stabilized by proteins that hold it in an organized conformation. Prokaryotic cells divide by binary fission, duplicating the chromosomal DNA once for each cell division.

Nucleoid: contains bacterial chromosome as large circular DNA molecule
  No nuclear membrane (Figures 7.5)
  Occupies central region of cell
  Contains most of cell's genes
  E. coli chromosome 1530 micrometers in diameter (Figure 7.6)
  Chromosome structure (Figure 7.7)
Plasmid: small circular DNA in bacteria
  Bacterial cell may contain none, one or more
  Plasmid usually separate from chromosome
  Episome: plasmid integrated into chromosome DNA
Binary fission: (asexual reproduction) mode of cell division in prokaryotes
  Chromosome replicates
  Each daughter chromosome attached to cell membrane
  Cells grows and divides pulling daughter chromosomes apart

7.3 DNA TRANSFER AND RECOMBINATION

Central ideas:
- There are three types of DNA transfer in bacteria: transformation, conjugation, and transduction.
- Transformation is the uptake of DNA into a bacterial cell from the cell's surroundings. The introduced DNA recombines with its homologous counterpart on the chromosome. Recombination can be used to map genes relative to one another on the chromosome.
- Conjugation is the transfer of bacterial DNA from one cell to another through a conjugation bridge. The transferred DNA is contained within an F factor, a plasmid that is becomes an episome when it inserts itself into the chromosomal DNA. A bacterial cell with an F factor is an F+ cell, while a cell without the F factor is an F- cell.
- In conjugation, DNA is transferred in one direction only: from an F+ cell to an F- cell. The F factor replicates in the F+ cell using σ–mode replication, and one copy of the F factor passes through the conjugation bridge to the F- cell, converting it into an F+ cell.
- The F factor can remain separate from the chromosome and replicate autonomously using θ-mode replication, or it can insert into the chromosome where it is replicated along with the chromosomal DNA. A bacterial cell with an integrated F factor is called an Hfr cell.
- The integrated F factor in an Hfr cell may initiate DNA transfer to an F- cell during conjugation. The F factor causes σ–mode replication of the chromosome and carries the chromosomal DNA along with it into the F- cell. Usually mating ceases before transfer of the entire chromosome, meaning that a part of the F factor along with a piece of the chromosome is transferred.
- The transferred chromosomal DNA may recombine with its homologous counterpart in the chromosome. The time at which genes enter the cell and recombine during conjugation between an Hfr cell and an F- cell allows the genes to be mapped on the chromosome. Numerous genes on the *E. coli* chromosome have been mapped in this way providing

detailed maps of the *E. coli* chromosome.

- An integrated F factor may excise from the chromosome. Sometimes the excision is faulty and the F factor takes some chromosomal DNA along with it. An F factor with chromosomal DNA integrated into it is called an F' factor. The F' factor may be transferred during conjugation resulting in two copies of the integrated DNA in the cell: one in the F' factor, the other in the chromosome. A cell with two copies of part of its chromosome DNA is called a merozygote or partial diploid.
- A single strand of DNA that has been introduced into a bacterial cell may recombine with the chromosomal DNA by displacing a homologous strand and incorporating into the chromosomal DNA.

(See Example 7.1 Experiments demonstrating recombination in bacteria.)
        Bacterial genetic recombination
        Binary fission and genetic variation (Figure 7.8)
            Genetic variation achieved by mutation
            No recombination of genetic information
        Bacteria can acquire DNA from other cells
        Segments of acquired DNA may recombine with bacterial DNA

Mechanisms of DNA recombination in bacteria
    Recombination by Single-strand displacement
        Cell degrades acquired DNA to single strand
        Single strand segment can displace homologous bacterial strand
        Displaced strand forms **D-loop**
        Enzymes can degrade D-loop and integrated strand with DNA
        Integrated DNA strand may be heteroduplex in some regions
        Replication produces recombinant and parental-type daughter cells
(See Example 7.2 Single-strand displacement in bacteria.)
    Recombination of double-stranded DNA (Figure 7.11)
    Acquired double strand may form Holliday junction with chromosome DNA
DNA transfer mechanisms
    Transformation: DNA uptake from cell environment
        Permits transfer between species
        More closely related DNAs transfer best
    Conjugation: direct transfer between connected bacterial cells
        Transfer between strains of same species
        Requires cell-cell contact
    Transduction: transfer via bacterial virus
        Transfer between strains of same species
        Transfer between cells by infecting viruses

7.4 TRANSFORMATION

Central idea:
- Transformation is the uptake of DNA into a bacterial cell from the cell's surroundings. The introduced DNA recombines with its homologous counterpart on the chromosome. Recombination can be used to map genes relative to one another on the chromosome.

Competent cells
    Transformation is rare event

Frequency increased by manipulating cell competency

Transformation by plasmids

Plasmids remain intact and self-replicate

Functional genes can be introduced into plasmids and expressed in host bacterium

No need for homology between plasmid DNA and bacterial DNA

Bacterial cells made competent for plasmid transformation

Transformation-based gene mapping

Frequency of cotransformation of two markers index of map distance

Close markers cotransform more frequently than distant markers

(See Example 7.3 Transformation-based gene mapping in *Bacillus subtilis*.)

7.5 CONJUGATION

Central ideas:

- Conjugation is the transfer of bacterial DNA from one cell to another through a conjugation bridge. The transferred DNA is contained within an F factor, a plasmid that is becomes an episome when it inserts itself into the chromosomal DNA. A bacterial cell with an F factor is an F+ cell, while a cell without the F factor is an F⁻ cell.

- In conjugation, DNA is transferred in one direction only: from an F+ cell to an F⁻ cell. The F factor replicates in the F+ cell using σ–mode replication, and one copy of the F factor passes through the conjugation bridge to the F⁻ cell, converting it into an F+ cell.

- The F factor can remain separate from the chromosome and replicate autonomously using θ-mode replication, or it can insert into the chromosome where it is replicated along with the chromosomal DNA. A bacterial cell with an integrated F factor is called an Hfr cell.

- The integrated F factor in an Hfr cell may initiate DNA transfer to an F⁻ cell during conjugation. The F factor causes σ–mode replication of the chromosome and carries the chromosomal DNA along with it into the F⁻ cell. Usually mating ceases before transfer of the entire chromosome, meaning that a part of the F factor along with a piece of the chromosome is transferred.

- The transferred chromosomal DNA may recombine with its homologous counterpart in the chromosome. The time at which genes enter the cell and recombine during conjugation between an Hfr cell and an F⁻ cell allows the genes to be mapped on the chromosome. Numerous genes on the *E. coli* chromosome have been mapped in this way providing detailed maps of the *E. coli* chromosome.

- An integrated F factor may excise from the chromosome. Sometimes the excision is faulty and the F factor takes some chromosomal DNA along with it. An F factor with chromosomal DNA integrated into it is called an F′ factor. The F′ factor may be transferred during conjugation resulting in two copies of the integrated DNA in the cell: one in the F′ factor, the other in the chromosome. A cell with two copies of part of its chromosome DNA is called a merozygote or partial diploid.

- An F⁻ cell may conjugate with an F+ cell and transfer the F factor to the F⁻ cell converting the F⁻ cell to an F+ cell .

- Complementation analysis can be done in merozygotes to determine whether or not two mutations belong to the same gene. If the two mutations fail to complement each other, they are probably alleles of the same gene. If they do complement each other, they are probably alleles of different genes.

The F factor

(See Example 7.4 U-tube experiments.)

The F plasmid DNA moves from cell to cell via conjugation bridge (Figures 7.13, 7.14)

F plasmid may integrate into bacterial chromosome DNA (an episome, Figure 7.15)

Plasmid controls DNA transfer between cells (Figure 7.17)

Established conjugation bridge through pilus

Integrated F plasmid replicates bacterial DNA by σ method

Moves replicated single strand through bridge

Integrated F plasmid DNA transferred last

F+ cell **donor,** F⁻ cell **recipient**

Hfr cells: cells with integrated F factor (episome)

Hfr means "high frequency recombination"

Chromosome DNA treated like large F factor

Hfr forms conjugation bridge with F⁻

σ-mode replication transfers chromosome DNA first

F factor transfers last (takes about 100 minutes)

Recipient cell remains F⁻ (unless F factor transferred)

Exogenote: introduce chromosome fragment

Endogenote: recipient chromosome DNA

Principle of "time of entry gene mapping"

Homology of exo- and endogenote allows gene recombination

First genes entering F⁻ recipient recombine first

Interrupted mating: mating time is timed by disruption

Cells immediately plated on selective media

Leading genes on exogenote transfer first (Figure 7.17)

(See Example 7.5 Mapping four genes in *E. coli* with time-of-entry mapping)

Hfr strains differ in chromosomal position of episome (Figure 7.19)

Orientation of episome does not change gene sequence (Figures 7.20, 7.22)

Reverse orientation of episome reverses gene order

Different position of episome changes time of entry

Maps still internally consistent and can be superimposed

(See Example 7.6 Overlapping maps from two Hfr strains.)

F' factors and sexduction

Excision of F factor

Sometimes not precise (Figure 7.23)

Carries some adjacent chromosome DNA with it

F' factor carries chromosome DNA piece

Can carry few genes to nearly half chromosome DNA

Conjugation with F' factor efficient gene transfer to F⁻ strain

Recipient cells with F' factor: called "partial diploids", "merozygotes"

Complementation analysis

Merozygotes can be used for gene complementation analysis (Figure 7.24)

Partial diploids for two different mutant genes will complement

Partial diploids for two mutant alleles will not complement

Partial diploid shows complementation:

F' factor: *lacY⁻ lacZ⁺*

Recipient: *lacY⁺ lacZ⁻*
Merozygote can metabolize lactose

Merozygote contains effective *lacY⁺* and
lacZ⁺ alleles

Partial diploid does not show complementation

F' factor: *lacY⁺ lacZ⁻*

Recipient: *lacY+ lacZ-*
Merozygote has defective *lacZ-* alleles
Alleles do not complement
Cannot metabolize lactose
Complementation tests determine allelic relationship
Intragenic complementation
Sometimes mutant alleles of same gene complement
Enzyme usually a multimer with same polypeptide
The two or more mutant polypeptides restore enzyme

7.6 PHAGE LIFE CYCLES (Figure 7.27)

Central ideas:
- Bacteriophages are bacterial viruses. They may be either virulent or temperate. A virulent phage multiplies into numerous progeny phage particles soon after infection, then lysis the cell releasing the progeny phage particles to infect other cells. Temperate phages may also enter the lytic cycle soon after infection, or they may enter lysogeny, where the phage integrates into the chromosomal DNA and is replicated along with the chromosomal DNA as the bacterium divides. An integrated lysogenic phage is called a prophage. At some point, the prophage may excise from the chromosome and enter the lytic cycle.
- DNA may be transferred from one cell to another through a phage intermediate, a process called transduction.
- There are two types of transduction: Specialized transduction in which phage particles contain a specific segment of chromosomal DNA connected to the phage DNA. In generalized transduction, a phage capsid mistakenly packages chromosomal DNA instead of phage DNA. The phage particle that contains chromosomal DNA injects the chromosomal DNA into another cell when the phage infects the cell.
- The complete nucleotide sequences of several bacterial and phage genomes have been determined. These sequences are the first step toward understanding the complete biology of an organism.
- Phages may be virulent or temperate. A virulent phage enters the lytic cycle soon after infection. A temperate phage may enter the lytic cycle soon after infection, or it may enter the lysogenic cycle where it integrates into the host chromosomal DNA and replicates as part of the chromosomal DNA.

Bacterial viruses (Figure 7.26)
Bacterial viruses are "bacteriophages" or "phages"
Capsid: virus protein coat that encapsulates virus DNA
Phage particle: one capsid with enclosed DNA
Genes in phage chromosome
Genes regulate phage reproduction in the cell
Genes specify capsid protein coat
Transcription of phage genes
Some phages have gene(s) for own RNA polymerase
Use bacterial RNA polymerase for first gene
First gene is phage RNA polymerase
Some phages use bacterial RNA polymerase for transcription
Translation always uses bacterial ribosomes
Phages take command of bacterial genome

Many phages degrade bacterial DNA after infection

Use nucleotides for synthesis of phage chromosomes

Many phage copies are assembled

Lysis: family of completed phage particles burst cell

Growth of phage infection on bacterial "lawn"

Lawn of bacteria grown on solid agar plate

"Plaque": infection cycles from single phage clears spot in lawn

Some phages can become episomes (Figure 7.29)

Prophage: phage integrated into bacterial chromosome

Lysogeny: process of phage DNA insertion into chromosome DNA

Lytic cycle: excision, phage reproduction, cell lysis

Induction: process of entrance into lytic cycle

Classification of phages according to capability of lysogeny

Virulent phage: relies on lytic cycle only for reproduction

Temperate phage: phage capable of lysogeny

Virulent phages make clear plaques on lawn

Temperate phages make turbid plaques on lawn

Some infected cells immediately undergo lytic cycle

Some infected cells become lysogenic

7.7 TRANSDUCTION

Central Ideas:

- Transduction is the transfer of DNA from one cell to another through a phage intermediate. Specialized transducing phages transfer bacterial DNA that is attached to phage DNA. Generalized transducing phages package and transmit bacterial DNA in the place of phage DNA.

- DNA may be transferred from one cell to another through a phage intermediate, a process called transduction.

- There are two types of transduction. In specialized transduction, phage particles contain a specific segment of chromosomal DNA connected to the phage DNA. In generalized transduction, a phage capsid mistakenly packages chromosomal DNA instead of phage DNA. The phage particle that contains chromosomal DNA injects the chromosomal DNA into another cell when the phage infects the cell.

Transduction: capsid may transmit bacterial DNA to host bacterium

Bacterial DNA may be packaged in capsid

Capsid injects bacterial DNA into host cell

1952: transduction discovered by Zinder and Lederberg (*Salmonella*)

Distinguished transformation from transduction of genes

Transducing capsid: DNA resistant to deoxyribonuclease

Transforming DNA: susceptible to deoxyribonuclease

(See Example 7.7 Discovery of transduction.)

Specialized transduction (Figure 7.30)

Temperate phage λ: phage capable of specialized transduction

Phage transduces specific region of DNA

λ DNA inserts at attB (BOB') site between *gal* and *bio* genes

attP (POP') site in λ DNA homologous to attB

BOB' and POP' sites align at integration

Integrated phage and bacterial DNA: *gal* BOP′ phage DNA POB′ *bio*

Excised λ capsid may carry *gal* or *bio* genes (Figure 7.31)

Generalized transduction (Figure 7.32)

P1 phage fragments bacterial chromosome

Random fragments may be encapsulated into capsid

7.8 GENOME SEQUENCING

Central idea:

- The complete nucleotide sequences of several bacterial and phage genomes have been determined. These sequences are the first step toward understanding the complete biology of an organism.

(See Example 7.8 Assignment of a DNA sequence to a mapped gene in *E. coli*.)

Ultimate genetic map: nucleotide sequence of entire genome

Several bacteria and virus genomes sequenced (Figure 7.33)

DNA sequence reveals promoters and reading frames for genes

Chapter 8
Regulation of Gene Expression

KEY CONCEPTS

- Cells regulate expression of their genes at the transcriptional, post-transcriptional, translational, and post-translational levels.
- Many prokaryotic genes are organized in operons, a tandem array of genes that are transcribed as a single mRNA. This organization permits the coordinated regulation of the proteins encoded by genes in the operon.
- Interactions between transcription factors and DNA sequence elements regulates eukaryotic genes at the transcriptional level.
- Regulation at the transcriptional level is usually combined with regulation beyond transcription to ultimately determine gene expression.

KEY TERMS

gene regulation
transcriptional regulation
post-transcriptional regulation
translational regulation
post-translational regulation
operon
operator
repressor
inducer
constitutive promoter
repressible operon
inducible operon
DNA-binding site
palindrome
allolactose
inducer-binding site
constitutive mutation
polar mutation
cis-acting element
trans-acting element
merozygote
negative regulation
positive regulation
catabolite activator protein (CAP)
cAMP
attenuation
attenuator
rho-dependent termination
corepressor
autogenous regulation
leader peptide
transcription factors

sequence elements
activators
enhancers
silencers
response elements
zinc fingers
helix-turn-helix domain
leucine zipper
DNA methylation
transcript processing
allosteric feedback inhibition

CHAPTER TOPICS

8.1 THE *lac* OPERON
    Function of the *lac* operon
    Structure and regulation of the *lac* operon
8.2 MUTATIONS IN THE *lac* OPERON
    Repressor gene mutations
    Operator mutations
    Mutations in enzyme genes
    Trans and cis effects of mutations in merozygotes
    Negative and positive regulation of the *lac* operon
8.3 THE *trp* OPERON
    Function and regulation of the *trp* operon
    Attenuation of the *trp* operon
8.4 REGULATION OF LYSIS AND LYSOGENY
8.5 TRANSCRIPTIONAL GENE REGULATION IN EUKARYOTES
    Transcription factors and eukaryotic gene regulation
    Environmental stimuli that activate gene expression
    DNA methylation
8.6 GENE REGULATION BEYOND TRANSCRIPTION
    Transcript processing
    Translational regulation
    Posttranslational regulation

CHAPTER OUTLINE

Introduction
    Four levels of gene regulation
        Transcriptional regulation
        Posttranscriptional regulation
        Translational regulation
        Posttranslational regulation
    Most genes and products regulated at all four levels

8.1 THE *lac* OPERON
The operon: a common transcription regulation mechanisms in prokaryotes
    A cluster of genes transcribed together

Transcribed as one mRNA

Genes of operon encode several enzymes of a pathway

Each gene translated separately (Figure 8.1)

All operon genes share single promoter

Each gene in the mRNA has Shine-Dalgarno sequence and is translated separately

Operon transcription blocked when genes not needed

First operon discovered: *lac* operon

Function of the *lac* operon

E. coli must sometimes use lactose as reduced carbon source

Milk sugar may be main source of carbon in baby mammal gut

Change in diet after weaning supplies other sugars

lac operon responds to lactose or presence of other sugars (see CAP, cAMP below)

Lactose present (absence of glucose)

Operon genes transcribed

mRNA translated into lactose metabolizing enzymes

Lactose absent operon genes not transcribed

Structure and regulation of the *lac* operon (Figure 8.2)

Three regulated genes

lacZ: encodes b galactosidase

Converts disaccharide lactose to glucose and galactose

Converts some lactose to allolactose (inducer)

lacY: β galactoside permease

Required for lactose utilization

Transport of lactose into cell

lacA: β galactoside transacetylase

Function unknown

Acetylates lactose and similar molecules

Promoter site (Figure 8.3)

Binding site for RNA polymerase

Transcription initiation

Operators: O_1, O_2, O_3

O_1: principle repressor binding site

O_2, O_3: repressor binds to O_1 and either O_2 or O_3

lacI gene: specifies repressor protein (Figure 8.4)

Repressor protein: tetramer four identical subunits

Two active sites per subunit

Has constitutive operator

The way the *lac* operon works (Figure 8.5)

lacI promoter is constitutive

RNA polymerase has low affinity for promoter

About 10 repressor molecules per cell

Repressor protein and operators

Palindrome at each O locus (Figure 8.6)

Each side of palindrome binds to a repressor subunit

Effects of bound repressor

Aids binding of RNA polymerase

Prevents transcription of operon

Repressor and inducer interaction

Inducer: allolactose

β-galactosidase converts some lactose to allolactose
Allolactose binds to site on each repressor subunit
Binding causes allosteric 3-D change in repressor
Repressor leaves operator and transcription begins
Repressor binds operator when lactose is removed
Transcription and translation *lac* operon mRNA ceases
Degradation exceeds production of *lac* mRNAs and enzymes
Cell uses other reduced carbon sources
How induction of *lac* operon is initiated (Figure 8.8)
Induction requires allolactose
Lactose can't enter cell without permease
Without β-galactosidase no inducer
Repression of *lac* operon imperfect
Few β-galactosidase and permease enzymes present

8.2 MUTATIONS IN THE *lac* OPERON

Central ideas:
- The *lac* operon is subject to positive as well as negative regulation. Glucose is the preferred source of carbohydrate and when it is present it is preferentially utilized instead of lactose. Glucose exerts positive regulation through a protein called catabolite activator protein (CAP) that activates transcription when it binds to the *lac* operon promoter. CAP is induced by cyclic AMP (cAMP), which is regulated by the concentration of glucose. When glucose levels are low, cAMP is high, activating CAP and activating transcription of the *lac* operon. When glucose levels are high, cAMP is low, reducing transcription of the *lac* operon.
- With positive and negative regulation acting together, transcription is repressed when lactose is absent regardless of glucose levels. When glucose concentration is high, the *lac* operon is not transcribed, even in the presence of lactose, because glucose is the preferred carbon source. The lac operon is transcribed only when lactose is present and when glucose concentrations are low.
- The *lac* operon encodes a single mRNA that contains three genes, each encoding an enzyme for lactose metabolism. The organization of the *lac* operon is such that transcription is repressed (but not perfectly) in the absence of lactose, and permitted in the presence of lactose.
- Imperfect repression of *lac* operon permits initiation of induction when cell is exposed to lactose
- The lac repressor protein is trans acting, and the operators are cis acting. These observations contributed to the development of the operon model.

Repressor gene mutations (Figure 8.9)
Mutations affecting repressor binding sites
DNA binding site function
Inducer binding site function
lacI- defective repressor lacks DNA binding function
*lacI*s "super-repressed" repressor lacks inducer binding function
Operator mutations
*lacO*c constitutive mutations do not bind repressor
Most *lacO*c constitutive mutations affect *lacO*$_1$
Operator mutations that increase binding strength of repressor

Mutations in enzyme genes

    lacZ- mutations

        Lac⁻ phenotype

        b-galactosidase defective

        Allolactose (inducer) not produced

        Repressor remains bound to operator

        Operon cannot be transcribed

    lacY- mutations eliminate permease

        Lac- phenotype

        Lactose cannot enter cell

    lacA- mutations

        Lactose metabolism not affected

        Lack of transacetylase activity

    Polar mutations

        Mutations affect expression of other genes in operon

        lacZ- and *lacY-* can be polar mutations

        Frameshift mutation in *lacZ* affects transcription of *lacY*

Trans and cis effects of mutations in merozygotes

    Trans-acting mutation: affects genes on different DNA

    Cis-acting mutation: affects genes only on same DNA

        Most cis-acting mutations: binding sites for operon control elements

        Most trans-acting mutations: regulator protein genes

    (See Example 8.1 Interaction of *lacI* and *lacZ* genes in *E. coli*.)

Negative and positive regulation of the *lac* operon

    Negative regulation:

        lac repressor inhibits transcription when bound to DNA

    Positive regulation:

        Regulator protein stimulates transcription when bound to DNA

        CAP stimulates transcription of *lac* operon when bound to DNA

            CAP DNA binding site: upstream of *lac* promoter

            CAP–cAMP form binds at CAP binding site (Figure 8.12)

            CAP alone does not bind DNA

                cAMP low when glucose high

                cAMP high when glucose low

lac operon is both inducible and repressible (Figure 8.13)

    High concentrations of lactose induce *lac* operon (repressor-allolactose)

    High concentrations of glucose repress *lac* operon (CAP–cAMP)

8.3 THE *trp* OPERON (Figure 8.14)

    Central ideas:

- The *trp* operon encodes five polypeptides that form three enzymes for tryptophan synthesis. The *trp* operon is a good example of attenuation, an additional type of gene regulation in operons. The attenuator is an intrinsic terminator of transcription in the mRNA upstream of the enzyme-encoding genes. A short leader peptide sequence precedes the attenuator. When tryptophan is in short supply, the ribosome stalls at two tryptophan codons and prevents the attenuator from assuming its terminator conformation. Transcription then continues on into the enzyme genes. When tryptophan is abundant, the ribosome translates past the tryptophan codons and allows the attenuator to assume its terminator conformation. Transcription terminates at the attenuator before the enzyme genes are transcribed.

- The *trp* operon is regulated by a combination of repression and attenuation.

The *trp* operon is negatively regulated by repressor and with attenuation
  trp operon is repressed by corepressor tryptophan (Figure 8.15)
  Attenuation terminates transcription before operon genes (Figure 8.16)
  Attenuation occurs in several operons
Nature of tryptophan synthesis pathway
  Tryptophan supply inadequate: trp synthesis pathway turned on
  Tryptophan supply adequate: trp synthesis pathway turned off
  Control of tryptophan synthesis at two levels
    Feed-back end-product (tryptophan) inhibition of pathway
    Repression of transcription of *trp* operon
trp operon system has *trpR* gene, *trp* promoter, *trp* operator and five *trp* genes
  trpR gene specifies *trp* repressor protein
    trpR gene has promoter and operator
      trp repressor protein negatively regulates own synthesis
      trp repressor protein binds *trpR* operator
        trp repressor low: *trpR* operon transcribed full speed
        trp repressor high: *trpR* operon repressed
  trp repressor-corepressor (tryptophan) repress *trp* operon transcription
    Repression imperfect (70-fold repression)
    Transcription further repressed by attenuation
Attenuation of the *trp* Operon (Figure 8.17)
  Attenuation reduces transcript 10-fold
  Attenuation occurs within 180 nucleotides at 5′ end mRNA
  Function of leader peptide sequence (Figure 8.18)
    Three hairpin forming sites involved at 5′ end
      Hairpin #1 nucleotides 54-92
      Synthesis of leader peptide begins in hairpin #1
        AUG codon begins at nucleotide 27
        Two tryptophan codons UGGUGG nucleotides 54-59
      Hairpin #2 nucleotides 74-119
      Hairpin #3 nucleotides 114-134
      Hairpin #3 is attenuator (has string of uridines 3′ end)
  How attenuation works
    Formation of Hairpin #1 and #3 blocks transcription
    Formation of hairpin #2 prevents formation Hairpin #3
    Hairpin #1 formation blocked by stalled ribosome
      Ribosomes stall at UGGUGG codons when tryptophan is low (trp-tRNA is low)
      Stalling allows formation of hairpin #2
      Formation of hairpin #2 blocks formation hairpin #3
      Transcription proceeds through attenuator
    Tryptophan low: translation stalls at Trp codons in hairpin #1

8.4 REGULATION OF LYSIS AND LYSOGENY
  Central ideas:
  - Gene regulation determines whether the temperate phage lambda (λ) will enter the lytic pathway or lysogenic pathway after it infects a cell. There is a competition between the pro-

teins pcI and Cro. If pcI succeeds first in binding to operators, lysogeny is established. If Cro succeeds first in binding to operators, lysis proceeds.

Regulation of lambda (λ) lysis and lysogeny in *E. coli* (Figure 8.19)(Table 8.1)
    Turbid plaques because of lysis and lysogeny in different cells
        Lysogenic cells
            λ *cI* gene encodes pcI repressor protein
            pcI represses lytic pathway genes
        Lytic cells *cI* gene not expressed (no pcI repressor protein)
            cI means "clear plaques" when *cI* mutant or not expressed
            Lytic pathway genes expressed
        Sequence of λ DNA units controlling lysis or lysogeny
            cIII-t_L-*N*-P_L_O_L-*cI*-P_M-O_R3-$O_R2O_R1$$P_R$-*cro*-$t_R$-$P_E$-*cII*
    Control of expression of *cI* gene
        cI gene flanked by promoter-operator complexes
            Left side O_L and P_L (L means "left", R means right side P_R, P_M, O_R3, O_R2, O_R1, P_E)
                P_R, P_M, , P_E, and P_L functions
                    P_R initiates transcription to the right
                        First part of mRNA transcript: *cro* gene
                        Transcription terminates at terminator t_R
                    P_L initiates transcription to the left
                        First part of mRNA transcript: *N* gene
                        Transcription terminates at terminator t_L
                    P_M promoter for *cI* gene
                    P_E initiates transcription backwards to left
                        cI only segment this transcript transcribed in right direction
                        cI translated to pcI repressor protein
                  O_R3, O_R2, O_R1 operator functions
                    Control transcription of *cI* and *cro*
                    pcI has high affinity for O_R1, O_R2 and O_L
                      Prevents RNA polymerase binding at P_R
                      Binding prevents transcription of *cro*
                      Binds O_L: prevents transcription to left
                  cro has high affinity for O_R3
                    Prevents RNA polymerase binding at P_M blocking *cI* transcription
                    Binding prevents transcription of *cI*
    Genes to the right of *cI*
        cro: repressor for transcription of *cI*
        cII: initiates the backward transcription at P_E
            cI gene only gene mRNA transcript transcribed in right direction
            pcII causes initial production of repressor pcI
    Genes to the left of *cI*
        N gene: pN antiterminator for t_L and t_R
            Allows transcription to continue through *cII* on right
            Allows transcription to continue through *cIII* on left
                (pcII initiates backward transcription through *cI* gene transcrib-

ing for first pcI)

pcIII protects pcII from degradation

cIII gene: pcIII protects pcII from degradation in cell

How control of lysogeny or lysis works

Two important points:

pcI repressor protein represses lytic cycle

cro protein represses lysogenic cycle

λ infection of *E. coli* cell

λ circularizes

Cell RNA polymerase binds P_L and P_R

Transcription is initiated

P_L initiates transcription of *N* gene on left of *cI*

P_R initiates transcription of *cro* gene on right of *cI*

pN allows transcription to continue through *cII* and *cIII*

pcII allows backward transcription at P_E promoter

Backward transcription for P_E

mRNA through *cro* is nonsense until *pcI* gene

pcI only gene transcribed in right direction

pcI protein binds to O_L and O_R1 and O_R2

pcI shuts off *cro, N, cII* and *cIII* genes

Transcription at P_M-*cI* continues indefinitely

pcI represses cro

The *int* gene is now transcribed producing integrase

Integrase controls integration of λ into bacteria chromosome and lysogeny

Lysogeny maintained while pcI is present

Repressor pcI prevents infection by other λ phages

cro and pcI interact to control lytic and lysogeny pathways

cro and pcI have affinity for right operators

pcI regulates its own synthesis

pcI high affinity for O_R1, O_R2, low affinity for O_R3

Binding pcI at O_R1 prevents transcription of *cro*

Binding at O_R2 enhances transcription of *cI*

Binding at O_R3 represses transcription of *pcI*

pcI binding at O_R3 effective when pcI conc. high

cro has increasing affinity for O_R1, O_R2 and O_R3

high affinity for O_R3 shutting off *pcI*

With pcI shut down lysogenic λ enters lytic cycle

Transcription goes beyond λ*cII* and *cIII* genes

Genes controlling lytic cycle are transcribed

UV light interrupts lysogeny

UV light activates bacterial RecA protein

RecA protein rapidly degrades pcI

Repression of O_R1 is relieved

RNA polymerase binds to P_R and transcribes *cro*

cro binds to O_R3 blocking transcription of *pcI*

Blocking of *pcI* relieves repression of right and left promoters

Transcription continues beyond *cII* and *cIII* genes

Lytic cycle genes are transcribed

λ enters lytic cycle

λ enters lytic cycle

(See Example 8.2 Mutation that turns Cro into a transcription activator.)

8.5 TRANSCRITPIONAL GENE REGULATION IN EUKARYOTES

Central ideas:
- Eukaryotic gene regulation has some similarities with prokaryotic gene regulation, but is much more complex.
- Eukaryotic gene regulation at the transcriptional level includes interactions between transcription factors and DNA response elements. When bound to a DNA response element, transcription factors may activate or repress transcription.
- Transcription factors may contain DNA binding and protein binding domains. Common DNA binding domains include, zinc fingers, leucine zippers, and helix-turn-helix motifs.
- Response elements are DNA sequence elements that are common to certain genes that have similar functions. These elements bind transcription factors that are specific to the gene or group of genes that they regulate. In this way, a set of genes can be coordinately regulated by a single signal, such as a hormone.
- Gene regulation is associated with DNA methylation in many species. Actively transcribed genes are undermethlyated while genes that are transcriptionally inactive tend to be methylated.
- Most genes are regulated at the transcriptional level and at levels beyond transcription.

Transcription factors and eukaryotic gene regulation Figure 8.20)

    Transcription factors function in regulation of all eukaryotic genes

        DNA sequence elements

            Enhancer elements bind activator proteins

            Coactivators facilitate binding of activators to DNA

            Repressor elements bind silencer proteins

            Activators and coactivators bind with basal transcription complex stimulating transcription initiation

            Some transcription factors are general

            Some transcription factors specific for certain genes

                Steroid receptors bind steroid hormone (Figure 8.21)

                Steroid receptor-hormone bind DNA response element

                Glucocorticoid DNA response element conserved sequence: TGGTACAAATGTTCT

        Most transcription factors have two active sites

        DNA binding sites of transcription factors

    Zinc fingers (Figure 8.22)

        Two β and two α polypeptide strands

            Held together by zinc ion

            Zinc bound to cysteines and histidines

        Fingers protrude into major grooves of DNA at conserved sites

    Helix-turn-helix domain (Figure 8.23)

        Two α-helices in protein

            Recognition helix: fits DNA major groove at specific sites

            Stabilization helix lies across DNA helix

    Leucine zipper (Figure 8.24)

Zipper teeth: leucine every 7 amino acids in protein subunit

Zipper holds two protein subunits together

DNA recognition helices extend from the two polypeptides

Bind major groove

Bind at conserved sequences

Protein binding domains

Many transcription factors have protein binding domains

Bind with regulator proteins to affect transcription

Sp1 has DNA and protein binding domains (Figure 8.26)

DNA domain: zinc fingers bind GC rich DNA

Binding site GC-rich region

Glutamine-rich domain binds coactivator protein

Complex binds basal transcription complex

Environmental stimuli that activate gene expression

GAL4/80 system in yeast (Figure 8.27)

Metabolism of galactose requires enzymes from autonomous genes

Coordinating expression of autonomous genes

Each gene responds to factors GAL 4 and GAL 80

GAL 4 binds to regulatory regions of genes

GAL 80 binds to GAL 4 in absence of galactose

GAL 4/GAL 80 inhibit transcription of each gene

Galactose or derivative binds and removes GAL 80

DNA loop joins GAL4 and factor on TATA box together

Complex stimulates basal eukaryotic transcription system

(See Example 8.3 GAL4 and its response element.)

DNA methylation

Cytosines converted to 5-methyl cytosine

CG/GC doublets most frequently methylated

Sometimes only one C methylated in C*G/GC doublet (hemimethylated doublet)

Methylated CG doublets in promoter regions may prevent transcription

Methylation perpetuated through cell division

Methylated CG doublets become hemimethylated doublets after DNA replication

Methyl transferase methylates hemimethylated CG doublets

Inactive genes may be activated by demethylation

(See Example 8.4 The role of methylation in gene inactivation.)

8.6 GENE REGULATION BEYOND TRANSCRIPTION

Central ideas:

- Most genes are regulated at the transcriptional level and at levels beyond transcription.
- Expression of some genes is regulated with pre-mRNA processing. Alternative splicing of the pre-mRNAs from the same gene may be used to produce different, but related, proteins.
- In translational regulation, cells regulate mRNA longevity and the rate of translation.
- Allosteric feedback inhibition is a form of post-translational regulation of enzymes after they have been translated and have assumed their function. Typically the first enzyme in a pathway is inhibited by the end product of the pathway. Thus, when the end product is abundant, the first enzyme is inhibited, blocking the synthesis of the end product at the step catalyzed by that enzyme. When the end product is deficient, the enzyme remains active allowing synthesis of the end product to proceed.

Transcript processing
    Alternative intron splicing in pre-mRNA (Figure 8.29)
        Differences in smooth and striated muscle fiber proteins
            α-tropomyosin gene pre-mRNA 13 exons, 12 introns
                Smooth muscle mRNA: 10 exons
                Striated muscle mRNA: 9 exons
                Seven exons in common
                Same gene pre-mRNA transcript
    Differential stability of mRNA in the cytoplasm
        mRNA with increased stability:
        Gene transcripts regulated by hormones
        Example: prolactin effects casein mRNA stability
            Increases stability of casein mRNA
            Increased translation rate casein mRNA
Translational regulation
    Storage of maternal mRNA stored in some animal eggs
        Fertilization frees maternal mRNAs for translation
    AIDS virus mRNAs favored in host cell
        Virus protein attaches to 5′ end virus mRNA
        Attachment favors translation virus mRNA
Posttranslational regulation
    Allosteric feed-back inhibition (Figure 8.31)
        Inhibition of first pathway enzyme by end product
        Allosteric enzymes have active site and allosteric site
            Active site: catalytic site
            Allosteric site: binds end product of pathway
            Binding end product reversibly inactivates enzyme
        Example: isoleucine biosynthetic pathway in *E. coli*
            First of five pathways steps: threonine → α-ketobutyrate
            Enzyme: threonine dehydratase inactivated by isoleucine
        Example: tryptophan biosynthetic pathway in *E. coli*
            First enzyme: anthranilate synthetase inhibited by tryptophan
            Enzyme product of *trpE* and *trpD* genes
            Three mechanisms regulate tryptophan biosynthesis
                Operon repression and attenuation
                Allosteric feedback inhibition
        High lysine or threonine inhibit synthesis of four amino acids in plants
            Single biosynthetic pathway for lysine, threonine, isoleucine, and methionine
                Aspartate kinase: first enzyme of pathway
                Lysine and threonine feedback inhibit first enzyme
                Other pathway enzymes feedback inhibited
                      Homoserine dehydrogenase: feedback inhibited by threonine
                      Dihydrodipicolinate synthase: feedback inhibited by lysine
        High lysine plant cells in tissue culture
        Selection for high lysine plant cells in tissue culture
            Mutations that eliminate high lysine-threonine feedback functions
                Tissue masses grown in high lysine and threonine
                Nonmutated cells die because of methionine starvation
                Pathway should not be feedback inhibited in surviving cells

Chapter 9
Recombinant DNA and Molecular Analysis

KEY CONCEPTS

- DNA from any species may be recombined with DNA from any other species *in vitro*.
- DNA from any species may be inserted into bacterial or yeast cells and replicated.
- Under certain conditions, genes from other species, including humans, may be inserted and expressed in bacteria, yeast, or mammalian cells.
- Several methods exist to amplify specific sequences of DNA using cellular DNA as a source.
- Researchers can determine the nucleotide sequence of a DNA fragment.

KEY TERMS

DNA clone
recombinant DNA
restriction endonuclease
restriction site
palindromic
restriction mapping
cohesive ends
sticky ends
cloning vector
plasmid cloning vector
phage cloning vector
BAC
cosmid vector
selectable markers
recombinant plasmid
blunt-end ligation
homopolymer tailing
linker DNA
blue-white screening
polylinker
stuffer fragment
shotgun cloning
genomic library
reverse transcriptase
cDNA
genomic DNA library
cDNA library
expression vector
fusion gene
polymerase chain reaction (PCR)
PCR primer
gel electrophoresis
SDS-PAGE
IEF
2D-PAGE

native protein gel electrophoresis
Southern blotting
northern blotting
western blotting
DNA sequencing
Sanger dideoxy sequencing
automated DNA sequencing
GenBank
BLASTN
BLASTX

CHAPTER TOPICS

9.1 RECOMBINANT DNA
    Restriction endonucleases and methylases
    Recombination of DNA fragments
9.2 PLASMID CLONING VECTORS
    An example of a plasmid cloning vector: pBR322
    Blunt-end ligation
    Homopolymer tailing
    Linker DNA
    Plasmid vectors with polylinkers and marker genes for blue-white screening
9.3 VECTORS FOR CLONING LARGE DNA INSERTS
    Phage cloning vectors
    Bacterial artificial chromosomes
9.4 CLONING STRATEGIES
    Shotgun cloning
    cDNA cloning
    Probe identification and synthesis
9.5 EXPRESSION VECTORS
9.6 THE POLYMERASE CHAIN REACTION
9.7 GEL ELECTROPHORESIS
    Gel electrophoresis of DNA
    Gel electrophoresis of proteins
9.8 DNA, RNA, AND PROTEIN BLOTTING
    Southern blotting and analysis
    Northern and Western blotting
9.9 DNA SEQUENCING
    Sanger dideoxy sequencing
    DNA sequence information on the Internet

CHAPTER OUTLINE

Introduction
    Implications of universality of DNA and genetic code
        Genetic information can be transferred among bacteria and eukaryotic organisms
        Genetic information can be rewritten and replaced
    Present applications of genetic engineering are numerous

Fundamental methods will be covered

9.1 RECOMBINANT DNA

Central ideas:
- DNA manipulation is possible because of the universality of DNA replication and the genetic code. It includes the transfer of DNA from one species to another, the *in vitro* modification and replication of DNA, and determination of the nucleotide sequence of DNA fragments.
- Restriction endonucleases cleave DNA at specific sites. Researchers may recombine DNA from different sources at the sites cut by the restriction endonucleases to make recombinant DNA.
- Geneticists use recombinant DNA technology to insert DNA fragments into bacterial vectors where the DNA replicates easily in bacterial cells. Bacterial vectors include specially designed plasmids, phages, cosmids, and bacterial artificial chromosomes. The choice of a vector depends on the size of the DNA fragment.
- After a restriction endonuclease cuts DNA at a restriction site, DNA fragments with cohesive ends can be joined, forming recombinant DNA.

Universality of DNA chemistry Makes DNA manipulation possible
    Genetic code
    DNA replication and recombination
Challenge: overcome barriers to DNA transfer between species
    Transfer of DNA between broad species categories
    Cloning eukaryotic genes in bacterial hosts
    Expressing eukaryotic genes in bacteria
    Selection of specific fragments of DNA
    Determination of nucleotide sequences
Advantages of DNA manipulations
    Practical applications such as development of human insulin
    Applications address almost all fundamental biological questions
Chapter discussion
    Recombinant DNA defined
    Purpose and design of cloning vectors
    How specific fragments of DNA are found
    How eukaryotic genes are expressed in bacteria
    The polymerase chain reaction is a useful tool
    How DNA fragments are identified, characterized and sequenced
    Management of DNA sequence information in data bases
Restriction endonuclease and methylases
    Restriction endonucleases cleave DNA at specific sites
    Methylases protect host DNA from host restriction endonucleases
        Methylation prevents recognition of restriction site
        Specific methylases methylate specific DNA restriction sites
        Methylation distinguishes bacterial DNA from foreign DNA
    Restriction endonuclease nomenclature
        *Eco*RI restriction endonuclease
            Eco refers to native species: *E. coli*
            RI refers to the RI endonuclease/methylase system
            Other restriction endonuclease from *E. coli: Eco*RV

81

*Eco*RV endonuclease/methylase system differs from *Eco*RI

Nature of *Eco*RI restriction site

Palindrome: six nucleotides GAATTC/CTTAAG

DNA cut between G and A (staggered cut)

Cut leaves 5′ AATT overhanging ends

*Eco*RI methylase methylates middle adenines

Types of restriction endonuclease systems

Type II system: *Eco*RI

Separate restriction and methylase enzymes

Cut or methylate same restriction site

Have great value in DNA manipulation

Type I and type III systems

Single enzyme cleaves or methylates DNA site

Binds at restriction site and cleaves elsewhere

Have limited value so far for DNA manipulation

Many different type II systems are being used in laboratories (Table 9.1)

Each system has specific palindromic restriction site

Restriction mapping (Figure 9.1 Restriction mapping of DNA molecules.)

Example: human mitochondria chromosome

Single and double digests of DNA: *Eco*RI and *Eco*RV

Map of restriction fragments put together using logic

(See text Example 9.1)

Recombination of DNA fragments (Figures 9.2, 9.3, 9.4)

Cuts with overhanging ends can be used for recombining cut DNA fragments

Many restriction endonucleases make staggered cuts

Restriction sites are palindromic

Staggered cuts of palindromic sites leave **cohesive ends**

Complementary cohesive ends can be rejoined

Cohesive fragments are cut with same restriction endonuclease

Cohesive ends will anneal leaving nicks

Nicks joined by DNA ligase forming recombinant DNA

Recombinant DNA: DNAs recombined in vitro

No limit to combinations of DNA

Vectors genetically redesigned to perform specific functions

Cloning vectors: Cloning of recombinant fragments in living cells

Clone: Replicated vectors containing same piece of recombinant DNA

Expression vectors: testing recombinant fragment for genetic expression

9.2 PLASMID CLONING VECTORS

Central ideas:

- Geneticists choose a cloning strategy to identify and isolate a desired clone from other clones that may be present.
- Expression vectors are plasmids that have been modified for expression of foreign genes in bacteria. They often contain a promoter and a transcription terminator that can be recognized by the bacterial host. They also are constructed so that the inserted gene can be easily turned on or off by altering culture conditions. Eukaryotic genes must be modified before insertion into an expression vector in order to produce the desired product in bacterial cells.
- DNA cloning is the replication of a DNA fragment contained within a vector. The most frequently used vectors are bacterial plasmids that have been specifically designed for DNA

cloning.

Researchers need many copies of DNA fragments
DNA fragment cloning strategies
 Replication of DNA fragments in bacterial cells
 Cloning vectors carry DNA fragments into bacterial cells
 Characteristics of **plasmid cloning vector pBR322**
  Circular DNA with origin of replication sequence
   Permit autonomous replication in host
   Several copies of plasmid extracted from each host cell
   pBR322 has two antibiotic resistance genes: amp^r and tet^r
  Antibiotic resistance genes (**selectable markers**)
   Noninfected cells can be eliminated by selective media
   Used to identify cells infected with recombinant plasmid
  Unique restriction sites (**linker sites**)
   Single sites: Ava I, Pst I, BamHI, Pvu I, Cla I, Sal I, Eco RI, Hind III
   Insertion antibiotic resistance inactivation sites:
    Amp^r: Pst I, Pvu I
    Tet^r: BamHI, Hind III (variable), Sal I
   Modern vectors have **polylinker sites**
 Example use of pBR322 cut with *Pst* I (Figure 9.5)
  Formation of "cohesive ends" (*Pst* I restriction digest)
   Human DNA fragment and pBR322 cut with *Pst* I
   Anneal plasmid and DNA fragment mixture
   Bond annealed ends with ligase
   Transform host with recombinant plasmids
  Competent *E. coli* cells transformed with plasmid mixture (figure 9.6)
   One plasmid per cell
   Cells plated on selective gelled growth media with tetracycline
    All transformed cells grow
   Transformed cells replica plated on tetracycline plus ampicillin
   Ampicillin sensitive cells contain recombinant plasmids
  Position of chimeric colonies noted and isolated from master
  Colonies with chimeric plasmids reproduced in liquid media with tetracycline
  Recombinant plasmids (about 10 per cell) isolated after reproduction
  Cloned DNA fragment cut out with *Pst* I and isolated for study
Blunt end ligation
 Blunt ends of DNAs joined by blunt end ligation
  T4 DNA ligase joins blunt ends
  Blunt ends of DNA fragment and vector DNA joined
Homopolymer tailing
 Synthesis of artificial cohesive ends on blunt ends
 Terminal transferase adds complementary nucleotides
  Fragment DNA (dATP + DNA → DNA-AAAAA)
  Vector DNA (dTTP + DNA → DNA-TTTTT)
  Mix (poly A ends pair with poly T ends) and ligate
  Clone chimeric plasmid in host
  Select hosts with recombinant plasmid by selective markers

Linker DNAs
      Fragments containing specific restriction sites
      Blunt end ligated to vector or DNA fragment to be cloned
      Artificial sites can be constructed in DNA synthesizer
Plasmid vectors with poly linkers and marker gene for blue-white screening (Figure 9.7)
      Blue-white vectors eliminate replica plating step
      Blue-white screening based on genes from *lac* operon
      Example: pUC19 plasmid cloning vector
         Plasmid contains:
            modified *lac* operon containing *lacI*, *lacZ'*, mutant *lacZ*;
               lacZ' encodes first 146 codons of *lacZ* gene (first 146 amino
                  acids of b-galactosidase)
               lacZ' protein is inactive by itself
               Mutant *lacZ* gene encodes inactive β-galactosidase
               lacZ' and mutant *lacZ* gene products produce functional β-
                  galactosidase
            amp^r ampicillin antibiotic resistance gene
            Specialized host bacteria modify X-gal only with intact pUC19 (colony
               turns blue)
            IPTG (analog of lactose) induces *lac* operon in pUC19
               X-gal (5 bromo-4 chloro-3 indole-ß-D-galactoside)
               X-gal substrate for active ß-galactosidase
         How the pUC19 system works
            Transformed cells are plated on medium with IPTG, X-gal and ampi-
               cillin
            Transformed colonies with intact pUC19, X-gal and IPTG turn blue
               (colonies contain nonrecombinant plasmids)
            Insertion of DNA fragment in poly linker of plasmid disrupts *lacZ'* gene
               (recombinant plasmids)
             X-gal is not chemically altered
               Colonies transformed with recombinant plasmids are white
               Cells without plasmids are killed by ampicillin
            Researchers isolate white colonies from plate
      Modern vectors provide higher yields of recombinant DNA
         pBR322: 15 copies per cell
         pUC19: 500-700 copies per cell
      (See text Example 9.2. Organization of the pUC19 polylinker)

9.3 VECTORS FOR CLONING LARGE DNA INSERTS
Sizes of DNA molecules for cloning varies
DNA sizes that can be cloned in cloning vectors
      Plasmid vectors: up to 10 kb
      Phage vector: up to 23 kb
      Cosmid vector: up to 46 kb
      BAC or YAC (YAC—see Chapter 10): >100 kb
Phage cloning vectors (Figure 9.10)
      Modified λ phage
         Region between *J* and *N* genes removed (lysogeny genes removed)
         Lytic cycle genes remain

     Stuffer fragment inserted between *J* and *N* genes
      Two purposes of stuffer fragment:
      Keeps λ at correct size for propagation;
      Insertion of foreign DNA modifies selective markers
    Charon 4A λ vector (Figure 9.11)
     15 kb stuffer fragment with *lac5* and *bio 256* genes
     DNA insertion site
      *Eco*RI site left end *lac5* and right end *bio 256* genes
      Insertion of foreign DNA inactivates *lac5* and *bio 256*
     lac5 encodes β-galactosidase and *bio256*
     E. coli host cell is *lacZ*⁻
      Host infected with Charon 4A in culture with X-gal
       Action of phage β-galactosidase on X-gal
       Plaques are blue
      Host infected with recombinant Charon 4A phage
       No enzyme action on X-gal
       Plaques are white
   Many special λ vectors with redesigned hosts available
    Choice depends on:
     DNA fragment size
     Restriction sites needed
     Recombinant phage selection methods
    (See Example 9.3 The *lacZ* gene as a marker in plasmid and phage vectors.)
Cosmid vectors, a combination of λ and plasmid vectors (Figures 9.12, 9.13)
Cosmid characteristics ("cos" for "cos" sites, "mid" for plasmid)
   4-6 kb circular DNA with λ cohesive joining ends (**cos sites**)
   Origin of replication sequence
   Antibiotic resistance gene
   Several unique restriction sites
Use of cosmids for cloning
   Fragment inserted using restriction endonuclease and ligase
   Linearized at cos sites
   Packaged into λ capsids (nonrecombinant cosmids too small)
   Capsids inject cosmid into bacteria
   Infected bacteria resistant to antibiotic due to recombinant cosmid
   Cosmid circularizes and replicates in host
Bacterial artificial chromosomes (BACs)
Characteristics of BACs
   Reengineered F factors
   Can carry > 300 kb recombinant DNA
   Genes control replication and copy number
   Chloramphenicol resistance gene serves as selectable marker
   Cloning segment
    Several common restriction enzymes
    Two eight-nucleotide recognition sites
Use of the system
   Recombinant BACs inserted into *E. coli* by electroporation
   Transformed cells antibiotic resistant
   Recombinant BAC circularizes and replicates in cell like F factor

9.4 CLONING STRATEGIES

Shotgun cloning

    Genomic DNA library: collection of clones from genomic digest

    Worker clones fragments from restriction digest of genomic DNA

    Selection and isolation of DNA clone from library

        DNA probe identifies desired clone (Figure 9.15)

        Screening for desired clone

cDNA cloning (an efficient method for making gene (cDNA) library)

    Making cDNA library

        mRNA isolated from selected organs or tissues (Figure 9.16)

        Poly-A mRNA tails bound to poly T column

        Displace bound mRNAs from column

        Make "complementary cDNAs" using reverse transcriptase

        Clone cDNA fragments for cDNA library etc.

    Probe blots of clones for desired cDNA

Probe identification and synthesis

Finding a probe

    Use homologous probe from different species

        Goal: find human insulin gene

        Known mouse insulin gene sequence used as DNA probe

        Probe human cDNA library from pancreas cells

    DNA probe logic based on partial sequence similarities of proteins with like functions

        Make degenerate set of probes based on codon sequence (if necessary)

        Number of degenerate probes can be reduced (numerous strategies)

            Select amino acid sequence with lowest redundancy

                Tryptophan and methionine: one codon each

                Avoid leucine, serine, arginine (six codons each)

                Some species use more of one codon in a set

            Make longer probe (30 nucleotides or more)

            (Some nucleotide mismatch tolerated with longer probes)

        (See text example 9.4. Degenerate probes.)

9.5 EXPRESSION VECTORS

Expressing eukaryotic genes in bacterial host

    DNA sequences needed at splice site in vector

        Bacterial promoter-operator sequence

        Shine-Dalgarno sequence

        Rho-dependent termination signal (not always needed)

    Plasmid expression vector pPLa2311 (Figure 9.17)

        P_L promoter, O_L operator from λ

        Selective genes for ampicillin and kanamycin resistance

        Several unique restriction sites

        Most useful sites: *Eco*RI and *Pst*I restriction sites

        Cut *Pst*I site inactivates ampicillin gene

    Genes in bacterial host

        Permanently lysogenic for mutant λ

        Defective lysogenic λ cannot enter lytic cycle

        Temperature sensitive *cI* gene in mutant λ

Active at 32°C (*pcI* blocks P_L promoter)

Inactive at 42°C (turns on P_L promoter)

Insert cDNA in plasmid at *Pst*I site inactivating *amp^r* gene

Transformed host cells kanamycin resistant and sensitive to ampicillin

Culture at 32°C (P_L promoter off)

Transfer to 42°C (P_L promoter on transcribing DNA insert)

Assay for protein specified by recombinant DNA

Using fusion genes (Figure 9.18)

(See example 9.5 Producing human growth hormone in bacteria using fusion gene.)

9.6 THE POLYMERASE CHAIN REACTION (PCR)

Central Ideas
- The polymerase chain reaction (PCR) replicates a specific fragment of DNA, just as cloning, but more rapidly and efficiently.
- The polymerase chain reaction (PCR) is a rapid and effective method for replicating specific fragments of DNA.

Used to replicate specific fragment of DNA (target region) quickly and easily

Fifteen-30 nucleotides at ends of target region identified

Single-stranded PCR primers matching target ends are made

Use of PCR to amplify target sequence in genomic DNA

Reaction mix:

Buffer

Modified DNA polymerase from thermophilic bacterium

dNTPs

Magnesium (polymerase cofactor)

Genomic DNA

Steps of PCR cycle (in PCR machine, Figure 9.22)

Reaction mix heated to 92-94°C (DNA strand separation)

Reaction mix cooled to selected primer annealing temperature

Annealing temperature: 25-65°C (usually 50°C)

Primers anneal to complementary primers sites on DNA

Reaction mix heated to 72°C for chain extension (DNA polymerase reaction temperature)

First cycle generates two copies of target region

Cycle 25-40 times

Each cycle doubles copies of target DNA fragments

Analysis of PCR products (figure 9.23)

Some values of PCR

Does not require pure DNA substrate

Minute amounts of target DNA can be amplified

Primer sequences determine target DNA to be amplified

DNA not RNA is used as primer (no need to cut out primer since primer is part of the sequence)

9.7 GEL ELECTROPHORESIS

Central ideas:
- DNA fragments can be separated from one another and their lengths estimated using gel

electrophoresis.
- Electrophoresis can separate proteins from one another by molecular weight alone, by net charge alone, or by a combination of molecular weight and net charge.

Gel electrophoresis of DNA
DNA or RNA fragments separated by size (Figures 9.24, 9.25)
    Gel slabs either agarose or polyacrylamide (depending on DNA fragment size)
        > 200 nucleotide pairs: agarose usually used
        < 500 nucleotide pairs: polyacrylamide usually used
        Wells for DNA formed at one end of gel slab
    Gel ends immersed in buffer trays with platinum electrodes
    Dense (due to added glycerol) DNA samples placed in gel wells under buffer
    Electrical current passed through gel
        Negative pole at well-end of gel
        Negative DNA moves toward positive end
        DNA separated according to fragment size
            Larger pieces move slower
            Smaller pieces move faster
    Current stopped when DNA reaches gel end
    Visualizing DNA bands
        Ethidium bromide staining
            Bands fluoresce at peak UV 260 Å
            Gels viewed and photographed
    Uses of DNA electrophoresis
        Determine fragment size
        Purify DNA
        Comparing genetic differences
        (See text Example 9.6 Estimating size of a DNA fragment with electrophoresis.)

Gel electrophoresis of proteins (polyacrylamide gels)
    Proteins separated by molecular size (figure 9.27)
        SDS-polyacrylamide electrophoresis (SDS-PAGE)
            Proteins denatured in sodium dodecyl sulfate
            SDS-proteins electrophoresed in SDS-polyacrylamide gels
            Polypeptides separated by size
    Proteins separated by molecular charge
        Isoelectric focusing (IEF)
            Proteins electrophoresed in pH gradient in gel
            Proteins migrate to isoelectric point in gel
    Proteins separated by size and charge
        Two-dimensional polyacrylamide electrophoresis (2D-PAGE (Figure 9.26)
            Combination IEF and SDS-PAGE
            Net Charge of protein X weight polypeptides
        Native gel electrophoresis (PAGE)
            Protein structure retained
            Separated by size and charge
            Enzyme activity retained in most proteins
            Position identified by enzyme activity
            Position identified by antibodies

9.8 DNA, RNA, AND PROTEIN BLOTTING

Central idea:
- After DNA or RNA fragments are separated by electrophoresis, they may be transferred from the gel to a filter on which the DNA or RNA can be hybridized to a labeled probe. Proteins may also be transferred from gels to filters for identification of specific proteins with antibodies.

DNA, RNA or proteins can be transferred from gel to filter
Southern blotting and analysis (Figure 9.31)
    Restriction digested human DNA electrophoresed in gel
    The many fragments form smear of DNA in gel lane
    DNA fragments transferred from gel to filter
        Gel placed on filter
        Buffer slowly flows through gel and filter
        DNA trapped on filter
        Bind DNA to filter (DNA immobilized on filter)
        Filter position same as gel position
    Probe hybridized to DNA fragment on filter (Figure 9.32)
        Probe sequence and DNA fragment similar
        Position of DNA fragment noted for study
Northern and Western blotting
Northern blotting: RNA is blotted on filter
    Probe identifies specific RNA fragment on blot
    Procedures similar for DNA Southern blotting
Western blotting: protein is blotted on filter for proteins (figure 9.33)
    Specific proteins detected by antibodies

9.9 DNA SEQUENCING

Central ideas:
- Cloned fragments of DNA can be sequenced with chain termination methods. Automated DNA sequencing has been developed and permits rapid and inexpensive DNA sequencing.
- DNA sequencing is based on chain termination by dideoxynucleotides. Automated DNA sequencing has made possible rapid and inexpensive acquisition of DNA sequences. Scientists may submit DNA sequence information for inclusion in centralized databases that are freely available to scientists worldwide.

Sanger dideoxy sequencing (Figure 9.34)
    Method uses modified DNA synthesis mixture on cloned DNA
        Cloning vector: DNA inserted next to DNA polymerase primer site
        Cloned DNA is amplified from primer
            Automated reaction mix in DNA sequencer:
                Four dNTPs
                Four fluorescent dye-labeled ddNTPs
                    Dideoxy NTPs have unavailable 3' carbon
                    Strand synthesis stopped at insertion of a ddNTP into new
                      DNA chain
                DNA polymerase

Buffer

Primer DNA

Primer insures replication of one DNA strand only

ddNTPs: block synthesis of strands of varying length from primer

Each DNA piece ends with ddNTP

Reaction products size fractionated and assayed by electrophoresis

Fragments come off gel in order of size (Figure 9.37)

ddNTP on fragment end identified by fluorescent color in laser beam

The machine identifies terminal nucleotide and position in sequence

DNA sequence information on the Internet (Figure 9.38)

Scientists submit DNA sequences to central computer

Information cataloged and made available

GenBank: largest US DNA sequence data base

Scientists can compare sequence with many other known sequences

(See Example 9.7 Use of GenBank, BLASTN, BLASTX)

Chapter 10
Eukaryotic Genome Organization

KEY CONCEPTS

- Eukaryotic genomes consist of linear DNA molecules organized into chromosomes through orderly hierarchical packaging of DNA.
- Eukaryotic DNA sequences may be unique or repeated within the genome. Most genes are within the unique fraction.
- Chromosomes have characteristic structural features that carry out specific functions.
- Some genes are organized in clusters called gene families.
- DNA sequencing of eukaryotic genomes provides important information about genome organization.

KEY TERMS

complexity
repetitive DNA sequences
nonrepetitive DNA sequences
unique DNA sequences
single copy DNA
transposable elements
LINES (long interspersed nuclear elements)
SINES (short interspersed nuclear elements)
retrotransposition
C-value paradox
Cot curve
chromatin
histone
nonhistone
nucleosome
10 nm fiber
30 nm fiber
solenoid
core DNA
linker histone
centromere
kinetochore
metacentric
submetacentric
subtelocentric
acrocentric
telocentric
chromosome arm
long arm
short arm
p arm
q arm
primary constriction
chromosome satellite

knobs
chromatid
sister chromatid
nonsister chromatid
telomere
chromosome banding
G-band
NOR banding
polytene chromosome
chromosome puff
in situ hybridization
FISH (fluorescence *in situ* hybridization)
euchromatin
heterochromatin
facultative heterochromatin
constitutive heterochromatin
short tandem repeats (microsatellites)
YAC (yeast artificial chromosome)
NOR (nucleolus organizer region)
gene family
pseudogene
unprocessed pseudogene
processed pseudogene

CHAPTER TOPICS

10.1 REPETITIVE AND NONREPETITIVE DNA
      Repetitive DNA
      Transposable elements
      Functions of repetitive and unique DNA
      The C-value paradox
      DNA renaturation experiments
10.2 EUKARYOTIC CNA PACKAGING
      Nucleosomes
      DNA packaging and regulation of transcription
      Nucleosomes and DNA replication
10.3 THE EUKARYOTIC CHROMOSOME
      Structural features of eukaryotic chromosomes
      Chromatids
      Centromeres
      Telomeres
      Chromosome banding
      In situ hybridization
      Euchromatin and heterochromatin
      Yeast artificial chromosomes
10.4 GENE ORGANIZATION IN CHROMOSOMES
      Gene families
10.5 WHOLE GENOME ORGANIZATION

CHAPTER OUTLINE

Introduction
Eukaryotic complexity requires more genes and larger genomes
> Prokaryote genome size
>> *Mycoplasma genitalium* 580,000 nucleotide pairs
>> *e. coli* genome 4.2 million nucleotide pairs
> Eukaryotic genome size
>> *Pyrenomas salina* unicellular alga 660,000 nucleotide pairs
>> Brewers yeast 13 million nucleotide pairs
>> Multicellular eukaryotes genome size
>>> *Caenorhabditis elegans* 80 million nucleotide pairs
>>> *Drosophila melanogaster* 140 million nucleotide pairs
>>> Some amphibians some higher plants exceed 75 billion   nucleotide pairs
>>> Diploid cells have double the amounts

Examine organization of eukaryotic genes and genomes

10.1 REPETITIVE AND NONREPETITIVE DNA

Central ideas:
- Most eukaryotic genomes are significantly larger than prokaryotic genomes.
- Eukaryotic genomes may be described in terms of complexity. Repeated sequences contribute only once to a genome's complexity.
- Eukaryotic genomes have three general classes of DNA sequences: unique (or single copy) DNA sequences, moderately (or middle) repetitive DNA sequences, and highly repetitive DNA sequences.
- A major proportion of eukaryotic genomes contains repetitive DNA.
- The DNA in a eukaryotic genome can be divided into three general classes: 1) unique (or single copy) DNA sequences 2) moderately (or middle) repetitive DNA sequences, and 3) highly repetitive DNA sequences. Most genes are within the unique sequences.

Genome complexity
> Total length (in nucleotide pairs) of different DNA sequences (sequences that aren't repeated)
> Contribution of repeated sequences to genome complexity
>> Three hundred nucleotide sequence repeated 100 times
>>> Total length: 30000 nucleotide pairs
>>> Contribution to complexity: 300 nucleotide pairs
>> **Repetitive DNA sequences:** sequences repeated in genome
>> **Unique DNA sequences:** sequences that appear once in genome
> Eukaryotic genomes have unique and repetitive sequences
>> Brewers yeast: few repetitive sequences (small genome)
>> Multicellular species: major fraction in repetitive sequences
>> Some plants and amphibians: up to 70% repetitive sequences
> DNA sequences classified according to degree of repetition
>> Unique (single copy) DNA
>> Moderately repetitive DNA (tens to thousands of times)
>> Highly repetitive DNA (typically > 100,000 times)

Repetitive DNA
Repeats range from two to millions of times in most genomes

Example:

Highly repeated sequence in *Drosophila viridis*

Repeated millions of times in genome:

5' ACAACT 3'

5' ATAACT 3'

5' ACAATT 3'

Transposable elements

Sequence can insert itself in several sites in genome

Some elements leave one site and move

Some elements replicate a movable copy

Some cause insertion mutations in genes

LINEs (long interspersed nuclear elements) and SINEs (short interspersed nuclear elements)

LINEs thousands of nucleotides long (Figure 10.1)

Repeated as much as 100,000

Interspersed in genome

SINEs < 500 nucleotides long

Repeated hundreds of thousands of times

Interspersed in genome

Both called **retroposons**

Move by **retrotransposition**

Transcribed into RNA from promoter

RNA reverse transcribed into DNA

Reverse transcribed DNA inserts at new site

Original transposon remains at original location

Increase in number as they spread generation after generation

LINE L1 best known human LINE 100,000 copies/genome

Structure suggests origin

6000 nucleotide pairs

Contains AATAAA polyadenylation signal

Poly-A sequence

Origin: reverse transcription of mRNA

Two genes

Left gene nonfunctional

Right gene like virus reverse transcriptase gene

SINEs and the *Alu* family in human genome (Figure 10.2)

Alu structure provides clue to origin

The *Alu* family of SINEs have *Alu*I restriction sites

One of two gene copies encodes 7S snRNA

One functional copy with polymerase III promoter

One insertion mutated copy

Alu sequences vary by 14%

Small fraction capable of retrotransposition

Transposed SINEs may cause some cancers

Functions of repetitive and unique DNA

Some repetitive sequences have known functions

Repeated sequences located in telomeres

Used for finishing replication

Constructed by telomerase

Centromere repeats

Some moderately repeated sequences

    Genes for rRNA

    Genes for tRNA

Unique DNA sequences encode most mRNAs

C-value paradox

C value = total amount of DNA per species genome

C value and number of genes per genome

    Prokaryotes C value close to number of genes per genome

    Eukaryotes C values higher than estimated number of genes

C-value paradox: discrepancy between number of genes and genome size

    Large fraction of genome highly repetitive

    Spacer regions between genes: repetitive and unique DNA

    Some spacer DNA regulates gene expression

    Introns are non-gene sequences

    Five percent human DNA encodes amino acid sequences

DNA renaturation experiments

Determine proportions of single copy, moderately repeated and highly repeated sequences

    Denaturation: separation of double helix DNA into single strand DNA

        Heat denatures DNA (complete at about 92°C, Figure 10.3)

        Denaturation temperature depends on A=T and G≡C proportions

            Lower temperature: higher proportion of A=T pairs

            Higher temperature: higher proportion of G≡C pairs

            Temperature plot of DNA denaturation curve

                Denaturation begins at about 70°C

                T_m = temperature at half denaturation of DNA sample

                Denaturation complete 92-95°C

    Renaturation rate at 25°C below T_m

        Denatured DNA is allowed to renature

        Rate is concentration dependent (Figure 10.4)

        $t_{1/2}$ = time when half DNA is renatured

Performing renaturation experiments

    DNA sheared to 100 to 300 kb fragments

    DNA completely denatured by heat 92–95°C

    Renatured at 65°C

        Rates depend on DNA concentrations

            Unique DNA slowly renatures

            Repeated sequences faster (weeks or months)

                Highly repeated sequences fastest

                Moderately repeated sequences fast

Relative proportions determined from shape of renaturation curve (Figure 10.5)

(See Example 10.1 DNA renaturation experiments and genome complexity.)

10.2 EUKARYOTIC DNA PACKAGING

Central ideas:

- Linear DNA molecules in the nucleus are packaged into chromosomes. Chromosomes are composed of chromatin, an orderly winding of DNA with proteins that hold the DNA in a condensed state.
- DNA packaging follows a set hierarchical organization. First, the linear double-stranded

DNA molecule is would around cores of histone proteins to form a string of nucleosomes. Second, the nucleosomes coil to form a solenoid. Third, the solenoids loop our from a scaffold of non-histone proteins. Degree of DNA packaging is dynamic.
- Metaphase chromosomes have certain structural characteristics that define their size, shape, and function. These include the primary constriction or centromere, chromosome arms, telomeres, secondary constrictions, knobs, and chromosome satellites.
- DNA packaging follows a set hierarchy. The DNA winds around histones to form the 10 nm fiber, that coils to form a solenoid of histones called the 30 nm fiber. DNA may further condense into loops held in place by non-histone proteins.

Large eukaryotic genomes require highly organized DNA packaging
> **Chromatin** contains DNA and associated proteins
> Packaging DNA depends on proteins
> Tremendous amount of DNA is held tightly in small space
> Removal of proteins releases enormous amount of DNA (Figure 10.7)
> Pattern of hierarchical packaging
>> First level **(nucleosome)** compresses helix 1/6
>>> **2 nm DNA fiber** (DNA helix) wound around histones core (**10 nm fiber**)
>>> **Nucleosome:** DNA plus histone core (10 nm fiber, Figure 10.8a)
>> Second level **(solenoid)** compresses helix 1/40
>>> Nucleosomes coil into helix (**solenoid, 30 nm fiber**)
>>>> (Figure 10.8d)
>>> Chromatin condensed to third level at cell division (Figure 10.8 d, e)
>>>> Super coiled solenoid
>>>> Chromatin at metaphase
>> Packaging levels not constant
>>> Varies between interphase and cell division
>>> Varies at transcription and replication
>>> Varies within chromosome

Nucleosomes
> DNA wound twice around histone core (140-180 nucleotide pairs)
> Core DNA: DNA within histone (140-180 nucleotide pairs)
> Linker DNA: DNA between nucleosomes (about 50 nucleotide pairs)
> Nature of histones
>> Basic amino acids give net positive charge
>> DNA negative phosphate groups bind histones
>> Nucleosome core:
>>> Eight histone molecules
>>> Two each of H2A, H2B, H3, H4 (Figures 10.10, 10.11)
>> Linker histone H1 (H5 or H^0, Figure 10.11)
>> Histones are highly conserved (evolution)

DNA packaging and regulation of transcription
> DNA packaging prevents transcription
> Intensely transcribed genes (i.e., rRNA) free of nucleosomes (Figure 10.12)
> Transcription mRNA genes: nucleosomes remain in place
>> 30 nm fiber uncoiled
>> Nucleosome structure temporarily altered during transcription

Nucleosomes and DNA replication
> Replication fork: nucleosome disrupted

Nucleosomes quickly reorganized after replication fork
(See example 10.2 Nucleosome conservation during DNA replication.)

10.3 THE EUKARYOTIC CHROMOSOME

Central ideas:
- Chromosomes have two major types of chromatin: euchromatin and heterochromatin. Euchromatin is generally less condensed and contains nearly all of the active genes. Heterochromatin is more condensed and contains few active genes.
- Many eukaryotic genes are organized into gene families. A gene family is a series of identical or similar genes that are clustered. The genes within a gene family are often expressed differently at predetermined stages during the organism's development.
- Eukaryotic chromosomes have centromeres that function in chromosome separation during mitosis and telomeres that protect the ends of the linear chromosomes.
- Chromatin may be classified as euchromatin or heterochromatin. Euchromatin is less condensed than heterochromatin and contains most of the genes. Heterochromatin is highly condensed and contains repetitive DNA.

Structural features of eukaryotic chromosomes
    Structural features defined in highly condensed state (i.e., mitotic metaphase)(figure 10.14)
        X-shape of metaphase chromosomes
            Two replicated DNA molecules attached at **centromere**
            Kinetochores: protein structure at centromere
        Chromosome shape defined by centromere position
            Metacentric: centromere in middle
            Submetacentric: centromere off center
            Subtelocentric or acrocentric: centromere near one end
            Telocentric: centromere located at end
        Position divides chromosome into "arms"
            In humans:
                "short arm" is "p" arm
                "Long arm" is "q" arm
        Constricted sites in metaphase chromosomes
            Primary constriction: centromere region
            Secondary constriction: constriction near chromosome end
            Satellite: chromatin beyond secondary constriction
    Chromatids: identical duplicated chromatin after DNA replication
        Chromatid contains one linear DNA molecule
        Two chromatids of duplicated chromosomes: **sister chromatids**
    Centromeres (Figure 10.16)
        DNA sequences of yeast chromosome centromeres
        Elements of yeast CENs (conserved centromere regions)
            CDEI consensus sequence: $^A/_C$TCA$^A/_C$TG
            CDEII conserved sequence: about 90% A/T pairs
            CDEIII conserved sequence: TGTTTTTTGN<u>TTTCCGAAA</u>NNNAAAAA
        CEN elements highly diverse among eukaryotes
    Telomeres
        Specialized ends of eukaryotic chromosomes
        Telomere stabilizes chromosome ends from "stickiness"

Structure

> Short repeated sequences (chapter 2 sections 2-4)
>
> Sequences similar in all eukaryotic species studied

Chromosome banding

> Alternate light/dark staining regions metaphase chromosomes
>
> Peculiar banding pattern for each chromosome
>
> Giesma stain reveals G-bands human chromosomes (Figure 10.18)
>
>> Dark bands AT rich highly condensed
>>
>> Light bands GC rich
>>
>> Genes usually grouped in light band regions
>
> NOR banding: staining NOR regions

Polytene chromosomes of *Drosophila* larvae

> Giant interphase chromosomes
>
> Many identical chromatids lying parallel (Figure 10.19, 10.20)
>
> **Chromosome puffs**: transcribing decondensed DNA

In situ hybridization

> Hybridizing DNA probe homologous to chromatin DNA region
>
> Detecting chromosome position of genes (Figure 10.22)
>
> Highly sensitive system
>
>> **FISH**: fluorescence *in situ* hybridization
>>
>> Detects small quantities of hybridized probe

Euchromatin and heterochromatin (in the interphase chromosome, Figure 10.23)

> Euchromatin: region of less condensed chromatin
>
>> Most transcribed genes in euchromatin
>>
>> Mostly unique sequence DNA
>
> Heterochromatin: region of highly condensed chromatin
>
>> Mostly repetitive DNAs
>>
>> Mostly nontranscribed regions
>
> **Facultative heterochromatin**
>
>> Not always heterochromatin
>>
>> Condensed X chromosome in mammalian females
>
> **Constitutive heterochromatin** (Figure 10.24)
>
>> Large blocks of highly repetitive DNA
>>
>> Condensed in all chromosomes
>>
>>> Known to contain some genes
>>>
>>> *Drosophila* centromere regions (see example 10.3)
>>
>> Usually found in centromere and telomere regions
>
> Euchromatin contains scattered repetitive DNAs
>
>> **Short tandem repeats (microsatellites)**
>>
>> Microsatellites can be found within genes
>>
>>> CGG repeat found in *FMR1* gene (fragile X)
>>>
>>> Repeat numbers vary

Yeast artificial chromosomes (YACs) (Figure 10.25)

> YACs are large DNA fragment cloning vectors
>
>> Replicated in bacteria as plasmids
>>
>> Replicates in yeast as chromosome (with inserted DNA)
>
> Structure of YAC
>
>> Yeast centromere and telomeres
>>
>> Bacterial origin of replication

Chromosome origins of replication
DNA insertion site (*Eco*RI)
Circular DNA cleavage site (two *Bam*HI sites)
Liberates telomere ends
Linearizes YAC
Bacteria selectable markers
Function as a cloning vector (see example 10.4)

10.4 GENE ORGANIZATION IN CHROMOSOMES
Central idea:
- Many eukaryotic genes are organized into gene families. A gene family is a series of identical or similar genes that are clustered. The genes within a gene family are often expressed differently at predetermined stages during the organism's development.

No known operons in eukaryotic genomes
Biochemical pathway genes are scattered
Same regulatory proteins may coordinately regulate scattered genes
Eukaryotic genes organized into clusters
rRNA precursor genes clustered in NOR
Humans have five NORs
tRNA genes are clustered in chromosome regions
Gene families
Many mRNA genes are clustered in **gene families**
Gene families common for abundant proteins
Histones
Globins (Figure 10.26)
α globin cluster (four genes, three pseudogenes)
β globin cluster (five genes, one pseudogene)
Storage proteins in plants
Pseudogenes
Sequences similar to true genes
Insertions, deletions, point mutations render locus nonfunctional
Unprocessed pseudogenes
Arise by duplication of a gene
Mutation render inactive
Processed pseudogenes
Lack introns
Often have poly A tails
Probable origin
Arise by reverse transcription of mRNAs
Reverse transcribed DNA inserted into genome
Features of expressed globin gene clusters (Figure 10.27)
Developmental times of expression
Large number of repetitive sequences between genes
Presence of *Alu* segments between genes
About 8% of DNA in globin clusters transcribed
(See example 10.5. Comparison of pseudogene with true gene)

10.5 WHOLE GENOME ORGANIZATION

Central ideas:

- Whole genome DNA sequencing is underway in several eukaryotic species and has been completed in *Saccharomyces cerevisiae*. The DNA sequence of an entire genome reveals much about genome organization and is the first step toward understanding the complete biology of an organism.

- Entire genome sequencing has been completed in one eukaryotic species (*Saccharomyces cerevisiae*) and will soon be completed in several others. Whole genome sequencing reveals many important aspects about eukaryotic genome organization.

Sequencing whole eukaryotic genomes

    Brewer yeast (*Saccharomyces cerevisiae*) first complete sequence (1996)

    Other projects underway

        Human (scheduled completion 2005)

        Drosophila melanogaster

        Arabidopsis thaliana

    Some values of complete genome nucleotide sequences

        Total number of genes revealed

        How genes are organized within genomes

        Relation of noncoding DNA to coding DNA

        Evolutionary relationships of DNA sequences

    Features of brewers yeast genome

        13 million nucleotide pairs among 16 chromosomes

        5885 sequences of potential mRNA genes

        140 rRNA genes

        275 tRNA genes

        40 snRNA genes

        (See example 10.6 Function of repeated sequence)

    Human genome

        3 billion nucleotides pairs among 23 chromosomes

        Estimated 50,000 to 100,000 mRNA genes

Chapter 11
Mitosis, Meiosis, and Life Cycles

KEY CONCEPTS

- Life continues from one generation to the next because cells and organisms reproduce.
- A particular species reproduces sexually, asexually, or in both ways.
- Somatic cells reproduce through mitosis (the division of the nucleus) and cytokinesis (division of the cell).
- Each cell from a mitotic division receives a complement of chromosomes that are genetically identical to those in the parent cell.
- Meiosis consists of two cell divisions that form haploid cells that develop into sperm or egg cells.
- In the life cycles of most eukaryotes, a haploid stage alternates with a diploid stage.

KEY TERMS

mitosis
meiosis
Life cycle
diploid
homologous chromosomes
nonhomologous chromosomes
homologues
homologs
haploid chromosome number
n
karyotype
cell cycle
G_1
S phase
G_2
interphase
prophase
spindle fibers
asters
centrioles
spindle equator
kinetochores
metaphase
sister chromatid cohesion
anaphase
telophase
cytokinesis
somatic cells
germ line
synapsis
crossing over
non-sister chromatid exchange
metaphase I

anaphase I
segregation
prophase II
metaphase II
anaphase II
telophase II
segregational division
equational division
leptonema
zygDNA
P-DNA
zygonema
synaptonemal complex
pachynema
chiasma
diplonema
diakinesis
terminalization
spermatogenesis
oogenesis
double fertilization
zygote

CHAPTER TOPICS

11.1 THE CELL CYCLE AND MITOSIS
- Chromosome number and homology
- The cell cycle
- Mitosis

11.2 MEIOSIS

11.3 A CLOSER LOOK AT PROPHASE I
- Stages of Prophase I
- Crossing-over

11.4 LIFE CYCLES
- Life cycle of animals
- Life cycles of flowering plants
- Life cycles with a predominant haploid phase

CHAPTER OUTLINE

Introduction

Life perpetuates by replication
- DNA replication precedes cell division
- Fertilized egg to adult
- Adult replacement of cells (i.e., lining small intestine, wound healing)

Mitosis produces genetically identical cells
- Eukaryotic process of cell division
- Mitosis followed by cytoplasm division
  - Each cell has identical chromosomes
  - Same genes in adult cells as fertilized egg
  - Genetic differences acquired by mutation only

Vegetative reproduction is by mitosis
Meiosis produces new genetic combinations (sexual reproduction)
Specialized somatic cell (a mitotic cell) undergoes meiosis
Gametes (egg and sperm) form from meiotic cells
Gametes: n chromosome number
Gamete mother cell: $2n$ chromosome number
Fertilization between egg and sperm: restores $2n$ chromosome number
Chapter focus
The cell cycle and mitosis
Meiosis
A close look at prophase I of meiosis
Life cycles of animals and plants

11.1 THE CELL CYCLE AND MITOSIS
Central ideas:
- A diploid cell contains of two sets of chromosomes, one inherited from the maternal parent, the other from the paternal parent. Each chromosome from the maternal parent is similar (but not identical) to a homologous chromosome from the paternal parent.
- Organismal reproduction may be sexual or asexual. Sexual reproduction allows for recombination of genetic material at each generation, whereas asexual reproduction does not.
- The somatic cells of most plants and animals are diploid which means there are two copies of each chromosome in the nucleus, one copy inherited from the maternal parent, the other from the paternal parent. These two chromosomes are said to be homologous, because they are similar in structure, location of genes, and nucleotide sequence, although there are often some differences in nucleotide sequence.
- The number of chromosomes in a haploid genome is designated as n. A diploid cell has $2n$ chromosomes in the nucleus. Diploid human cells, for example, have $2n = 46$ chromosomes.
- Conventions for chromosome numbering vary among species, but are often numbered consecutively from the largest to the smallest chromosome. Human chromosomes are numbered in this manner, except for the X and Y chromosomes which are not numbered. 5. Somatic cells pass through a series of events called the cell cycle. The cell cycle consists of two main stages: mitosis and interphase, which are divided into substages.
- Interphase begins with G_1 during which most cells carry out their function. Cells that are not in the process of dividing are typically in the G_1 phase. When a cell prepares to divide, it enters the S phase during which the DNA is replicated. Following the S phase, is a relatively short G_2 phase before the cell enters mitosis.
- Mitosis begins with prophase during which the nuclear envelope dissipates and the duplicated chromosomes condense. At metaphase, the duplicated chromosomes align at the equatorial plate of the cell. During anaphase, the duplicated chromosomes separate, with one copy of each chromosome moving to each of the two cell poles. In telophase, the chromosomes reach the poles, nuclear envelopes reform surrounding each set of chromosomes. Cytokinesis (cell division) typically begins during telophase. Mitosis ensures that each daughter cell receives an identical complement of chromosomes.

Chromosome number and homology (Figure 11.1)
Drosophila melanogaster
Diploid somatic cells ($2n$): eight chromosomes
Female: two each of X, II, III, and IV chromosomes
Two sets of **homologous** chromosomes

103

The two Xs are homologous

The two IIs are homologous etc.

Male: one X, one Y and two each of II, III, and IV

Egg and sperm cell(n): 4 chromosomes each

Female egg: one each of X, II, III, and IV chromosomes

Male sperm: X or Y, one each of II, III, and IV chromosomes

Homologous chromosomes

Identical in size, shape and closely or exactly similar in nucleotide sequence

May differ slightly in nucleotide sequence due to mutations

Carry same genes normally in same linkage order

Homologues or homologs: the two chromosomes of homologous pair

X and Y chromosomes behave as homologous chromosomes

Small part of nucleotide sequences match

X and Y carry different genes (except for homologous nucleotide segment)

Y much smaller with few genes

Gamete chromosome number = n (haploid chromosome number)

Drosophila $n = 4$, $2n = 8$ (Figure 11.1)

Humans $n = 23$, $2n = 46$ (Figure 11.2)

Human chromosome numbering: largest to smallest 1–22, plus X and Y

The cell cycle (Figure 11.3)

Interphase: G_1, G_2, and S

G_1: gap between last mitosis (last cell division) and DNA synthesis

S phase: DNA synthesis phase

Chromosomes duplicate (single DNA/chromosome → two DNAs/chromosome)

Chromosome → two chromatids each (each with one long DNA molecule)

G_2: gap between DNA synthesis and mitosis

Interphase: G_1, S, and G_2

M phase: mitosis and cytoplasmic division (cytokinesis)

Mitosis (Figure 11.4)

Prophase

Chromosomes condense (shorten and thicken)

Sister chromatids seen attached at centromere

Nucleolus disappears

RNA transcription nearly ceases

Spindle begins to form outside nucleus

Centrioles (seen in almost all eukaryotes except higher plants, Figure 11.5)

Divide and migrate to opposite poles

Radiating microtubules form **Asters**

Nuclear envelope (membrane) dissipates

Spindle fibers and chromosomes make contact

Metaphase

Spindle equator: spindle fibers radiate from two opposite poles meeting mid-cell

Kinetochores: spindle fiber attachment structure on chromosome centromeres (Figure 11.6)

Attachment site on each chromatid

Attachments align sister chromatid to poles

Chromosomes moved into equator between poles of cell

Sister chromatid cohesion: sister chromatids adhere through prophase and metaphase

Anaphase

        Separation of chromatid centromeres identifies anaphase

        Centromeres pulled to opposite poles

        (At this point former chromatids are called "chromosomes")

        Chromosome arms dangle behind centromeres during movement to poles

Telophase

        Chromosomes cluster at opposite poles

        Chromosomes decondense to interphase state

        Nuclear envelopes form around chromosome clusters

Cytokinesis (division of cytoplasm)

        Plant cells: new cell membranes and cell walls form dividing cells

        Animal cells: new membranes form dividing cells

        Cells shift into G_1 phase of cell cycle

(See example 11.1 Replication of centromeric DNA in yeast.)

11.2 MEIOSIS

Central ideas:

- Haploid gametes arise from meiosis, a series of two cell divisions with one round of DNA replication. The two divisions of chromosomes are called meiosis I and meiosis II.
- Meiosis I begins with prophase I during which the chromosomes condense, duplicated homologous chromosomes pair with each other to form tetrads, and the nuclear membrane dissipates. At this stage, non-sister chromatids exchange segments. During metaphase I, the tetrads align at the cell equator, and at anaphase the tetrads separate to each pole. Non-homologous chromosomes assort independently. The cell is in telophase I when the chromosomes arrive at the poles.
- Meiosis II begins shortly after telophase I with an abbreviated (or sometimes nonexistent) interphase. During prophase II the chromosomes condense and the nuclear envelope dissipates. The duplicated chromosomes align at the cell equator during metaphase II and chromatids separate from each other toward opposite poles during anaphase II, becoming true chromosomes. During telophase II, the chromosomes arrive at the poles and the nuclear envelopes reform. The cells are now haploid and may develop further into mature gametes.
- Prophase I is one of the most lengthy and important stages of meiosis. It is subdivided into several phases. During leptonema, the chromosomes condense and begin to pair, but do not synapse. During zygonema, further the chromosomes condense further and begin to synapse. By pachynema, chromosome synapsis is complete and chiasmata form at the sites of crossing over. During diplonema, chromosomes decondense in order to be transcribed. Diakinesis is the final stage of prophase I when the chromosomes condense once again and prepare to complete meiosis.
- Crossing over recombines genes on paired homologous chromosomes.
- In cells that will give rise to gametes, meiosis reduces the number of chromosomes to one set. Meiosis proceeds through two cell divisions, each divided into prophase, metaphase, anaphase, and telophase. Nonsister chromatids of paired homologous chromosomes may exchange segments during prophase I.

Contrast between mitosis and meiosis

    Genetic results of mitosis:

        Daughter cells genetically identical to parent cell ($2n \rightarrow 2(2n)$)

        Somatic cells genetically identical to zygote ($2n \rightarrow 2(2n) \rightarrow 4(2n) \rightarrow 8(2n)$)

Genetic results of meiosis:

        Parent cell 2*n*, 4 gametes *n*: ($2n \rightarrow n + n + n + n$)

        Forms new combinations of chromosomes in gametes

        Forms new genetic recombinations within chromosomes

Where meiosis takes place

    Animals:

        Specialized cells in reproductive organs undergo meiosis

        (Reproductive organs (testes and ovaries) differentiate from embryo **germ line** cells)

    Flowering plants:

        Male and female organs (anthers and ovaries) differentiate in new floral buds

        Meiosis occurs in specialized tissues of anthers and ovaries

Stages of meiosis (Figure 11.7)

    Specialized cell prepares for meiosis: DNA replicates in S phase

    Meiosis I (segregational division)

        Prophase I

            Chromosomes decondense, homologous chromosomes **synapse (synapsis)**

            Dissipation of nuclear envelope

            Crossing over between nonsister chromatids of homologous chromosomes

                (nonsister chromatid exchange)(figure 11.8)

            Spindle attachments to kinetochore: one attachment per chromosome

            Paired chromosomes (tetrad) move into spindle equator (Figure 11.9)

        Metaphase I

            Tetrads aligned in spindle equator (Figures 11.9, 11.11)

            Orientation of nonsister chromatids of tetrads to opposite poles of cell

            Maximum condensation of chromosomes

        Anaphase I

            Sister chromatids pulled together to same pole

            Nonsister chromatids separate toward opposite poles of spindle

            Segregation of homologous chromosomes begins at separation of centromeres

            Nonhomologous chromosomes (different tetrads) assort independently (Figure

                11.10)

        Telophase I

            Nuclear envelopes form around each cluster of chromosomes at the cell poles

            Cells may enter brief interphase

            No DNA replication before meiosis II

            Chromosomes may decondense

    Meiosis II (equational division)

        Prophase II (no DNA replication between telophase I and prophase II, Figure 11.7 on

            page 329)

            Condensing of chromosomes in each nucleus

            Formation of spindles in each nucleus

            Dissipation of nuclear envelopes

            Spindle fibers attach to kinetochores

        Metaphase II

            Chromosomes (two chromatids/chromosome) pulled into spindle equators

            (One spindle for each group of meiosis II chromosomes)

        Anaphase II

            Sister chromatids separated at centromeres

            Chromosomes moved to opposite poles of spindles

Telophase II
>   Nuclear membranes organize around four clusters of chromosomes at poles
>   Chromosomes decondense
>   Cytokinesis separates the four nuclei
(See example 11.2 Positioning of kinetochores during meiosis I.)

11.3 CLOSER LOOK AT PROPHASE I

Central idea:
- Prophase I is the stage at which synapsis and crossing over take place. It is longest an most complex of the stages in meiosis I and can be divided into five stages, leptonema, zygonema, pachynema, diplonema, and diakinesis.

Stages of prophase I (Figure 11.12)
>   **Leptonema** (Figure 11.12a)
>>   Chromosomes appear as single threads
>>   Sister chromatids adhere tightly (Figure 11.13)
>>   Telomeres attach to nuclear envelope
>   **Zygonema** (Figure 11.12b)
>>   Synapsis of homologous chromosomes
>>   Formation of **synaptonemal complex** (Figure 11.14)
>>   Replication of zygDNAs
>   **Pachynema** (Figure 11.12c)
>>   Nonsister chromatid crossing over probably at this point
>>   Tetrads shorten and thicken in appearance (condensing)
>>   Crossing over creates **chiasma**
>   **Diplonema** (Figure 11.12d)
>>   Chromosome segments (including centromeres) separate between chiasma
>>   Homologous chromosomes held together at chiasma points
>   **Diakinesis** (Figure 11.12e)
>>   Chromosomes continue condensation
>>   Chiasma **terminalize** (move) toward telomeres (Figure 11.15)
>   **Crossing over**
>>   Consequences of crossing over:
>>>   Recombination of genetic differences in homologous chromosomes
>>>   Several crossovers can occur between nonsister chromatids
>>>   Crossing over produces hybrid patchworks of maternal and paternal homologous chromosomes
>>>   Occurrence at different points each meiosis
>   (See Example 11.3 Crossing over and the synaptonemal complex.)

11.4 LIFE CYCLES

Central idea:
- Life cycles consist of a haploid stage and a diploid stage. Animals have a short haploid stage in which the haploid products of meiosis develop into gametes with no mitotic divisions. The haploid cells of flowering plants undergo a few mitotic divisions before the gametes develop. Many fungi spend most of their life cycles as haploid cells that divide mitotically.

Alternating diploid and haploid stages of life cycles
    The need for understanding life cycles
    Variations in haploid and diploid stages
Life cycle of animals (Figure 11.17)
    Great diversity of developmental stages
    Underlying alternation of haploid and diploid stages similar
        Gamete formation from specialized cells of sex organs
            Spermatogenesis (Figure 11.18)
                Diploid spermatogonium becomes primary spermatocyte
                Diploid primary spermatocyte goes through meiosis I
                Two haploid secondary spermatocytes undergo meiosis II
                Meiosis II forms four spermatids
                Spermatids mature into motile sperm
            Oogenesis (Figure 11.19)
                Diploid oogonium becomes primary oocyte
                Primary oocytes goes through meiosis I
                    Products of meiosis I: secondary oocyte and first polar body
                    Both go through meiosis II
                    Products of meiosis II: ovum and three polar bodies
            Fertilization in animals (Figure 11.20)
Life cycles of flowering plants (Figure 11.21)
    Meiosis produces haploid spores from specialized cells in sex organs
    Haploid spores undergo mitotic division(s) and differentiate gametes
    Differentiation of male gametes
        Anther is male reproductive organ
            Microspore mother cell undergoes meiosis
            Each of four haploid spores undergo one mitosis
            Two cells differentiate into pollen grain (no gametes yet)
                Tube nucleus
                Generative nucleus
                    Generative nucleus undergoes mitosis in pollen tube
                    Produces two male gametes
    Differentiation of female gametes
        Ovary is female reproductive organ
            Megaspore mother cell ($2n$) in ovule undergoes meiosis
            Four haploid spores (n each) formed (three usually disintegrate)
            Haploid spore divides mitotically forming multicelled embryo sac (often 8
                cells)
            One cell becomes egg cell
            Two embryo sac cells fuse ($n + n \rightarrow 2n$) forming endosperm mother cell
    Double fertilization in plants
        Pollen tube grows into embryo sac in ovule
        Two sperm nuclei released (mitotic division of generative nucleus)
        Egg fertilized by one sperm nucleus
        Endosperm mother cell fertilized by second sperm nucleus ($2n + n \rightarrow 3n$)
        (Double fertilization)
        Embryo plant ($2n$) from fertilized egg cell
        Seed endosperm ($3n$) from fertilized endosperm mother cell\
    Life cycles with predominant haploid (gametophyte) phase

Chapter 12
Mendelian Genetics

KEY CONCEPTS

- Mendelian principles of inheritance reflect the fundamental patterns of chromosome partitioning during meiosis and can be explained at the molecular level.
- The principle of segregation describes how alleles located on homologous chromosomes segregate from each other during meiosis.
- The principle of independent assortment describes how genes on nonhomologous chromosomes assort during meiosis.
- Mendelian principles function in accordance with the laws of probability

KEY TERMS

true breeding
monohybrid experiments
parental generation
F_1 generation
monohybrid
F_2 generation
dominant phenotype
recessive phenotype
Mendel's principle of segregation
dihybrid experiments
Mendel's principle of independent assortment
alleles
locus
homozygous
heterozygous
genotype
Punnett square
phenotype
Punnett square
monohybrid testcross
parental equivalence
reciprocal cross
trihybrid
forked-line method
linked genes
probability
product rule
sum rule
binomial distribution
binomial coefficient
Pascal's triangle
multinomial distribution
sampling error
chi-square analysis

significant

highly significant

type I error

CHAPTER TOPICS

12.1 MENDEL'S EXPERIMENTS
    Monohybrid experiments and the principle of segregation
    Dihybrid experiments and the principle of independent assortment

12.2 MOLECULAR BASIS OF DOMINANCE
    Basic genetic terminology
    Genotype, phenotype, and dominance

12.3 CELLULAR BASIS FOR SEGREGATION
    Monohybrid testcross experiments
    Parental equivalence

12.4 CELLULAR BASIS FOR INDEPENDENT ASSORTMENT
    Dihybrid testcross experiments
    Trihybrid experiments
    Linked genes

12.5 MENDELIAN INHERITANCE IN HUMANS

12.6 MENDELIAN GENETIC AND PROBABILITY
    The rules of probability
    Binomial distribution
    Multinomial distributions
    Sampling error
    Chi-square analysis

12.7 ABOUT MENDEL
    Rebirth of Mendelian genetics
    Criticisms of Mendel's work

CHAPTER OUTLINE

12.1 MENDEL'S EXPERIMENTS

Central ideas:
- Mendel's experimental results led him to develop mathematical theories to explain the basic principles of inheritance, including the principle of segregation and the principle of independent assortment. Mendel confirmed his theories through additional experimentation.
- Mendelian genetics is a central theme of genetics. It is named after Gregor Mendel who formulated the basic principles of inheritance in the 19th Century based on hybridization experiments with pea plants.
- Several key terms in Mendelian genetics can be defined in the context of molecular biology. A locus is the position of a gene in the DNA of a chromosome. Different DNA sequences at the same locus are called different alleles. Because there are two homologues for each chromosome, there are two copies of each locus, one on each of the homologues. If both homologues have the same allele at a locus, the individual is homozygous for that allele. If the alleles differ between homologues at a locus, the individual is heterozygous for those alleles. If one allele masks the effect of another in a heterozygous individual, then the masking allele is dominant to the other allele. The masked allele is recessive to the dominant allele.

Genotype describes the genetic composition of alleles at a locus, whereas the phenotype is what we actually see in the individual.

"Hybrids follow a definite law"
- Segregation of dominant and recessive characters predictable
- Independent assortment of characters predictable

Self pollinating , **true breeding** pea varieties selected
- Different alleles seldom introduced during reproduction
- Mendel chose 22 pea varieties with different traits
- Confirmed "true breeding" by growing for two seasons
- Mendel selected 7 traits with contrasting forms (Figure 12.2)

Mendel's monohybrid experiments and the principle of segregation
- Monohybrid experiments and segregation ratios (See Table 12.1)
    - True breeding parents differ for one trait
    - **Parental generation:** true breeding parents
    - First generation progeny: each F_1 **generation** was monohybrid
        - **Dominant** phenotype expressed in F_1 (Figure 12.3)
        - **Recessive** phenotype not expressed in F_1
    - F_2 **generation:** progeny of self pollinated or intercrossed F_1s (Figure 12.7)
        - Mathematical series of all possible combinations of gametes from F_1 parents
        - 3/4 dominant phenotype
        - 1/4 recessive phenotype like the recessive parent
    - **Mendel's principle of segregation of differing alleles**
        - "Differing elements" segregate at gamete formation
        - Differing elements recombine at fertilization (F_2 ratios)
            - Proof of genotypes of dominant F_2 plants (all seven traits)
            - F_3 generation genotypes (F_2 allowed to self-pollinate)
        - Progeny from dominant F_2 plants (Table 12.2)
            - 1/3 homozygous for dominant factor like the dominant parent
            - 2/3 heterozygous for both factors like the F_1 hybrid
        - Progeny from recessive F_2 plants
            - All recessive phenotypes
            - All pure breeding

Mendel's dihybrid experiments and the principle of independent assortment
- **Dihybrid experiment**
    - Parents differ by two pairs of contrasting traits (round, yellow seeds x wrinkled, green seeds)
        - Gametes: one genotype from each pure breeding parent
        - Gametes combine to produce heterozygous offspring
    - F_1 offspring had both dominant phenotypes (round, yellow seeds)
    - Selfing or intercrossing F_1 produced F_2 generation (Figure 12.4)
- F_1 generation is **dihybrid** (See in-text diagrams page 352)
    - Four kinds of gametes produced in equal proportions
    - Recombine at random in fertilization
    - Gametes: four haploid genotypes from each parent sex
    - Gametes combine at random
- F_2 generation segregates as predicted by **"Mendel's principle of independent assortment"**
    - Different pairs of alleles assort independently of each other at gamete formation
    - F_2 phenotypes follow mathematically predictable proportions:

9/16 both dominant traits (yellow, round seeds)
3/16 dominant trait and recessive trait (yellow,. wrinkled seeds)
3/16 recessive trait and dominant trait (green, round seeds)
1/16 both recessive traits (green ,wrinkled seeds)
(See example 12.1 Matching observed and expected ratios.)

12.2 THE MOLECULAR BASIS OF DOMINANCE
Central idea:
- Most dominant alleles encode a functional product and most recessive alleles are mutant and fail to encode a functional product. When an individual is heterozygous for dominant and recessive alleles, the dominant phenotype appears because the functional product encoded by the dominant alleles compensates for the recessive allele's failure to encode a functional product.

Basic genetic terminology
    Locus (plural: loci)
        Synonymous with "gene"
        Chromosome location of gene (See in-text diagram page 353)
    Alleles:
        Different DNA sequences of the same gene locus on homologous chromosomes
        Different DNA sequences at the same nucleotide positions in homologous DNAs
    Homozygous: identical alleles on homologous chromosomes
        True breeding individuals are homozygous
        Example: *AA* and *aa* plants in Mendel's F_2 for flower color
    Heterozygous: different alleles on homologous chromosomes
        Hybrid F_1s for flower color were heterozygous at one locus
        Hybrid F_1s for seed shape and seed color had heterozygous alleles at two loci
    Genotype: a description of alleles an individual is carrying
    Phenotype: observed features of an individual

Genotype, phenotype, and dominance
    Purple flowers contain anthocyanin (Figure 12.6)
        Anthocyanin synthesized by enzymes in biochemical pathway (Figure 12.5)
        White flowers due to a defective pathway enzyme
        Gene *A* on short arm of chromosome I encodes enzyme
        Allele *a* encodes defective enzyme
        AA encodes functional enzyme (flowers purple)
        Aa encodes functional and defective enzymes (*A* is dominant, flowers purple)
        aa encodes defective enzyme (flowers white, Figure 12.6)
    A allele is dominant to *a* allele in *Aa* heterozygote
        (See Example 12.2: Molecular basis of seed shape)

12.3 THE CELLULAR BASIS FOR SEGREGATION

Central ideas:
- Stated in modern terms, the principle of segregation is: Because homologous chromosomes segregate from each other during meiosis, alleles at the same locus on homologous chromosomes also segregate from each other so that half the gametes receive one allele and half receive the other.

- Because homologous chromosomes segregate from each other during meiosis, alleles at the same locus on homologous chromosomes also segregate from each other so that half the gametes receive one allele and half receive the other.

Mendel's segregation: a consequence of chromosome segregation at meiosis (See text diagrams page 356)
>	Purple flowered plant is male parent (AA, diploid)
>	White flowered plant is female parent (aa, diploid)
>>		All sperm nuclei of purple flowered plant (AA) carry A allele
>>		All egg nuclei of white flowered plant (aa) carry a allele
>>		Pollination produces Aa hybrid seed (F_1 generation)

$$AA \times aa \text{ (pure breeding diploid parents)(two copies of each allele)}$$
$$\downarrow \quad \downarrow \text{ (egg and sperm genotypes follow chromosomes in meiosis)}$$
$$\text{(sperm) } A \quad a \text{ (egg, each have haploid genotype—copy of one allele)}$$
$$\backslash \quad /$$
$$Aa \text{ (diploid } F_1 \text{ hybrid, Figure 12.7)}$$
>	Summarizing these events by **Punnett square**
>>		Union of F_1 gametes produce F_2 generation (Figure 12.7)
>>		Four equally likely possibilities segregate in F_2 genotypes
>>>			25% chance of AA homozygote (purple flowers)
>>>			50% chance of Aa heterozygote (purple flowers)
>>>			25% chance of aa homozygote (white flowers)
>	(See example 12.3: Testcross experiment in mouse, Figure 12. 8)
Parental equivalence
In the formation of both male and female gametes, segregation of alleles is the same.
The **reciprocal** cross (female written first, male on right,)

$$AA \times aa \text{ and } aa \times AA \text{ (female written first)} \rightarrow \text{same results in } F_1 \text{ and } F_2$$

12.4 THE CELLULAR BASIS OF INDEPENDENT ASSORTMENT

Central ideas:
- Using modern terms, the principle of independent assortment may be stated: Because genes located on nonhomologous chromosomes assort independently during meiosis, the inheritance of alleles at one locus does not influence the inheritance of alleles at another locus.
- Genes that are closely linked to each other on the same chromosome do not assort independently during meiosis.

Explanation of Mendel's principle of independent assortment (Figure 12.9)
>	Based on events during meiosis
>>		Segregation of homologous chromosomes
>>		Independent assortment of nonhomologous chromosomes
>	Mendel's seed color and seed shape in peas
>>		RR, Rr: seeds round
>>		rr: seeds wrinkled
>>		II, Ii: seeds yellow
>>		ii: seeds green
>>		Homozygous diploid parents and F_1 hybrid

113

$IIRR \times iirr$ (*I* and *R* loci on nonhomologous chromosomes)

   ↓   ↓

IR ir (haploid gametes from pure breeding parents)

  \   /

F_1 *IiRr* (diploid dihybrid)

    ↓ (segregation and independent assortment of chromosomes)

IR Ir iR ir (meiosis produces four gamete genotypes in equal proportions, Figure 12.11)

Self-pollinated or intercrossed F_1 plants produces F_2 (Figure 12. 10)

    Phenotype ratios: 9:3:3:1

    Genotype ratios: 1:2:1:2:4:2:1:2:1

Dihybrid testcross experiments

    Purpose: Identify genotype of individual with dominant traits

    Purple flowered tall plant homozygous or heterozygous

        Plant with dominant traits crossed with homozygous recessive

        (Purple flowered tall plant x white flowered dwarf plant)(Figure 12.11)

    Phenotypes in first generation progeny

        Reveal genotypes of dominant parent

        If dominant parent is *AaBb*:

            Four genotypes: *AaBb, Aabb, aaBb, aabb*

            Four phenotypes: purple tall, purple dwarf, white tall, white dwarf

        If dominant parent is *AaBB* or *AABb*:

            Two genotypes

            Two phenotypes

Trihybrid experiments (Figure 12.12)

    Original true breeding parents differ by three traits ($AABBCC \times aabbcc$)

    Gametes produced by pure breeding parents: *ABC* and *abc*

    Kinds of gametes produced by F_1 *AaBbCc*: 8 kinds

    Sixty-four ways 8 kinds of gametes can unite at random

        F_2 genotypes: use forked-line method

        Determine expected proportions of genotypes

            AaBbcc: $1/2 \times 1/2 \times 1/4 = 1/16$

        Genetic variation among parents and variation in offspring

            Few parent differences lead to great progeny variation

                Differ by two loci: $3 \times 3 = 9$ genotypes

                Differ by three loci: $3 \times 3 \times 3 = 27$ genotypes

        Determine the number of gametes, genotypes, phenotypes

        (any number of independently segregating loci)

            n = number heterozygous loci (Mendel's formulas)

            2^n gametes

            3^n F_2 genotypes

            2^n phenotypes (complete dominance at all loci)

Linked genes

    Linked loci tend to remain associated in gamete formation

    Likelihood of crossing over increases with linkage distance

    Distantly linked genes assort independently

    Two of Mendel's seven pea traits on chromosomes I, two on chromosome IV, three loci are on different chromosomes (seven chromosomes in pea, Figure 12.13)

(See Example 12.4: Deviation from independent assortment)

12.5 MENDELIAN INHERITANCE IN HUMANS

Central idea:
- Mendelian inheritance in humans can be studied by analysis of existing pedigrees

Mendelian genetics in plants and animals
    1900 Mendelian inheritance rediscovered in plants by three scientists
    1902 Mendelian inheritance demonstrated in animals
Mendelian inheritance in human pedigrees (Figures 1214, 12.15, 12.16, Table 12.3)
    1905: brachydactyly dominant trait
    1913: albinism demonstrated in numerous pedigrees
    Molecular biology circumvented past limitations on human genetics
        Human among best understood species genetically (Table 12.3)
        (Internet link to OMIM website at www.brookscole.com/biology)

12.6 MENDELIAN GENETICS AND PROBABILITY
Central ideas:
- *The product rule*: When two events are independent of one another, the probability that they will occur together is the product of their individual probabilities.
- *The sum rule*: If two events are mutually exclusive, the probability that one of the two events will occur is the sum of their probabilities.
- Binomial and multinomial distributions allow researchers to determine the probability of any possible outcome in genetic experiments.
- Chi-square analysis is used to determine whether or not sampling error can reasonably explain the deviation of observed data from hypothesized values.

The rules of probability
    The **product rule**: the chance two independent events will occur at the same time is a product of their separate probabilities of occurrence
        Applied to coins
            Flip two coins (penny and nickel)
            P of heads = 50%, tails = 50%
            P both heads $0.5 \times 0.5 \times 100 = 25\%$
            P one heads one tails $2 \times 0.5 \times 0.5 \times 100 = 50\%$
        Applied to Mendelian genetics (Figure 12.10)
            P of green seed 1/4, wrinkled seed 1/4
            P of green-wrinkled seed $1/4 \times 1/4 = 1/16$
            P of yellow-wrinkled seed $3/4 \times 1/4 = 3/16$
    The **sum rule**: if two events are mutually exclusive, the probability that one of the two events will occur is the sum of their probabilities.
        Applied to one coin
            Flip one coin: either heads or tails
            P of either heads or tails $= 0.5 + 0.5 = 1.0$
        Applied to rolling a six-sided die
            P of either 1 or 4: $1/6 + 1/16 = 2/6$
        Applied to genetics (Mendel's purple/white flower color)
            P of F_2 heterozygote (Aa) = 1/4 Aa + 1/4 aA = 2/4
            P of dominant phenotype = P of AA + P of Aa: $1/4 + 2/4 = 3/4$

Binomial distribution used to determine probabilities (uses product and sum rules)

$(p + q)^n$

p and q = probabilities of outcomes p and q and n = number of trials

Required assumptions

Outcomes mutually exclusive

All events or trials independent

Binomial distribution sexes in families of five children (Figure 12.17)

Six mutually exclusive outcomes possible

5 f, 4f + 1 m, 3 f + 2m, 2f + 3m, 1f + 4 m, 5 m

P of any outcome in a binomial distribution: $P = (n!/x!y!)(p^x q^y)$

n = total number of individuals (e.g., family of five children)

x = number of individuals in one class (e.g., number of females)

y = number of individuals in other class (e.g., number of males)

p = probability of occurrence of one class (e.g., P of male = 1/2)

q = probability of occurrence of other class (e.g., P of female = 1/2)

"!" = "factorial"

$p + q = 1$

The binomial coefficient: $n!/x!y!$

Number of ways (i.e., birth orders) a specified $x + y$ (i.e., two boys three girls) can occur

(See example 12.5 The binomial distribution: Recessive alleles in human families.

Example 12.6 The probability of genotypic misclassification in Mendel's experiments.)

Multinomial distributions

Trinomial distribution $P = (n!/x!q!z!)(p^x q^y r^z)$

Values have same meaning as above

More classes can be added accordingly

Sampling error

Deviation of expected ratios

Error greater with smaller sample sizes

P of all girls with five children greater than P of all girls in ten children

Large samples expected closer to 3:1 ratio than smaller samples

Mendel's monohybrid flower color experiments

Observed: 705 purple: 224 white

Expected 697 purple: 232 white

Deviation is sampling error

Chi-square analysis

$X^2 = \Sigma((O - E)^2/E)$ value for each class

The greater the sampling error the higher the chi-square value

X^2 = "chi-square", O = number observed, E = number expected

Chi-square table and degrees of freedom

Level of significance (how much error can we accept?)

Meaning of two levels of significance (0.05 and 0.01)

Type I error (rejection of a correct hypothesis)

(Example 12.7 Chi-square analysis: significance testing. Example 12.8 Chi-square analysis applied to genetics.)

12.7 ABOUT MENDEL

1822: born Heinzendorf bei Odrau (Hyncice, Czech Republic, Figure 12.18, peasant family, farming, orchards, etc.)

1843: Entered St. Thomas Monastery, Brünn (Brno, Czech Republic)

116

1850: Failed examination for teacher certification

Enrolled Univ. Vienna to study mathematics, physics, chemistry, biology

1853: returned to Monastery, studied peas

1856: began experiments with peas and with beans (8 years)

1865: results presented Brünn Society of Natural History

Published paper: *Versuche über Pflanzen-Hybriden* (*Experiments on plant hybrids*, Figure 12.19)

Some commentaries on his work

    William Bateson

    Mendel's own comments on his work

Mendel's further studies and correspondence with Karl von Nägeli

    The hawkweed paper

    Concluded pea findings not universal

Increased administrative duties interfered with research and publishing

    Other scientific researches

        Bees, mice, sunspots and weather patterns, ozone in air, groundwater levels, scientific paper on observed tornado

Much of original research data burned after Mendel's death

Rebirth of Mendelian genetics

    Hugo DeVries, Carl Correns, Erich von Tschermak 1900

        confirmed Mendel's experiments in plants

    Confirmation in animals 1902 (William Bateson and L. Cuénot)

        fowl and mice

    Mendelism accepted rapidly throughout world

    1905: term *genetics* coined (Bateson)

    1909: first textbook in genetics

1913: first department of genetics in US est. Univ. California, Berkeley

Criticism of Mendel's work

    Sir Ronald A. Fisher

    (Example 12.9 Statistical justification of Mendel's interpretation of his experiment with flower color in beans.)

    Most criticism dismissed by careful reading of Mendel's paper

    Mendel observed many additional principles of inheritance

        Genetic basis of inbreeding

        Heterosis of some hybrids

        Described pleiotropy

    Conclusion: Mendel can be remembered as a careful and meticulous scientist (example 12.9)

    Mendel also remembered as mindful, devoted teacher, used position and resources to assist those in need (Hugo Iltis)

Chapter 13
Variations on Mendel's Theme

KEY CONCEPTS

- Alleles are inherited according to Mendelian principles, but the traits encoded by some alleles do not appear in typical Mendelian ratios because of variations in the ways in which genes are expressed phenotypically.
- Different types of gene expression and gene interaction can be detected phenotypically.
- DNA markers are inherited like alleles that affect physical characteristics, but are free of many of the limitations for genetic analysis that physical traits may have.

KEY TERMS

       multiple alleles
       incomplete dominance
       wild-type alleles
       mutant alleles
       gain-of-function mutation
       loss-of-function mutation
       constitutive
       threshold effects
       codominance
       antigens
       Bombay phenotype
       leaky recessive alleles
       compound heterozygote
       dominance series
       lethal alleles
       pleiotropy
       epistasis
       complementary gene action
       duplicate gene action
       dominant suppression
       dominant epistasis
       recessive epistasis
       penetrance
       nonpenetrant
       expressivity
       modifier genes
       genetic background
       non-genetic factors
       DNA markers
       restriction fragment length polymorphisms (RFLPs)
       tandem nucleotide repeat markers
       minisatellites
       variable number tandem repeats (VNTRs)
       microsatellites (short tandem repeat polymorphisms (STRPs)
       PCR-based markers

random amplified polymorphic DNA (RAPDs)

CHAPTER TOPICS

13.1 MULTIPLE ALLELES AND DOMINANCE RELATIONS
   Incomplete dominance
   Dominant mutant alleles
   Codominance
   Leaky recessive alleles
   Compound heterozygotes and dominance series
   Lethal alleles
   Pleiotropy
13.2 EPISTASIS
   Complementary gene action
   Duplicate gene action
   Dominant suppression
   Dominant epistasis
   Recessive epistasis
13.3 PENETRANCE AND EXPRESSIVITY
   Penetrance
   Expressivity
   Causes of nonpenetrance and variable expressivity
13.4 DNA MARKERS IN GENETIC ANALYSIS
   Restriction fragment length polymorphism (RFLP) analysis
   RFLPs and tandem nucleotide repeats
   PCR based markers
   Random amplified polymorphic DNA (RFLP)

CHAPTER OUTLINE

Introduction
   Inheritance of a trait does not always follow simple patterns
      Eye color in humans
         Brown and blue eyes can be Mendelian
         Gray, green, hazel, some blues and browns may not be Mendelian
      Biochemical pathways have several enzymes
         Eye color varies because several gene loci are involved
         Each enzyme specified by different gene locus or loci
         Several genes may affect the same trait
         Alleles can each affect structure same protein differently
         One enzyme may be common to other pathways
         Single gene locus my affect more than one trait
   Phenotypes depart from Mendelian ratios for two basic reasons
      Genetic and biochemical complexities of gene products
      Affects of environment on development of phenotype
   Segregation and assortment of chromosomes and gene loci still universal

13.1 MULTIPLE ALLELES AND DOMINANCE RELATIONS

Central ideas:

- Most recessive alleles are mutant alleles in that they differ from the dominant wild-type alleles most often found in nature. However, there are many known cases of dominant mutant alleles.
- Different alleles at a locus do not always show a simple dominant-recessive relationship. Incomplete dominance is a situation in which a heterozygote has a phenotype that is intermediate between the phenotypes of the two homozygotes. Codominance is a situation in which a heterozygote has the phenotypes of both homozygotes.
- Although a diploid individual carries only two alleles at a locus, there may be more than two alleles for a single locus in a population of individuals. Multiple alleles may show various dominance relationships with one another, in some cases forming a dominance series.
- Some recessive alleles do not completely eliminate the dominant phenotype, but cause reduced expression of the phenotype. These alleles are often called leaky recessive alleles.
- Dominance is not always complete. Alleles may show incomplete dominance or codominance.
- Although a diploid individual carries only two alleles at a locus, a population may have more than two alleles at a locus.
- Some recessive alleles do not completely eliminate the dominant phenotype, but cause reduced expression of the phenotype. These alleles are often called leaky recessive alleles. When homozygous, leaky recessive alleles allow some of the dominant phenotype to appear, but at reduced levels.
- The dominance relations of multiple alleles at a locus may form a series.
- The phenotype associated with lethal alleles is death, often in zygotic or embryonic stages. Lethal alleles are usually recessive and are only expressed in homozygotes. They are usually detected as the absence of an expected class of progeny. Dominant lethal alleles are much more rare because their carriers usually die before reproducing. However, dominant lethal alleles with delayed onset may be transmitted from one generation to the next.
- A pleiotropic gene affects the phenotype of more than one trait.

More that two alleles can exist for each gene locus
- Single diploid can carry only two of many possible alleles for each locus
- New allele created by any alteration of DNA at a locus
- More than two alleles called **Multiple alleles**
- Multiple alleles can have hierarchy of dominance relations

Incomplete dominance
- Dominance not always complete
- F_1 intermediate between pure breeding parents
- Inheritance of flower color in snapdragons (Figure 13.1)
  - Pure breeding parents: red (R^1R^1) and white (R^2R^2) flowers
  - F_1 hybrid pink (R^1R^2) flowers
  - Underlying cause
    - R^1 allele codes for functional enzyme
    - R^2 allele fails to codes for functional enzyme
    - Amount of functional enzyme limiting in hybrid
    - Limiting enzyme levels produce less pigment in this case (threshold effect)
- Products of many genes have **threshold effects**

Dominant mutant alleles (See GENETIC NOTATION page 384)

Mutations can produce dominant mutant alleles

    Alleles most often found in nature are called "**wild-type alleles**"

    Typical features of wild-type alleles and mutant alleles

        Wild type usually encode functional product and are dominant

        Mutant alleles fail to encode functional product and are recessive

    Mutant alleles that are exceptions

        Some mutations responsible for human cancers

            Proto-oncogenes (mutations may cause cancers)

                Function: gene protein product stimulates cell division

                Gene regulated at transcription level

            Mutation in regulator region of gene stimulates transcription

                Called "**gain of function mutation**"

                Gain of function mutations are often **constitutive** mutations

                Gain of function mutations act as dominant mutations

                (Recessive mutations are often "**loss of function**")

    Some genes may have some dominant loss of function mutant alleles

        TP53 gene in humans (tumor suppresser gene)

            Dominant loss of function mutation due to protein structure

                Gene product is tetramer of same polypeptide

                Some mutations permit tetramer assembly but eliminate function

                  (Figure 13.3)

                Wild-type and mutant polypeptides in heterozygote

                    One mutant peptide in tetramer destroys function of tetramer

                    Chance for fully normal tetramer is low

                      15/16 tetramers with mutant peptide

                      1/16 normal tetramers

                      Normal tetramers more quickly degraded

            Some *TP53* loss of function mutations are recessive (Figure 13.3)

                Mutant product cannot assemble with tetramer

                Heterozygote can assembles only normal tetramer

Codominance

    ABO histo-blood groups in humans

        Blood groups differ by alteration of cell surface oligosaccharide (Figure 13.4)

        FUT1 locus makes H antigen (adds fifth sugar on oligosaccharide)

        ABO locus adds sixth sugar to H antigen

            ABO*A allele adds N-acetylgalactosamine

            ABO*B allele adds galactose to H antigen

            ABO*O no sugar is added to H antigen

        Effects of *ABO* genotypes on blood group phenotype (Figure 13.5)

        Phenotypic responses to blood transfusions (Table 13.1)

    Bombay phenotype and expression of *ABO* alleles

        Due to mutant *FUT1* allele

        Lacks H antigen structure (*ABO* enzyme has no substrate on cell surfaces)

        Blood type appears as O (called O_h, Figure 13.6)

    Structure of the *ABO* alleles

        (See Example 13.1. Molecular characterization of the *ABO* alleles)

Leaky recessive alleles

    Mutant enzyme may retain some function

    Final product leaks through

Over 100 alleles at white locus *Drosophila melanogaster*

w^1 blocks synthesis brown and red eye pigments

Other *w* alleles allow synthesis of some pigment (leak through, Figure 13.7)

Compound heterozygotes and dominance series

Heterozygous for two different mutant alleles

Example: *PAH* gene in humans

Several mutant forms (190 forms) cause same disorder (PKU)

Heterozygotes for different alleles (**compound heterozygotes**) have same disorder

Dominance series among mutant alleles

Example: dominant hierarchy at the *c* locus in rabbits

$C > c^{ch} > c^h > c$ (agouti, chinchilla, Himalayan, white phenotypes, respectively)

Genotypes at the *C locus* and phenotypes of rabbit coat colors(Figure 13.9)

Agouti: CC, Cc^{ch}, Cc^h, cc

Chinchilla: $c^{ch}c^{ch}$, $c^{ch}c^h$, $c^{ch}c$

Himalayan: c^hc^h, c^hc

White: cc

Lethal alleles: mutant alleles that eliminate a function essential to survival

Persistence of dominant and recessive lethal mutants in population

Recessive lethals persist (active only when homozygous)

Dominant lethal alleles usually eliminated first generation

Delayed-action dominant lethals may persist (Huntington disease)

Affects of lethal mutations on Mendelian ratios

Segregation of recessive lethal alleles

Parents must be heterozygous

Living progeny segregate: 1/3 homozygous dominant, 2/3 heterozygous (homozygous recessive dies)

Coat color in mice (Figures 13.10, 13.11)

A^WA^W wild-type color

A^y recessive lethal

A^WA^y yellow coat

A^yA^y dies

(Example 12.2. Molecular structure of the A^y recessive lethal allele)

Pleiotropy: single gene responsible for several phenotypic effects

Pleiotropic genes

Mendel observed flower color gene affected leaf axil and seed coat colors (Figure 13.12)

The *A* gene enzyme expressed in leaf axils and seed coats

Sickle-cell anemia gene (Figure 13.13)

13.2 EPISTASIS

Central idea:

- Epistasis is the interaction of alleles at two or more loci that affect a single trait. It is often detected by observing ratios such as 9:7, 15:1, 13:3, 12:3:1, or 9:3:4 in the offspring of doubly heterozygous parents.
- In complementary gene action, the dominant phenotype is encoded by the presence of at least one dominant allele at each locus.
- In duplicate gene action, the dominant phenotype is encoded by the presence of at least one dominant allele at each locus.

Effects of biochemical pathways

   Several enzymes encoding genes help form pathway final product

   Each gene of pathway influences expression of other pathway   genes

Example of epistasis

   Comb shape in chickens (William Bateson)

   RRPP walnut, *R_pp* rose, *rrP_* pea, *rrpp* single (Figure 13.14)

Complementary gene action

   Purple flower color in sweet pea (Figure 13.17)

   Independent loci *A* and *B*

   Each encodes different enzyme of anthocyanin synthesis pathway

   F_2 ratio (progeny of cross: *AaBb x AaBb*)

   3/16 *aaB_* white flowers (defective pA enzyme)

   3/16 *A_bb* white flowers (defective pB enzyme)

   1/16 *aabb* white flower (defective pA and pB enzymes)

   9/16 *A_B_* purple flowers (has both pA and pB enzymes producing functional pathway)

   F_2 ratio 9 purple: 7 white

   Alternative explanation (Figure 13.18)

   Independent loci *A* and *B* (anthocyanin biosynthesis pathway)

   Each encodes different polypeptide of same enzyme

   Same results as above

   (See Example 13.3. Testing the ratio for complementary gene action.)

Duplicate gene action

   Two independent gene loci segregating in F_2 (*A* and *B*)

   Only *aabb* genotype expresses recessive phenotype

   F_2 ratio is 15 dominant phenotype: 1 recessive phenotype

   Growth habit in wheat

   Spring growth: *A_B_, A_bb, aaB_*

   Winter growth: *aabb*

   Biochemistry of growth habit in wheat (Figure 13.20)

Dominant suppression

   Dominant allele suppresses dominant expression at other locus

   Feather color in chickens

   C gene encodes enzyme for colored feathers

   cc blocks pigment formation (feathers are white)

   I locus suppresses pigment formation

   ii homozygote allows color (need *C* allele at other locus)

   C colored feathers (other F_2 genotypes are white)

   F_2 ratio: 13 white: 3 colored (Figure 13.21)

Dominant epistasis

   Bulb color from onions (red, yellow and white colors)

   Colors controlled by two independent loci (*R* and *I*)

   *R_* gives onion dark red color

   rr leaky recessive giving yellow color

   I is dominant inhibitor of color

   __ii allows color determined by *R* locus

   *__I_* is white

   F_2 segregation ratio: 12 white: 3 red: 1 yellow (Figure 13.22)

Recessive epistasis

   An example from Labrador retrievers

Two independent loci *B* and *E*

*BB E_* or *BbE_* produces black coat

bb is leaky recessive reduces pigment in coat (chocolate colored)

Dominant allele *E* allows normal color development in coat

ee is leaky recessive allows small amount of pigment

B_ee, bbee are yellow

F_2 9 black: 3 chocolate: 4 yellow (Figure 13.23)

13.3 PENETRANCE AND EXPRESSIVITY

Central ideas:
- Penetrance is the proportion of individuals with a particular genotype that have the phenotype typically associated with the genotype.
- Expressivity is the degree to which a phenotype is expressed in individuals with a given phenotype.

Penetrance (phenotype is either expressed or not expressed)

Phenotype is expressed: trait is penetrant

Phenotype is not expressed: trait is nonpenetrant

Bombay phenotype:

Type A, B and AB phenotypes not express (nonpenetrant)

Nonpenetrance

Examples: dominant suppression, dominant epistasis, recessive epistasis

A phenotype is lacking although gene for trait is present

Penetrance can be expressed as a percentage of population showing trait

If 975/1000 people with *ABO*A* gene show type A phenotype

Penetrance is 97.5%

Expressivity (defines degree of expression of an expressed trait)

Figure 13.24 shows variable expressivity in pea seeds

Phenotypes may vary in degree of expressivity due to **modifier genes**

Over 20 modifier genes for seed coat color known in pea

Causes of nonpenetrance and variable expressivity

Genetic background (all genes in individual except one under study)

Non-genetic factors (external and internal environments)

Expression of the *c^h* allele in Himalayan rabbits

Dark color fur depends on temperature of tissue

Extremities are dark

Warmer portions of body are light colored (Figure 13.25)

(Example 13.4. Type-D brachydactyly in humans)

13.4 DNA MARKERS IN GENETIC ANALYSIS

Central ideas:
- DNA markers detect differences in nucleotide sequence and do not rely on analysis of phenotypes associated with genes.
- Restriction fragment length polymorphisms (RFLPs) and PCR-based markers are among the DNA markers most often used. DNA markers are usually inherited as codominant markers although some are inherited as fully dominant and recessive markers.

Restriction fragment length polymorphism (RFLP) analysis

  Detection of allelic differences in DNA directly

  DNA alleles are called **DNA markers**

  Detection of sickle cell anemia allele by RFLPs (*HBB*S* allele)

    A → T transversion mutation 2nd nucleotide 6th codon

    Restriction digest by *Dde*I restriction endonuclease

      Digest yields millions of fragments

      Electrophoresis, Southern blotting, and probing with allele specific probe

        HBB*A allele yields two fragments (175 and 201 nucleotides long)

        HBB*S allele yields a 375 nucleotide fragment (Figure 13.28)

      Homozygotes and heterozygotes identified (Figure 13.29)

  RFLPs are inherited in codominant fashion (note heterozygote pattern in Figure 13.29)

  Used for genetic analysis like standard alleles

  DNA markers are not affected by gene interactions or environment

  Used for finger printing individuals, forensics, determining parentage, evolutionary studies,
    mapping chromosomes, tracking important genes in breeding etc.

RFLPs and tandem nucleotide repeats

  Based on tandem repeated segments of DNA

  Regions vary in length due to slippage during replication or crossing over

  Over many generations variable length alleles gradually increase in number

    Minisatellites (variable number tandem repeats, VNTRs)

      Repeated segment of 10–100 nucleotide pairs

      Bordered by unique DNA sequences

      Often present in many locations within genome

      VNTR probes may identify many different loci in same Southern blot of restricted DNA (Figure 13.30)

    Microsatellites (short tandem repeat polymorphisms, STRPs)

    Shot repeated segments (i.e., ACACACACACACAC etc.)

    Microsatellite markers detected same way as minisatellite markers

    Like other RFLPs both are codominant markers

PCR based markers

  PCR can be used to generate markers for DNA analysis

  Advantages over RFLP techniques

    Less time consuming

    Less expensive

    Products detected directly by electrophoresis (Figure 13.31)

    PCR primers are made from sequenced DNA fragments

  (See example 13.5. Use of microsatellite markers identify the Huntington disease allele)

Random amplified polymorphic DNA (RAPD)

  PCR amplification uses single 10-nucleotide primer of arbitrary sequence

  Amplification is based on genome DNA matches to RAPD primer

  Different RAPD primer is used for each RAPD reaction

  Reaction products are viewed by electrophoresis and staining

  RAPD markers are usually dominant (Figures 13.32, 13.33)

Chapter 14
Sex Determination and Sex-related Inheritance

KEY CONCEPTS
- Sex determination may be genetic or nongenetic.
- Genetic sex determination is usually governed by genes on sex chromosomes.
- The inheritance of genes on sex chromosomes differs in males and females.
- Mechanisms known as dosage compensation equalize the effect of genes located on the X chromosome in males and females.
- Sex-influenced and sex-limited traits are expressed differently in males and females, but are governed by genes that are not on sex chromosomes.

KEY TERMS
cross-fertilization
hermaphrodites
self-incompatibility
autosomes
homogametic sex
heterogametic sex
ZZ-ZW system
heterogametic sex
XX-XY system
mosaics
gynandromorphs
testis determining factor or TDF
H-Y antigen
sex-determining region
testicular feminization
pseudohermaphroditism
true hermaphroditism
Y-linked or holandric genes
X-linked gene
hemophilia A
deuteranopia
protanopia
fragile-X syndrome
genetic anticipation
pseudoautosomal
dosage compensation
X-chromosome inactivation
Barr body
sex-influenced trait
sex-limited trait

CHAPTER TOPICS

CHAPTER OUTLINE

Introduction
Sexual reproduction produces novel combinations of genes
    Mutation only source of variation without sexual reproduction
    Low mutation rates produce limiting genetic diversity
Cross fertilization encourages heterozygosity
    Heterozygosity facilitates gene recombinations
    Array of mechanisms encourage cross fertilization

14.1. PROMOTION OF CROSS-FERTILIZATION

Central idea:
- There are many mechanisms in nature that promote cross fertilization which makes possible exchange and recombination of genes.

Means of encouraging cross fertilization
    Dioecy: individual is either male or female
        Most animals
        Many plant species are dioecious
    Hermaphrodites: individual has both male and female organs
        Animals: snails, earthworms, etc.
        Plants: many plant species of conifers and angiosperms
            Some mechanisms for promoting cross fertilization
                Differential maturity of sexual organs
                Insect pollination
                Self incompatibility anatomy and physiology (Figure 14.2)
                Monoecy: male and female flowers separated (Figure 14.1)
    (See Example 14.1. Self incompatibility in plants.)

14.2. SEX DETERMINATION

Central ideas:

- Sex determination may be genetic or non-genetic. Non-genetic sex determination may be influenced by such factors as temperature or proximity to females.
- Genetic sex determination may be controlled by a two alleles of a single gene, by multiple alleles of a single gene, or by genes on heteromorphic sex chromosomes.
- There are three general types of sex determination caused by heteromorphic chromosomes: 1) the XX-XO system where females have two X chromosomes and males have one, 2) the XX-XY system where females have two X chromosomes and males have one X and one Y chromosome, and 3) the ZZ-ZW system where males have two Z chromosomes and females have one Z chromosome and one W chromosome.
- Heterogametic sex determination usually ensures that the numbers of males and females are essentially equal.
- In species with an XX-XO or XX-XY system, females are the homogametic sex and males are the heterogametic sex. In the ZZ-ZW system, males are the homogametic sex (ZZ) and females are the heterogametic sex (ZW).

Environmental sex determination

Sex of fertilized eggs affected by temperature

Sea turtle species and species of geckos

< 25°C eggs hatch as females

> 32°C eggs hatch as males

25° to 30°C males and females hatch

Effects of site of attachment: slipper limpet (Figure 14.3)

Attachment to sea floor: matures as female

Attachment to other limpets: mature as male

Genetic sex determination by one gene

Sex determined by two alleles at a single locus

Many dioecious plant species

Asparagus is dioecious

MM and *Mm*: male phenotype

mm: female phenotype

Ploidy and sex determination

Number of chromosome sets determine sex

Bees, wasps, and ants

Queen is diploid

Drones are haploid

Fertilized eggs produce queens or sterile workers

Unfertilized eggs produce drones

Genetic basis: multiple allele series at single locus

Homozygosity of diploids is rare (male)

Nearly all diploids are heterozygous at this locus (females)

Chromosomes and sex determination

Sex determination associated with **sex chromosomes** (all other chromosomes are called "**autosomes**")

Most animals and many dioecious plants

Heteromorphic sex chromosomes (Figure 14.4)

Chromosomes differ in size, shape and gene content

Designated X and Y or Z and W sex chromosomes

Three major sex chromosome systems: XX-X0, XX-XY and ZZ-ZW

Meiosis insures sex ratios are equal

XX-X0 system: grasshoppers and some other insects

XO males produce X and O sperm (heterogametic sex)

Females XX produce X eggs (homogametic sex)

XX-XY system: all mammals, many animal species, and some plants

Males XY (heterogametic sex, females XX homogametic sex)

Females produce X eggs, males produce X or Y sperm

ZZ-ZW: gallinaceous bird species (chickens, turkeys, pheasants) moths, butterflies and some fish

Heterogametic sex is female ZW (produce Z and W eggs)

Males homogametic sex ZZ

(see Example 14.2. Sex determination in a dioecious plant.)

14.3. HETEROMORPHIC CHROMOSOMES AND SEX DETERMINATION

Central idea:

- The mechanism of XX-XY sex determination may differ among species. In *Drosophila melanogaster*, sex is determined by the ratio of X chromosomes to autosomes. When the ratio is 0.5, the individual is male. When the ratio is 1.0, the individual is female. When the ratio is between 0.5 and 1.0, the individual is an intersex. In mammals, sex is determined by the presence of a gene on the Y chromosome called the sex determining region Y (*SRY* in humans). When *SRY* is present, the individual has a male phenotype. When *SRY* is absent, the individual has a female phenotype.

Best studied systems: *Drosophila melanogaster* and mammals

Sex determination in *Drosophila melanogaster*

Sex determination based on ratio of sets of autosomes to X chromosomes

Calvin Bridges (1920s) developed the model (Figure 14.7)

Abnormal segregation of chromosomes at meiosis in female

Autosomes diploid:

XXY female, XO sterile male

XXX: metafemale (weak, infertile)

YO: die soon after fertilization

Y chromosome: little to do with sex determination

Sex: ratio autosome sets to X chromosomes (**X/A ratio)**

Males: 1/2 (0.5 causes male phenotype)

Females: 2/2 (1.0 causes female phenotype)

X/A = 2/3 = intersex

Autosome genes and X chromosome genes interact to determine sex

Numerator elements (sex determining genes on X chromosome) influence the numerator of X/A ratio

Denominator elements (sex determining autosomal genes) influence the denominator value of the X/A ratio

Sex mosaics

Sex determination due to genotype of cell not hormones

Gynandromorphs (Figure 14.8)

XX females with XO cells

XO cells have male characteristics

Gynandromorphs observed in many insect species

Sex determination in mammals (Y-linked genes and male determination in mammals)

Y chromosome is male determining (two gene loci on Y chromosome and male determination)

TDF **gene**

Location discovered in XY females and XX males

Factor responsible for stimulus of testis development

XY females lack small portion of short arm of Y (small deletion)

XX males carry that small portion of Y short arm on X (translocation)

Short arm of Y carries TDF gene

H-Y antigen gene

Antigen present in males absent in females

Locus in long arm of Y

Not male determining

Antigen discovered in mouse male-female reciprocal skin grafts

Inbred females sensitive to inbred male skin grafts

Inbred males accept inbred female skin grafts

t(XX +Yp;X) human males do produce carry H-Y antigen

SRY **locus** (sex-determining region)

Present in all XX human males studied

Found in nearly all male mammals

SRY sufficient to initiate development of male phenotype

ZFY gene product is not male determining

(See Example 14.3 Introduction of *SRY* gene into XX mice)

Other male determining genes located on X and autosomes

Recessive X chromosome mutation: testicular feminization

Absence of cell receptors that bind male determining hormones

Males develop outward female phenotype and characteristics

Develop internal testes and no ovaries

Absence of uterus, vagina is present

Do not ovulate

Other sex differentiation disorders: Pseudohermaphroditism

14.4 SEX-LINKED INHERITANCE

Central ideas:

- Genes on the Y chromosome are transmitted from father to son and are expressed only in males.

- Genes on the X chromosome may be expressed in both males and females. Because females have two X chromosomes, they may be homozygous or heterozygous for X-linked alleles. Males have only one X chromosome, so they can be neither homozygous or heterozygous for X-linked alleles. Instead, males are hemizygous for X-linked alleles.

- Recessive X-linked alleles are typically expressed more often in males than in females because females may carry a recessive allele in the heterozygous condition. Hemophilia and red-green colorblindness are examples of human genetic disorders caused by recessive X-linked alleles.

- Alleles on the X chromosome are inherited in a predictable pattern that does not conform to the principle of parental equivalence. Females may be homozygous or heterozygous for X-linked alleles, and males are hemizygous for X-linked alleles.

- X and Y chromosomes pair during meiosis due to a region of shared homology. Genes in this homologous region are inherited in a pseudoautosomal fashion.
- An attached X chromosome in *Drosophila melanogaster* is designated as X^X. Flies with the genotype X^XY are females. When they are mated to XY males, the X chromosome from the males is transmitted to male progeny and the Y chromosome is transmitted to female progeny.
- In species with a ZZ-ZW form of inheritance, Z-linked traits are inherited in the same manner as X-linked traits, but the homogametic and heterogametic sexes are reversed.

X- and Y-linked inheritance

Genes on X chromosome do not follow parental equivalence

Genes on X chromosome more often expressed in males

    Genes on Y chromosome transmitted father to son

        Holandric genes or Y-linked genes

        Very few Y-linked genes are known

    Genes located on X chromosomes

        X-linked genes

        Males are hemizygous for X-linked genes (Figure 14.10)

        Females are homozygous or heterozygous for X-linked genes

        Mendel's principle of parental equivalence does not apply

            Males transmit X only to daughters

            Females transmit X to both male and female offspring

    1910: X-linked genes in *Drosophila* reported by Thomas Hunt Morgan (Figure 14.11)

        w^1 recessive allele causes white eyes

        White eye male × pure breeding wild-type female (red eyes)

            F_1 males hemizygous with red eyes

            F_1 females heterozygous (red-eyed phenotype)

        F_1 males × F_1 females

            F_2 males red eyes:white eyes 1:1 ratio

            F_2 females have red eyes (half are heterozygous)

            Only males have white eyes

            The reciprocal cross: red-eyed males × white-eyed females

                F_1 males white eyed hemizygous

                F_1 females red eyed heterozygous

             F_2 females: 1/2 red eyes: 1/2 white eyes

            F_2 males: 1/2 red eyes: 1/2 white eyes (Figure 14.12a)

Examples of X-linked genetic disorders in humans (Table 14.1)

    Hemophilia A: 1 per 7000 males (Figure 14.12)

        Absence of blood clotting factor VIII

        Gene locus: *factor VIII c (F8C)*

    Hemophilia B (Figure 14.13)

        Lack blood clotting factor IX (*F9* gene)

        Scientists working for genetically engineered factors VIII and IX

    (See Example 14.4. X-linked inheritance of the *F8C* and *F9* genes in humans.)

    Red-green colorblindness

        Can be X-linked or autosomal

            Two closely linked X-linked loci

            GCP locus (deuteranopia-failure of green perception)

RCP locus (protanopia-failure of red perception)

GCP and *RCP* loci encode color sensing pigment proteins

Alleles known that cause less severe colorblindness

Fragile X syndrome

Afflicts 1/1500 humans (Figures 14.14, 14.15)

Genetic anticipation (frequency increases each generation in family line)

Caused by increasing a trinucleotide repeat region

Normal number of repeats six to 52

Greater than 50 has potential for expansion

Full mutation = 700 or more repeats (fragile X syndrome)

Homology between X and Y chromosomes

Small segment of X homologous to Y (pseudoautosomal segment)

Meiotic pairing occurs in homologous regions X and Y

Inheritance of pseudoautosomal gene in *Drosophila* (Figure 14.17)

Crossing over in homologous region may cause XX males and XY females in humans

At least one crossover always occurs in homologous region

SRY located near homologous region

An errant crossover can translocate *SRY* gene to X

XY without *SRY* female determining

X X with *SRY* male determining

Attached X chromosomes in *Drosophila melanogaster*

Attached Xs behave as single chromosome with double dose of X

$X^{\wedge}XY$ is female (X/A ratio 1.0)

$XY \times X^{\wedge}XY$ (Figure 14.19)

Z-linked inheritance

Barred feathers in chickens

B dominant allele for barred

b recessive allele for nonbarred (Figure 14.19)

14.5. DOSAGE COMPENSATION

Central ideas:

- In mammals, dosage compensation is accomplished by inactivation of one X chromosomes in each somatic cell. The inactivated chromosome is called a Barr body. X chromosomes are usually inactivated early in development, so a mosaic pattern of expression may appear in females who are heterozygous for X-linked alleles.
- In *Drosophila melanogaster*, X chromosomes are not inactivated in females. Instead, dosage compensation is accomplished by regulation of individual X-linked genes.

Potential chromosome imbalance evident in XX-XY, XX-X0, and ZZ-ZW inheritance

Several mechanisms compensate for gene dosage imbalance

Dosage compensation in mammals

X-chromosome inactivation

The Barr body in female nuclei (Figure 14.20)

Facultative heterochromatin genes not transcribed

Lyon hypothesis: heterozygous females for X-linked genes are mosaic

Tortoiseshell cats are females

Calico cats heterozygous for X-linked coat color alleles

Differential inactivation of X chromosomes cause mosaic of X-linked gene activity in tissues

(See Example 14.5. Rare cases of tortoiseshell and calico male cats)

Exceptional males are XXY

Patches of hidrotic ectodermal dysplasia in human females

Glucose-6-phosphate dehydrogenase activity in female cells

Tissue culture of heterozygous human female cells

Only one allele is active

Mitotic progeny tend to retain the same active allele as parent cell

Result: patches of cells with activity of same X-linked allele

Dosage compensation in

Transcription rate of X-linked genes

XX female X-linked genes transcribed at half the level of XY males

XXX females X-linked genes transcribe at 1/3 level of XY males

Dosage compensation on translocated X-linked and autosomal   genes

X genes translocated to autosome are still regulated

Autosomal genes translocated to X chromosome are not regulated

14.6. SEX-INFLUENCED AND SEX-LIMITED TRAITS

Central idea:
- Sex-influenced and sex-limited traits are expressed differently in males and females, but are controlled by genes on autosomes rather than sex chromosomes. Sex-influenced traits are expressed in both sexes, but preferentially in one sex. Sex-limited traits are expressed exclusively in one sex.

Sex influenced traits

Sex influences expression of an autosomal gene

Pattern baldness

Trait appears in both sexes but more often in males

Allele is dominant in males, recessive in females

Bald females are homozygous

Sex limited traits

Genes are expressed only in one sex

Secondary sex characters

Milk production

Antlers in male deer

Breast development in humans

Male and female plumage in birds

Beard growth in human males

(See Example 14.6. Inheritance of spotting in the pea weevil.)

Chapter 15
Chromosome Mapping

KEY CONCEPTS

- Linked genes are located close to each other on the same chromosome which prevents them from assorting independently.
- The genetic map distance between linked genes is measured as the recombination frequency of the genes.
- Genetic maps are constructed by consolidating map distances among genes and genetic markers.
- Physical chromosome maps show the positions of genes and genetic markers on a chromosome viewed microscopically.
- Chromosome mapping has several applications including marker-assisted selection, genetic testing, and chromosome walking and jumping.

KEY TERMS

genetic recombination
syntenic genes
linked genes
chromosome mapping
centimorgans (cM)
two-factor linkage analysis
recombinant chromosomes
nonrecombinant chromosomes
recombination frequency
coupling conformation
repulsion conformation
cytological markers
double crossover
interference
mapping functions
Haldane function
Kosambi function
coefficient of coincidence
linkage group
polymorphic markers
deletion mapping
somatic cell hybridization
marker-assisted selection
cystic fibrosis
chromosome walking
chromosome jumping
rare cutting restriction enzyme

CHAPTER TOPICS

15.1. THE DISCOVERY OF LINKAGE AND CROSSING-OVER

CHAPTER OUTLINE

Introduction

Genes located on same chromosome recombine by crossing over
    Syntenic genes: genes located on same chromosome
    Linked genes: syntenic genes that do not assort independently (Figure 15.1)
Chromosome mapping: determining the linkage order of syntenic genes
    Chromosome map: a diagram showing relative gene loci on chromosomes
    Principles of chromosome mapping

15.1. THE DISCOVERY OF LINKAGE AND CROSSING-OVER

Central ideas:
- Linked genes are located on the same chromosome and do not assort independently. Genes that are located on the same chromosome are syntenic, but are not necessarily linked because genes that are distant on the same chromosome may assort independently.
- Genetic map distances between linked genes are measured in centimorgans (cM) which are defined as the percentage of crossing over between linked genes. The genetic map distances between many linked genes can be combined to construct a genetic map.

1900: first case of linkage (Carl Correns in stocks (flowers)
    Purple flowers hoary leaves x white flowers smooth leaves
    F_1: purple flowers hoary leaves
    F_2: Correns expected independent assortment
        Only two classes of progeny observed (3:1 ratio):
            Purple flowered plants: hoary leaves
            White flowered plants: smooth leaves
        Strains of recombined phenotypes were known

Concluded assortment not independent

1908: first case of incomplete linkage (William Bateson and Reginald Punnett)

Purple vs. white flowers and long vs. round pollen grains

Traits failed to assort independently in F_2

Thomas Hunt Morgan: linkage correctly identified and described

Deviations from independent assortment caused by linkage

Believed homologous chromosomes "crossed over" during meiosis (see text example page 447)

Coined the term "crossover"

Alfred H. Sturtevant (Morgan's student) calculated first linkage map

Relative positions of six X-linked genes determined in *Drosophila melanogaster*

Distances related to frequency of crossing over (Figure 15.2)

Sturtevant and Calvin Bridges demonstrated linkage on autosomes (Figure 15.3)

Units used for mapping genes (Figure 15.3)

Centimorgans (cM): frequency of crossovers as a percentage

Chromosome mapping: one of the more active areas of genetic research

15.2. TWO-FACTOR LINKAGE ANALYSIS

Central ideas:

- Alleles of linked genes may be in coupling or repulsion conformation. Alleles that are coupled are on a single chromosome of a homologous pair of chromosomes. Alleles in repulsion to one another are on different chromosomes of a homologous chromosome pair.

- Analysis of two linked genes is called two-point linkage analysis. Recombinant chromosomes are those chromosomes that arise from a crossover between the two genes under consideration. Nonrecombinant chromosomes are those chromosomes that do not arise from a crossover between the genes under consideration and are, therefore, the same as the original parental chromosomes.

- Linkage is best analyzed in a testcross situation in which recombinant and nonrecombinant chromosomes are represented by recombinant and nonrecombinant phenotypes in the progeny. Under these conditions, the recombination frequency can be determined by totaling the number of recombinant progeny and dividing by the total number of progeny.

- Linkage may also be measured in F_2 progeny, although the procedure is not as accurate as in testcross progeny. Testcross situations should be used whenever possible for linkage analysis.

- Genetic map distances between linked genes are measured in centimorgans (cM) which are defined as the percentage of crossing over between linked genes. The genetic map distances between many linked genes can be combined to construct a genetic map.

Two factor linkage analysis: linkage analysis of two linked genes

Linkage analysis usually done with testcross progeny

All testcross data are informative

Most F_2 data are not informative (unless codominant markers are used)

Important terms

Recombinant chromosomes: arose from crossover (recombinant type chromosomes)

Nonrecombinant chromosomes: no crossover (parental type chromosomes)

Recombination frequency:

(# recombinant chromosomes) ÷ (total chromosomes)

Use two-factor linkage notation to diagram cross (use notation as used in Example 15.1)

Use two-factor linkage notation to identify progeny genotypes

Two-factor linkage in testcross progeny

    (See example 15.1. Two factor linkage in maize)

        Measure significance of deviation from independent assortment with chi-square

        Identify recombinant chromosomes in progeny

        Identify **coupling or repulsion conformation** of linked markers (see in-text diagrams on page 450)

            Coupling: two dominant alleles together in nonrecombinant

            Repulsion: one dominant one recessive allele together in nonrecombinant

        Calculate map distance

            Number recombinant chromosomes/ total chromosomes

            Place markers on map diagram showing cM distance

    (See Example 15.2. Two-point linkage in repulsion conformation)

        Sex of individual can affect map distances (Figure 15.9)

Genetic recombination and physical detection of crossovers

    Harriet B. Creighton and Barbara McClintock

(See Example 15.3 Association of genetic recombination with a physical exchange of chromosome segments.))

        Compared recombination of linked genes with physical exchanges between homologous chromosomes in maize (Figure 15.6)

Crossing-over in duplicated chromosomes

    Sister chromatid crossing over of no consequence (Figure 15.7)

    Nonsister chromatid crossing over causes recombination of linked genes (Figure 15.8)

15.3. MAP DISTANCE CORRECTION

Central idea:

- Genetic map distances may be underestimated when recombination frequencies exceed 0.2 because of undetected double crossovers. Underestimations can be corrected with mapping functions.

- There is a tendency to underestimate the map distance when distances exceed about 20 cM because of undetected double crossovers. Map function equations compensate for undetected crossovers and make it possible to estimate map distances more accurately.

Factors that alter crossovers affect map distances

    Chromosome location of genes

    Age, sex, genotype, and environmental influences (Figure 15.9)

    Double crossover **interference**

Mapping function (two-point linkage data)

    Effects of single crossover (Figure 15.8, Figure 15.5)

        Each chromatid becomes a chromosomes in four gametes

        Two of four chromatids are recombinant chromosomes

        Two chromatids remain nonrecombinant chromosomes

    Double crossover and recombination of two markers (Figure 15.10)

        No recombinants (two-strand double)

        Two recombinants, two nonrecombinants (three-strand double)

        Four recombinants (four-strand double)

        Half the crossovers cannot be detected phenotypically

    Effects of double crossover on map distances

        Underestimates map distance

Expected frequency of double crossovers: map distance squared
Probability of double crossovers: increases exponentially with distance
Small distances: very low probability
Double crossover interference
Within 5 cM interference almost 1 (chance for double crossover is zero)
Double crossovers become significant at ca. 20 cM (Figure 15.11)
Mapping functions attempt to correct two-point linkage data
Haldane function (Figure 15.11)
$$x = -0.5\ln(1-2y)$$
y = observed crossover frequency, x = correction
Kosambi function (Figure 15.12)
$$x = 0.25 \ln ((1 + 2y) \div (1 - 2y))$$
x and y mean the same
(See Example 15.4. Mapping function)
Chromosomes can be mapped by adding two-point linkage data

Two-factor linkage analysis in F_2 progeny
With dominance linkage calculation from F_2 data is not efficient
Several genotypes make up one phenotype in F_2
Some genotypes in a phenotypic class carry two recombinant or two nonrecombinant chromosomes
Linkage manifest by deviation from 9:3:3:1 ratio
Table 15.1a used for calculating coupling linkage with F_2 data
Table 15.1b used for calculating repulsion linkage with F_2 data
(See Example 15.5. Using F_2 data for two-point linkage analysis)
If markers are codominant (i.e., RFLP data) F_2 data can be informative

15.4. THREE-FACTOR LINKAGE ANALYSIS

Central idea:
- Three-point and higher linkages can be calculated in progeny of the same cross. It is also possible to estimate the degree of interference in three-point crosses.
- Three-factor linkage analysis is used to determine the order and genetic map distances among three linked genes in the progeny of a single testcross.
- The coefficient of coincidence (C) is calculated as the frequency of observed double crossovers divided by the expected frequency of double crossovers. Interference (I) is calculated as $1 - C$.

Chromosomes can be mapped by adding two-point linkage data
Three or more loci can be mapped in a single testcross (three-point testcross)
Eight genotypes in testcross progeny (Figures 15.13, 15.14, see in-text diagrams)
Two nonrecombinant genotypes
Two crossover genotypes in one interval
Two crossover genotypes in other interval
Two double crossover genotypes
Affect of linkage on assortment of eight genotypes (Figure 15.14)
Not linked: 1:1:1:1:1:1:1:1 ratio (independent assortment for testcross of three independent loci)
Linked loci show significant deviation from independent assortment
Most frequent class: two nonrecombinant classes

Least frequent class: double recombinant classes
Determine gene order: compare noncrossover classes with double crossover classes
Indicates which locus in the middle of the linkage group
Relative positions of three markers can be determined by comparing two-point linkage
distances among the three markers
Calculate map distances
(See Example 15.6. Three-point linkage with complete coupling)
(See Example 15.7. Three-point linkage with repulsion)

Interference
Predicting frequency of double crossovers (dco) in three-point testcross
Without double crossover interference
Expected dco = observed freq. crossover region 1 (A-B in Figure 15.14) x
observed freq. crossover region 2 (B-C Figure 15.14)
Measuring interference
Coefficient of coincidence (C) quantifies interference
C = observed dco ÷ expected dco
Interference: I = 1 – C

Mapping genes on heteromorphic chromosomes
Genes on X or Z chromosomes
Heterozygous homogametic sex crossed to hemizygous sex
If hemizygous parent is recessive all progeny show recombination
If hemizygous parent is dominant only hemizygous progeny show recombination
(See Example 15.8. Three-point linkage on the X chromosome in *Drosophila melanogaster*)

15.5. MULTIFACTOR CHROMOSOME MAPPING

Central idea:
- Multifactor chromosome mapping is typically done using computer programs that construct
genetic maps from data sets. With DNA marker analysis, it is possible to construct a genetic
map of all chromosomes from the progeny of a single cross.
- Chromosome mapping has several practical applications which include marker-assisted
selection, DNA testing, chromosome walking, and chromosome jumping.

Calculating map distances with four or more linked genes
Each added locus increases number of genotypes by factor of 2
Coupling-repulsion relationships must be determined
Noncrossover, single, double, triple crossover classes identified
Linkage groups (Figures 15.3, 15.15, 15.16, 15.17)
Chromosome segment that contains two or more linked markers
Linkage group can contain all markers on a single chromosome
All linkage groups of a species will ultimately equal the haploid chromosome number of the
species
Each locus to be mapped must have **polymorphic markers**
Polymorphic markers: distinguishable alleles
DNA markers

15.6. GENETIC MAPPING IN HUMANS

Central idea:
- Human chromosome mapping progressed very slowly until DNA marker analysis was available. With DNA marker analysis, chromosome mapping in humans has progressed at a rapid pace and many genes have been mapped.

Use of DNA markers overcomes limits of family population sizes in humans
    Codominant DNA markers permit use of human family data
    Codominant markers permit accurate linkage calculation from multigenerational data
    (See Figure 15.17)
Values of genetic maps
    Marker assisted selection
        DNA markers can be used to tag genetic traits for selection
        Use of DNA markers for finding gene DNA sequences
    Use of linkage groups for evolutionary studies
        Use of linkage groups to understand the genetic architecture
        Use of linkage groups to track phylogenetic relations

15.7. PHYSICAL CHROMOSOME MAPPING

Central idea:
- Genetic maps do not reflect exact linear distances of chromosome DNA or chromatin
- Exact chromosome position of a locus is determined by physical mapping
- Genes can be mapped to their physical locations on the chromosome using deletion mapping or *in situ* hybridization. Although the order of genes in genetic and physical maps correspond with each other, genetic map distances do not necessarily correspond with physical map distances.

Deletion mapping
    Identification of genes located in deleted map segments of chromosomes
        Hybridize homozygous recessive to strain with dominant phenotype and heterozygous for chromosome deletion (Figure 15.18)
            F_1: recessive: dominant 1:1, gene is in deleted segment
            F_1: all dominant: gene not in deleted segment
        Used to determine regional location of gene within chromosome
        Other uses of deletion stocks
Somatic cell hybridization mapping
    Used to determine chromosome association of genes
    Somatic cell hybridization: culture human cells fused to rodent cells (mouse or Chinese hamster cells)
    Mapping based on losses of human chromosomes as fusion cells divide
        Chromosome loss is random among cell lines
            Chromosome losses detected cytologically and biochemically in each cell line
            Loss of enzyme activity correlated with chromosome loss in cell culture line
        (see Example 15.9. Identification of the human chromosome that carries a particular gene using somatic cell hybridization.)
Physical chromosome mapping with *in situ* hybridization
    Labeled DNA probes are hybridized to chromosome DNA

Cytological position of probe on chromosome reveals physical position of homologous chromosome DNA sequence (Figures 10.22 and 10.23)

Correspondence of genetic and physical maps

Map orders of loci correspond

Map distances based on cytological picture of chromosomes do not correspond perfectly

Reasons for noncorrespondence of map distance and physical distance

Varied levels of chromatin condensation along chromosome length

Map distances vary among species and between sexes (human)

One cM in yeast: 3000 nucleotide pairs

One cM in humans: 1,000,000 nucleotide pairs

15.8. PRACTICAL APPLICATIONS OF CHROMOSOME MAPPING

Central ideas:

- Human chromosome mapping progressed very slowly until DNA marker analysis was available. With DNA marker analysis, chromosome mapping in humans has progressed at a rapid pace and many genes have been mapped.
- Chromosome mapping has several practical applications which include marker-assisted selection, DNA testing, chromosome walking, and chromosome jumping.
- Mapped DNA markers can be used for marker-assisted selection, genetic testing, and chromosome walking and jumping.

Tracking the inheritance of an allele with coupled DNA markers

Marker assisted selection

Detection and tracking of mutant allele using homologous probe to closely linked polymorphic DNA marker

Tracking mutant allele using homologous probe

(See Example 15.10. Identification of DNA markers coupled to the *Sw-5* allele in tomato)

Chromosome walking and jumping

Walking: reconstruction of long chromosome sequence using overlapping sequences (Figure 15.22)

Jumping: detecting two linked segments of chromosome DNA that do not overlap (Figure 15.22)

Chapter 16
Genetic Fine Structure

KEY CONCEPTS

- Tetrad analysis in fungi has provided much information about the mechanism of crossing-over and gene conversion.
- The gene is a linear segment of DNA that is divisible by crossing-over.
- The units of recombination and the units of mutation are the individual nucleotides of DNA.
- Alleles can be placed into complementation groups by complementation analysis.

KEY TERMS

spores
ascus (plural asci)
tetrad
octad
unordered spores
ordered spores
first-division segregation
second-division segregation
parental ditype
tetratype
non-parental ditype
gene conversion
Holliday model
heteroduplex DNA
Holliday junction
Meselson-Radding model
asymmetric strand-transfer model
double-strand-break repair model
recombination hotspots
polar
nonreciprocal
intragenic recombination
allelic
non-allelic
complementation test
mutational hotspots

CHAPTER TOPICS

16.1. TETRAD ANALYSIS
 Spore formation in *Neurospora crassa*
 Centromere mapping
16.2. UNORDERED TETRAD ANALYSIS
16.3. GENE CONVERSION AND THE MECHANISM OF CROSSING-OVER
 The Holliday model of crossing-over
 The Meselson-Radding model of recombination

CHAPTER OUTLINE

Introduction
Early concepts of the gene
> Genes seen as points on a line
> Crossing over occurred between genes

The modern concept of a gene in relation to recombination
> Gene is part of the linear sequence of DNA that is the chromosome
> Crossing over events break and rejoin linear molecules of DNA
> The unit of recombination is a nucleotide in the chromosome

16.1. TETRAD ANALYSIS

Central idea:
- Ascomycetes are used as model organisms for studying the direct products of meiosis which are present within the ascus.
- Ordered tetrad analysis in ascomycetes makes it possible to map a gene to its centromere.
- The genetic map distance between a gene and the centromere can be estimated as half of the second-division-segregation asci divided by the total number of asci.

Analysis of sexual fungal spores provide a close look at mechanisms of meiosis
> Life cycle of *Neurospora* (Figure 16.1)
>> The ascus: a membranous sac that carries ascospores produced by meiosis
>>> Tetrad: the four direct products of meiosis
>>> Tetrad cells each divides once mitotically producing octad of ascospores
>>> The tetrad and octad are **ordered** according to planes of division spindle
>>> The spore order identifies meiosis I, meiosis II and mitotic division (Figures 16.2, 16.4)
> *Saccharomyces cerevisiae*: the four meiotic products are unordered
>> The four meiotic products mature into ascospores
>> The centromere cannot be mapped

Centromere mapping using *Neurospora crassa* ascospores
> Developing ascus firsts contains a diploid meiocyte
> The meiocyte undergoes meiosis to produce four ascospores (tetrad) in line with ascus
> Four ascospores divide mitotically producing linear array of eight ascospores(octad)
>> Segregation and independent assortment readily seen in octad
>>> Mutant allele phenotypes observed
>>>> Visible: white spore phenotype (Figure 16.2)
>>>> Many mutants studied are auxotrophs
>>>>> Spores dissected form asci by position in ascus
>>>>> Germinated on complete media

Plated to selective media for assay of auxotrophic mutants (figure 16.3)
Measuring gene to centromere map distances
First division segregation spore pattern: *aaaaAAAA*, etc. (Figure 16.4a, b)
Second division segregation spore pattern: *AAaaaaAA*, etc. (Figure 16.5a, b)
Second division asci arise from single crossover between gene locus and centromere
Map distance = 1/2 (# 2nd division asci/ total asci) x 100
(See Example 16.1. Mapping a gene to the centromere in *Neurospora*)

16.2. UNORDERED TETRAD ANALYSIS (Figure 16.6)

Central idea:
- Unordered tetrad analysis can be used to map genes in relation to one another. The frequency of undetected double crossovers can estimated directly from the data.

Three types of unordered tetrads following meiotic distribution of two gene loci (Figure 16.7)
Parental ditype
All spores identical to parental type (nonrecombinant)
AB x *ab* → *AaBb* meiocyte → *AB ab AB ab*
Tetratype
Meiotic products all different (half ascospores recombinant)
AB x *ab* → *AaBb* meiocyte → *AB aB Ab ab* ascospores
Nonparental ditype
All spores recombinant
AB x *ab* → *AaBb* meiocyte → *Ab aB Ab aB* ascospores
If two loci are not linked
Parental ditypes equal nonparental ditypes
Tetratypes arise by crossing over between either locus and centromeres
Two alleles would assort independently 1:1:1:1 (*AB, aB, Ab, ab*)
If two loci are linked
Effects of crossing over
Single crossover tetrad of four spores
Two spores are recombinant, two are nonrecombinant
The tetrad class would be tetratype
Double crossover tetrad of four spores
Two-strand doubles cannot be detected
Seen as parental ditype tetrads
Three-strand double detected as single crossover
Seen as tetratype tetrads
Four-strand doubles detected as nonparental ditype
Mapping two loci by tetrad analysis (*AB* x *ab*)
Mapping based on (no. crossovers/ total strands) x 100
The number of crossovers must be counted
Include single and double crossovers
Counting undetected double crossover tetrads
Four-strand doubles = 1/4 total double crossovers
1/4 = two-strand double
2/4 = three-strand double

$1/4$ = four-strand double

Let x = number of tetratypes (four-strand double crossover)

$2x$ = number of tetratypes that arose from three-strand double crossovers

x = number of parental ditypes that arose from two-strand double crossovers

Compensating for undetected double crossovers

Parental ditype class has $2x$ undetected crossovers

Tetratype class has $2x$ undetected crossovers

Number crossovers in nonparental ditype: $2x$

Total correction is $6x$ or 6 (nonparental ditypes)

Calculation of map distance in cM with dco correction:

= ((number tetratypes + 6(number nonparental ditypes)) ÷ 2) ÷ total number of asci x 100

(See Example 16.2. Two-factor mapping using unordered tetrad analysis.)

16.3. GENE CONVERSION AND THE MECHANISM OF CROSSING-OVER

Central ideas:
- Most intragenic recombination events in fungi are gene conversions in which one allele is converted to another. Unlike intragenic crossing over, gene conversion is nonreciprocal.
- About one-half of all gene conversions are associated with crossing over between flanking markers. In fungi, gene conversions are usually polar because of crossing over at recombination hotspots.
- Gene conversion data and molecular analysis have led to several models for recombination at the DNA level. The most widely accepted model for fungi is the double-strand-break repair model.
- Gene conversion has also been demonstrated in multicellular eukaryotes, although it is very difficult to study in these species.
- Models of recombination at the DNA level explain crossing over and gene conversion. All models propose the formation of heteroduplex DNA at the site of recombination.

Aberrant spore patterns and **gene conversion** in *Neurospora*

Expected spore pattern (Figures 16.4, 16.5)

Aberrant spore patterns (Figures 16.8, 16.10)

Gene conversion more frequent than mutation rate

Gene conversion is related to crossing over

50% gene conversions associated with crossing over

One allele is converted to other allele on homologous chromosome

(See Example 16.3. Gene conversion in *Sordaria brevicollis*.)

The Holliday model of crossing-over (Figure 16.9)

DNA single strand nicks, and formation of **heteroduplex DNA**

Nicks are sealed

Two DNA molecules (nonsister chromatids) connected by **Holliday junction**

Junction migration extending heteroduplex DNA segments

Cutting Holliday junction in one of two ways

East-west cut and sealing

Restores flanking markers to nonrecombinant type

Leaves heteroduplex regions on both chromatids

North-south cut

Causes recombination between flanking markers

Leaves heteroduplex region on both chromatids

Heteroduplex segment near original Holliday junction in both cases

One of three conversion patterns can appear due to mismatch repairs or failure of repair (heterozygous *A* vs. *a* in heteroduplex region)

Converts *A* to *a* or *a* to *A*

3:5 spore pattern: one of two molecules is repaired before mitotic division

2:6 spore pattern: both molecules are repaired (Figures 16.10 a, b, c)

The Meselson-Radding model of recombination

Proposes transfer on one DNA strand rather than two (Figure 16.11a)

Strand breaks and displaces homologous strand of nonsister chromatid

Displaced strand is digested

Vacancy on homologous strand filled by DNA synthesis (Figure 16.11 b, c)

Crossed strands may or may not migrate (Figure 16.11d)

No migration heteroduplex limited to region of displacement in one DNA molecule (chromatid)

Strand migration heteroduplex region potentially increases (Figure 16.11e)

Crossed strands are cut as in Holliday model

Effects of cutting on crossing over

Same as Holliday model

Effects on gene conversion predicted by both models

Holliday: frequency of gene conversion equal on both DNAs

Meselson-Radding: conversion on one DNA more frequent

The double-strand-break repair model of recombination (Figure 16.12)

Model accounts for several observations

Double stranded break creates two Holliday junctions

Observations supporting model in fungi

Recombination hot spots prone to double stranded breaks

Gene conversion in fungi is polar

Crossing over rare within fungi alleles

Gene conversion in *Drosophila*

Comparing crossing over/gene conversion detected when all products of one meiosis can be analyzed as in ascomycetes

Crossing over proven to be a reciprocal exchange

Gene conversion shown to be non reciprocal

Gathering evidence for gene conversion in higher eukaryotes difficult if not impossible

Chovnick and coworkers demonstrated gene conversion in *Drosophila*

Method of analysis beyond scope of chapter

16.4. INTRAGENIC RECOMBINATION

Central ideas:
- Although intragenic crossing over is rare in fungi, it is common in higher eukaryotes.
- Intragenic crossing over between two mutant alleles restores the wild-type allele.

Crossing over and gene locus relative to crossing over

Can occur within a gene locus as well as between gene loci

Different alleles represent different positions of mutation within gene locus

Alterations of different nucleotides create different alleles

Crossing over between mutant sites rearrange alleles

Crossing over in compound heterozygotes (two mutant alleles)

Can create wild-type recombinant allele

Intragenic recombination (Figure 16.14)

Intragenic recombination demonstrated in *Drosophila*

1940: Clarence P. Oliver (Figure 16.15)

Intragenic recombination in compound heterozygote for *lz* alleles

Wild-type offspring associated with recombination of flanking markers

1949: M. M. and K.C. Green demonstrated double mutant *lz* allele

Intragenic crossing over produces wild-type allele and expected reciprocal: double mutant *lz* allele

The wild-type allele was dominant because crossing over restored enzyme function (Figure 16.16)

Mapping mutation site positions within different mutant alleles

Intragenic map distances are small

0.01 to 0.05 cM (Figure 16.17)

Intragenic crossing over absent in fungi

Gene conversion accounts for intragenic recombinations in fungi

Fungal gene conversion explained best by double-strand break model

16.5. COMPLEMENTATION

Central ideas:
- Two mutant alleles of the same gene usually fail to complement one another in a trans test.
- Mutant alleles of different genes that cause the same phenotype complement one another.
- In most cases, complementation means that the mutant alleles belong to different loci.
- When recessive mutant alleles fail to complement one another, they usually belong to the same locus.

Different mutant alleles may cause the same phenotype but are not alleles

Mutant alleles of same gene affect the same enzyme (**allelic**)

Mutant alleles of different genes affects different enzymes of same biochemical pathway (**non-allelic**)

Cis-trans test tests for difference between alleles and non-alleles

Setting up trans **complementation test** (Figure 16.18)

Cross between m^1m^1 and m^2m^2

m^2m^1 wild-type phenotype: assume mutants are non-allelic

m^2m^1 mutant phenotype: assume mutants are alleles (Figure 16.19)

Cis test more difficult to set up (used for control experiment)

If m^2 and m^1 are alleles need to isolate double mutant allele

If m^2 and m^1 are not alleles set up a little easier

Complementation group

All alleles that fail to complement each other

(See Table 16.3)

(See Example 16.4. Complementation of osmotic mutants in x Neurospora *crassa*.)

16.6. FINE STRUCTURE MAPPING

Central idea:
- Analysis of intragenic recombination in large numbers of progeny permits fine-structure mapping of genes.

Fine-structure mapping in bacteriophages
>   1955: Seymour Benzer reported maps of *r*II plac mutants T4 phage
>   *r*II phenotypes ("*r*" means "rapid lysis mutants", Figure 16.20)
>>   Wild-type phage reproduce in *E. coli* K12
>>   Mutant *r*II do not reproduce in K12
>>   Both reproduce in *E. coli* strain B
>   Found two complementation groups within *r*II region
>>   Created recombination map (Figure 16.22)
>>   Recon: minimum distance: 0.01% recombination
>>   Mutations sites that would not recombine were included in deletions (figure 16.21)
>>   (See Example 16.5. Fine-structure mapping of the *rosy* locus in *Drosophila melanogaster*)

16.7. MITOTIC CROSSING-OVER

Central ideas:
- Crossing over between sister chromatids during mitosis is frequent, but has no genetic consequence because sister chromatids are identical.
- Mitotic crossing over between homologous chromosomes is very rare, but is possible when homologous chromosomes are close enough for partial pairing during mitosis.

1936: Curt Stern recognized mitotic crossing over in *Drosophila*
>   X-linked *Yellow* and *singed* loci (*y* and *sn*)
>   Females heterozygous for *y* and *sn* alleles (phenotypically wild-type)
>>   Twin spots: yellow spot adjacent to singed spot in female body (Figure 16.25)
>>   Diagram of crossover (figure 16.26)

Chapter 17
Alterations in Chromosome Number and Structure

KEY CONCEPTS

- Alterations in chromosome number and structure influence phenotypic expression of traits and speciation.
- Aneuploidy is an aberration in which chromosomes are missing or added so that chromosome sets are unbalanced.
- Polyploidy, in which there are three or more sets of chromosomes in a cell, is common in plants and is important in plant evolution, but is rare in animals.
- Alterations in chromosome structure include deletions, duplications, inversions, translocations, fissions, and fusions. These alterations have important genetic consequences.
- Most chromosome alterations in humans do not permit survival of the fetus. Those chromosome alterations that permit survival usually have medical syndromes associated with them.

KEY TERMS

ploidy
euploidy
balanced
aneuploidy
unbalanced
trisomy
monosomy
trisomy 21
nullisomy
double trisomy
tetrasomy
nondisjunction
polyploidy
monoploid
unreduced gamete
parthenogenesis
endoploidy
autopolyploidy
bivalent
trivalent
univalent
quadrivalent
allopolyploidy
homeologous chromosomes
amphidiploid
allotetraploid
colchicine
triticale
digenic
trigenic
tetragenic

deletion (deficiency)
terminal deletion
interstitial deletion
acentric fragment
duplication
tandem duplications
unequal crossing-over
pericentric inversion
paracentric inversion
dicentric chromatid
chromatid bridge
simple terminal translocation
reciprocal translocation
alternate-1 segregation
adjacent-1 segregation
alternate-2 segregation
adjacent-2 segregation
chromosome fission
chromosome fusions
isochromosome
position effect
cri-du-chat syndrome
Down syndrome
Turner syndrome
Kleinfelter syndrome
triple-X karyotype
47, XYY karyotype
Philadelphia chromosome

CHAPTER TOPICS

Edward syndrome and Patau syndrome
Aneuploidies for X and Y chromosomes
Chromosomal alterations and cancer

CHAPTER OUTLINE

Introduction
Alterations in chromosome structure and number are common
  Down syndrome 1 in 1000 births (Figure 17.1a)
  Wild and domesticated polyploid plants
  Chromosome alterations have major genetic and phenotypic effects

17.1 ANEUPLOIDY

Central ideas:
- Chromosome number is described using the term ploidy. Euploid individuals have complete sets of chromosomes with no missing or extra chromosomes. Aneuploid individual have missing or extra chromosomes in their somatic cells. Polyploid individuals are euploid, but have three or more sets of chromosomes in each somatic cell.
- Aneuploidy is an imbalance in chromosome number. Monosomy and trisomy are the two most common forms of aneuploidy. Monosomy is the absence of one chromosome from a set and trisomy is the presence of one additional chromosome.
- Aneuploidy often arises from nondisjunction in meiosis. The end result is a gamete with one extra chromosome ($n + 1$) and a reciprocal gamete that is missing a chromosome ($n - 1$). The $n + 1$ gamete causes trisomy ($2n + 1$) when it unites with a normal haploid (n) gamete. The $n - 1$ gamete causes monosomy ($2n - 1$) when it unites with a normal haploid (n) gamete.

Definitions
  Ploidy: number and proportions of chromosome sets in cell
  Euploidy: number of complete chromosome sets
  Balanced: all genetic material is in correct proportion (euploidy)
  Aneuploidy: extra or missing chromosome(s)
  Unbalanced: genetic material not in correct proportions for species (aneuploids)
  n = number of chromosomes in balanced gamete
  Trisomy: one extra chromosome $2n + 1$
  Monosomy: one chromosome less $2n - 1$
Nondisjunction
  Failure of homologous chromosomes or chromatids to disjoin during meiosis
    Nondisjunction is reciprocal event at meiosis
      One daughter cell gains chromosome ($n + 1$)
      Other daughter cell lacks chromosome ($n - 1$)
    Higher frequency of trisomics than monosomics
  (See Example 17.1. Genetic segregation in a trisomic plant)

17.2 POLYPLOIDY

Central ideas:
- Polyploidy is rare in animals, but common in plants. About one-half of all flowering plant species are polyploid.

- Polyploids are designated by the multiple number of chromosome sets they contain. The symbol n is the number of chromosomes in a gamete, and x is to the number of chromosomes in one complete set. In diploid individuals, $2n = 2x$ = the number chromosomes in a somatic cell. In a tetraploid individual (four chromosome sets per somatic cell) $2n = 4x$ = the number of chromosomes in a somatic cell.
- Polyploidy typically arises from unreduced gametes that unite with one another or with normal, reduced gametes.
- Polyploid species may be either autopolyploids or allopolyploids. Autopolyploids arise from a single species. Allopolyploids arise from two or more different species.
- Patterns of inheritance in allopolyploids resemble those in diploid species. Patterns of inheritance in autopolyploids are more complex.

The arisal of polyploidy

Union of **unreduced gametes** (same chromosome number as somatic cells)
    Unreduced gamete plus haploid gamete = triploid zygote
    Two unreduced gametes unite = tetraploid zygote
Endoploidy in plants: chromosomes replicate and cell fails to divide mitotically
    Tetraploid cell then divides producing sector of tetraploid tissue
    Fertile tetraploid flower arises from tetraploid tissue
        Self-fertile tetraploid flower may produce tetraploid seed
        Self-incompatible tetraploid flower must outcross
            $2n$ gametes x $1n$ gametes: triploid offspring
            $2n$ gametes x rare $2n$ gametes: tetraploid offspring
Fertility of polyploid
    Triploids produce unbalanced gametes
        Seedless bananas, watermelons
        Can reproduce asexually
        Development of triploid varieties
            Select at tetraploid and diploid levels
            Cross tetraploid and diploid
        Triploid animals
            Whiptail lizard
            Offspring arise from unreduced gametes **Parthenogenesis**
    Tetraploids can produce balanced diploid gametes

Autopolyploidy and allopolyploidy

Autopolyploid
    All chromosomes come from same ancestral diploid species
    Four homologous copies of each chromosome
    Meiotic pairing of homologous chromosomes
        Can form bivalents, trivalents, quadrivalents, univalents (Figure 17.6a, b, c, forms partially sterile gametes)
        Some species form only bivalents (fully fertile gametes)
Allopolyploidy
    Chromosomes from different ancestral species
    Ancestral species are closely related
        Hybrid sterility due to chromosome pairing failure at meiosis
        Similar chromosomes are **homeologous** but not homologous
    Development of fertile **amphidiploid** plant species hybrids
        Endoploidy in hybrid and production of fertile allopolyploid flowers

Endoploidy produces allotetraploid tissue sectors

Has diploid set of chromosomes from each parent

Formation of amphidiploid allotetraploid (one of several possible ways)

Cross between two diploid species ($x + x$ gametes)

$2x$ hybrid is sterile (two homeologous sets of chromosomes)

Endoploidy produces $4x$ hybrid cells ($2x + 2x = 4x$)

Homolog for each chromosome

Normal meiotic pairing

n gametes are $2x$ (balanced, Figure 17.7)

Natural amphidiploids

Wheat is an allohexaploid amphidiploid

Three diploid sets of genomes A, B, and D

$x = 7$ for each diploid species

Somatic cells of wheat $6x = 42$ chromosomes

n gametes are $3x$

Development of artificial $8x$ amphidiploid in plants

Development of allooctaploid **triticale**

Parents: rye ($2x$) x bread wheat ($6x$)

Hybrid ($1x + 3x$ gametes = sterile $4x$)

Artificial endoploidy $\rightarrow$ 2 x $4x = 8x$ hybrid

Endoploidy induced with colchicine

(See Example 17.2. Polyploidy and natural interspecific hybridization)

Genetics of polyploidy

Typical Mendelian inheritance patterns in allopolyploids

Meiosis: allopolyploids behave as diploids

Some traits controlled by more gene loci

Epistatic interactions more common

Duplicate gene action for spring and winter wheat (Figure 13.19)

Inheritance patterns in autotetraploids

Example: duplex inheritance pattern from AAaa parents

Gamete array: 1 AA: 4 Aa: 1 aa

Offspring segregation pattern with dominance: 35:1

More than two alleles at a locus

Definition of digenic, trigenic and tetragenic genotypes

(See Example 17.3. Chromosome mapping in polyploids.)

17.3 ALTERATIONS OF CHROMOSOME STRUCTURE

Central ideas:

- Alterations in chromosome structure include deletions, duplications, translocations, inversions, and fissions, and fusions.
- Large deletions are often lethal, but small deletions may allow survival of heterozygotes. Most deletions are homozygous lethal.
- Duplications may or may not have phenotypic effects. Tandem duplications may participate in unequal crossing over, which serves to increase or reduce the number of tandem duplications.
- Inversions are of two types: pericentric in which the centromere is within the inversion, and paracentric in which the centromere is outside of the inversion. Chromosomes loop within the inversion region to pair in inversion heterozygotes. Crossing over within the inversion

loop in inversion heterozygotes results in gametes that are unbalanced.

- Translocations are typically reciprocal. Altered pairing in reciprocal translocation heterozygotes causes a quadrivalent to form. The chromosomes in the quadrivalent may segregate in one of four possible ways: alternate-1, adjacent-1, alternate-2, and adjacent-2 segregations. Alternate segregations result in balanced gametes and adjacent segregations result in unbalanced gametes. Fertility is typically reduced by about 50% in translocation heterozygotes.
- Chromosome fissions are rare. Fusions are more common. A Robertsonian translocation is fusion that is a specialized type of reciprocal translocation in which the long arms of telocentric chromosomes fuse at their centromeres to form a single chromosome.

Six major types of chromosome structure alterations
> Deletion: loss of segment
> Duplication: repeated segment, often tandem
> Inversion: reverse orientation of segment
> Translocation: transfer of segment to other chromosomes
> Fission: splitting of one chromosome into two
> Fusion: two chromosomes joined into one

Deletions (figure 17.12)
> **Terminal deletion** (one break)
>> Loss of end of chromosome arm (figure 17.12a)
>> Failure of end to join with other chromosomes
> **Interstitial deletion** (two breaks)
>> Loss of chromosome segment between breaks
>> Telomeric piece rejoins main chromosome
> Deletion produces **acentric fragment** (piece without centromere)
>> Acentric fragment lost at cell division
>> Fragment cannot be replaced
> Use of deletions for gene mapping
> Lethality of deletions when homozygous

Duplications (Figures 17.13, 17.14)
> **Tandem duplications** (adjacent duplications)
>> Few repeats: i.e., some gene families
>> Many repeats: i.e., rRNA genes in NOR
>> Mini and micro satellite regions
>> Tandem repeats can increase or decrease
>>> **Unequal crossing over** (Figure 17.13)
>>> Mismatch of template DNA during DNA synthesis
> Duplications may or may not have phenotypic effects
>> Phenotypic effects at the *Bar* locus (Figure 17.14)
>> Dosage effects and degree of Bar phenotype

Inversions
> Origin (Figure 17.15)
> Chromosome pairing and inversions (Figure 17.16)
>> Inversion homozygote
>>> Pairing is normal
>>> No phenotypic effects (usually)
>> Inversion heterozygote (Figure 17.16)
>>> Pairing chromosomes form loop of inversion segment
>>>> Crossing over in loop creates duplication and deficiency chromatids

Pericentric inversion (Figure 17.17)
Paracentric inversion (Figure 17.18)
Tracing effects of crossovers on chromatids
Dicentric chromatids
Chromatid bridge at anaphase I
Acentric fragments with two telomeres
Inversions suppress formation of recombinant chromosomes
Suppression of recombination in inverted segment
May hold some favorable gene combinations together
May favor heterozygosity in population for inverted segment
Reproductive disadvantage inversions

Translocations
Reciprocal translocation: the most common form
Acentric fragments exchanged between nonhomologous chromosomes
Requires breaks in two chromosomes (Figure 17.19a, b)
Meiotic segregation patterns in reciprocal translocation heterozygote (Figure 17.22)
Alternate-1 segregation: balanced gametes (Figure 17.21a)
Adjacent-1 segregation: unbalanced gametes (Figure 17.21b)
Alternate-2 segregation: balanced gametes (Figure 17.21c)
Adjacent-2 segregation: unbalanced gametes (Figure 17.21d)
Significance in speciation
Translocation heterozygote is semisterile (adjacent-1, -2 segregation patterns have unbalanced gametes))
May form initial isolation barriers between ecotypes
(See Example 17.4 Alternate-1, adjacent-1, adjacent-2 and alternate-2 segregation frequencies in reciprocal translocation heterozygotes.)
Chromosome fission and fusion
Fission: rarely observed
One chromosome from fission needs new centromere
Break near centromere and fission of centric fragment
Fusion
Robertsonian translocation:
Fusion of long arms of two acrocentric chromosome
Position effect

17.4 CHROMOSOME ALTERATIONS IN HUMANS
Central ideas:
- There are several known chromosome alterations in humans. Reciprocal translocations are among the most common. Most chromosome imbalances (either for chromosomal segments or entire chromosomes) cause spontaneous abortion of embryos or fetuses that carry the aberration. The alterations that permit survival typically have medical syndromes associated with them.
- *Cri-du-chat* syndrome is caused by a short terminal deletion in the short arm of chromosome 5.
- Down syndrome is usually due to trisomy-21. Rarely, it is caused by trisomy for the long arm of chromosome 21 in a Robertsonian translocation.
- Edward syndrome is due to trisomy 18 and Patau syndrome is due to trisomy 13. Both are severe syndromes and usually cause death within days to weeks after birth.
- Aneuploidies for X and Y chromosomes are associated with syndromes that are typically

less severe than the syndromes associated with autosomal trisomies. The most common are Turner syndrome (45, XO), Kleinfelter syndrome (47, XXY), and some karyotypes not associated with syndromes such as 47, XYY and 47, XXX.

- Chromosomal aberrations in somatic cells may promote certain types of cancers.

Human karyotype nomenclature

Abbreviated set of rules (Table 17.4)

47,XX,+21 = female Down syndrome

46,XY,4p– = male with deletion in short arm chromosome 4

Reciprocal translocations and inversions

About 20% of hemophilia A have inversion in *F8C* gene

Robertsonian translocation

Cri-du-chat syndrome

46,XX or XY,5p– = deletion in short arm chromosome 5

1/50000 births

Down syndrome

47, XX or XY, +21

Formerly about 1/700 births, now about 1/1000 recorded (maybe due to voluntary abortions)

Relationships to age of mother (Figure 17.26)

Robertsonian translocation (Figures 17.28, 17.29)

(See Example 17.5 Inheritance of translocation Down syndrome, Figure 17.30)

Edward syndrome and Patau syndrome

47,XX or XY,+18 Edward syndrome

47,XX or XY,+13 Patau syndrome

Aneuploidies for X and Y chromosomes

Only monosomy in humans: Turner syndrome (X0) female (45,X0)

Kleinfelter syndrome (47,XXY)

47,XXX female with no unusual phenotype

47X YY male with no unusual phenotype

Chromosomal alterations and cancer

Philadelphia chromosome (46,XX or XY,t(22q;9q)

Breakpoint chromosome 9 in *ABL* gene

Breakpoint in chromosome 22 in *BCR* gene

Fusion gene *BCR -ABL* under control of *BCR* promoter (Figure 17.33)

Fusion gene product encourages development of a leukemia

Other cancers associated with chromosome aberrations

Wilms tumor

Acute nonlymphocytic leukemia

Acute myeloblastic leukemia

Ovarian cancers

Retinoblastoma

(See Example 17.6 Retinoblastoma caused by an inversion-induced deletion.)

Chapter 18
Extranuclear Inheritance

KEY CONCEPTS

- Mitochondria and plastids are cellular organelles that are essential for energy conversion.
- Mitochondria and plastids have circular genomes with genes that are expressed within the organelles.
- Mitochondrial inheritance is usually uniparental-maternal in both animals and plants.
- Plastid inheritance in plants may be uniparental-maternal, uniparental-paternal, or biparental.
- When mitochondria or plastids of two or more genotypes are present in the same cell, the different types of organelles segregate during mitotic cell divisions.
- The inheritance of some nuclear genes may mimic uniparental-maternal inheritance.

KEY TERMS

mitochondria
plastids
chloroplast
chromoplasts
amyloplasts
elaioplasts
proplastids
extranuclear inheritance
endosymbiotic hypothesis
outer boundary membrane
inner boundary membrane
intermembrane compartment
stroma
thylakoids
grana
stromal lamellae
thylakoid compartment
light-dependent reactions
light-independent reactions
photosystem I
photosystem II
electron transport chains
chlorophylls
photolysis
C_3 cycle
Calvin-Benson cycle
outer boundary membrane
inner boundary membrane
cristae
intermembrane compartment
matrix
cellular respiration
citric acid cycle

Krebs cycle
oxidative phosphorylation
Cytochrome oxidase
L strand
H strand
biparental inheritance
budding
homoplasmic
heteroplasmic
somatic segregation or sorting out
random segregation model
petite mutants
segregational petite
neutral petite
supressional petites
uniparental-maternal inheritance
cytoplasmic male sterility
cytoplasmic-nuclear male sterility
kappa particles
maternal sex ratio
maternal effect

CHAPTER TOPICS

18.1 THE ORIGINS AND CELLULAR FUNCTIONS OF MITOCHONDRIA AND PLASTIDS
    Chloroplast structure and function
    Mitochondrial structure and function
    Organellar proteins
18.2 ORGANELLAR GENOMES
    Mitochondrial genomes
    Plastid genomes
18.3 MITOCHONDRIAL INHERITANCE
    Mitochondrial inheritance in yeast
    Petite mutants in yeast
    Recombination of mitochondrial genes
    Mitochondrial inheritance in animals
    Mitochondrial inheritance in plants
18.4 MITOCHONDRIAL DNA AND GENETIC DISORDERS IN HUMANS
    Disorders caused by deletions in the mitochondrial genome
    Point mutations in protein-encoding genes
    Point mutations in tRNA and rRNA genes
    Mutations in mitochondrial DNA and human aging
18.5 PLASTID INHERITANCE
18.6 OTHER TYPES OF EXTRANUCLEAR INHERITANCE
18.7 CORRECTLY RECOGNIZING EXTRANUCLEAR INHERITANCE

CHAPTER OUTLINE

18.1 THE ORIGINS AND CELLULAR FUNCTIONS OF MITOCHONDRIA AND PLASTIDS

Central ideas:
- Mitochondria and plastids contain circular DNA genomes that contain genes.
- The genes on organellar genomes are transcribed and translated within the organelle and the products of these genes are utilized within the organelle.
- Proteins encoded by genes in organellar genomes are usually subunits of enzymes that contain organellar and nuclear-encoded subunits.
- The similarity of organellar genomes to prokaryotic genomes suggests that mitochondria and plastids have remote prokaryotic origins, a concept called the endosymbiotic hypothesis.

Endosymbiotic hypothesis
- Free-living prokaryotes ancestors to chloroplast and mitochondria organelles
- Prokaryotes invaded primitive eukaryotic cells
- Development of symbiotic relationship over time
- Evidences for hypothesis
  - Circular genomes
  - Genes similar to prokaryotic genes
  - Systems of DNA synthesis, transcription, translation similar to prokaryotes
- Lost genes: functions covered by host genome

Chloroplast structure and function (Figure 18.3)
- Chloroplast membranes
  - **Outer boundary membrane**
  - **Inter membrane compartment** between the two membranes
  - **Inner boundary membrane**
    - **Stroma:** enclosed by inner boundary membrane
    - **Thylakoids:** stacks of membrane compartments in stroma
    - **Grana:** stacks of thylakoids
    - **Stroma lamellae:** membrane connections between stacks of thylakoids
- Chloroplast biochemistry
  - Light reactions take place on thylakoid membranes (Figure 18.3)
    - Photosystem I: chlorophylls and electron transport
    - Photosystem II: chlorophylls and electron transport
    - Photolysis of water and formation of ATP and NADPH
  - Light independent reactions in stroma (CO_2 fixation)
    - Utilize ATP and NADPH: $CO_2 \rightarrow$ carbohydrate (Figure 18.4)
    - ATP and NADPH formed by light reactions

Mitochondrial structure and function
- Outer and inner boundary membranes (Figure 18.5)
- Inner boundary membrane folded into cristae
- Matrix enclosed by inner membrane cristae
  - Electron transport on inner membrane
  - Mitochondrial function (Figure 18.6)
    - Oxidative cellular respiration
    - Formation of ATP and NADH for cell metabolism
    - Electron transport consumes O_2

Cytoplasmic enzymes make substrate for mitochondria
>Glycolysis converts glucose to pyruvate (Figure 18.7)
>Pyruvate oxidized by mitochondria (Figure 18.8)

Organellar proteins
>Compare organelle genome size and function with prokaryotic genomes
>Coding sequences transferred to nuclear genomes
>>Organelle genome greatly reduced compared to prokaryote ancestors
>>Organelle depends on nuclear genes for most enzymes
>>Some enzyme subunits come from organelle and nuclear genes
>>>Example: ribulose 1-5, bisphosphate carboxylase (rubisco)
>>>>Function: port of entry of CO_2 into cell metabolism
>>>>Most abundant protein in nature
>>>>Most abundant protein in plant cells
>>>Structure: eight large and 8 small subunits (ca. 550,000 daltons)
>Encoding of rubisco in eukaryotic and prokaryote genomes
>>Blue-green algae
>>>Genome encodes both large and small subunits
>>Eukaryote genomes
>>>Large subunit encoded in chloroplast genome
>>>Small subunit encoded in nuclear genome
>>Organelle and nuclear genomes cooperate in construction of other multiple subunit enzymes

18.2 ORGANELLAR GENOMES

Central ideas:
- Animal mitochondrial genomes are smaller than plant mitochondrial genomes and nearly all nucleotides are within genes. The arrangement of mitochondrial genes is highly variable among species. Plastid genome arrangement is similar among species that have plastids.
- Inheritance of organellar genomes does not follow Mendelian principles. Patterns, termed extra-nuclear inheritance, depend on the way cytoplasms are inherited from the two sex cells at fertilization.

Small fraction of cell's genes in organellar genomes
Encoded proteins in organelle genomes essential for survival of cell/organism
Mitochondrial genomes
>Genomes are circular and many copies per mitochondrion (Figure 18.10)
>Variable genome sizes among species (Table 18.1)
>>Plant mitochondria may have heterogeneous DNAs (Figure 1811)
>>Animal and fungal mitochondrial genomes smaller and uniform
>Human mitochondrial genome has no wasted nucleotides (16,569, Figure 18.12)
>>About 13 protein encoding, 2 rRNA, 22 tRNA genes
>>Some genes overlap
>>Transcription
>>>Two large RNAs (few promoters)
>>>**L** and **H** RNA strands cleaved to mRNAs, rRNAs, and tRNAs
>All eukaryote mitochondrial genomes have essentially same genes
>Differences due to reorganizations during evolution

Plastid genomes

Genomes are circular similar in size among species

Largest genomes in algae

Over 120 genes per genome

Encodes over 50 proteins

Genes have prokaryotic-like promoters and some operon-like segments

Most proteins are subunits for multi-subunit enzymes

Nuclear genes specify protein subunits for enzymes

Plastid and nuclear subunits assembled together in plastids

Most rRNAs and tRNAs used in plastid

Own *E. coli*-like RNA polymerase

The two inverted repeats

10,000 to 25000 nucleotides (variable sizes account for genome size differences)

18.3 MITOCHONDRIAL INHERITANCE

Central ideas:

- A cell with only one type of mitochondrion or plastid is homoplasmic. A cell with two or more types of mitochondria or plastids is heteroplasmic.
- Mendel's principles of inheritance do not apply to extranuclear inheritance.
- In yeast, mitochondria are inherited biparentally and undergo somatic segregation during mitotic cell generations.
- Somatic segregation produces homoplasmy in the progeny of a heteroplasmic cell after several mitotic cell generations.
- Mitochondrial inheritance in animals is typically uniparental-maternal
- Mitochondrial inheritance in plants is usually, though not always, uniparental-maternal. Mitochondrial genes may interact with nuclear genes to produce a particular phenotype.

Mendel's principles do not apply

Plastid and mitochondrial genomes follow cytoplasmic divisions

Inheritance pattern is called **extranuclear inheritance**

Sex cells transmit cell cytoplasms differently

Depends on relative amounts of cytoplasm transferred to zygote

Sperm, flowering plant pollen, often little or no cytoplasm transferred to egg

Organelle genomes do not follow nuclear inheritance patterns

Mitochondrial inheritance in yeast

Inheritance of yeast mitochondria is **biparental** in sexual reproduction

Asexual budding transmits small samples of cytoplasm (Figure 18.14)

Genetic constitutions

Heteroplasmic: genetically mixed organelles

Homoplasmic: genetically identical organelles

Somatic segregation (sorting out) of heteroplasmic mitochondria

Budding offspring of heteroplasmic cells become homoplasmic

Homoplasmy achieved in 10-20 cell generations

(See Example 18.1. Mitochondrial inheritance in yeast.)

Petite mutants in yeast

About 2% brewer's yeast cells culture as petite colonies

1950s: Boris Ephrussi—first yeast mitochondrial mutants

Petite mutants lack aerobic respiration, respire anaerobically

Some petite colonies controlled by nuclear gene mutations

Some follow cytoplasmic inheritance—neutral petites

Neutral petites: mitochondria lack DNA

Normal x neutral petite → all normal offspring

Normal mitochondria outcompete neutral petite mitochondria

Inheritance pattern not Mendelian

Some petites are **supressional petites**

Mutant mitochondrial DNA

Normal x supressional petites → variable ratio offspring

Recombination of mitochondrial genes

Mitochondria may fuse and heteroplasmic DNAs may recombine

Rates of recombination of mitochondrial genes vary

Only close linkage can be detected

Mitochondrial inheritance in animals

Inheritance of mitochondrial genes is uniparental

Source of zygote mitochondria

Sperm contributes little if any mitochondria

Egg contributes most if not all cytoplasm

(See Example 18.2. Paternal inheritance of mitochondrial DNA in mouse)

Mitochondrial inheritance in plants

Transmission of mitochondria to zygote

Mitochondrial transmission is maternal for most flowering plant species

Cytoplasmic male sterility is a mitochondrial trait (maize, Figures 18.17, 18.18)

Interaction between mitochondrial and nuclear genes

Nuclear pollen restorer allele is (R)

RR and Rr produce fertile pollen in male-sterile cytoplasm

rr in male-sterile cytoplasm produces male-sterile plant

18.4 MITOCHONDRIAL DNA AND GENETIC DISORDERS IN HUMANS

Central idea:

- Several human genetic disorders, most of which affect the neural, muscular, and skeletal systems, are caused by mutations in mitochondrial DNA.

Disorders caused by deletions in the mitochondrial genome

Deletions appear in cells lines during development

Cells are heteroplasmic for normal and defective mitochondria

Homoplasmic cell lines die out

Deletions vary in size: 1-9 kb, include at least one tRNA gene

Mutants mitochondria lack oxidative phosphorylation

Point mutations in protein-encoding genes

Affect electron transport chain

LHON degeneration of optic nerve

(see Example 16.3 Investigation of a possible nuclear-mitochondrial gene interaction in Leber hereditary optic neuropathy (LHON) in humans)

Point mutations in tRNA and rRNA genes

Affect protein synthesis in mitochondria

Most common of detected mitochondrial disorders

Mutations in mitochondrial DNA and human aging

Mitochondrial mutations tend to increase with age

Mitochondrial deletions increase in nondividing tissue cells
Threshold for disease symptoms
> Greater than 60% mutant mitochondria
> Proportion rarely more than 0.1%

18.5 PLASTID INHERITANCE

Central idea:

- Plastid inheritance in plants varies among species. It may be uniparental-maternal, uniparental-paternal, or biparental.

Variegated leaves (Figures 18.19, 19.20)
> Crosses involving green, variegated and white tissue sectors (Table 18.3)
> (See Example 18.4. Biparental inheritance of plastids in alfalfa.)
> Plasmid inheritance in *Chlamydomonas* depends on gene linked to mating type gene

18.6 OTHER TYPES OF EXTRANUCLEAR INHERITANCE

Kappa particles are bacteria in paramecium cell cytoplasm
> Cells with kappa are killer cells
> Kappa transmitted during sexual conjugation
> Cells with *K* Mendelian allele can harbor kappa
> *kk* cells cannot harbor kappa
> *kk* cells killed in vicinity of cells with kappa

Maternal sex ratio in *Drosophila*
> Trait transmitted maternally only
> Affected female produces female offspring with few males
> Trait due to virus

Cytoplasmic male-sterility in *Vicia faba*
> Due to a cytoplasmic double-stranded RNA
> No effect of plastid or mitochondrial genomes

18.7 CORRECTLY RECOGNIZING EXTRANUCLEAR INHERITANCE

Central idea:

- Maternal effects may mimic extranuclear patterns but in reality are governed by nuclear genes.

Extranuclear inheritance does not adhere to Mendelian principles
> Segregation
> Independent assortment
> Parental equivalence

Maternal effect is by nuclear genes
> Inheritance of shell coiling in snails (Figure 18.21)
>> Coil direction follows genotype of female parent
>> Effects of reciprocal crosses with same genotypes
> (See Example 18.5 Maternal effect in *Limnaea peregra*)

Chapter 19
Population Genetics

KEY CONCEPTS

- Hardy-Weinberg equilibrium, which represents no change in allele frequencies in a population, serves as the foundation for a study of population genetics.
- For Hardy-Weinberg equilibrium to apply there must be no mutation, no migration, random mating with respect to genotype, no selection, and the population must be infinitely large.
- The violations of these five assumptions are the factors that cause deviations from Hardy-Weinberg equilibrium in populations. These factors fall into five general categories: mutation, migration, non-random mating, selection, and drift.
- It is possible to describe the effects of these factors mathematically.

KEY TERMS

population genetics
population
allele frequency
Hardy-Weinberg equilibrium
genotype frequencies
mutation
migration
non-random mating
selection
random genetic drift
assortative mating
disassortative mating
inbreeding
inbreeding coefficient (F)
consanguineous mating
positive selection
negative selection
directional selection
artificial selection
natural selection
fitness
selection coefficient (s)
relative fitness
stabilizing selection
disruptive selection
underdominance
heterozygote advantage or overdominance
balanced polymorphism
random genetic drift
systematic
dispersive
fixation
founder effect

CHAPTER TOPICS

CHAPTER OUTLINE

Introduction
The principles of Mendelian genetics in populations
    Establishment of theoretical framework (Hardy-Weinberg equilibrium)
    Compare genotypic effects of selection, migration, mutation, drift

19.1 HARDY-WEINBERG EQUILIBRIUM

Central ideas:
- Hardy-Weinberg equilibrium is an equilibrium for allele frequencies and genotype frequencies in a population. It adheres to the equations $p + q = 1$ and $p^2 + 2pq + q^2 = 1$, where p and q represent frequencies of different alleles at the same locus.
- The equations for Hardy-Weinberg equilibrium can be expanded to account for more multiple alleles.
- When a population is in Hardy-Weinberg equilibrium allele and genotype frequencies remain constant in each generation. Certain assumptions are met to maintain Hardy-Weinberg equilibrium. Because there is no genetic change, Hardy-Weinberg equilibrium represents the absence of evolution.

Hardy-Weinberg equilibrium for two alleles
    Definition of a **population**
    Definition of **allele frequency**

Definition of **genotype frequency**

Based on Hardy-Weinberg assumptions of equilibrium

Two alleles at a locus: $p + q = 1$

Five hundred individuals: $a = 300$, $A = 700$, $p = 0.3$ $q = 0.7$

Distribution of a and A alleles in population (equilibrium frequencies)

$p^2 + 2pq + q^2 = 1 = (0.3)^2 + 2(0.3)(0.7) + (0.7)^2$

$p^2 = AA$, $2pq = Aa$, $q^2 = aa$ (genotype frequencies)

$AA = 0.09$, $Aa = 0.42$, $aa = 0.49$ $(0.09 + 0.42 + 0.49) = 1$

Calculation of p and q and genotype frequencies in a population

(See Example 19.1 Hardy-Weinberg equilibrium for alleles at the *MN* locus in humans.)

Hardy-Weinberg equilibrium for three alleles

Application to multiple alleles

$p + q + r = 1$ (gene frequencies)

Genotype equilibrium frequencies with three alleles

$p^2 + 2pq + 2pr + q^2 + 2qr + r^2 = 1$ (equilibrium genotype frequencies)

Calculations with three alleles in a population

(See Example 19.2 Determining allele frequencies for multiple alleles.)

(See Example 19.2 Determining allele frequencies for multiple alleles.)

Assumptions for maintenance of Hardy-Weinberg equilibrium

Five assumptions: no mutation, no migration, random mating, no selection, infinitely large population

Deviation from equilibrium assumptions are natural

Establishment of Hardy-Weinberg equilibrium

Equilibrium for two autosomal alleles (assumptions are met or nearly met)

BB or *Bb* = black coat, *bb* = brown coat

4000 *bb* rabbits mated at random with 6000 *BB* rabbits

Genotype equilibrium ($p^2 + 2pq + q^2$) reached in one generation of random mating (.36 *BB* + .48 *Bb* + 0.16 *aa*, equilibrium genotype frequencies)

p of *B* allele = 0.6; q of *b* allele = .4

($p^2 + 2pq + q^2$) calculated by random mating (Figure 19.1)

$0.4 \times 0.4 = 0.16$ *bb*

$2 \times 0.4 \times 0.6 = 0.48$ *Bb*

$0.6 \times 0.6 = .36$ *BB*

X-linked alleles and Z-linked alleles

X and Z linked alleles reach equilibrium in several generations

Allele frequencies oscillate between sexes until equilibrium is reached (Figure 19.2)

19.2 GENETIC CHANGE IN POPULATIONS

Central Ideas:

- Hardy Weinberg equilibrium is dependent on the assumptions of no mutation, no migration, random mating with respect to genotype, no selection, and a population of infinite size.

- The violations of these five assumptions represent the factors that disrupt Hardy-Weinberg equilibrium.

Five factors that disrupt equilibrium

Mutation

Migration

Nonrandom mating
Selection
Random genetic drift

19.3 MUTATION AND MIGRATION
Central ideas:
- Mutation is the only original source of genetic variation. It alters allele frequencies at slow rates over many generations.
- Migration alters allele frequencies when there is a net flow of a particular allele into or out of a population.

Mutation
Short term effects on allele frequencies
Long term effect on allele frequencies
> Forward and reverse mutation rates
> Establish allele frequency in favor of mutant allele

Migration
Conditions that change allele frequencies
> Particular genotypes move out
> Unique genotypes move in
Random small migrations among genotypes do not affect equilibrium (large populations)

19.4 NON-RANDOM MATING

Central idea:
- Nonrandom mating includes assortative mating, inbreeding, and disassortative mating.
- Assortative mating is preferential mating between individuals of like genotypes. It promotes homozygosity and isolation of alleles. Inbreeding is a type of assortative mating in which individuals with common ancestry mate with one another. Disassortative mating is preferential mating between individuals of different genotypes. It promotes heterozygosity.

Assortative mating
Preferential mating of similar kinds
Increases frequency of homozygotes
Inbreeding
Mating between related individuals
Form of assortative mating
Increases homozygosity for all alleles
Self-fertilization: most extreme form of inbreeding (Figure 19.3)
> Mendel predicted decrease in heterozygosity in peas selfing F_2 to F_7th generation
> Heterozygosity deceased by half each generation
Inbreeding coefficient (F) (Figure 19.4, Figure 19.6)
> F = probability any two alleles of locus are alike by descent
> F can be calculated by tracing pedigree paths to individual (Figure 19.4a, b)
> $F_A = \Sigma(1/2)^n(1 + F_A)$
> n = number of individuals in path
> F_A = inbreeding coefficient of common ancestor (often set at 0)
(See Example 19.3 Consanguinity in the British monarchy.)
Disassortative mating

Preferential mating of individuals of dissimilar genotypes
Favors heterozygosity

19.5 SELECTION
Central ideas:
- Selection alters allele frequencies by favoring or disfavoring the reproduction of individuals with a particular phenotype.
- The effectiveness of selection is dependent on the intensity of selection, the degree of dominance, and allele frequency.

Directional selection
Allele frequencies move in one direction (ultimately to 1.0 or 0, Figure 19.10a)

Artificial selection is conducted by plant or animal breeders

Populations are altered in specific ways by breeders

Natural selection (without aid of humans)

Example of natural selection: moths (Figure 19.7)

DDT resistance increased each generation exposed

Fitness and selection coefficient (s) (Table 19.3)

Selection coefficient: the intensity of selection against a genotype

$s = 1$ (no individuals of genotype reproduce)

Fitness: relative ability to survive and transmit genes

w = relative fitness

$w = 1 - s$ (Table 19.3)

h = coefficient used in calculating fitness with incomplete dominance

Directional selection against recessive homozygotes

Allele exposed to selection when homozygous

Fitness of homozygous recessive (q^2) is $1 - s$

Change in q of recessive allele:

$$q_1 = (q - sq^2) \div (1 - sq^2)$$

q = frequency in parent generation

q_1 = frequency after 1 generation of selection

$q_1 - q = \Delta q$ (change in q in one generation of selection)

$$\Delta q = (- spq^2) \div (1 - sq^2)$$

(See Example 19.4 Change in allele frequency in peppered moths due to natural selection.)

Compare Δq when $s = 1$ and $s = 0.5$ (Figure 19.8)

(See Example 19.5 Effect of selection against a recessive allele.)

When s is small selection becomes ineffective (Figure 19.8)

q after t generations (q_0 = initial q)

$$q_t = q_0 \div (1 + tq_0) = t = (1/q_t) - (1/q_0)$$

(See Example 19.5 Effect of selection against a recessive allele)

Directional selection against a completely dominant allele

p = frequency of dominant allele

$$\Delta p = (- spq^2) \div (1 - s + sq^2)$$

If $s = 1$ dominant allele is eliminated in 1 generation

Directional selection with partial dominance

$$\Delta q = (- spq^2[q + h(p - q)]) \div (1 - 2hspq - sq^2)$$

Heterozygote genotype half way between homozygote ($h = 1/2$)

$$\Delta q = (- 1/2 \, spq \div (1 - sq)$$

(See Example 19.6 Selection and partial dominance)

Stabilizing and disruptive selection (Figure 19.10b, c)
Stabilizing selection
Wild coyote phenotype vs. dog breeds (disruptive and directional selections)
Heterozygote advantage (Figure 19.11)
Selection favors heterozygotes against both homozygotes
Called **heterozygote advantage** or **overdominance**
Maintains two alleles in population
Heterozygote has greater fitness, homozygote have lower fitness
$1 - s$ = fitness of one homozygote, $1 - t$ = fitness of other homozygote
(See Example 19.7 Equilibrium with overdominance in a human populations.)
Balance between selection and mutation
Mutation rate (u) and selection pressure (s) can affect allele frequency
Equilibrium equation ($p + q = 1$):

$$up = spq^2 \div 1 - sq^2$$

If q is small (usually when selection-mutation equilibrium is important)
p is close to 1, the denominator is close to 1, the equation is:

$$u = sq^2$$

q at equilibrium between mutation and selection against q

$$q = \text{square root of } (u \div s)$$

When $s = 1$

$$q = \text{square root of } u$$

19.6 RANDOM GENETIC DRIFT

Central ideas:
- Random genetic drift causes alterations in allele frequencies because of sampling error.
- The magnitude of random genetic drift is inversely related to population size.
- Random genetic drift is predictable in magnitude, but unpredictable in direction.

Random genetic drift (or drift)
Gene frequency change due to sampling error
Drift is dispersive not systematic change in gene frequency (Figure 19.12)
(See Example 19.8 Random genetic drift in *Tribolium castaneum*.)
Dispersive effects of drift in *Drosophila* (Figure 19.13)
Founder effect
Small number of individuals found a new population
Significant change in gene frequencies from parent population
(See Example 19.9 The consequences of founder effect.)

Chapter 20
Quantitative Genetics

KEY CONCEPTS

- Qualitative characters can be classified into discrete non-numerical categories while quantitative characters are often distributed continuously and are measured in numerical units.
- Quantitative characters are often influenced by several genes and by environmental factors.
- Description of quantitative inheritance typically relies on statistical summaries such as means and variances.
- Phenotypic variation may be subdivided into genetic and environmental components which are then used to analyze inheritance of quantitative characters.

KEY TERMS

qualitative description
quantitative description
continuous variation
polygenic inheritance
quantitative genetics
metric character
continuous trait
meristic trait
threshold trait
distribution
histogram
sampling
random sampling
systematic sampling
mean
mode
symmetric distribution
asymmetric distribution
skewed
bimodal distribution
median
variance
standard deviation
theoretical terms
observed terms
normal distribution
additive gene action
transgressive segregation
transgressive segregants
heterosis or hybrid vigor
overdominance
genetic load
inbreeding depression
inbred line

environmental variation
norm of reaction or range of reaction
genotype by environment interaction
phenotypic variance
components of variances
broad-sense heritability
dominance
epistasis
narrow-sense heritability
point of truncation
selection differential or S
response to selection or R
marker-assisted selection
quantitative trait locus (QTL)
realized heritability
reverse selection

CHAPTER TOPICS

20.1 STATISTICAL DESCRIPTIONS OF METRIC CHARACTERS
    Distributions
    Sampling
    Mean, mode, and variance
20.2 ADDITIVE GENE ACTION AND CONTINUOUS VARIATION
    Transgressive segregation
20.3 HETEROSIS AND INBREEDING DEPRESSION
    Inbreeding depression and heterosis
20.4 ENVIRONMENTAL VARIATION
    Genotype by environment interaction
20.5 BROAD-SENSE HERITABILITY
20.6 NARROW-SENSE HERITABILITY AND SELECTION
    The effect of dominance on selection
    The effect of epistasis on selection
    The effect of environmental variation on selection
    Narrow-sense heritability
    Quantitative trait loci and DNA markers
    Realized heritability
20.7 LIMITS ON SELECTION

CHAPTER OUTLINE

Introduction

Quantitative and qualitative genetics
    Qualitative: nonnumerical description of trait (tall, short, pink, white)
        Discontinuous variation (tall, short, red, white)
    Quantitative: phenotype described numerically (64 mm, 150 g, 100 decibels)
    Quantitative traits exhibit **continuous variation**
        Individuals differ by small increments over wide range
        Combined effects of several genes on single trait

Polygenic inheritance
Quantitative genetics studies quantitative traits
Effects of environment
Effects of genetic factors

20.1 STATISTICAL DESCRIPTIONS OF METRIC CHARACTERS

Central ideas:
- Many inherited traits may be described in qualitative or quantitative terms. Quantitative descriptions use units of measurement to describe a trait.
- Quantitative traits are often influenced by several genes acting together to give the final phenotype, which together with environmental factors determine the phenotype.
- Quantitative traits may be classified as continuous or meristic. Continuous traits vary from one extreme to another without discrete classes. Meristic traits are measured by counting rather than applying incremental units of measurement.
- Researchers usually analyze quantitative inheritance with summary statistics rather than attempting to determine the individual effects of genes. Common statistical values are the mean, mode, and variance.

Metric character: character that can be measured
> **Continuous character:** traits measured by units of measure (grams weight, millimeters, meters, pigment intensity)
> **Meristic trait:** trait measured by counting (number of bristles, leaves, scales)
> **Threshold trait:** qualitative trait with polygenic inheritance
> > Trait develops if additive effects exceed critical value
> > Susceptibility to certain diseases

Distributions
> Representation of metric characters as two-dimensional **distribution** (Figure 20.1)
> > Plotting distribution
> > > x axis = increments of measure
> > > y axis = numbers or frequency
> **Histogram:** groupings of classes in predefined ranges of increments
> Each class grouping becomes bar on histogram

Sampling
> **Random sampling:** random selection of individuals for measurement
> **Systematic sampling:** selection according to predetermined criteria

Mean, mode, and variance
> **Mean,** $x = M = \Sigma x_i/n$ (Σx_i = sum of phenotypic measurements on each individual, n = number of individuals and x and M = "mean")
> **Mode** is the value (value at the peak of the distribution, usually the most frequent class)
> > **Symmetric distribution:** mean and mode same
> > **Asymmetric distribution:** different mode and mean
> > **Bimodal distribution:** two modes
> **Variance:** sum of all deviations from mean squared in sample divided by total number of individuals minus 1.
> > $s^2 = V = \Sigma (x_i - x)^2 \div n - 1$
> Variance expressed as standard deviation s
> > s = square root of s^2
> Statistical symbols (Table 20.1)

Quantitative genetics often based on normal distributions
    Key features of normal distributions
        Symmetrical
        68% one standard deviation from mean
        95% 1.96 standard deviations from mean

20.2 ADDITIVE GENE ACTION AND CONTINUOUS VARIATION

Central ideas:
- Additive gene action is the most straightforward situation in quantitative genetics. When present, the number of genes that vary for the a trait in a population can be estimated.
- Additive gene action is the influence of alleles with no dominance or epistasis. Progeny means may sometimes exceed parent means because of transgressive segregation.

Additive genes
    Alleles have equal additive effects on phenotype
    No dominance among alleles
    Estimating number of additive alleles affecting a trait
        $n = D^2 \div 8V_G$
        n = number of genes
        D = difference between parent means (parents are homozygous)
        V_G = genetic variance of F_2
    Three assumptions must be met (rarely met actually)
        Alleles have equal, additive effects
        Independent assortment
        Original parents homozygous for genes affecting trait
Additive gene action in wheat: three independent loci and kernel color
    (See Figures 20.3, 20.4 and Example 20.1 Estimating number of genes that govern inheritance of quantitative character.)
Transgressive segregation
    Offspring from heterozygous parents can exceed parental traits
    Transgressive segregation can be due to fortuitous combinations of additive genes
    Plant and animal breeders rely on transgressive segregation

20.3 HETEROSIS AND INBREEDING DEPRESSION

Central ideas:
- Deleterious recessive alleles may be protected from selection in the heterozygous condition. Inbreeding causes an increase in homozygosity allowing recessive alleles to be expressed at higher frequencies. The expression of deleterious recessive alleles due to inbreeding is called inbreeding depression. The degree of potential inbreeding depression is directly related to the degree of dominance in a population.
- Heterosis is the opposite of inbreeding depression. It occurs when deleterious recessive alleles are masked in heterozygous individuals. Hybrid varieties of plants and animals have been developed to exploit the productivity conferred by heterosis.
- Inbreeding depression is the expression of deleterious recessive alleles in the homozygous condition that arises because of inbreeding. Heterosis is the genetic opposite of inbreeding depression and appears in individuals that are highly heterozygous so that dominant alleles mask deleterious recessive alleles.

Heterosis: increased vigor in heterozygotes; also **hybrid vigor**

> Causes of heterosis
>> **Overdominance**: interaction between heterozygous alleles exceeds phenotype of homozygotes (a few cases known)
>> Heterozygosity for dominant alleles and their recessive alleles (probably most cases)
>>> Six genes determine trait A, B, C, D, E, F
>>> Dominant alleles contribute to trait, recessive alleles do not
>>> Parents $AABBCCddeeff$ x $aabbccDDEEFF$
>>> Hybrid trait: $AaBbCcDdEeFf$ is superior to both parents

Inbreeding depression

> Cause: homozygosity for recessive alleles
> Recessive alleles usually encode defective proteins
>> Recessive remain in cross-fertilizing populations for at least two reasons
>>> Lowered fitness is minor for some recessives (selection less efficient)
>>> Rarer deleterious recessive alleles shielded from selection in heterozygous carriers (homozygosity is rare)
> Cross-fertilizing species thus carry numerous deleterious recessives at low frequencies (**genetic load)**
>> Inbreeding increases homozygosity
>> Homozygous recessive loci decrease fitness (Figure 20.8)
> Self-fertilizing species do not suffer inbreeding depression
>> Self-fertilized species are homozygous for most loci
>> Homozygous deleterious recessives exposed and removed by selection

20.4 ENVIRONMENTAL VARIATION

Central ideas:

- Effects of environment on phenotypes of offspring can begin in the maternal parent during development of the egg or as soon as the egg becomes a zygote.
- Every genotype has a potential range of phenotypic expression which can be modified by nurturing and other environmental exposures during maturation and senescence,
- Genotype by environment interaction is a nonadditive response of phenotypes to varying environmental conditions

Causes of environmental variation

> Subtle effects such as female environment on offspring
>> Resources for seed development during flowering season
>> Maternal health during gestation period
>> Environment during maturation
> Predictable environmental effects
>> Observed correlation between environment and phenotype
>> Calorie intake and body weight in mammals
>> Fertilizer and yield in crop plants and lawns
> Phenotypic response curve within range of environments
>> **Norm of reaction** or **range of reaction**
>> Effects of water on plant height (Figure 20.9)

Genotype by environment interaction

> Norms of reaction for two genotypes (Figure 20.10)

Genotype responses may vary drastically

Additive and nonadditive reactions

Detection and interpretation of environmental interactions

(See Example 20.3 Genotype-by-environment interaction in soybeans.)

20.5 BROAD-SENSE HERITABILITY

Central ideas:
- Heritability is among the most important concepts in quantitative genetics. Broad-sense heritability is the proportion of the phenotypic variation in a population attributed to genetic variation. Narrow-sense heritability is the proportion of the phenotypic variation attributed to variation for the additive effects of genes.
- Broad-sense heritability is the proportion of the phenotypic variation that is caused by genetic variation

Broad-sense heritability (H^2): proportion of total phenotypic variance due to genetic causes

Total phenotypic variance contains two variances

$V_P = V_G + V_E$

V_P = total phenotypic variance

$V_G + V_E$ = genetic variance plus environmental variance

Broad-sense heritability = H^2

$H^2 = V_G/V_P$

Estimating broad-sense heritability in wheat

(See Example 20.4 Estimating broad-sense heritability for mineral uptake in wheat.)

Estimation of broad-sense heritability in humans

Estimation of environmental variance

Identical twins are compared to fraternal twins

Phenotypic difference in identical twins due to environmental causes $V_P = V_E$

(because V_G is 0)

Differences in fraternal twins due to $V_G + V_E$

Estimation of H^2 from twin data

$V_G = V_P$ (from fraternal twins) − V_E (from identical twins)

$H^2 = V_G/V_P$ (from fraternal twins)

Twin data can be compared to sequential siblings, adopted siblings etc. to develop other estimates of broad-sense heritability

Problems are associated with these estimates particularly with IQ

20.6 NARROW-SENSE HERITABILITY AND SELECTION

Central ideas:
- Narrow-sense heritability predicts the effectiveness of selection. Narrow-sense heritability identifies the proportion of the selection differential gained by selection.
- Narrow-sense heritability is the proportion of the phenotypic variation attributed to variation for the additive effects of genes. Narrow-sense heritability predicts the efficiency of selection.

Narrow-sense heritability predicts effectiveness of selection

Based on correlation between genotype and phenotype

Factors that produce lower correlations

Dominance among alleles
Epistatic gene interactions
Environment

Lower correlations and reduced effectiveness of selection

The effect of dominance on selection

Dominance: nonadditive interaction of alleles of the same locus (Figure 20.12)

Dominance shelters recessive alleles from selection pressures

Trait due to multiple genes: any degree of dominance masks recessives

The effect of epistasis on selection

Epistasis: nonadditive interaction of alleles of different loci

Epistasis reduces effectiveness of selection by masking other loci

Example: flower color in sweet pea

$P\_C\_$ colored flowers

$ppC\_$, P_cc, $ppcc$ produce white flowers

Selection for white flowers does not eliminate $ppC\_$, P_cc

The effect of environmental variation on selection

Environmental variation may cause inferior genotypes and superior genotypes to look alike reducing effectiveness of selection

Environmental variation may allow individuals to escape selection

Narrow-sense heritability (h^2)

The proportion of genetic variance due to additive effects of genes

$V_G = V_A + V_D + V_I$ (subscripts = additive, dominance, epistasis [interaction])

Narrow-sense heritability = $h^2 = V_A/V_p$

V_P includes: $V_A + V_D + V_I + V_E$

Effects of h^2 on genetic improvement ((Figure 20.13)

Variance of trait is standard normal curve with mean M

Breeder selects parents from high end of distribution (**Point of truncation**)

Point of truncation set to avoid genetic drift in selected parent sample

M^S = mean of selected parents

M to M^S = **selection differential** or S (Figure 20.13a)

Progeny mean is between M and $M^s = M^*$

M to $M^* = R$ **response to selection**

Response to selection is related to h^2

$$R = h^2 S$$

Progress continues until h^2 becomes zero

Breeder can increase h^2

Selection of genetically diverse parents

Decrease V_E cultivating uniform environment

Marker assisted selection: track DNA markers linked to genes controlling trait

Quantitative trait loci and DNA markers

Gene that controls trait: **QTL (quantitative trait locus)**

$V_E = 0$ for DNA markers

$V_D = 0$ for DNA markers that are codominant (most are codominant)

Use of DNA marker assisted selection to identify QTLs

(See Example 20.5 Identification of a potential QTL associated with susceptibility to alcoholism in humans.)

Realized heritability

Realized heritability: $h^2 = R/S$ (Figure 20.13)

Value of realized heritability

Determines general h^2 of trait when determined on many populations

Predicts degree of success of further selection from selected generation (i.e., keep selection cycles going until R nears 0)

20.7 LIMITS ON SELECTION

Central idea:
- Exhaustion of genetic variation may cause a selection plateau, or physiological limits may prevent selection from exploiting genetic variation.

Reasons for reaching a selection plateau

    Selection reduces genetic variation

        Frequencies of favored alleles increased

        Disfavored alleles decrease

    Reaching physiological limits of organism

        Selection for litter size in mice (Figure 20.14)

        Female can successfully gestate limited number of offspring

    Distinguishing exhausted genetic variation from physiological plateau

        Reverse selection

            Disfavored alleles become favored

            Physiological plateaus stop selection before disfavored alleles are eliminated (Figure 20.15)

Chapter 21
Evolutionary Genetics

KEY CONCEPTS

- Speciation, the formation of new species, arises when populations are reproductively isolated from one another.
- Evolution can be studied at the molecular level. The rate of nucleotide and amino acid substitution is relatively constant over evolutionary time.
- Evolutionary forces may reduce or increase genetic diversity in a species depending on which forces predominate.
- Evidence of genetic divergence can be used to reconstruct phylogenies, the evolutionary histories of groups of organisms.

KEY TERMS

evolution
species
gene pool
reproductive isolation
reproductive isolating mechanisms
prezygotic reproductive isolating mechanisms
postzygotic reproductive isolating mechanisms
geographic isolation
allopatric speciation
sympatric speciation
parapatric speciation
ecological isolation
temporal isolation
behavioral or ethological isolation
mechanical isolation
gametic isolation
quantum speciation
hybrid swarm
flush-crash cycle
bottleneck effect
silent mutations
selectively neutral
molecular clock
neutrality theory
selection theory
phylogenetic tree
multiple origins theory
single origin theory or "out of Africa" theory

CHAPTER TOPICS

21.1 SPECIATION
Reproductive isolation

CHAPTER OUTLINE

Introduction
Evolution, the process of genetic change within and among species
Need for reproductive isolation
Genetic differentiation of the DNA and chromosomes
Genetic variation intertwined with:
Population and quantitative genetics
Ecology of populations, communities, ecosystems
Piecing together the evolutionary puzzle
Early studies based on morphological similarities
Population and quantitative genetics added
Cytogenetics added
Molecular evolution added with discovery of DNA and development of DNA and protein bio-chemistries
We begin with discussion of speciation
Examine molecular evolution
Reconstruction of ancestral relationships and divergence

21.1 SPECIATION

Central ideas:
- A species is defined as a group of interbreeding individuals that produce fully fertile off-spring and are isolated reproductively from other such groups. Some form of reproductive isolation is necessary for speciation.
- Selection requires form of reproductive isolation. Reproductive isolation may be either prezygotic or postzygotic.
- There are several types of reproductive isolating mechanisms. They can be divided into two general categories: prezygotic and postzygotic.
- Prezygotic mechanisms prevent or inhibit formation of zygotes. They typically prevent or inhibit mating. Examples include geographic isolation, mechanical isolation, and isolation in

time.

- Postzygotic mechanisms do not prevent mating and zygote formation, but cause a loss of viability or fertility in the zygote, embryo, of hybrid offspring. Examples include physiological imbalance, chromosomal incompatibilities such as inversions, translocations, and differences in ploidy.
- Drift and selection may operate to heightened degrees in small populations to reproductively isolate populations.

Definitions of **species** and **gene pool**

Species: group of interbreeding individuals reproductively isolated from other groups

Gene pool: all genes shared exclusively (or nearly so) by members of the species

Reproductive isolation

Reduction or complete exclusion of gene flow between two populations

Speciation requires some form of reproductive isolation

Reproductive isolating mechanisms contribute to allopatric, sympatric, and parapatric speciation patterns

Prezygotic reproductive isolating mechanisms

Prevent or inhibit fertilization

Geographic isolation (Figure 21.1)

Land or water barriers

No gene flow between isolated populations

Allopatric speciation: results from geographic isolation

Sympatric speciation; groups occupy same geographic locality (no geographic isolation)

Parapatric speciation: extremes of range geographically isolated but areas overlap permitting gene flow

Ecological isolation: habitat separation in same territory

Temporal isolation: separated by time (flowering times, etc.)

Behavioral isolation: males and females not attracted

Mating rituals

Color differences

Release of mating-specific pheromones

Mechanical isolation

Cleistogamy in plants

Floral preferences of insect pollinators (Figure 21.2)

Gametic isolation: incompatibility between gametes

Biochemical interactions limit pollination to pollen from species flowers

Postzygotic reproductive isolating mechanisms: reduced fertility and/or viability of hybrids

Frequent cause: alterations of chromosome structure or number

Example: fixation of translocation homozygotes in small founder populations by genetic drift

Crossing back to homozygous normal population produces semisterile hybrids

Further crossing totally sterile if parent or founder population diverge with more inversion or translocation homozygosity (Figure 21.3)

(See Example 21.1 Chromosomal evolution in primates.)

Horse x donkey → sterile mule

Horse $2n = 64$

Donkey $2n = 62$

Hybrid mule has 63 ($n = 32 + n = 31$) chromosomes (poor meiotic pairing)

Patterns of chromosome evolution in *Drosophila* species (Figure 21.5)

Chromosome rearrangement may be first step in evolution

Reproductive isolation set up by chromosome rearrangement

Rearrangement fixed because of drift in small colony

Small colony can now diverge from parent population

Quantum speciation: rapid speciation in one or few generations

Speciation is often gradual

Reproductive isolation leads to accumulation of isolating mechanisms

Often takes many generations (sometimes spanning thousands of years)

Speciation can also be sudden

Caused by polyploidy

Example of new allopolyploid (Figure 17.9)

Development of hybrid swarm

Two polyploids come in contact

Hybrids partially sterile but vigorous

Best genotypes may stabilize become more fertile

Arising by extremes of drift and natural selection

Flush-crash cycles and bottlenecks

Migration when flush may produce geographic isolations

(See Example 21.2 Reproductive isolation from flush-crash cycles in *Drosophila*.)

21.2 MOLECULAR EVOLUTION

Central ideas:

- After speciation is complete, gene pools of different species evolve independently. Mutations may appear and become fixed in one group but not another. The genetic divergence of reproductively isolated species that share common ancestry is correlated with the amount of time that has passed since reproductive isolation. Thus, differences in DNA and amino acid sequence can be used to determine how long ago species, or major groups of species, diverged from common ancestry.

- Nucleotide and amino acid substitutions appear at about the same rate for a particular gene or site in DNA. The number of substitutions can be used to estimate when two groups or species diverged, a concept known as a molecular clock.

- Because of selection, genes may evolve at different rates, so molecular clocks for genes and regions within genes may tick at different rates.

- The forces that drive evolution have their ultimate effect at the DNA level. Evolution can be reconstructed by comparing DNA and protein polymorphism's.

Gene pools of incipient species evolve independently

Distinguishing mutations and selection occur with time

Genetic divergence correlated with time

Number of amino acid or nucleotide substitutions indicate genetic distance

Amino acid sequence divergence in proteins

Hemoglobins among first proteins compared among species

Human vs. chimpanzee identical hemoglobins

Chimpanzee and great ape differ by one amino acid in a an b subunits

Humans vs. cattle = 17 amino acids a subunit, 24 amino acids b subunits

Evolution of hemoglobin constant with time (Figure 21.7)

Similar pattern of straight line relationships occurred with other proteins

Rate of protein divergence depends on the effects of amino acid substitutions on protein activity

Hemoglobin: 1.55 % per 5.8 million years

Cytochrome *c*: 1% per 20 million years (Figure 21.8)

Fibrinopeptides: diverge rapidly (1% per 1.1` million years)

Histones: hardly diverge at all (1% per 600 million years)

Usefulness of rate of protein divergence

Fibrinopeptides: distinguishing relatedness among mammals

Cytochrome c: distantly related groups

(See Example 21.3 Molecular evolution in cytochrome c.)

Nucleotide sequence divergence in DNA

Rate of change depends on effects of mutations in region

Highly conserved sequences for comparing distantly related groups

Not highly conserved sequence for comparing closer related groups

Silent mutations may be selectively neutral

Do not change amino acid sequence

More useful than amino acid sequences in proteins

(See Example 21.4 Codon usage bias in *Drosophila*.)

Molecular clocks

Timing molecular clocks

Conserved sequences tick slowly

Neutral sequences tick faster

Estimation of time of divergence of two species

Molecular clocks compared to confirm conclusion and set the time scale

Large-scale DNA sequence comparisons

DNA sequences are accumulating in DNA libraries

Courtesy US government DNA sequences available for comparison

Molecular-marker analysis

Markers used for evolution studies

Isoenzymes

RFLPs, minisatellites, microsatellites, DNA sequencing

Markers selected to represent the genome

DNA hybridization

DNA renaturation can be used to determine degree of similarity

$t_{1/2}$ of species DNA compared with $t_{1/2}$ of mixture of species denatured DNAs

Single copy DNA isolated from each species and denatured

Single copy DNA from one species is radioactively labeled

Labeled DNA is mixed with excess unlabeled DNA and renatured

The $t_{1/2}$ for labeled species DNA alone and $t_{1/2}$ for mixed DNAs compared

Difference is $\Delta t_{1/2}$ each degree difference is about 1% difference in nucleotide sequence (Figure 21.9)

Gene organization

Hemoglobin gene family can serve as molecular clock

Compare lampreys, shark and mammal hemoglobins

Evolutionary pattern emerges

Pattern based on oxygen carrying efficiency needs

Ancient DNA

Recovery of ancient DNAs has several problems

DNA is quickly degraded at death

Claims of DNA preservation in amber and other kinds of fossilizing encasements have been difficult to replicate and rule out modern DNA contamination

21.3 MAINTENANCE OF GENETIC DIVERSITY

Central idea:

- Drift, selection, and inbreeding are mechanisms that cause fixation of alleles and loss of genetic diversity. Although many alleles are fixed in each species, other alleles may be maintained at high levels of heterozygosity. Neutrality and selection theories explain how genetic diversity can be maintained.

Factors that drive evolution decrease genetic diversity

Direction is toward homozygosity and fixation of alleles

Directional selection, drift, inbreeding, assortative mating

Eliminate some alleles

Fix other alleles

In species many alleles and chromosome rearrangements are fixed

Factors that increase or maintain diversity in populations

Mutation, immigration, some forms of stabilizing selection

Uniform appearing wild populations contain have high levels of heterozygosity for DNA markers and enzyme markers

Forces that maintain diversity

No consensus among scientists and in nature

Some species are highly heterozygous some are not

Mutation, neutrality, selection theories are discussed

These theories suggest possible ways diversity is maintained

21.4 PHYLOGENETIC ANALYSIS

Central idea:

- Information gathered from a variety of sources, such as analyses of morphological characteristics, chromosome organization, DNA sequences, and amino acid sequences, can be synthesized to identify phylogenetic relationships and reconstruct evolutionary histories.

Construction of a phylogenetic tree

Evolution analysis often based on comparison of species

Genetic similarities imply common ancestry

Degrees of similarity depicted by phylogenetic tree

Simplest path races or species descended from common ancestry

Basic premise for tree construction

Paths requiring least mutations most correct

Construct phylogenetic tree from Figure 21.8

Data summarized Tables 21.3, 21.4

Connect groups based on number of amino acid substitutions (see text example page 650)

(See Example 21.5 Construction of a phylogenetic tree from amino acid sequence diversity in cytochrome *c*.)

Comparison of data from different sources in phylogenetic analysis

Evolutionary histories obtained from wide variety of data

Molecular sequences in DNA and proteins

DNA hybridization

Chromosome organization (banding for instance)

Chromosome structure (inversions , translocations, etc.)

Chromosome numbers

Comparative anatomy
Information obtained by one method usually confirms other methods
Human evolutionary history
>Fossil record suggests African origin
>Two major theories about spread from Africa
>>Multiple origin theory
>>>Several origins from an extant *Homo erectus*
>>>Aided by migration and gene flow between rising groups
>>>Fossil record suggests migration from Africa 1.8 m years ago
>>>Fossil record: *H. erectus* in near east 200,000 years ago
>>>Fossil features similar to certain features of indigenous population
>>>Suggest humans arose from several *H. erectus* groups
>>Single origin theory
>>>Modern humans arose once in Africa and migrated
>>>Migrants displaced related species
>>>Argument based on highest diversity theory
>>>>Highest diversity at center or origin
>>>>Lower diversities away from origin due to founder effect
>>>Studies of nuclear and mitochondrial DNA
>>>>Show greater diversity in indigenous Sub-Saharan African populations than all other human populations combined
>>>Mitochondrial DNA studies
>>>>First studies suggested African origin from one woman (assuming uniparental inheritance)
>>>>>Set time of divergence 100,000 to 300,00 years ago
>>>>Later studies have confirmed African origin (assuming some biparental inheritance of mitochondria)
>>>>>Set time of divergence 60,000 to 100,000 years ago
>>>Studies based on minisatellite markers
>>>>Support single-origin theory
>>>>Greater diversity among Sub-Saharan Africans than the rest of world combined
>>>>Set time of migration 150,000 years ago
(see Example 21.6 Genetic diversity for coupled nuclear mutations in humans.)

Chapter 22
Transposable Elements

KEY CONCEPTS

- Genomes are not stable entities. Certain segments of DNA, called transposable elements, may move from one site to another in the genome.
- Transposable elements cause mutations when they insert themselves into a gene and often cause the gene to revert to its former function when the element excises itself from the gene.
- Many transposable elements have characteristic features such as inverted or direct terminal repeats and a gene within the element that encodes a transpose, an enzyme that catalyzes transposition.
- Some elements transpose by excising themselves, then moving to a new site in the genome. Others transpose by replicating and inserting the new copy at a new site, leaving the original copy in its site. Others transpose by means of an RNA intermediate that is reverse transcribed to make a new DNA element.
- Transposable elements have been used in research to tag genes of interest for cloning. They also have been used as vectors for introducing foreign genes into the genome.

KEY TERMS

transposons
retrotransposons
retroposons
conservative transposition
replicative transposition
mutable alleles
autonomous transposon
nonautonomous transposon
breakage-fusion-bridge (BFB) cycle
dysgenesis
P elements
dysgenic cross
retrotransposition
long terminal repeats (LTRs)
polyproteins
insertion sequences
composite transposons
composite transposon
terminal modules
transposon tagging

CHAPTER TOPICS

CHAPTER OUTLINE

Introduction

Barbara McClintock (1950s): pieces of chromatin move within maize genome
      Years later **transposable elements** confirmed in *Drosophila* and *E. coli*
      Transposable elements probably part of genomes of all species
Significance of transposable elements
      Important in cancer disease and genetic disorders
      Important in evolution
Types of transposable elements in chromosome DNA
      Transposons: pieces of chromosome DNA that can change location
      Retrotransposons: resemble retroviruses and code own reverse transcriptase
      Retroposons: segments of DNA that resemble reverse transcribed mRNA and snRNA
Mode of transposition (Figure 22.1)
      Conservative transposition
            DNA element excised and moved to new location
            Element does not increase in number
      Replicative transposition
            Original element remains at initial site and is copied and moved
            Elements increase in number
Most studied transposable elements
      Maize, *Drosophila*, and *E. coli*
      Transposable elements resemble elements in other genomes

22.1 EUKARYOTIC TRANSPOSONS

Central ideas:
- Transposable elements may be divided into three general classes: transposons, retrotransposons, and retroposons.
- Transposons are segments of DNA that can move from one location of the genome to another and move as a DNA entity.
- Transposons have characteristic common features. The most important are inverted terminal repeats and a gene that encodes a transposase. Transposons that encode functional transposase may transpose in the absence of other transposable elements and are said to be autonomous. Transposons with a mutant transposase gene that does not encode functional transposase are nonautonomous and can transpose only when an autonomous element is present in the genome.

Effects of insertion of transposable elements

Insertion mutation in gene locus (Figure 22.2)

Insertion near gene may disrupt transcription regulation

Effects of mobility of inserted transposons

Elements can remove and restore activity of "mutated" gene locus

Recessive transposon alleles are **mutable alleles**

Mutable alleles revert to wild-type dominant alleles

Reversion to wild-type much higher than natural mutation rate

AC-DS system in maize and P elements in *Drosophila*

Typical of transposable elements in other genomes

Detection of transposable element activity in maize

Purple spots on "Indian corn" kernels led to discovery of transposable elements (Figure 22.3, see kernel rendering on page 660)

Purple kernels due to anthocyanin pigment

Several loci encode enzymes for anthocyanin synthesis

Homozygosity at any of several loci causes lack of purple in aleurone of kernel (aleurone is triploid endosperm tissue)

One locus (A_1) has transposable element that produced recessive allele (homozygosity $a_1a_1a_1$ produces light kernels)

Removal of transposable element causes reversion to dominant allele $a_1a_1a_1 \rightarrow A_1a_1a_1$ (purple tissue sector in aleurone, Figures 22.4 and 22.5)

The *Activator-dissociator* (*Ac-Ds*) transposon system in maize

Ac element is an **autonomous transposon** element

Ac can transpose by itself

Transposition can cause recessive mutable alleles

Ds element is a **nonautonomous transposon**

Ds transposition requires presence of *Ac* transposon in genome

Ds transposition can cause recessive mutable allele

Ds mutable alleles are stable in absence of *Ac* transposon

Ds transposon at the *c1* locus in maize

c1 locus encodes enzyme for anthocyanin pathway

c-m1 recessive mutable allele contains *Ds* transposon

Ac containing line crossed with *c-m1* line

F_1 carries *Ac* in genome with *c-m1* gene

Dc can now transpose in somatic cells and aleurone (Figure 22.5, *c-m1* converts to dominant allele)

Result: spotted kernels in hybrid ears of corn (Figure 22.6)

1980s: Nina Federoff and workers cloned sequenced *Ac* and *Ds* elements

Common features of autonomous elements

Bordered by imperfect terminal repeats

Codon sequence for transposase

Function of repeats and transposase codon (Figure 22.7)

Features of nonautonomous elements (*Ds*, Figure 22.8)

Ds has deletion of transposase codons

Terminal repeats intact

Presence of transposase allows *Ac* and *Ds* to transpose (Figure 22.9)

Insertion of transposon

Transposon inserted into a staggered cut leaving single strands at both ends of inserted transposon

Polymerase repairs the single stranded ends

Leaves repeats at both ends of inserted transposon (Figure 22.10)

Excision of transposon

Repeats are imperfectly joined

Repeats are called footprints

Reading frame reestablished if repeats are multiples of three

Enzyme activity is restored if the added amino acids don't have a drastic affect

Ds elements and chromosome breakage

Chromosome breakage associated with some *Ds* elements (McClintock)

Ds element in chromosome 9 with *C1, Wx, Sh* alleles

Genes distal to *Ds* element

Ds line crossed to homozygous recessive (*c1, wx, sh*) *Ac* line

Development of **breakage-fusion-bridge cycle** in somatic cells

Excision of *Ds* may cause chromosome break at excision site

Results of breakage at *Ds* site

Distal dominant genes (*C1, Wx and Sh*) lost (acentric fragment) recessive alleles on intact 9 now expressed

Recessive allele expression produces variegated somatic tissue (appears aleurone in kernel in this case because the genes affect kernel phenotype)

Broken chromatid ends can rejoin forming dicentric chromosome

Dicentric chromosome forms bridge at mitotic anaphase

Bridge breaks again at anaphase

Broken ends fuse again next cell division etc.

Only certain *Ds* elements break chromosomes

P elements in *Drosophila*

McClintock proposed *Ds* elements in *Drosophila* (1940s)

P elements found in wild strains

P elements entered wild populations within last 50 years

Wild flies crossed with laboratory strains

Wild males (**P-cytotypes)** crossed with laboratory females (**M-cytotypes**)

Hybrids infertile and **hybrid dysgenic**

Effects of fly culture temperature on hybrid progeny

29° all hybrids are sterile

21° hybrids partially fertile

Progeny of hybrids highly mutant

Chromosome breaks etc.

P-cytotype eventually acquired

Dysgenesis result of frequent transposition of P elements

Acquiring P-cytotype cytoplasm

P-cytotypes have 30 to 50 P elements

Initial crosses into M-cytotype liberates P element transposition

P elements accumulate each generation by transposition until P-cytotype is established

Molecular structure and function of P elements

Basis for P-cytotype inhibition of P element transposition

Inhibitor codons are part of transposase gene

Intron between exons 2 and 3 not removed in somatic cells (Figure 22.13)

Intron contains translation termination sequence
Translated polypeptide is truncated form of transposase
Presence in somatic cell cytoplasm inhibits transposase
Reciprocal cross (wild females (P-cytotypes) × lab males (M-cytotypes))
Hybrids have normal fertility no hybrid dysgenesis
P-cytotypes carry transposition inhibitor in cytoplasm
(See Example 22.2 The *snᵂ* allele in *Drosophila melanogaster*)

22.2 RETROTRANSPOSONS AND RETROPOSONS

Central ideas:
- Retrotransposons are segments of DNA that resemble retroviruses and code for a reverse transcriptase. They transpose by means of an RNA intermediate that is transcribed from the retrotransposon. The RNA is then reverse transcribed into DNA which is made double stranded and inserted into a new position in the genome.
- Retroposons, like retrotransposons, are pieces of DNA that are transcribed into an RNA intermediate that is then reverse transcribed into DNA and inserted into the genome. Unlike retrotransposons, they do not encode their own reverse transcriptase, nor do they resemble retroviruses.
- Retroposons also transpose by means of an RNA intermediate, but they have no reverse transcriptase gene. Instead, they rely on reverse transcriptase produced by retrotransposons or by retroviruses present in the cell.
- The *copia* element of *Drosophila melanogaster* is a well-studied example of a retrotransposon. Unlike *Ty*, it does not form virus-like particles. It comprises about 15% of the *Drosophila melanogaster* genome.
- Retroposons are present in humans and include LINEs and SINEs, retroposons that are present in many copies in the human genome.

Retrotransposons
Resemble retroviruses that have lost ability to invade and lyse cells
General structure of retroviruses from yeast and *Drosophila* (Figure 22.14)
    Ty elements in yeast and *copia* elements in *Drosophila*
    Process of retrotransposition (Figure 22.15)
        DNA is transcribed into mRNA and polyadenylated
        mRNA is translated into capsid proteins and four enzymes
        The reverse transcriptase makes DNA copy of RNA
        RNase removes RNA template from DNA
        DNA strand circularizes and becomes double stranded
        The integrase integrates new copy into new site

Retroposons
Retroposons resemble mRNAs with poly A tails and snRNAs
Transposition of retroposons
    Most require presence of integrase and reverse transcriptase from retroviruses or retro-
        transposons
    Examples: mammalian LINEs and SINEs
    Alu elements (common SINE in humans) constitute 5% of genome
    Most are transpositionally inactive
(See Example 22.3 A new germ-line mutation from transposition of an *Alu* element.)

22.3 PROKARYOTIC TRANSPOSONS

Central ideas:
- Transposons are also found in prokaryotes. The best studied are insertion sequences that have the same general features as maize and *Drosophila* transposons.
- Insertion sequences are prokaryotic transposons with the same general features as eukaryotic transposons. Some insertion sequences utilize conservative transposition and others utilize replicative transposition.
- Two insertion sequences may border a segment of DNA and transpose as a single unit with the DNA between them. Such a unit of transposable DNA is called a composite transposon.

Insertion sequences
Several families of transposons found in bacteria
> Insertion sequences (more than 50 characterized, *IS* sequences)
> > Bordered by repeats
> > Contain gene for transposase or transposase subunits
> > Cells can contain 10 to 200 copies
> > Found in plasmids, bacteriophages
> > Insertion can cause gene mutations
> > Excision can restore gene activity or leave stable mutant
> > > Excision leaves footprint
> > > Excision can leave deletion
> > Transposition can be conservative or replicative

Composite transposons
Two transposons can transpose bacterial DNA between them (Figure 22.18, **composite transposon**)
Rearrangements of bacteria genomes with composite transposon (Figure 22.19)
> Recombination can produce plasmids with bacterial genes
> May carry genes for antibiotic resistance
> Natural selection may favor formation of plasmid with antibiotic resistance genes
> Outbreaks of antibiotic resistant *Salmonella*
> > Attributed to selection of composite transposons
> > Antibiotic selective agent applied to either livestock or humans

22.4 USING TRANSPOSABLE ELEMENTS IN RESEARCH

Central idea:
- Transposable elements have several applications in research. Among the most important are transposon tagging and transposon-mediated transformation

Transposon tagging
Probing genomic or cDNA library for a gene mutated by a transposon insertion
> Probe library from mutant for DNA clones containing transposon
> Manipulate clone to obtain gene probe free of transposon
(See Example 22.4 Cloning bronze locus in maize by transposon tagging.)

Transposon-mediated transformation
Transposable elements can integrate genes into eukaryotic cell genomes
(See Example 22.5 P-element mediated transformation in *Drosophila melanogaster*)
P-element transformation now routinely used for transforming *Drosophila*

Chapter 23
Developmental Genetics

KEY CONCEPTS

- Genes govern the differentiation of somatic cells into specialized tissues and organs.
- In the nematode *Caenorhabditis elegans* the somatic lineage of every cell in the adult is known. Mutations in genes that regulate development have provided information about the function of those genes.
- Much is known about gene expression and development in *Drosophila melanogaster*. Maternal and segmental genes establish the number and positions of body segments, whereas homeotic genes determine segmental identity.
- There are many similarities in DNA sequence, function, and organization between the genes that regulate development in *Drosophila* and mammals.
- Genes that govern plant development are different from those that govern animal development.

KEY TERMS

differentiation
totipotent
positional developmental regulation
autonomous developmental regulation
heterochronic mutations
fusion genes
reporter gene
polarity
bicoid (bcd)
morphogen
homeodomain
segmental genes
gap genes
pair-rule genes
stripes
segment polarity genes
homeotic genes
Antennapedia complex (ANT-C)
bithorax complex (BX-C)
Ultrabithorax domain
Infraabdominal domain
heat-shock genes
homeobox
Hox clusters
paralogous
meristems
floral meristem identity
floral organ identity
MADS box
K domain

CHAPTER TOPICS

CHAPTER OUTLINE

Introduction
Single celled zygote give rise to complex organism
    Genes that control developmental pathways
    Use of recombinant DNA to study development
Similarities at gene levels among widely different organisms will be discussed
    Basic aspects of developmental genetics
    Developmental genetics in *C. elegans* and *D. melanogaster*
    Developmental genetics in mammals
    Field of plant developmental genetics

23.1 DIFFERENTIATION AND TOTIPOTENCY

Central ideas:
- Developmental genetics is the study of genes that govern cell differentiation and organismal development.
- A cell that can divide and give rise to an entire multicelled organism is said to be totipotent.
- During somatic cell differentiation, totipotency is often lost as cells become specialized to carry out the function of the tissue in which they reside.

Specialization of the genetic information and totipotency
    Regulation targets cells for specialized functions
    Somatic cells contain entire genetic compliment but become specialized
        Many specialized cells lose totipotency (especially in complex animals such as insects and mammals)
        Loss of totipotency without loss or rearrangement of genes in cell
Cell specialization depends upon regulation of small fraction of all genes
    Small number of total genes expressed in specialized cells
    Different genes are expressed in cells with different specialization

23.2 GENETIC CONTROL OF DEVELOPMENT IN *Caenorhabditis elegans*
Central ideas:
- The nematode worm *Caenorhabditis elegans* and the insect *Drosophila melanogaster* are the two

best studied species in developmental genetics.

- In *C. elegans*, the developmental fate of every cell is known and the effect of many genes that govern cell development has been determined through analysis of mutations in the genes.

Tracing cell lineage's in a simple multicelled organism *C. elegans* (Figure 23.1)

At some point in development two daughter cells must diverge

Tracing developmental fate of cells

XO males have 1031 nuclei

XX hermaphrodites have 937 nuclei

Assigning distinct developmental stages to nuclear mitotic divisions

Nuclei are tracked by noting plane of division relative to axis of embryo (Figure 23.2)

Lineage's of all nuclei are known

Nuclear divisions, mutations, and development of vulva in hermaphrodites (Figure 23.3) positional vs. autonomous developmental regulation

Vulva develops from seven cells (anchor cell and six cells)

Seven cells become either 1°, 2°, and 3°

1° and 2° differentiate into vulva tissue

3° cells become hypodermis surrounding vulva

Genes in anchor cell control genes in precursor cells

Cell fate determined by distance from anchor cell

Called **positional development regulation**

(**autonomous developmental regulation**: cell fate determined within cell)

Mutations disrupt development of four stages

1. Anchor cell and precursor cells

   At least five genes

   Mutations change timing and direction of differentiation

2. Formation of three primary types (1°, 2°, and 3°)

   About 15 genes

   Mutations prevent formation of primary precursor cells

   May eliminate signal from anchor cell

   Calls may become only 3° cells

3. Execution of cell division of each primary type

   Mutations govern only one cell lineage

   i.e., mutations affect only 2° lineage not other lineage's

4. Formation of structures (morphogenesis)

   Mutations affect only final outcomes of lineage's

   i.e., only malformed vulva and other tissues normal

(See Example 23.1 The role of *lin-12* in *C. elegans*.)

23.3 GENETIC CONTROL OF DEVELOPMENT IN *Drosophila melanogaster*

Central ideas:

- Maternal genes establish the initial anterior-posterior and dorsal-ventral orientation of the embryo. The products of these genes interact with gene products produced by the embryo's genes.
- Development in *Drosophila melanogaster* follows a hierarchical pattern beginning with a gradient of maternal gene products that influences embryonic genes. The embryonic genes that were activated by maternal proteins activate another set of genes that determine the pattern for development.

- There are several types of segmental genes. These genes establish the number, position, and polarity of the segments in the larva and eventually the adult.
- Mutations in homeotic genes may cause replacement of one structure with another body part. For example, certain homeotic mutations may cause legs to form in place of antennae.
- The homeotic genes of *Drosophila* are located in two clusters on chromosome 3 called the antennapedia complex (ANT-C) that determines structural development in the head and anterior portion of the thorax and the bithorax complex (BX-C) that regulates structural development in the posterior portion of the thorax and the abdomen.

Techniques for studying development in *Drosophila*
> Major developmental stages (Figure 23.5)
> Mutations
>> Studying gene promoters and their sites of action
>>> P-element transformations with fusion genes
>>> Fusion gene: fly promoter fused to harmless reporter gene
>>> Inject into embryos to determine control of promoters
>> Studying DNA interactions with regulatory proteins
>>> Cloning and expressing *Drosophila* regulatory genes in *E. coli*
>>> Regulatory proteins and their interaction with DNA studied

Maternal effects in early development
> Maternal genes and first stages of development
>> Embryo's anterior and posterior polarity maternally controlled
>>> Anterior: head, thorax
>>> Posterior: abdomen, telson
>> Evidences for maternal **morphogen** that determines polarity
>>> Offspring from homozygous *bicoid* females (Figure 23.9)
>>>> All with *bicoid* phenotype regardless of genotype
>>> Removal of anterior fertilized egg cytoplasm
>>>> Embryos without anterior structures etc.
>> Morphogens, proteins encoded by maternal mRNAs
>>> DNA probe from *bicoid* gene hybridizes with mRNA at anterior pole
>>> Anterior morphogens form gradient (anterior pole to midline)
>>> **Homeodomains** of anterior morphogens
>>> Homeodomains bind to zygotic DNA regulator sites
> About 30 maternal genes govern first stages of development
>> Genes cloned and protein products analyzed
>>> The *nos* and *dl* genes and their products
>>> *nos*: posterior development, abdomen formation
>>> *dl*: dorsal ventral orientation of embryo

Segmental gene expression (Figure 23.8)
> Early embryos and reliance on maternal mRNAs for proteins (*Drosophila*)
>> Division of embryo nuclei throughout initial cell cytoplasm
>> Maternal morphogens and transcription of genes in embryo nuclei
>> Embryo genes assume task of differentiation
>>> **Segmental genes**: early activated embryo genes
>>> Mutations of segmental genes and faulty formation of body segments
>> **Gap gene expression**: first segmental genes expressed
>>> Mutations and missing segments (called gaps)
>>>> Well studied mutants: *hunchback, Krüppel, knirps*

Several gap genes regulated by *bicoid* product

knirps: short larvae, 7 abdominal segments fused (Figure 23.10, Figure 23.11a)

hunchback: extreme posterior (Figure 23.11b)

Krüppel: midline (Figure 23.11c)

(see Example 23.2 Regulation of the *hunchback* gene by the *bicoid* gene protein.)

Pair-rule gene expression (Figure 23.12, Figure 23.14)

Formation of adjacent paired segments

Pair-rule genes and formation of stripes in embryos (Figure 23.12)

Gap genes regulate pair-rule genes

Complex regulator regions of pair-rule genes (Figure 23.13)

hairy gene mutations

Coding region mutations eliminate function in all stripes

Some eliminate function in one stripe

Hierarchical nature of gene regulation

bicoid gene product and regulation of *knirps, hairy, Krüppel* genes

knirps gene product and regulation of *hairy* gene

Segment polarity gene expression

Anterior (A) and posterior (P) compartments of each segment

Loss of one or other compartment and mutant genes

wingless, engrailed, gooseberry

Homeotic gene expression

Homeotic genes and segmental identity

Mutations cause body parts to appear in wrong places (Figure 23.6)

Two large complexes

ANT-C and **BX-C**

Location of mutations: two complexes on chromosome 3

ANT-C genes head and thorax segments (T1, Figure 23.15)

BX-C genes, second anterior thorax segment to abdomen (Figure 23.16)

Homeotic gene functions (23.17)

Regulatory and protein coding segments (three DNA binding proteins)

BX-C 300,000 nucleotides, four transcribed genes

***Ultrabithorax* domain**

Ubx; encodes DNA binding protein

***Infraabdominal* domain**

abd-A and Abd-B (encode DNA binding proteins)

23.4 COMPARISON OF MAMMALIAN AND *Drosophila* DEVELOPMENTAL GENETICS

Central idea:
- The DNA sequences and spatial arrangement of genes in ANT-C and BX-C in insects are similar to paralogous sequences and arrangements of homeotic genes in vertebrates. The similarity suggests a common evolutionary origin and arrangement of these genes.

Some basic principles are similar

Homeobox DNA probes hybridize with mammalian development genes

Similarities within and outside of homeoboxes

Similarity of gene sequences on chromosomes

Hox clusters of human and mouse homeotic genes

Human, mouse, *Drosophila* hox cluster are **Paralogous** (Figure 23.18)
Similarity of order of gene expression
Function of hox clusters in mouse
Homeotic mutations and tendency to take on more anterior structure
P-element *Drosophila* transformants with hox cluster mouse mutants
Developmental genes similar in structure and function
Same effects as paralogous *Drosophila* homeotic mutants
Similarities of development genes include much of animal kingdom
Communality suggests evolutionary advantage of the organization
But specific arrangement not always necessary
(See Example 23.3 Special placement of *pb* in ANT-C.)

23.5 PLANT DEVELOPMENTAL GENETICS

Central idea:
*   Plant development genetics is an emerging field that has produced much information in recent years. Among the most extensively studied genes are those that regulate floral development.

Accelerating pace of plant developmental genetics
Genome sequencing of *Arabidopsis* and recent progress in plant developmental genetics
Floral differentiation in *Arabidopsis*
Meristems at tip of shoot and root
Shoot meristem and stem, bud, leaf, (vegetative organs) and flower differentiation (reproductive organs)
Change of shoot meristem from stem, leaf to floral differentiation
Initiation of vegetative to floral differentiation transition
Stimulus of day length (long day and short day plants)
Rise in environmental temperature
Genes governing transition to **floral meristem identity**
AP1, CAL, LFY, CLV1, CLV2
Second step: genes governing **floral organ identity**
Types of floral organs: sepals, petals, stamens, carpels
Four concentric whorls of cells on floral meristem
MADS boxes: conserved 56 amino acid regions of control proteins (found in yeast, plant and mammalian development control genes)
MADS boxes are DNA binding sites
MADS box genes
Over 20 MADS box genes in Arabidopsis
Most known to govern floral development
Gene duplication and origin of MADS genes
MADS box genes and homeotic floral mutations
The *AG* locus and homeotic mutations (Figures 23.20 and 23.21)
PAN gene: number of organs and organ positions
pan-1 (Figure 23.22)
(See Example 23.4 MADS box genes in *Arabidopsis*.)

23.6 COMPARISON OF PLANT AND ANIMAL DEVELOPMENTAL GENETICS

Central idea:
- The patterns of development and the genes that govern development in plants differ from those of animals. Among the best studied plant-development genes are the MADS-box genes, which perform functions that are analogous to the functions of the homeobox genes in animals.

Pattern of animal development genes determined early in evolution history
    Plants and animals share same types of genes
    Gene functions are different
Comparison of gene functions
    Homeobox genes in both
        Animals: several homeobox genes
            Determine organ identity
        Plants: few homeobox genes
            Proteins activate cell division
    MADS box genes
        In plants many MADS box genes
            Determine organ identity
        In animals few MADS box genes
            Govern generalized cell division
    An evolutionary picture
        Animals and plants diverged as single cell eukaryotes
        Gene requirements of multicelled plants and animals
            Genes needed that regulate differentiation and development
            Developmental roles by genes
                Genes duplicated and diverged
                Groups of similar genes took on different regulation aspects in plants and animals

Chapter 24
Genes and Cancer

KEY CONCEPTS

- Cancerous cells have lost the controls that normally inhibit cell division so that the cells grow and divide to form a tumor.
- Cancerous tumor cells may spread to other parts of the body and begin growing as new tumors.
- Mutations in oncogenes and tumor-suppressor genes are responsible for cancer.
- Research on the genetic basis of cancer is leading to new forms of detection and treatment.

KEY TERMS

cancer
tumor
oncogenesis
benign
malignant
metastasis
angiogenesis
cyclins
cyclin-dependent kinases (CDKs)
cyclin D
CDK4 or CDK6
pRB
restriction point (R)
master brake
p21
p53
apoptosis
proto-oncogenes
tumor-suppressor genes
DNA-repair genes
oncogenes
retinoblastoma
g-proteins
signal transduction proteins
polyps
Gardner syndrome
familial adenomatous polyopsis (FAP)
telomerase
senescent
immortal
carcinogens
radiation therapy
chemotherapy
antiangiogenesis compounds
gene therapy

CHAPTER OUTLINE

Introduction
Understanding the molecular basis of cancer
   One third US populations affected in lifetime
   Methods for detection, prevention, treatment
Cancer tumors invade tissue and spread
   Oncogenesis: cell changes that cause cancer tumors
   Benign tumors remain localized
   Metastasis: breaking free and spreading of cells
   Angiogenesis: elaboration of blood vessels around tumor
   Benign-cancer progression (Figure 24.1)
Cancer is a genetic disease
   Cancer susceptibility may be inherited
   Cancer tumors caused by cell mutations
   Mutations cause normal cells to lose control of division and growth
      Genes that regulate cell cycle
      Cancer usually requires mutations in several genes

24.1 GENETIC CONTROL OF THE CELL CYCLE
   Central idea:
   • Proto-oncogenes are essential genes that govern the cell cycle. Their products include nuclear regulatory proteins, protein kinases, growth factors, growth factor receptors, and G-proteins. These products may interact with the products of tumor-suppressor genes.

Cell division, organ, and tissue development
   As cells differentiate cell division is controlled and eventually arrested
   Controlling elements are inter- and intracellular

Signals from adjacent cells bind to neighbor cell receptors
Bound receptors activate chain of events inside cell
Events may terminate or initiate cell division (Figure 24.2)
Regulator gene products govern complex steps in cell
Some steps inhibit cell division (Figure 24.3)
Some steps promote cell division
Control genes act at all stages of cell cycle (G_1 to M)
Cyclins among most important regulating proteins
Complex with **kinases (CDKs)**
Cyclin dependent kinases catalyze steps to cell division (Figure 23.3)
Cell gets growth promoting signal in G_1
Signal induces **Cyclin D** gene cyclin D levels rise
Cyclin D binds to CDK4/6
pRB becomes heavily phosphorylated
pRB is **master brake (restriction point)**
Underphosphorylated inhibits division
Inhibits transcription factors for cyclins A and E genes
Phosphorylated stimulates division
Releases transcription factors for A and E
Cyclins A and E rise in cell
Cyclins A and E bind to CDKs
Cells passes through S to G_2
Cyclin A binds to CDK 1 stimulates cyclin B binding CDK 1
B-CDK 1 induces mitosis
Essential roles of inhibitory proteins
Several proteins inhibit cyclin-CDK complexes
p15, p27, p21 inhibit cyclin D-CDK4/6 complex
p21 inhibits cyclin-CDK complexes throughout cell cycle
p53 regulates production of p21
Most cells have low levels
p53 rises when cell is in danger causing eventual apoptosis
p53 can decrease if cell is repaired
(See Example 24.1 Cancer due to mutations in genes that encode p53 and pRB.)

24.2 THE MOLECULAR BASIS OF CANCER

Central idea:

- Cancerous tumors are caused by mutations that change cell cycle regulatory proteins and signal receptors.
- Due to medical advances, deaths due to infectious diseases have declined in more developed countries resulting in longer life spans. As a consequence, cancer has become one of the leading causes of death in these countries.
- Cancer can be considered a genetic disease because it is always the result of mutations in genes.
- Mutations that influence cancer often convert proto-oncogenes into oncogenes. Oncogenes are mutant versions of genes that govern cell growth and division.
- Mutations in more than one gene are required for a tumor to become malignant and to metastasize.
- Tumor-suppressor genes encode products that suppress cell division. Most cancers are due to mutations that create oncogenes as well as mutations in at least one tumor-suppressor

gene.

- Because cancers are due to mutations, susceptibility to cancer may be inherited. A person who inherits a mutant oncogene has an elevated risk for cancer because the first step toward cancer has already been passed.

Three classes of gene mutations and cancer
    Proto-oncogenes
        Gene products stimulate normal progress through cell cycle
        Encode Cyclins and CDKs
    Tumor suppresser genes
        Prevent or inhibit progress through cell cycle
        Encode p53, p21, pRB for example
    DNA repair genes
        Encode proteins that repair damaged DNA
        May promote cancer by allowing damage in proto-oncogenes
    Oncogenes products promote tumors (defined by function not sequence)
        Oncogenes are gain-of-function mutations (dominant mutations)
        Mutations in tumor suppressor genes may stimulate cell division
        Mutations in cyclin and CDK genes may stimulate cell division

The discovery of oncogenes
    First discovered in viruses 1911 (Peyton Rous)
    Rous sarcoma virus (RSV) caused tumors in chickens
        Many tumor causing viruses have been discovered
    Genetic basis of tumor viruses
        Viral oncogenes have counterpart in eukaryotic animal cell proto-oncogenes
        Evidence suggests virus acquired oncogene of animal tumor cells
        (See Example 24.2 Vertebrate counterparts of the *v-src* gene.)

24.3 EXAMPLES OF GENES THAT INFLUENCE CANCER
    Central ideas:
    - Oncogenic mutations may include point mutations as well as deletions and chromosome rearrangements.
    - Many genes that influence cancer have been well characterized. They encode many different types of proteins, most of which govern the cell cycle.

TP53
Importance of *TP53*
    TP53 encodes tumor suppressor protein p53 (53,000 daltons)
    At least one mutant *TP53* allele in many cancers
    Function of p53 (Figure 24.3) a very key point in cell cycle
        Activates transcription of several genes
            CDKN1A gene → p21 (suppressor of cyclin-CDK complexes, S-stage DNA polymerases)
            Inhibits proteins that stimulate progression G_1 to S
        Stimulation of apoptosis (cell death)
            Cell stresses stimulate synthesis of p53
            DNA damage, oxygen starvation, nutrient starvation
        Activates transcription of anti-angiogenesis gene
    Structure of p53

Tetramer of identical subunits

Subunit: 393 amino acids four functional domains

First 42 subunits transcription activator with TFIID

Binds to TAATA box

Basal transcription complex

Amino acids 102-292

DNA binding domain

Promoters of genes that respond to p53

Over 90% mutations related to cancers

Amino acids 324-355 tetramer forming domain

Last 26 amino acids regulatory domain

Some mutations in *TP53* are dominant or partially dominant

DNA binding domain

Heterozygote produces mixture tetramers

One mutant peptide/3 wild-type reduce DNA binding

Heterozygous cells have high risk of cancer

RB1

pRB is cell cycle master brake

Binds transcription factor of several proto-oncogenes

Arrests cell cycle at G_1

RB = "retinoblastoma" gene first found in retinoblastoma cases

Often childhood disease

Often affecting both eyes

Humans only mammal so affected by mutant *RB1*

Mutants basis for several cancers

Structure of *RB1* gene

180 kb mostly introns

27 exons encode 4.7 kb mRNA

pRB 928 amino acid chain phosphoprotein

(See Example 24.3 Penetrance of mutant *RB1* alleles.)

E2F1

Member of set of transcription factor genes

Factors known as E2F factors

p53 binds to E2F factors

Releases them when fully phosphorylated

Genes with E2F binding sites

Genes that govern transition from G_1 to S

Cyclin A, D and E genes

DNA replication genes

E2F1 is a proto-oncogene

Overexpression correlates with tumor development

Mouse tumors develop when *E2F1* is eliminated

RAS three genes in humans

Encode **G-proteins** a class of **signal transducer proteins**

Function when growth factor binds to plasma membrane receptor protein

Structure and function of G-proteins (Figure 24.4)

Convert GDP to GTP

have α, β, γ subunits

Levels of GTP regulate activity of G-proteins

a subunit plus GDP = inactive state (remains bound to other subunits of G-protein)

GTP displaces GDP and a subunit disassociate from protein

GTP-α subunit is active form passing signal

α subunit has GTPase activity (GTP → GDP + P_i)

GDP-α subunit is inactive form (rejoins with G-protein subunits)

RAS mutants

GTPase activity loss (dominant loss of function mutations)

Mutant G-proteins remain activated

Most mutations are in the GTP binding domains

Codons 12, 13, 59, 61, 63 crucial in GTP to GDP

APC

Mutations often associated with colorectal cancer

Tumors begin on benign rectal polyps (common in elderly, Figure 24.5)

Mutations first identified by deletions in q arm chromosome 5

pAPC promotes cell adhesion

Inheritance

First identified by Eldon Gardner

Fully penetrant dominant allele

Gardner syndrome

FAP and Gardner syndrome alleles of *APC*

24.4 THE ETIOLOGY OF CANCER

Mutations that promote cancer

Cancer rarely caused by single proto-oncogene mutation

Example: colon cancer (Figure 24.6)

Mutations in most cancers

Mutation of at least one proto-oncogene and one tumor suppressor

Metastasis due to mutations in cell adhesion genes

Cancer cells gain **telomerase** activity

Usually active only in germ-line

Cell divisions of somatic cells limited to about 50 cycles per cell line

Addition of telomerase make cancers cell divisions immortal

Blocking telomerase could block most cancers

Tumors carry many kinds of mutations

All affect functions of proto-oncogenes, tumor suppressers and signal transducers

Rapid growth leaves little time for DNA repair

Point mutations may be transitions or transversions

Transversions can be caused by polycyclic hydrocarbons in tobacco smoke

Carcinogen interacts with guanines

Altered guanines can pair with adenine

Guanine is switched for thymine without DNA repair

Point mutations in functional domains can destroy function

Deletions, insertions and translocations

Associated with proto-oncogene mutations

Associated with tumor suppressor genes

Signal transducer genes

Disruptive insertions can be caused by retroviruses, transposons, retroposons, retrotransposons

Why is cancer so common?
Mutations are rare and cells have built in protection mechanisms
    Adults have 30 trillion cells
        Long life span
        Exposure to carcinogens and radiation accumulate in life time (Table 24.2)
        Rare mutations exist in thousands of cells in one adult
        Chance of cancer producing cluster of mutations in one cell are relatively high
    (See Example 24.4 Mutations in the *TP53* gene in skin cancer.)

Inherited susceptibility to cancer
Susceptible families carry inherited mutations in proto-oncogenes or tumor suppressor genes
    DNA analysis can be used to detect some familial cancer alleles
    Human breast cancer: *BRCA1* and *BRCA2*
        DNA probes allow early detection and treatment
        Physicians can closely monitor carriers
        Early treatment is essential

24.5 CANCER PREVENTION, DETECTION, AND TREATMENT
Cancer prevention
Change environment
    About 30% of all cancers attributed to smoking
        Rise in cancer 1973-1972 6.3% (Age factored out)
        Take out lung cancers rate declines 3.4%
    Airborne particulates contain carcinogens
        Automobile is major source
        Industry is serious source
    Change in diet can control many food borne carcinogens
        Some clearer but complex associations with diet
            Red meats and saturated fats and colon cancer
            High salt consumption and stomach cancer
            Alcohol consumption and liver, breast and colorectal cancers
        Diets that reduce cancer rates
            High in fruits and vegetables
    Dietary planning can reduce risk of many cancers
        Reduce red meat and fat intake
        Avoid alcohol
        Increase fruits and vegetables
    Cancers and radiation
        About 2% of all cancers
        Nonionizing radiation
            Overexposure to UVB accounts for 90% of skin cancers
            Incidence (Figure 24.9)
        Ionizing radiation less common (usually localized to certain environments)
        Hiroshima, Nagasaki, Southern Nevada and Utah
            Cancer rates are higher among exposed people
        People who work with X-rays radiation from radioactive elements are trained to avoid
            exposure
    Cancers and industrial carcinogens
        Workers should be trained to avoid contact
        People who live near industrial environments can be severely exposed unless waste

handling follows careful guidelines

Industries need to properly care for wastes

Traditional cancer treatments

Early detection is extremely important

Early detection

Advanced cancers that have spread and metastasized

Can be treated but rarely cured

Early detection methods

Prostate exams and biochemical tests

Pap smears

Breast examination routine mammography women over 40

Routine rectal exams in susceptible families and elderly

Development of biochemical tests for detection of altered proteins

Test for blood and urine

DNA probes to detect genetic susceptibilities

Traditional treatments

Radiation therapy

Based or radiation damage to DNA

Rapidly dividing cells have inefficient DNA repair mechanism

One hope is to restore p53 activity and induce apoptosis

Chemotherapy

Drugs detrimental to actively dividing cells (i.e., induction of DNA damage)

DNA damage could induce apoptosis

Drugs that interfere with DNA synthesis

These drugs do less damage to ordinary somatic cells

Serious and painful side effects on tissue with normal dividing cells

Dosages must be carefully monitored to limit side effects

Future treatments

Future treatments will tend to target cancer cells specifically

Antibodies can recognize and bind to cancer-specific cell surface antigens

Development of tumor-specific antibodies carrying anticancer drugs or genes

Development of chemicals that inhibit proteins necessary for cell division

Inhibition of telomerase activity

Protein kinase inhibitors

Chemicals that attack angiogenesis rather than attacking tumors

Gene therapy

Introduction of functional genes into loss-of-function mutant cells

(See Example 24.5 Successful treatment of lung tumors with gene therapy.)

Chapter 25
Genes and Immunity

KEY CONCEPTS

- Cells of the immune system recognize foreign substances as antigens and target for destruction those particles or cells that display the antigen.
- Antibodies are proteins that bind to specific antigens. Antibody genes are capable of a large number of rearrangements that produce a wide variety of possible antibodies.
- When an antibody binds to an antigen, it marks the antigen and the cell or particle to which the antigen-antibody complex is attached for destruction by the immune system.
- T cells distinguish normal cells in the body from cells that have been infected by a virus and mark the infected cells for destruction.
- Several human diseases result from immune system dysfunction.
- Antibodies have been used extensively as tools in genetics research.

KEY TERMS

antibodies
immunoglobulin or Ig
proteins
antigen
B cells
T cells
humoral immunity
cell-mediated immunity
macrophages
complement system
histocompatibility antigens
MHC markers
cytotoxic (killer) T cells
helper T cells
suppressor B cells
heavy (H) chains
light (L) chains
constant regions
effector domain
variable regions
antigen-binding sites (antigen-binding domains)
epitope
immature (or virgin) B cell
class switching
IgM
IgD
IgG
IgA
IgE
hypervariable regions
heptamer-nonamer sequence

RAG1

RAG2

non-productive arrangements

productive arrangements

primary immune response

memory cells

class I genes

self-recognition histoincompatibility antigens

class II genes

class III genes

allergic reaction

autoimmune diseases

insulin-dependent juvenile onset diabetes

rheumatoid arthritis

hyperthyroidism or Graves disease

immune deficiencies

X-linked agammaglobulinemia

human immunodeficiency virus (HIV)

acquired immune deficiency syndrome (AIDS)

myeloma cells

hybridomas

monoclonal antibodies

bispecific antibodies

CHAPTER TOPICS

CHAPTER OUTLINE

Introduction

First time infections and secondary immune response

Secondary immune response makes artificial immunity possible
Immune response is a joint effort among cell types
Cell types and specialized molecules
> **Antibodies**
>> Proteins encoded by genes
>> Kinds: potentially millions
>> Requires a few genes to rearrange themselves
> **Immunoglobulins** or **Ig proteins**
> **Antigens**

Chapter discussion
> Nature of the immune responses
> Antibody structure and genetic rearrangements
> Molecular diversity of immune system molecules
> Consequences of errors in the immune system
> HIV and alterations of the immune system
> The immune system as a tool for genetic research

25.1 IMMUNE RESPONSES

Central ideas:
- There are two major types of immune responses, humoral immunity and cell-mediated immunity.
- In humoral immunity, B cells express genes that encode antibodies. Antibodies are proteins that recognize and bind to a wide variety of substances that are foreign to the body called antigens. An antibody bound to an antigen marks the antigen and anything attached to it for destruction.
- Each B cell rearranges its antibody genes to encode a unique antibody. When an antibody encounters an antigen, the B cells that produce that antibody proliferate to mount an immune response.
- Cell-mediated immunity relies on the association of MHC antigens and viral antigens on a cell surface. The associated antigens attract cytotoxic T cells that destroy the infected cell.

Immune system a joint effort of several cell types and specialized molecules
Humoral immunity (Figure 25.1)
> B cells produce and use Ig antibodies
>> All Ig antibodies from a B cell have same variable regions
>> One B cell's Ig types differ only in structure of constant region
>>> IgM, IgD cell surface antibodies
>>> IgG secreted into blood stream
>>> IgD secreted into body fluids
>>> IgE stimulates histamine production
> Antibody-antigens interactions and detection of foreign particles
> Destruction of particles attached to antibodies
>> **Macrophages** engulf antigen-antibody complexes (Figure 25.2)
>> **Complement system** (specified by some of the class III MHC genes)
>>> About 20 proteins in blood
>>> Recognize antigen-antibody complexes
>>> Attract macrophages to complexes

Cell mediated immunity (Figure 25.3)

T cells coordinate the cell-mediated immune response

> T cells distinguish normal cells from infected cells
>> Detection based on recognition of two kinds of antigens
>>> Normal cells: **Histocompatibility antigens (MHC markers)**
>>> Foreign antigens

> Cells infected with virus display virus antigen on surface
>> Some virus macromolecules combine with infected cell's MHC markers
>> MHC marker-antigens move to cells surface
>> MHC marker-antigens attract T cells

Cytotoxic (killer) T cells recognize and destroy infected cells

> Receptors on T cells recognize and bind to antigen-MHC complexes on infected cell surfaces

Helper T cells

> Assist cytotoxic T cells with their attacks
> Assist B cells in recognition of infected cells

25.2 ANTIBODY STRUCTURE

Central idea:
- Antibodies consist of two identical heavy chains and two identical light chains that associate to form a Y-shaped antibody molecule. Each of the chains contains a constant (C) region and a variable (V) region. The constant regions are similar in all antibodies.
- The variable regions form the antigen binding sites and give each antibody a particular structure that causes it to bind with its specific antigen.

Structure of antibody (Figure 25.4)

> Antibody has two **light (L) chains** and two **heavy (H) chains**
>> Chain lengths
>>> L = about 220 amino acids
>>> H = about 440 amino acids

> Each chain has a variable and a constant region
>> Variable regions contain hypervariable immune response region
>>> Recognizes the **epitope** of the antigen
>>> Epitope on protein antigen fewer than 15 or 16 amino acids
>> Constant regions
>>> Similar in structure in all antibodies (with some slight differences)
>>> H chain constant region carries the **effector domain**
>>> Effector domain recognizes other agents of the immune system

25.3 ANTIBODY GENES FOR HUMORAL IMMUNITY
(The production of B cells and Ig antibodies they produce)

Central idea:
- Three genes encode antibodies: two light-chain genes called κ (kappa) and λ (lambda), and a heavy-chain gene. Each gene includes a variable region and a constant region.
- The κ chain gene consists of three regions: a variable (V_κ), a joining (J_κ) region, and a constant (C_κ) region. The V_κ region consists of a cluster of about 300 V_κ segments each preceded by its own promoter and by a leader (L_κ) segment. The V_κ region is followed by a spacer sequence which is followed by the J_κ region consisting of five J_κ segments. Following the J_κ

region is another spacer, that encodes an intron, followed by a single C_κ segment that codes for the constant region of the κ chain.

- During rearrangement, a single L_κ-V_κ segment is selected and fused to a J_κ segment with all intervening DNA deleted. The selected L_κ-V_κ-J_κ segment is joined to the intron separating the J_κ region from the C_κ region. The final gene has the order: L_κ-V_κ-J_κ-intron-C_κ. The mRNA is translated to produce a polypeptide with a κ light chain that has a leader sequence 17-20 amino acids long, a variable sequence 108 amino acids long (V_κ and J_κ segments), and a constant sequence of 112 amino acids.

- The λ gene is similar to the κ gene with a few differences. The human V_λ region is similar in size to the V_κ region with about 300 V_λ segments. Mouse has only three V_λ segments. In humans, about 60% of antibodies have κ light chains while 40% have λ light chains. In mouse, about 95% of the antibodies have κ light chains.

- There is much greater diversity in heavy chains than in light chains because there are a greater number of combinations of variable and constant segments, and the heavy-chain gene includes an additional class of segments called diversity (D_H) segments. The gene is divided into four regions: the V_H region, the D_H region, the J_H region, and the C_H region. The V_H, J_H, and C_H segments contained in these regions perform the same roles as their corresponding segments in the light chain genes. The D_H segments add additional diversity to the heavy-chain variable region in the antibody.

- Rearrangement of antibody genes is the responsibility of enzymes encoded by two linked genes, *RAG-1* and *RAG-2*. These genes encode enzymes that catalyze recombination.

Ig antibody genes in B cells
    Large genes consisting of many rearrangeable segments (Figure 25.6)
        Variable segments (V, about 300)
        Joining segments (J, about 5 or 6)
        Constant segments (C, light genes have one constant segment, heavy genes have about 10 C segments)
    Segments of antibody genes are rearranged before transcription
    Rearrangement of segments occurs in B cells
Gene rearrangement at three gene loci in B cells
    Rearrangement of Ig genes occurs only as B cells mature
    The *IGKC* (κ light-chain) gene
        Location and coding function (Figures 25.5; 25.6)
            Located in p arm near centromere chromosome 2 (Figure 25.5)
            Encodes *kappa* (κ) light chain
        Pre transcription IGHC gene rearrangement in new B cell
            (several P + L_κ-V_κ segments) + P + L_κ-V_κ + J_κ + intron + C_κ
            Function of transcription enhancer in intron
        Pre mRNA: L_κ-V_κ + J_κ + intron + C_κ
        mRNA: L_κ-V_κ + J_κ + C_κ + AAAAetc.
        Leader amino acids encoded by L_k later cleaved off
    The *IGLC1* (λ light-chain) gene
        Encodes segments for λ light chain
        Location: chromosome 22 q arm
        Organization and processing similar to IGKC gene and gene products
    The *IGHG1* (heavy-chain) gene
        V_H-D_H segment same size at V segment of light chains
        V_H segments also carry L (leader coding sequence)

Nine or ten alternative C_H segments including two pseudo segments (ψ)

Heavy chain gene rearrangement in B cell

    Rearranged gene (Figure 25.9)

        Ca. 300 V_H segments

        D_H segment

        J_H segment

        Intron

        Nine or ten C_H segments (depending on alleles)

    B cell makes several kinds of Ig antibodies

    All antibodies of B cell have same variable regions

    B cell antibody types differ by differences in heavy chain constant (C_H) segments (Table 25.1)

Heavy chain Pre-mRNAs

    Several classes of heavy chain pre-mRNAs are made

        Classes differ by number of C_H segments transcribed

        All classes have same L_H-V_H-D_H + J_H + intron segments

    Classes of heavy chain mRNAs

        L_H-V_H-D_H + J_H + C_{H*}

        *Classes differ by selected C_H segment (**class switching**) during pre-mRNA processing

            Class switching: alternative splicing of pre-mRNAs (Figure 25.9)

            Class switching produces five classes of heavy chains

                IgM: $C_{H\mu}$ segment

                IgD: $C_{H\delta}$ segment

                IgG: has either $C_{H\gamma1}$, $C_{H\gamma2}$, $C_{H\gamma3}$, $C_{H\gamma4}$ segments

                IgA: has either $C_{H\alpha1}$, $C_{H\alpha2}$ segments

                IgE: $C_{H\varepsilon}$ segment

    L_H-V_H-D_H + J_H segment same in all classes in one B cell

Hypervariable regions in the variable segments

    Contain the antigen interaction sites

    Always found in same positions

Antibodies are completed by combining 2 light chains with 2 heavy chains

Segment joining during gene rearrangement

    The **heptamer-nonamer** consensus sequences

    The sequences and precise joining of light chain V and J segments and heavy chain V, D, and J segments

    The function of RAG1 and RAG2 enzymes

Productive and non-productive arrangements

Matching specific antigens

    Antibodies are made by non-directed gene rearrangements

    Millions of possible antibodies exist in cell

    Match between antigen and antibody is fortuitous event

25.4 CELL-MEDIATED IMMUNITY GENES

Central idea:

- The cell-mediated immune response is dependent on genes that produce receptors on T cells that recognize foreign antigens and histocompatibility markers. Histocompatibility markers are present on the surface of most cells in the body and are encoded by highly variable

MHC genes.

(The production of T cells which seek out and destroy infected or defective host cells)

T-cell receptor genes and MHC marker genes

The receptor proteins on cytotoxic T-cell surfaces

Rearrangement of receptor genes occurs during T-cell maturation

Receptor proteins bind MHC-antigen on surfaces of infected cells

Genes for T-cell receptor proteins include V, D, J, and C segments

Utilize heptamer and nonamer sequences for rearrangements

Four T-cell receptor genes

TCRA and TCRD (overlapping genes)

Rearrangements form two variable polypeptides

α polypeptides (TCRA gene)

δ polypeptides (TCRD gene, Figure 25.14)

Order of rearrangement during T cell maturation

TCRD rearranges first leaving TCRA intact

TCRA rearranges second

TCRA rearrangement deletes TCRD gene

Mature T cells produce only α polypeptide

During gene rearrangements only the α segments join and only the δ segments join

TCRB and TCRG genes (Figure 25.15)

TCRG gene rearranged and expressed in early T cell development

TCRB gene rearranged and expressed only in mature T cells

Mature T cells express only α and β chains (T-cell receptor proteins) from active, rearranged TCRA and TCRB genes (Figure 25.13)

T cells and pathogen antigen-MHC complex on infected cells

MHC markers produced by most body cells

Diversity of MHC markers not obtained by gene rearrangements

MHC marker diversity obtained from large gene family (**HLA locus**, chromosome 6)

Classes of MHC genes

Class I: encode **self-recognition histocompatibility antigens**

Surface antigens on most body cells

Vary substantially among individuals (identical twins excepted)

Class II: encode proteins on B cell, T cell and macrophages

Participate in cellular communication during immune responses

Class III: encode many proteins including complement system in blood

Recognition and attack by cytotoxic T cells

Attack only cells with MHC host pattern proteins and bound pathogen antigens on surfaces

T-cell receptors recognize and bind only to the antigen-MHC complex

T-cell binding to infected host cell initiates eventual destruction of host cell and pathogen

Cytotoxic T cells can recognize potential tumor cells

Tumor cells must overcome T-cell recognition

(See Example 25.1 Inhibition of transcription of MHC class I genes by the *JUN* oncogene)

25.5 IMMUNE SYSTEM MALFUNCTION

Central idea:

- Autoimmune disorders appear when the immune system mounts an immune response against the body's own substances. Infectious immune deficiency appears when a pathogen attacks part of the immune system.

Autoimmune diseases
Immune system incorrectly recognizes self substances
Insulin-dependent juvenile onset diabetes
Insulin-producing pancreatic β cells destroyed by immune system

Disorder associated with alleles of class II MHC genes
Rheumatoid arthritis
Rheumatoid factor: antibody that recognizes IgG in blood

Factor-IgG complex stimulates macrophages to attack joint membranes
Hyperthyroidism or Graves disease
Antibody recognizes TSH receptors and stimulates thyroid hormone overproduction

Immune deficiencies
X-linked agammaglobulinemia
Recessive allele at the *BTK* gene locus

pBTK coordinates B-cell maturation

Affected people have immature B cells and no Ig antibodies

Cell-mediated immunity is still effective
SCID severe combined immunodeficiency syndrome
Failure of immune system

Disorder affects lymphoblasts (B and T cell precursor cells)

Bone marrow transplants from near relatives and cure
Infectious defeat or destruction of immunity
HIV human immunodeficiency virus is a retrovirus
Responsible for **acquired immune deficiency syndrome**

Virus frequently mutates

Attacks T4 cells

25.6 ANTIBODIES AS TOOLS IN GENETICS RESEARCH
Development of monoclonal antibodies

Use of antibody-delivered drugs

Chapter 26
Genetics in Medicine and Forensics

KEY CONCEPTS

- The human genome project is an effort to map the human genome, identify human genes, and sequence the entire genome.
- Genetic testing identifies alleles that confer genetic disorders.
- DNA fingerprinting is valuable in forensics and paternity identification.
- Genetic pharmacology, the production of proteins in bacterial, yeast, or mammalian cells, provides proteins that are useful in medicine.
- Gene therapy, the genetic modification of cells to restore gene function, provides a means for treating some genetic disorders and cancer.
- Clinical genetics is a medical specialty that includes diagnosis of genetic disorders, treatment of patients with genetic disorders, and genetic counseling of patients and their relatives.

KEY TERMS

Human Genome Project
contigs
sequence tagged sites (STSs)
expressed sequence tags (ESTs)
DNA fingerprinting
recombinant human insulin
preproinsulin
proinsulin
recombinant human growth hormone (HGH)
somatic-cell gene therapy
in vivo therapy
ex vivo therapy
germline gene therapy
transfection
clinical genetics
genetic counseling

CHAPTER TOPICS

26.1 THE HUMAN GENOME PROJECT
    Human chromosome mapping
    Mapping cloned fragments into contigs
    Expressed sequence tags (ESTs)
    Human genome sequencing and data management
26.2 GENETIC TESTING
    Biochemical and cytological genetic tests
    DNA-based genetic tests
    Genetic testing for mutant alleles of the cystic fibrosis (CF) gene
26.3 DNA FINGERPRINTING
    DNA fingerprinting in forensic science
    DNA fingerprinting in paternity testing

CHAPTER OUTLINE

Introduction

Recombinant DNA has revolutionized many areas of medicine and biology
    Present basic knowledge due to advances in genetic technology
    Diagnosis of many diseases
    Early recognition of genetic disorders
    In vitro fertilization and embryo selection
    Genetically engineered pharmaceutical products
        Human insulin
        Pituitary dwarfism
        Cancer treatments (such as Onyx virus)
    Focus of chapter
        Practical applications
            Medicine
            Forensics
        Human genome project
            Effects on treatment of disorders
        Clinical genetics
            Diagnosis
            Treatment

26.1 THE HUMAN GENOME PROJECT

Central ideas:
- Applications of genetics in medicine have been important for many years. With improvements in genetic technology, applications of genetics in medicine are increasing in importance.
- The human genome initiative includes mapping the human genome with DNA markers, identification and characterization of previously unmapped or unknown genes, studies on model organisms with applications to human genetics, and determination of a consensus nucleotide sequence for the entire human genome.

Goal of human genome project
    Identify and map all human genes
    Determine nucleotide sequence of entire human genome
Laboratory techniques employed
    DNA sequencing

High resolution mapping

    RFLPs, PCR-based markers

    cDNA cloning and sequencing

    Cloning and sequencing large fragments

        Cosmid, BAC, and YAC cloning

        Comparing cloning and sequencing in model organisms

Information management

2001 target date

Human chromosome mapping

Rate of progress

    1990: 6,726 markers mapped (1867 known genes)

    1994: over 60,000 markers mapped

Benefits of map

    Genetic testing markers

    Markers used for chromosome jumping and walking to locate genes

Mapping cloned fragments into contigs

Contigs: overlapping clones (Figure 26.1)

Assigning cloned fragments to linkage groups using contig for alignment

Use of **sequence tagged sites (STS)**

    200-500 nucleotides assigned to chromosome locations

    Geneticists can locate chromosome locations of large cloned fragments for STS site using PCR

Comparing nucleotide sequences of large clones with mapped sequences

Sequences within clone compared to known mapped sequences in data base

Expressed sequence tags (ESTs)

Sequences of cDNAs are **expressed sequence tags** ESTs

Use of ESTs among scientists

    ESTs of human and model organisms in data base

    Provides access to work of many scientists on many organisms

        Workers in yeast provide information for human geneticists

            Placed nucleotide sequence of yeast telomerase in data base

            Human geneticists identified human telomerase in human EST data base using yeast sequence

    Human data base provides data for identifying ESTs in other organisms

(See Example 26.1 Identification of the cDNA sequence for human telomerase from the human EST database)

Human genome sequencing and data management

The world wide data base

GenBank as part of the data base

    Laboratory robotics daily provide enormous amounts of DNA sequence information world wide

    Project inspired lab automation and efficient methods of data-base management

Broad benefits of human genome project justify cost

26.2 GENETIC TESTING

Central ideas:

- Genetic testing is now available for detecting the mutant alleles that cause many genetic disorders. Genetic testing may be based on biochemical, cytological, or DNA tests. In many

216

cases, genetic testing may be used prenatally.
- Certain biochemical genetic tests are inexpensive and may be used in widespread screening programs. Mandatory testing of newborns for PKU in the United States is an example of inexpensive genetic screening.

Biochemical and cytological genetic tests
    Genetic tests based on chemical analysis
        Test for PKU (Figure 26.2)
        Test for sickle-cell anemia
    Tests based on cytological analysis
        Tests for aneuploidy
        Down Syndrome etc.

DNA-based genetic tests
    Alleles responsible for over 200 genetic disorders can now be detected

    Detection of heterozygotes
    Detection of delayed onset genotypes
        Detection by linked DNA RFLP markers
            Huntington disease (*HD* gene) first tracked by linked RFLP markers (95% accurate due to crossing over)
            Sequencing *HD* gene provided precise genetic tests
                HD alleles detected using *HD* gene-based PCR primers
                Sequence comparisons identified several alleles

Genetic testing for mutant alleles of the cystic fibrosis (*CF*) gene
    Genetic and clinical value for sequencing a gene
    Sequence information provides information for PCR primers
        Alleles can be quickly detected
        Correlation between alleles and genetic disease quickly assessed
    Cystic fibrosis common among European descendants
        $2pq = 0.043$
        $q^2 = 1/2000$
    1989: nucleotide sequence *CF* reported
        DNA sequence gave important clues
            Developing of accurate DNA tests for *CF* gene alleles (Figure 26.3)
            Protein structure and function developed from DNA sequence of gene
            Membrane transport of chloride affected
        Defective codon position within *CF* gene mapped
    Development of precise genetic tests for other defective *CF* alleles
    (See Example 26.2 Genetic testing for preimplantation diagnosis of cystic fibrosis.)

26.3 DNA FINGERPRINTING
Central idea:
- DNA fingerprinting is valuable for identity exclusion and inclusion in criminal cases and paternity testing.

DNA fingerprinting in forensic science
    DNA fingerprinting: specific pattern of DNA markers for an individual
        Use of minisatellites and microsatellites
        Only identical twins share same DNA fingerprint

Identifying culprit in England in 1985 using DNA testing

    Minisatellite analysis of sperm samples exonerated suspect

    DNA analysis indirectly identified suspect

DNA fingerprinting is often used routinely (Figure 26.4)

    Used to identify or exonerate suspects

    Used to identify victims

DNA fingerprinting in paternity testing

DNA fingerprinting used in paternity testing

    Used to exclude or confirm suspected father

    (See Example 26.3 DNA fingerprinting)

Court challenges of DNA fingerprinting

Exclusion of suspects based on DNA fingerprinting rarely challenged

Proof of suspect identification using DNA fingerprinting gaining legal acceptance

26.4 GENETIC PHARMACOLOGY

Central idea:

- Genetic pharmacology is the production of a pharmaceutical product in a host organism or cell culture (usually bacteria) using recombinant DNA. Currently, several genetically engineered pharmaceuticals, such as human insulin, are in widespread use.
- Not all human proteins can be successfully produced and processed in bacteria. Yeast and animal cells are alternative hosts that may produce and process the gene products properly.

Many complex proteins cannot be assembled in bacteria

    Bacteria can assemble primary protein structure

    Post-translation processing often impossible in bacteria

Human insulin expression in bacteria

Production of human insulin using recombinant bacteria

    Normal cellular processing of insulin (Figure 26.7)

    Two-chain method (Figure 26.8)

        Construction of fusion genes with *lacZ* gene and promoter

        Processing and combining products *in vitro*

    The single-chain method (Figure 26.9)

        Construction of fusion gene with *lacZ* promoter system

        In vitro processing of proinsulin

Recombinant human growth hormone (HGH) (Example 9.5)

Foreign protein expression in yeast

Yeast is a eukaryotic cell that can produce and process some proteins

Production of hepatitis B antigen (vaccine)

Many other vaccines can be produced using yeast cells for expression

Human proteins produced in cultured mammalian cells

Production of proteins in cow's milk

Use of mammalian cell cultures to produce proteins

26.5 HUMAN GENE THERAPY

Central idea:
- Human gene therapy is the introduction of genetically engineered somatic cells into a patient to provide a genetic function that is missing in the patient. Gene therapy for ADA deficiency is an example of successful gene therapy. Currently, most applications of gene therapy are still in the experimental stages.

Kinds of gene therapy
>Focus of gene therapy
>>Correcting the disorder
>>Changing genetics of cells
>**Somatic-cell gene therapy**
>>**In vivo therapy**
>>>Virus vector introduces corrective gene into cells
>>>(See Example 25.5)
>>**Ex vivo therapy**
>>>Corrective gene inserted into body cell
>>>Transformed body cell reintroduced into body
>**Germ-line gene therapy**
>>Germ-line cells corrected
>>Developed in plants and animals so far

Viral vectors in gene therapy
>Retrovirus vectors for gene delivery (**transfection**)
>>Deletion of destructive genes in virus
>>Virus can only infect actively dividing cells
>>Potential uses for selective distraction of cancer cells
>Use of adenoviruses for gene transfection
>>Virus will insert DNA into chromosomes
>>Cells need not be actively dividing

Treatment of ADA deficiency with gene therapy
>ADA ideal genetic disorder for gene therapy
>ADA deficiency causes SCID
>(See Example 26.4 Genetic engineering of a retroviral vector for gene therapy.)

26.6 CLINICAL GENETICS

Central idea:
- Clinical genetics is a medical specialty that focuses on the diagnosis and treatment of genetic disorders. Trained genetic counselors provide genetic counseling to families whose members are at risk for a genetic disorder. With the added importance of genetics in medicine, the need for genetic counseling has increased.

Clinical genetics as medical specialty
>Diagnose genetic disorders
>Recommend care and treatment by physicians
>Provide access the genetics counseling

Chapter 27
Genetics in Agriculture and Industry

KEY CONCEPTS

- The origins and locations of genetic diversity for most domesticated plants and animals are found in less developed parts of the world.
- Breeding and biotechnology of domesticated plants and animals have contributed substantially to increases in agricultural production and will continue to be a major part of agricultural improvement.
- There are numerous applications of genetics in industry. And with the development of recombinant DNA technology, industrial applications of genetics are increasing.

KEY TERMS

center of origin
center of diversity
green revolution
gene banks
two-parent cross
three-parent crosses
four-parent crosses
backcrossing
donor parent
recurrent parent
marker-assisted selection
multiple-parent cross
complex population
diallel cross
circular cross
synthetic population
synthetic varieties
recurrent selection
true-breeding line
pure-line varieties
F_1 hybrid variety
clonal line
clonal varieties
callus
explant
somatic embryos
somaclonal variation
cell selection
Ti plasmid
T-DNA
vir genes
quantitative trait loci (QTLs)
breeds
closebreeding

general combining ability
specific combining ability
superovulate
in vitro fertilization
somatic-cell nuclear transfer
eutrophication

CHAPTER TOPICS

27.1 GENETIC DIVERSITY
  Genetic erosion
  Conserving genetic resources
27.2 PLANT BREEDING
  Hybridization
  Self-pollination to achieve homozygosity
  Late-generation testing
  F_1 hybrid varieties
  Asexually propagated varieties
27.3 PLANT BIOTECHNOLOGY
  Plant cell and tissue culture
  Somaclonal variation
  Plant transformation
  Marker-assisted selection
27.4 ANIMAL BREEDING AND BIOTECHNOLOGY
  Animal breeding methods
  Animal biotechnology
  Animal cloning
  Transgenic animals
27.5 APPLICATIONS OF GENETICS IN INDUSTRY
  Land reclamation
  Genetically modified bacteria for hazardous-waste cleanup
  Biosynthesis of fuels and industrial products

CHAPTER OUTLINE

Introduction
  Hybridization and selection of breeds and varieties practiced for millennia
    Mendelian genetics provided basis for systematic breeding and selection
    Major increases in world production in past 50 years due to genetic selection
    Adequate food supplies and distribution problems
  Basis for present adequate world food production
    Improved cultural practices
      Irrigation, fertilization, weed, pest and disease control
    Improved genetic lines
      Comparison of old varieties and breeds to modern lines
      Over 50% of increases due to genetic selection
  Contribution of biotechnology to genetic selection
    Genetic engineering of plants and animals

Use of molecular markers to improve heritability
Industry, biotechnology and improved bacterial and yeast strains
Fermentation
Improvement of animal feeds and human food

27.1 GENETIC DIVERSITY

Central ideas:
- Worldwide, agricultural production has increased several fold in the past 50 years. Although many factors are responsible for the increases, genetic improvement has contributed more than any other factor.
- Continued genetic improvement is dependent on genetic diversity. Most genetic diversity for agricultural plants and animals is found in centers of diversity that correspond to the centers of origin.
- Most varieties and breeds of agricultural species grown throughout the world have narrow genetic bases.
- As genetically improved plants and animals replace their more diverse counterparts in the centers of diversity, genetic diversity is lost through genetic erosion.
- Scientists maintain genetic diversity in gene banks where seeds, plants, and animals with diverse genotypes are held for future use in breeding. Most gene banks are underfunded.

Cultivated plant and animal species spread from centers of origin
Center of origin
Domestication of cultivated crops can be traced to civilization centers
Major world centers of origin (Figure 27.2)
Center of diversity
Usual pattern: greatest genetic diversity found at area of domestication
Several major centers of origin (Table 27.1, Figure 27.2)
Genetic erosion
Genetic diversity provides raw material for genetic improvement
The limited genetic base of soybeans and potential for crop improvement
Success of plant and animal breeding threatens genetic diversity
Effects of the **green revolution** on plant diversity
Genetic uniformity and outbreaks of new diseases
Improved varieties and loss of older genetic lines
Conserving genetic resources
Establishment of **gene banks**
Underfunding for gene banks
Dedicated workers in the field
The Vavilov Institute and the siege of Leningrad
Worldwide coordinated efforts
Rights of nations to national genetic resources
Development of core collections
(See Example 27.1 Development of core collections in gene banks.)

27.2 PLANT BREEDING

Central idea:
- Plant breeding methods depend on the reproductive system of the species, the level of

inbreeding depression, and the cost of commercial seed production.

Important genetic features of plant breeding programs
    Utilization of quantitative genetics
    Breeding and the plant species breeding system
    Inbreeding depression
        Self pollinated species
        Open- or cross-pollinated species
    Development of methods for large-scale seed production
    Hybridization and selection
        Selecting the best genotypes
        Progeny testing

Hybridization
    Some hybridization schemes (Figure 27.3)
        The **two-, three- and four-parent crosses**
        Backcrossing (Figure 27.4)
            The **donor parent** and the **recurrent parent**
                Recurrent parent carries the major economic traits
                Donor parent usually donates one major trait
            Backcrossing and selection schemes vary if donor trait is dominant or recessive
            Backcrossing using **marker assisted selection**
        Multiparent crosses and **complex populations**
            Diallel cross and **circular crosses** (Figure 27..3)
            Synthetic populations and **synthetic varieties**
            Recurrent selection in multiparent crosses (Figure 27.5)
    (See Example 27.2 Single-seeded descent for development of true-breeding lines in self-pollinating plants.)

Self-pollination to achieve homozygosity
    Used in naturally self-pollinated species, wheat, barley, pea, soybean, etc.
    Near-homozygosity achieved by F_5 or F_6 selfed generations (**true-breeding lines**)
        F_1 plants and descendants allowed to self pollinate for several generations
        Purpose of self pollination: achieve homozygosity for all traits
    Advance-generation true-breeding lines tested in replicated trials
    Used in cross-pollinated plants to obtain homozygous inbred lines
    (See Example 27.2 Single-seeded descent for development of true-breeding lines in self-pollinating plants.)

Late-generation testing
    Line testing is often better than single seed descent testing
        Each line tested for performance in replicated field trials in several environments
        Importance of testing performance in several environments
        Saving seed from best performing lines each generation
    Best lines compared to existing varieties at F_{10} to F_{12} generation
    Seed companies usually sell **pure-line varieties** from self-pollinating species
        Pure-line varieties
            All plants genetically homozygous and identical
            All harvested seed genetically identical to parent crop
        Mendel's peas were homozygous because they came from pure-line varieties

F_1 hybrid varieties
    Inbreeding and loss of vigor in cross-pollinating plants

Examples: maize, sorghum and sugarbeets

Inbred lines lose vigor

Offspring of two inbred lines show heterosis depending on degree of heterozygosity

The F_1 **hybrid variety**

Breeders achieve maximum heterosis by crossing two inbred lines

Hybrid seed harvested from two inbred parents sold as F_1 hybrid variety

F_1 hybrid varieties are heterozygous, show heterosis and genetically uniform (parents were two homozygous inbred lines)

Seed from F_1 hybrid variety are segregating F_2 progeny

Plants from hybrid seed are highly productive (heterosis effects)

F_2 offspring show half the heterosis as F_1 generation

Criteria for hybrid varieties to be valuable economically

Inbred lines can be made and tested

Hybridization must be simple and efficient

Heterosis must out-perform standard varieties

Economic value of crop must justify extra cost of hybrid seed production

Asexually propagated varieties

Varieties propagated through cuttings

Examples

Potatoes, sugarcane, long lived perennials, fruit trees, small fruit (strawberries, raspberries, grapes, blue berries) and ornamentals

Propagating potatoes (Figure 27.6)

Breeding asexually propagated plants

Many are cross-pollinated and subject to inbreeding depression and heterosis

Permanent hybrids showing heterosis from crosses of inbred lines can be cloned as **clonal varieties**

F_1 hybrids showing heterosis can be cloned and (clonal line) serve as commercial **clonal varieties**

27.3 PLANT BIOTECHNOLOGY

Central idea:

- Plant biotechnology includes applications of cell and tissue culture, plant transformation, and marker-assisted selection. Plant biotechnology has created a greater need for traditional plant breeding.

Three general categories of plant biotechnology

Plant cell and tissue culture and its function in biotechnology

Callus cells can be cultured much like bacteria

Correct hormone balance maintained

Grow indefinitely

Callus cells form on wound surfaces of wounded plants

Explant: a piece of tissue cut from a plant

Callus forms on explant on culture medium

Somatic embryos can form from callus cells (Figures 27.7, 27.8)

Plantlets from somatic embryos (plant regeneration)

Plantlets grow roots when placed on rooting medium

Plantlet can mature into fertile adult plant

Somaclonal variation

Plant cultures tend to be mutagenic
Point mutations and chromosome rearrangements
Somaclonal variation and selective media for mutations expressed in cell culture (selection for salt tolerance)
Plant transformation and introduction of foreign genes into plant chromosomes
Introduction of foreign genes into plants
Introduction of genes by conventional breeding
Agrobacterium-mediated plant transformation (Figure 27.9)
Agrobacterium tumefaciens carries **Ti plasmid**
Bacterium infects host plant through wound (Figure 27.10)
Ti plasmid is inserted into host plant chromosomes
vir genes in plasmid control insertion of Ti plasmid into host chromosome DNA
Plasmid **T-DNA** causes gall formation in infected host tissue
T-DNA genes encode enzymes that control gall formation
T-DNA genes also encode enzymes that make compounds only the bacteria can use for energy
Reengineered TI plasmid (figure 27.11)
Most of T-DNA genes removed (cannot form crown galls)
Foreign DNA can be inserted into T-DNA region of plasmid
Intact *vir* genes in TI-plasmid vector control insertion of vector DNA into plant chromosomes
Breeders can use inserted genes in breeding programs
Genes that have been successfully incorporated are inherited
Gene conferring plant resistance to moth and beetle larvae
Source for toxin *Bacillus thuringensis*
Gene conferring resistance to glyphosate (Roundup)
Use of *Agrobacterium tumefaciens* limited mostly to broadleaf plants (some recent success in some grasses)
Marker-assisted selection
Selection of important traits by selecting for linked marker loci
Markers are usually DNA markers that have no phenotypic effects other than detectable changes in DNA sequences (RAPDs, RFLPs, mini- and micro-satellite PCR, etc.)
Use of DNA markers can improve heritability of economic traits
Used for tagging single genes and quantitative loci (**QTLs**)
(See Example 27.3 Marker assisted selection of QTLs.)

27.4 ANIMAL BREEDING AND BIOTECHNOLOGY

Central ideas:
- Animal breeding focuses on genetic improvement of existing breeds through selective breeding and minimization of inbreeding depression.
- Animal biotechnology has significantly impacted animal genetic improvement through applications such as in vitro fertilization, surrogate motherhood, and animal transformation.

Animal breeding methods
Animal Breeds are counterparts of plant varieties
Breed has group of genetically inherited characteristics

Holstein breed of cows selected for high volumes of high protein milk, usually have black and white spotting (Figure 27.13a, may be almost all white, Figure 27.14)

Black Angus breed is solid black, selected for beef, produces much lower volumes of milk (Figure 27.13b)

Animal breeding methods

Farmers and ranchers often practice animal breeding in cooperation with professionals

Plant breeding usually done by professionals at universities, seed companies, or federal and state plant breeding stations

Differences in breeding (plant and animal) technology due to reproductive differences

Many livestock animals require several years to sexual maturity

Cannot be self-fertilized to produce homozygosity

Homozygosity for some loci achieved by mating close relatives (i.e., full sibs or parent x offspring)

Balancing negative effects of inbreeding with positive effects of maintaining desirable genes in herd or flock

Closebreeding: avoiding the effects of inbreeding depression

Careful pedigrees (avoiding close relatives)

Bringing in a few new sires each generation

Coefficient of inbreeding of 6% acceptable (see section 19.4)

Value of parent based on performance of offspring

General combining ability

Offspring perform well in all or most matings

Parent with good general combining ability has higher value (i.e., semen of the breeding sire in large animals)

Specific combining ability

Two parents produce unusually outstanding offspring

Of little long-term value until recently

(See animal biotechnology below)

General and specific combining ability usually result of heterosis

Animal biotechnology

Use of specific combining ability for herd improvement

Cattle example (parents produce superior offspring)

Cow induced to **superovulate**

In vitro fertilization of cow's ova by bull's sperm

Embryos implanted into surrogate mothers (usually inferior performers)

Embryo splitting increases yield of fertilized eggs

Early stage embryos can be subdivided without loss of developmental potential

Subdivided embryos grown in vitro to implantation stage (Figure 27.14)

Animal cloning

1997: first cloning of an adult animal Roslin Institute in Scotland

Sheep adult somatic cell nucleus transferred to zygote cell

Transfer of zygote cell to surrogate mother

(See Example 27.4 Somatic cell nuclear transfer in sheep.)

Transgenic animals

Injection of genes into zygote cells

Grow zygote to embryo in vitro

Identify transgenic embryos by PCR

Transfer transgenic embryos to surrogate mothers

Example: growth hormone genes transferred into cattle

27.5 APPLICATIONS OF GENETICS IN INDUSTRY

Central idea:
- There are many industrial applications of genetics including breeding plants to reclaim mined lands, treatment of waste water with genetically improved microorganisms, and biosynthesis of industrial and pharmaceutical compounds.

Land reclamation

Reclaiming disturbed lands by breeding for plants that can grow on disturbed soils

Breeding of native wildland plants

Genetically modified bacteria for hazardous-waste cleanup

Bacteria that degrade petroleum crude oil spills

Genetically altered *E. Coli* strains that reduce phosphate pollution in lakes, ponds and streams

Biosynthesis of fuels and industrial products

Use of biomass as a resource

Synthesis of diesel fuels from algae that grow in saline water

Methane production from anaerobic digestion of biomass

Ethanol from sugar, starch and cellulose fermentation

Genetic engineering of more efficient organisms for biomass digestion

Development biodegradable plastics

BHP and PHA

(See Example 27.5 Genetic modification of plants for BHP production.)

Chapter 28
Legal and Ethical Issues in Genetics

KEY CONCEPTS

- Eugenics, the intentional hereditary improvement of the human population through selection, was popular at one time but is usually shunned today.
- Issues of informed consent and confidentiality are among the most important considerations in genetic testing and the treatment of genetic disorders.
- The legal admissibility of DNA fingerprinting has been challenged.
- To ensure public safety, institutional review and approval are required for many applications of recombinant DNA.
- To protect investments in research, scientists and corporations often patent a wide range of genetically altered organisms, the genes they carry, and the techniques used to produce them.
- At a time when progress in genetics is moving rapidly, appropriate science education is essential.

KEY TERMS

eugenics
prenatal testing
donor screening in sperm banks
sex selection
glucose-6-phosphate dehydrogenase (G6PD) deficiency
informed consent
confidentiality
utility patent
Plant Variety Protection (PVP) Act

Topics Discussed

CHAPTER OUTLINE

Introduction

Hope and fear are often part of genetics

    Developing effective treatments for genetic diseases and cancer

    Genetically improved plants and animals providing sufficient food

    Genetic development to improve well-being

    Concerns about legal and ethical questions

    Concerns about environmental dangers of genetically altered organisms

Increasing complexity and sophisticated nature of genetic research and public understanding

    Judges and juries and complex genetic evidence

    Disagreements among scientist (always basic to science) create public confusion

28.1 EUGENICS

    Improved people like breeders have improved animals

        Sir Francis Galton early advocate

        Galton coined term "eugenics" 1888

    Popular late 19th early 20th century (philosophers, scientists, politicians etc.)

        Laws in United States against marriages of imbeciles, epileptics, etc.

        US and Europe: Mandatory sterilization laws

        Between 1907 and 1960 60,000 people in US prisons and mental institutions sterilized

        Most US states have by now rescinded mandatory sterilization laws

    The effect of eugenic selection

        Basic human right covenants in US and Europe

        Little justification for laws that prevent people reproducing

        Most genetic disorders due to rare recessive alleles

    (See Example 28.1 Recognition of the ineffectiveness of eugenic selection against genetic disorders.)

    Contemporary selection in humans

        Eugenic selection of the past and present have little affect on overall allele frequencies

        Current eugenic practices

            Prenatal testing

                Have reduced births of children with Down syndrome and Tay-Sachs etc.

                Little or no effect on allele frequencies

            Donor screening in sperm banks

                Genetically screened individuals for heterozygosity of disorders

                Very mild selection and little effect on allele frequency

            Sex selection

                Process is expensive

                Few people use the technology

                Effect on sex ratio is negligible

28.2 GENETIC TESTING AND SCREENING

    Laws for certain kinds of genetic testing

        PKU testing has wide-spread acceptance

        Sickle cell anemia screening is seen as having ethnic and racial overtones

        Tay-Sachs disease screening has support among Jewish political groups

    Occupational genetic testing

G6PD deficiency and exposure to industrial oxidizing agents

1970's: several companies conducted genetic screening

> G6PD deficiency
>
> Sickle cell trait
>
> α-antitrypsin deficiency
>
> Adverse public attention has caused many companies to stop screening
>
> Possible effects of anti discrimination laws on genetic screening

Genetic testing and health insurance

> Costs of health insurance by employer give added incentives to genetic screening
>
> Number of genetic tests are increasing (PCR etc.)
>
> > Tests can be used to deny insurance or increase premiums
> >
> > Legislation has been recommended to prevent denial or premium increase

Legal challenges of DNA testing

> DNA fingerprinting and evidential technical errors
>
> > Purity of the DNA sample taken at crime scene
> >
> > Uniformity of methods of DNA analysis
>
> Use of rigorous controls
>
> > Training and licensing of technicians
> >
> > Rigorous replication and national establishment of standards

Informed consent and confidentiality

> Adequate counseling
>
> Protecting a persons rights of privacy
>
> > Employers, insurance companies, physicians, law enforcement agencies etc.
> >
> > Examples of breaching rights of privacy and confidentiality
>
> Many legal questions yet to be resolved

(see Example 28.2 Informed consent and confidentiality in genetic testing.)

28.3 LEGAL PROTECTION AND INTELLECTUAL PROPERTY RIGHTS IN GENETICS

Patenting microbes

> 1980: crude oil digesting microbes given patent
>
> Since then patented organisms have increased

Patenting genes

> Genes can be patented when someone clones or discovers sequence of gene
>
> Disclosure in article before patenting——gene becomes public domain
>
> Many genes have been patented (industry, universities, scientists)

Patenting traits

> Traits may be patented when sufficiently novel
>
> Phenotype and its use rather than gene can be patented

Patenting techniques

> Often much effort and funding used to develop new technique
>
> Patent protection has been sought and awarded

Plant genetic protection rights

> 1930: plant patent act passed
>
> > Used only for asexually propagated plants
> >
> > Seed-produced plants not protected under the act
>
> 1970: **plant variety protection act (PVP)**
>
> > Gave protection to genotype of pure-line variety or in-bred line for 18 years
> >
> > > Farmers could purchase variety and save and plant seed

Breeders could use variety as parent in breeding programs
Objections raised by countries where lines originated (usually centers of origin in third-world countries)
Laws have been enacted to protect genetic resources
Country compensated for transfer and use of genetic resources
Many scientists feel: any genotype must be freely available to breeding programs to anyone in the world
Seed companies usually oppose the policy (say patents should provide protection for variety use)
Opponents say policy discriminates against developing countries
Animal genetic protection rights
1987: patent protection for genetically altered animals through genetic engineering of genome (patent extends to progeny carrying the gene)
Animals developed by conventional breeding are not protected by patent
Implications of protecting genetic materials, traits, and techniques
Does legal protection promote or inhibit progress of research?
Without promise of legal protection many genotypes and techniques would not be developed
Private research would be seriously jeopardized
But restrictions on use of technique or genotype may inhibit beneficial research
Costs of techniques, enzymes, genotypes too high for limited funds
Research diverted from creative ideas by excessive costs for patented resources
Balancing conflicting needs
Many companies allow exemptions for use of patented resources
Non-profit research institution use
Need for patent protection has slowed publication of results (public domain laws)
Universities can use patents to generate needed funding for research and teaching
Perhaps the greatest beneficiary of biotechnology patents is the legal profession
(See Example 28.3 A patent dispute over recombinant human insulin.)

28.4 RECOMBINANT DNA AND SAFETY

Recombinant DNA research and public concerns
Creation of misguided fears
Movies and cartoons depict genetically engineered dangerous organisms
Fears about the possible misuse of genetic technology
Biological warfare and altered bacteria and viruses
1975: Asilomar Conference and adoption of strict recommendations
Release of recombinant organisms outside lab confines
Use of genetically altered organisms that cannot survive outside laboratory
Compliance was voluntary
1976: NIH Recombinant DNA Advisory Committee and guidelines for all NIH-funded research
Establishment of institutional biosafety committees
Other government funding agencies developed similar guidelines
Evidence accumulated that most applications posed little if any hazard

28.5 GENETICS AND SCIENCE EDUCATION

Pace of discovery in genetics has become very fast

    Applications of genetic research and technology have broadened extensively

    Public awareness of modern advances in genetics

        Avoidance of basic education in sciences

        Surveys indicate many students fail to see science as having any meaning to their lives

    Problem of ignorance not confined to the nonscientist

    Many scientists, physicians (other medical persons) and other specialists are not adequately informed of current trends in genetic engineering

    (See Example 28.4 Physicians' understanding of medical genetics.)

Section 4
Using the End-of-Chapter Questions and Problems

Each chapter in Genetics: The Continuity of Life has end-of-chapter questions and problems that help students learn genetic analysis. The questions and problems range in difficulty from easy conceptual questions that can be answered quickly to problems that require lengthy analysis. We have included a large number of questions and problems to allow professors to select those that are best adapted to their particular courses.

This section begins with a list of all questions and problems with ratings of their difficulty levels. It then provides detailed solutions to all end-of-chapter questions and problems.

Difficulty Ratings for Questions and Problems

We have given a difficulty rating from A to E for each end-of-chapter question or problem as follows:

A   Easy conceptual question that should require no more than a minute or two of study.

B   Conceptual question or problem that may require 2–10 minutes of study and analysis.

C   Conceptual question or problem that may require 10–20 minutes of study and analysis.

D   Moderately challenging problem that may require 20–30 minutes of study and analysis.

E   Very challenging problem that may require more than 30 minutes of study and analysis.

The times required to solve a question or problem are estimates for students who have read the chapter and are familiar with the concepts explained in the chapter.

Chapter 1	Chapter 2	Chapter 3	Chapter 4
1. A	1. B	1. A	1. B
2. B	2. B	2. A	2. B
3. C	3. B	3. B	3. B
4. A	4. A	4. A	4. B
5. B	5. A	5. B	5. B
6. B	6. B	6. B	6. B
7. C	7. A	7. B	7. C
8. B	8. B	8. B	8. A
9. A	9. C	9. B	9. A
10. B	10. B	10. B	10. B
11. C	11. B	11. B	11. B
12. A	12. B	12. B	12. B
13. B	13. A	13. B	13. A
14. C	14. B	14. A	14. C
	15. B	15. B	15. B
	16. B	16. C	16. B
	17. A	17. B	17. B
	18. B	18. B	18. C
	19. B	19. C	19. B
	20. C	20. B	20. B
	21. A	21. B	21. C
	22. A	22. B	22. C
	23. B	23. B	23. C
	24. B	24. B	24. C
	25. C	25. C	25. D
	26. C	26. C	26. B
	27. C	27. C	27. C
		28. C	28. D
		29. C	29. C
		30. C	30. D
		31. C	31. C
		32. C	
		33. C	

Chapter 5	Chapter 6	Chapter 7	Chapter 8
1. C	1. B	1. A	1. A
2. B	2. B	2. B	2. B
3. B	3. C	3. C	3. B
4. A	4. B	4. B	4. C
5. B	5. C	5. A	5. C
6. B	6. B	6. B	6. B
7. D	7. C	7. B	7. B
8. D	8. B	8. B	8. B
9. B	9. B	9. B	9. B
10. C	10. B	10. C	10. B
11. B	11. C	11. B	11. C
12. A	12. C	12. B	12. C
13. B	13. D	13. B	13. B
14. B	14. D	14. B	14. B
15. B	15. D	15. D	15. C
16. A		16. D	16. B
17. C		17. C	17. C
18. C		18. C	18. C
19. C		19. D	19. D
20. B		20. D	20. D
21. C		21. C	21. C
22. C		22. C	22. C
23. C			23. D
24. C			24. C
25. C			25. C
26. D			26. D
27. C			27. C
28. B			28. D
29. E			29. D
30. D			

Chapter 9	Chapter 10	Chapter 11	Chapter 12
1. A	1. B	1. B	1. C
2. B	2. B	2. B	2. B
3. B	3. A	3. B	3. C
4. B	4. B	4. B	4. A
5. B	5. B	5. B	5. C
6. C	6. C	6. B	6. B
7. C	7. B	7. B	7. B
8. B	8. C	8. C	8. C
9. B	9. B	9. B	9. C
10. B	10. B	10. C	10. B
11. B	11. A	11. B	11. B
12. D	12. B	12. B	12. A
13. A	13. B	13. B	13. B
14. A	14. B	14. C	14. B
15. B	15. C	15. D	15. B
16. B	16. C	16. D	16. B
17. B	17. B	17. C	17. D
18. B	18. B	18. B	18. C
19. B	19. B		19. C
20. E	20. C		20. C
21. B	21. B		21. C
22. D	22. C		22. C
23. E	23. C		23. C
24. C	24. B		24. C
25. D	25. B		25. E
	26. B		26. C
	27. C		27. D
	28. C		28. D
	29. C		29. D
	30. C		30. C
	31. C		31. B
			32. C
			33. C
			34. D
			35. E
			36. E
			37. C
			38. D
			39. D
			40. E

Chapter 13	Chapter 14	Chapter 15	Chapter 16
1. C	1. A	1. A	1. B
2. B	2. C	2. D	2. D
3. C	3. B	3. B	3. C
4. C	4. B	4. E	4. C
5. D	5. C	5. D	5. D
6. B	6. B	6. C	6. C
7. A	7. C	7. B	7. B
8. A	8. B	8. E	8. C
9. B	9. B	9. C	9. C
10. D	10. B	10. E	10. C
11. B	11. C	11. C	11. C
12. C	12. B	12. C	12. C
13. C	13. B	13. B	13. C
14. D	14. C	14. D	14. C
15. D	15. C	15. D	15. D
16. D	16. C	16. E	16. E
17. C	17. C	17. E	17. D
18. B	18. C	18. E	18. C
19. D	19. C	19. E	19. D
20. A	20. B	20. C	20. C
21. B	21. B	21. E	21. C
22. C	22. C	22. D	22. C
23. C	23. C	23. E	23. D
24. D	24. C	24. D	24. D
25. C	25. B	25. D	25. D
26. B	26. B	26. D	
27. C	27. A	27. D	
28. C	28. A		
29. D	29. C		
30. D	30. D		
31. D	31. C		
32. C	32. D		
33. C	33. D		
34. D	34. E		
35. E	35. C		
36. C	36. C		
	37. C		

Chapter 17	Chapter 18	Chapter 19	Chapter 20
1. B	1. B	1. C	1. A
2. C	2. B	2. B	2. B
3. B	3. B	3. C	3. B
4. D	4. B	4. D	4. B
5. D	5. B	5. B	5. B
6. C	6. B	6. C	6. B
7. C	7. C	7. C	7. B
8. C	8. D	8. C	8. C
9. D	9. D	9. D	9. B
10. C	10. C	10. C	10. B
11. D	11. C	11. C	11. C
12. C	12. C	12. C	12. C
13. C	13. C	13. C	13. B
14. C	14. C	14. C	14. C
15. C	15. D	15. C	15. D
16. D	16. C	16. D	16. C
17. C	17. C	17. C	17. C
18. C	18. D	18. D	18. D
19. C	19. C	19. B	19. D
20. E	20. C	20. C	20. C
21. D	21. D	21. E	21. C
22. D		22. D	22. C
23. C		23. E	23. C
24. C		24. E	24. C
25. C		25. D	25. C
			26. C
			27. C
			28. C

Chapter 21	Chapter 22	Chapter 23	Chapter 24
1. C	1. B	1. C	1. A
2. B	2. B	2. B	2. B
3. B	3. B	3. B	3. B
4. C	4. B	4. B	4. B
5. C	5. D	5. B	5. B
6. C	6. C	6. B	6. B
7. C	7. D	7. C	7. C
8. D	8. C	8. C	8. B
9. C	9. C	9. B	9. B
10. C	10. C	10. C	10. B
11. C	11. C	11. C	11. B
12. C	12. B	12. B	12. B
13. C	13. C	13. C	13. D
14. D	14. C	14. C	14. D
15. D	15. C	15. C	15. C
16. E	16. B	16. C	16. C
17. C	17. C	17. C	17. C
18. B	18. B	18. D	18. C
19. D	19. C	19. C	19. C
20. D	20. D		20. C
21. E			21. C
22. E			22. C
23. D			23. C
24. D			
25. C			
26. C			
27. D			

Chapter 25	Chapter 26	Chapter 27	Chapter 28
1. B	1. B	1. B	1. B
2. B	2. C	2. B	2. B
3. B	3. B	3. B	3. B
4. B	4. B	4. B	4. B
5. B	5. C	5. C	5. B
6. C	6. C	6. B	6. C
7. C	7. C	7. C	7. B
8. C	8. C	8. C	8. C
9. B	9. B	9. C	9. B
10. B	10. C	10. C	10. B
11. C	11. C	11. C	11. B
12. C	12. D	12. D	12. C
13. C	13. C	13. D	13. C
14. B	14. C	14. C	14. C
15. C	15. C	15. C	15. B
16. C	16. C	16. D	16. C
17. C	17. D	17. C	17. B
18. C	18. C	18. C	18. B
19. C	19. D	19. B	
20. D	20. B	20. B	
21. D	21. C		
22. D	22. D		
23. C			
24. C			

Detailed Solutions to End-of-Chapter Questions and Problems

The pages that follow contain detailed solutions to the end-of-chapter questions and Problems. The solutions are identical to those in the student solutions manual, *Student Companion to Genetics: The Continuity of Life*, except that the difficulty level for each question or problem is indicated in parentheses.

Chapter 1
Introduction

1. *(A)* Genetics is considered a twentieth-century science because scientists began to recognize it as a formal science at the dawn of the twentieth century. Biologists had attempted to study the basis of heredity before then, particularly in the seventeenth and eighteenth centuries, but generally they made little progress in understanding how traits are inherited. In the 1850s and '60s, Gregor Mendel, in a remarkable leap of insight, discovered and correctly described the patterns of inheritance of individual traits in peas and beans. But no one recognized the significance of his work until the year 1900, when three scientists, Hugo De Vries, Carl Correns, and Erich von Tschermak, independently rediscovered Mendel's principles. Genetics can also be considered an ancient science because the people of ancient civilizations understood enough about the principles of inheritance to make significant progress in the domestication and genetic improvement of agricultural animals and plants.

2. *(B)* Our present understanding of genetics has revolutionized medical, industrial, and agricultural research. For example, scientists have engineered genes that produce human insulin in bacteria for treatment of people afflicted with diabetes. Although the genes that encode genetically engineered human insulin were constructed by scientists, the insulin is identical to natural human insulin and does not cause allergic reactions, which were a problem with insulins derived from pigs and cattle. Several other pharmaceutical products produced in genetically altered bacteria are now on the market as well. In other medical applications, newborn babies are routinely screened for genetic disorders for which early medical intervention can prevent permanent damage. Certain genetic disorders can be identified in human fetuses before birth. Our understanding of the genetic basis of cancer has grown tremendously in the past few years, allowing for development of methods that permit earlier and more accurate detection of cancer. Early detection of cancer makes it possible to begin therapeutic treatments during the critical initial stages of the disease, when treatments are the most effective. The multinational project to determine the entire nucleotide sequence of the human genome, called the Human Genome Project, will soon be completed. It has already provided direct benefits in understanding the biochemical basis of inherited diseases and promises to deliver many more. It has indirectly benefited other areas of genetics through the development of techniques, such as automated DNA sequencing, that can be widely used.

Genetic improvement has been important in agriculture since before recorded history. In recent years, the development of modern breeding methods for animals and plants, and the introduction of agricultural biotechnology, have resulted in dramatic increases in the amount of food produced and in substantial improvements in quality. Industrial applications of genetics have given us improved products such as detergents and other industrial chemicals and have assisted in overcoming industrial damage to the environment.

There are many important legal and ethical issues related to applications of genetics. Among the most important are the safety and ethics of releasing genetically engineered organisms into the environment, the administration of patent rights and ownership of genetically modified organisms and the methods used to produce them, the introduction of foreign DNA into plants and animals, and the applications of genetic methodology in human health care.

3. (C) The answers to these questions will vary depending on the book chosen. Genetic topics likely to be found in a section on cell biology include DNA structure and replication, gene expression (transcription and translation of genes), gene regulation, and genetic control of the cell cycle. In a section on physiology, you may find topics such as gene expression, gene regulation, genetic disorders, and genetic control of metabolism. Sections on ecology and evolution typically include such topics as the genetic structure of populations, natural selection, genetic drift, inbreeding and heterosis, and the relative effects of genetic and environmental factors on phenotypes.

4. (A) Many principles of genetics are identical or similar across a wide range of species. For example, most of the principles that Mendel described in pea plants apply to other plant and animal species, including humans. All cellular species use DNA as the genetic material, and the mechanisms of DNA replication and gene expression are similar among all species.

5. (B) Some of the most important characteristics of a model organism are the following: It can be raised easily and inexpensively, it produces large numbers of progeny, its generation time is short, genetic variants within the species are readily available for study, and it has been the subject of previous studies that have produced relevant background information. The economic value of an organism is not an important consideration in selecting a model organism for genetic study because the principles learned from model organisms can usually be applied to the study of economically important species later. Some model organisms, such as *Drosophila melanogaster* and *Arabidopsis thaliana*, have little economic importance. Others, such as maize, *Saccharomyces cerevisiae* (yeast), and *Escherichia coli* are of great economic importance.

6. (B) Humans have relatively long generation times and do not produce large numbers of progeny. It can also be very expensive to conduct genetic research with humans. DNA analysis compensates for the limitations of traditional genetic analysis by allowing researchers to study human genes directly and conduct large-scale studies on human families.

7. (C) Pages 111–112 of the article (Redei, G. P. 1975. *Arabidopsis* as a genetic tool. *Annual Review of Genetics* 9:111–127) list the characteristics that make *Arabidopsis thaliana* a good choice as a model organism. Below is an abbreviated version of Redei's list with some explanations. We have placed an asterisk by each of the advantages that are listed on page 7 of your textbook.
a. The chromosome number is five pairs (which is a relatively small number).
b. All primary trisomics are morphologically distinguishable. (This means that if a chromosome is missing, the plant's morphology reveals which chromosome is missing.)
*c. The life cycle may be completed within a month. (Its generation time is short.)
d. Outcrossing (cross fertilization) is minimal (the plant is predominantly self-fertilizing).
*e. The seed output of a plant may exceed 50,000. (It produces large numbers of progeny.)
*f. Five to 10 plants may be grown in a square centimeter. (It can be raised easily and inexpensively.)
*g. Plants can be grown to maturity on simple media in test tubes. (It can be raised easily and inexpensively.)
*h. A large number of ecological variants are available. (Genetic variants within the species are readily available for study.)
i. It can be crossed with several species of different basic chromosome numbers.

A. thaliana has few disadvantages as a model organism. The only one mentioned by Redei is the small size of the chromosomes. At the time this article was written, there was not a large body of scientific literature on *A. thaliana*, which was a disadvantage. However, *A. thaliana* has been so intensively studied during the past 20 years that the current body of literature is very extensive.

8. (B) There are two differences between prokaryotes and eukaryotes mentioned on page 11 in Chapter 1. (1) The cells of eukaryotes have cellular nuclei, whereas prokaryotic cells lack cellular nuclei. (2) Eukaryotic cells contain linear DNA molecules in the chromosomes (located in the nucleus), whereas the

DNA in prokaryotic chromosomes is circular. There are many other differences between prokaryotes and eukaryotes that are not mentioned in Chapter 1. You can find them in most introductory biology books.

9. *(A)* Molecular genetics is the study of the molecules of heredity, which include DNA, RNA, and protein, and how the information in DNA is ultimately expressed as an outward phenotype. Transmission genetics is the study of how genes and the traits they govern are transmitted from parents to offspring. The genetics of populations is the study of inheritance in populations and how external forces influence that inheritance, the interactions of multiple genes with themselves and environmental influences, and how genetics influences evolution. Molecular genetics is genetics at its most fundamental level. A full understanding of transmission genetics and the genetics of populations is only possible when we study their molecular bases. Transmission genetics, in turn, is a foundation for the genetics of populations.

10. *(B)* A gene is a linear segment of DNA. The information in the DNA of a gene is transcribed into RNA, and in most cases the information in RNA is translated into a protein. Genes may mutate, and mutation is the underlying source of genetic variation. Genes are found in cell nuclei, mitochondria, chloroplasts, bacteria, and viruses. Genes and their interactions with environmental influences determine the phenotypes of discontinuously and continuously varying traits.

11. *(C)* Mendel was the first person to experimentally demonstrate the existence of genes as constant hereditary units. He did so through exhaustive experiments on the inheritance of easily observable traits in pea plants. Bateson was among the most ardent advocates for Mendel's principles and was instrumental in establishing the science of genetics. Bateson proposed that Mendel's principles could explain both discontinuous and continuous variation, and he recognized the link between genes and enzymes. Garrod recognized that enzyme deficiencies caused certain inherited disorders, establishing the evidence that genes were linked with enzymes. Sutton and Boveri proposed that genes are located on chromosomes and that each chromosome contains many genes. Morgan showed genetically that a gene that governs eye color in *Drosophila melanogaster* is located on the X chromosome. Sturtevant and Bridges, along with Morgan, mapped many nuclear genes to their respective chromosomes in *Drosophila melanogaster*. Beadle and Tatum demonstrated a relationship between genes and enzymes and hypothesized that each gene corresponds to one enzyme. Avery, MacLeod, and McCarty demonstrated that the transforming principle in bacteria is DNA. Hershey and Chase showed that the hereditary material of bacterial viruses is DNA. Franklin and Wilkins produced X-ray diffraction images that provided evidence about the structure of DNA. Chargaff obtained data on the composition of DNA that helped lead to the discovery of the structure of DNA. Watson and Crick discovered the structure of the DNA molecule based on information published by other scientists, including Franklin, Wilkins, and Chargaff. Yanofsky showed that there is a linear relationship between mutations in the nucleotide sequence of a gene and changes in the amino acid sequence of the protein encoded by the gene. Ochoa, Brenner, Jacob, and Meselson demonstrated that the information transfer from DNA to protein required an RNA intermediate. The work of Nirenberg, Matthaei, Leder, and Khorana was instrumental in deciphering the genetic code.

12. *(A)* Genetics is an analytical science and cannot be adequately studied as a body of theories and facts. Instead, it is best studied by examining how genetic experiments are conducted and their results interpreted.

13. *(B)* Mendel hybridized plants that differed for one characteristic (such as a tall plant hybridized with a dwarf plant). He conducted seven experiments, in each case testing one characteristic. In each experiment, all of the first-generation progeny resembled one of the parents and not the other. In the second generation, he observed a 3:1 ratio for the two contrasting parental traits in all seven experiments. From these results, he concluded that each plant carried hereditary factors that influenced the traits he was studying, and that those factors were transmitted unchanged from one generation to the next. He also concluded that one of the factors was dominant over the other. He showed mathematically that with dominance and random union of pollen and egg cells, all first-generation plants and three-fourths of the

second-generation plants should resemble the parent with the dominant characteristic, just as he observed. He then tested his hypothesis with further experimentation. Several aspects of his approach allowed him to discover the basic principles of inheritance, including his choice of an appropriate experimental organism, his choice of traits that could be analyzed easily and unambiguously and that were not influenced by environmental variation, his analysis of large numbers of individuals, his interpretation of his results in light of the scientific theory of his day, and his testing of hypotheses with further experimentation.

14. *(C)* The answers to these questions will vary depending on the issue of *Science* or *Nature* that you choose.

Chapter 2
DNA Structure and Replication

1. *(B)* The relationship between DNA and inheritance had not been demonstrated. To identify the molecular structure of genes it was necessary to show that a given chromosome chemical, such as DNA, RNA, or protein, was directly associated with inheritance of a phenotype. Scientists needed to prove that a given change (mutation) in one of these chemicals would affect phenotype and, of crucial significance, would be inherited from generation to generation. Before 1940, no scientist had been able to demonstrate this critical relationship for any chemical. Although known to be a major constituent of chromatin, DNA, consisting of only four different nucleotides, seemed to represent a structure that was too simple to qualify as the genetic information molecule. Protein, also a major constituent of chromatin, seemed to be a more logical choice because of its potential for much greater complexity.

2. *(B)* **(a)** Each DNA nucleotide contains a deoxyribose sugar (5 carbon atoms), a nitrogenous base (4–5 carbon atoms, 2–5 nitrogen atoms), and a phosphate group that contains a single phosphorus atom. With 3 phosphate atoms in Miescher's empirical formula, one could guess that the formula represents a molecule with three nucleotides. If this is so, the number of carbon atoms should be between 27 and 30, and the number of nitrogen atoms between 6 and 15. Miescher's formula of $C_{29}H_{49}N_9P_3O_{22}$ fits within these parameters and, therefore, represents three nucleotides. **(b)** $C_{39}H_{56}N_{15}P_4O_{32}$. **(c)** The relative proportions of carbon, hydrogen, nitrogen, oxygen, and phosphorus atoms correspond fairly closely to Miescher's basic empirical formula. **(d)** Each DNA nucleotide varies slightly from some of the other nucleotides in number of atoms of carbon, hydrogen, oxygen and nitrogen as well as number of nucleotides present in the molecule. Differences in sequence of the four nucleotides provide the basis of genetic diversity. A particular DNA molecule may vary in the proportions of the four nucleotides from another DNA molecule, so we expect the relative proportions of the atoms to vary slightly.

3. *(B)* Griffith used two strains of pneumococcal bacteria, S (virulent) and R (avirulent). Only the S cells caused pneumonia in the mice. The R cells, a closely related strain, could not cause the disease. Mice injected with either heat-killed S cells or live R cells were unaffected. Mice injected with living S cells died of the disease. These were the control experiments. When Griffith injected heat-killed S and live R cells together into mice, the recipient animals died of pneumonia. He recovered live S cells from these diseased mice. The living R cells incorporated something *genetic* from the killed S cells, transforming the R strain *and its descendants* to the S type. This latter point is the critical observation. Whatever the transforming principle was, after becoming incorporated into the living R cells, it transformed them to the S type. This change was permanent and genetic because each succeeding generation was also the S type.

4. *(A)* Deoxyribose has one less oxygen atom than ribose. The formula for ribose is $C_5H_{10}O_5$. The chemical formula for deoxyribose is $C_5H_{10}O_4$.

5. *(A)* As shown in Example 2.3, the A repels C and G repels T because positive charges align with positive charges, and negative charges with negative charges.

6. *(B)* In such a DNA double helix, the concentration of C would not necessarily equal the concentration of G. The same would be true for the relative concentrations of A and T. Chargaff showed that C = G and A = T. In addition, pyrimidines (C and T) are smaller than purines, so C-C and T-T pairs would be markedly less wide than A-A and G-G pairs. This kind of pairing would produce a nonuniform diameter along the double helix, which is contrary to the observations obtained by X-ray diffraction analysis.

7. *(A)* If the molar concentration of adenine is 30% in human DNA, then the molar concentration of thymine should also be 30%. The remaining 40% must consist of guanine and cytosine, which are also equal to one another in molar concentration, so the concentration of each must be 20%.

8. *(B)* It is known that the DNA in the virus particles of some viruses is single stranded. There are no base pairs in single-stranded DNA, so there is no relationship between the relative proportions of C and G, or A and T. Since A does not equal T, and G does not equal C in the virus's DNA, it would be reasonable to assume that the DNA is single stranded.

9. *(C)* Adjacent base pairs in the double helix of B-DNA are about 0.34 nanometers (nm) apart. A nanometer is 10^{-9} meters and is 1 millionth of a millimeter ($10^{-9} \div 10^{-3} = 10^{-6}$), so 50 mm of DNA equals 50 million nm. There should be a nucleotide pair every 0.34 nanometers, so $50{,}000{,}000 \div 0.34 = 147{,}058{,}824$ nucleotide pairs.

10. *(B)* The model is of a replication fork that is moving toward the left. Of the newly synthesized strands, the leading strand is synthesized continuously and the lagging strand is synthesized discontinuously. The leading strand is synthesized in the same direction in which the replication fork is moving. The letter "b" in the diagram is located on the end of the leading strand that is pointing toward the replication fork, so "b" must be the 3′ end of that strand. Because the DNA molecule is antiparallel, "a", "d", and "c" must all be 5′ ends.

11. *(B)* Topoisomerase relieves the tension of supercoiling that is generated ahead of the replication fork when a double-stranded DNA molecule is replicated. Without topoisomerase activity, the DNA molecule would become excessively supercoiled during DNA replication and could not be fully replicated. The cells could not divide without replicating their DNA, so elimination of topoisomerase activity is eventually lethal to the bacterial cultures.

12. *(B)* DNA ligase is essential for joining Okazaki fragments of the lagging strand during DNA replication. Absence of DNA ligase activity prevents completion of DNA synthesis and is eventually lethal to the cells.

13. *(A)* DNA polymerase requires a short polynucleotide primer annealed to the DNA template to initiate DNA replication. Thus, for DNA to replicate in a test tube, primers that are complementary to the DNA must be included along with the other components mentioned. In cells, the primers are composed of RNA. However, in a test tube, DNA primers also permit DNA polymerase to synthesize DNA.

14. *(B)* Meselson and Stahl grew cells for many generations on a medium containing ^{15}N as the sole source of nitrogen, then transferred the cells to medium with ^{14}N as the sole source of nitrogen. After one generation (one round of DNA replication) the DNA extracted from these cells formed a single DNA band of a density that was between the densities of DNA with only ^{15}N and DNA with only ^{14}N. This band would not have existed if DNA replication were conservative. If DNA replication were conservative, the extracted DNA would have formed two bands, one with DNA containing only ^{15}N and the other with DNA that contained only ^{14}N, as shown in part b of Figure 2.16.

15. *(B)* DNA polymerase II synthesizes DNA during repair of DNA damage and is not an essential enzyme for synthesis of undamaged DNA. Therefore, cells can survive in the absence of its activity. If left unrepaired, DNA damage can cause mutations (changes in the nucleotide sequences of DNA). In the absence of DNA polymerase II activity, DNA damage cannot be efficiently repaired, so mutations are more frequent.

16. *(B)* **(a)** Yes, it is possible, and it happens naturally in some circular DNA molecules. When the single replication fork migrates around the entire molecule to its point of origin, the DNA polymerase has synthesized two new DNA molecules. Each newly synthesized strand will be complete except for gaps where the 5′ and 3′ carbons of the two final adjacent nucleotides meet. Ligase joins the nucleotides at these gaps, forming two double-stranded molecules of DNA. **(b)** No. In unidirectional replication, a replication fork proceeds in one direction from the origin of replication. In a linear molecule, it proceeds in one direction from the origin of replication to the end of the molecule; the DNA on the other side of

the origin is not replicated.

17. *(A)* Less energy is required to separate AT-rich strands of the double helix because each A-T pair is held by only two hydrogen bonds, whereas each G-C pair is held by three hydrogen bonds. Regions rich in A-T pairs at origin of replication sites facilitate separation of the DNA strands for initiation of replication.

18. *(B)* Okazaki fragments do appear in the replication fork of a circular DNA molecule that is replicated unidirectionally. DNA synthesis within a replication fork is the same for unidirectional and bidirectional DNA replication. Unidirectional replication consists of a single replication fork that moves in one direction from the origin. Bidirectional replication consists of two replication forks that move in opposite directions from the origin. In each replication fork, one new strand is the leading strand and the other strand is the lagging strand, which is synthesized as Okazaki fragments.

19. *(B)* Replication fork movement in eukaryotic cells proceeds at about 2500 nucleotide pairs per second. For bidirectional replication, DNA synthesis proceeds at a rate of about 5000 nucleotide pairs per second per origin. The average length of a human chromosome is about 130 million nucleotide pairs. Thus, over 26,000 seconds (about 7 hours) would be required to replicate a chromosome of average size from a single origin of replication, which is too slow to accommodate cell division in eukaryotes. This limitation is overcome by the presence of several origins of replication in each eukaryotic chromosome. Researchers estimate that mice may have about 25,000 origins scattered throughout their DNA molecules to achieve DNA replication within the time required to accommodate cell division.

20. *(C)* One major problem is related to the source of energy required for establishing the phosphodiester bond between adjacent nucleotides. If replication were in the $3' \rightarrow 5'$ direction, the last added nucleotide on a DNA strand would have to carry the triphosphate group to furnish energy for the bond. If this last nucleotide were to lose one or more of the phosphate units (which are quite reactive), there would not be enough energy to bond to the $3'$ carbon of the new incoming nucleotide. There is no mechanism that will easily restore this chemical energy to the last nucleotide. This loss would block DNA replication. On the other hand, with replication proceeding in the $5' \rightarrow 3'$ direction, the loss of a phosphate from a single nucleotide triphosphate in the pool of nucleotide triphosphates does not inhibit DNA replication significantly because there are many nucleotide triphosphates in the pool that can continue to be utilized in DNA replication.

21. *(A)* **(a)** B-DNA. **(b)** The helix is right-handed. This means that if one were to sight along the helix from either end, the helix would appear to twist in a clockwise direction. **(c)** In the B form, the bases are nearly perpendicular to the axis of the helix.

22. *(A)* Z-DNA and H-DNA may also exist in living cells. In addition, a double-stranded nucleic acid molecule in which one strand is DNA and the other RNA may exist in the A form in living cells.

23. *(B)*

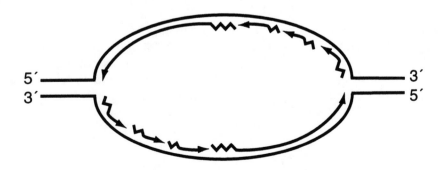

24. *(B)* The major structural feature of the double helix that suggested the mode of replication is the hydrogen bonding that holds the two complementary strands of DNA together. Hydrogen bonds can easily be broken and rejoined, whereas the covalent bonds holding adjacent nucleotides together within a strand are comparatively very strong bonds. So one could hypothesize that the two strands of the double helix could be easily separated from each other, exposing each of the four kinds of nitrogen bases within each strand for precise attraction of free nucleotide pairing partners during some kind of replication process.

25. *(C)* **(a)** Rolling circle replication is semiconservative; new strands are synthesized from conserved strands that are used as templates. **(b)** Rolling circle replication is unidirectional because there is a single replication fork that proceeds in one direction. **(c)** Rolling circle replication is semidiscontinuous because one newly synthesized strand is synthesized continuously and the other is synthesized discontinuously.

26. *(C)* If the 3´ end dissociated from the circle, the RNA primer that bound to that end could not be replaced with DNA because there would be no 3´ end on the newly synthesized strand to which new nucleotides could be added:

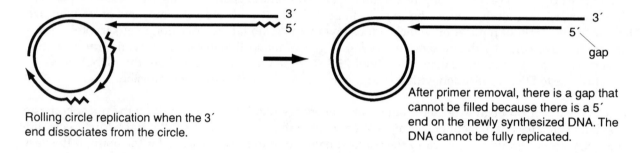

Rolling circle replication when the 3´ end dissociates from the circle.

After primer removal, there is a gap that cannot be filled because there is a 5´ end on the newly synthesized DNA. The DNA cannot be fully replicated.

On the other hand, when the 5´ end dissociates, the molecule can be fully replicated because one of the Okazaki fragments is synthesized all the way to the end of the molecule:

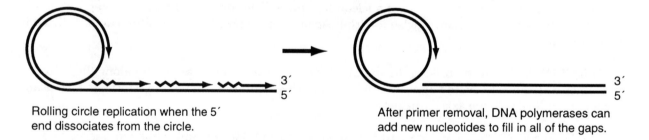

Rolling circle replication when the 5´ end dissociates from the circle.

After primer removal, DNA polymerases can add new nucleotides to fill in all of the gaps.

27. *(C)* Germ-line cells are the cells that give rise to sperm and eggs. Their DNA molecules are replicated through an unlimited number of cell divisions as life continues from one organismal generation to the next. In the absence of telomerase activity, the ends of the DNA molecules would undergo erosion at their telomeres with each round of replication. On the other hand, all other cells in the body (called somatic cells) undergo only a limited number of cell divisions. Most of the cells in your body will never divide again and will never replicate their DNA again. Thus, they do not require telomerase. They have undergone a limited number of cell divisions, and the degree of erosion of their telomeres, caused by the absence of telomerase, is insufficient to cause them any serious harm.

Chapter 3
Transcription and RNA Processing

1. *(A)* The central dogma addresses the fundamental question of how proteins in cells come into existence. The central dogma can be stated as follows: The coded information in DNA is transcribed into a complementary RNA. The information in the RNA is then translated into a polypeptide. According to the central dogma, the information flow is in one direction only: DNA → RNA → amino acid sequence in a polypeptide. The central dogma tells us that the information about amino acid sequence in a polypeptide cannot be transferred back to the gene. The only way amino acid sequence can be changed in the polypeptide is for a mutation to occur in the corresponding nucleotides in the DNA.

2. *(A)* Based on the central dogma, genes are specialized segments of DNA that serve as templates for the construction of different types of RNA, such as rRNA, tRNA, snRNA, and mRNA. Those genes that encode mRNAs carry the genetic message for construction of proteins.

3. *(B)* Almost all eukaryotic RNAs are processed after transcription. Eukaryotic mRNAs are processed extensively. They are capped on the 5′ end, the introns are removed, the exons are spliced together, and a poly (A) tail is added to the 3′ end. Prokaryotic mRNAs are not processed. In prokaryotes, transcription and translation occur almost simultaneously as the mRNA product is being transcribed. Just as soon as the 5′ end of the mRNA carrying sufficient information for ribosome attachment is transcribed, a ribosome assembles on the mRNA strand and initiates translation. Another ribosome will soon follow, so several ribosomes follow behind the RNA polymerase as it synthesizes the mRNA. In eukaryotes transcription and translation are separated in space and time. After eukaryotic pre-mRNAs are processed into mature mRNAs, the mRNAs are transported through pores in the nuclear membrane to sites in the cytoplasm where ribosomes translate them.

4. *(A)* They are called genes because they carry a genetic message for the construction of RNA molecules. In order to be called a gene, a DNA sequence must have the features that are necessary for it to be transcribed into an RNA molecule. However, a gene does not necessarily need to encode a protein.

5. *(B)* **(a)** Hemoglobin carries oxygen in the blood. **(b)** The nucleotide sequence in the DNA determines what the final sequence of nucleotides in the mRNA will be after processing. The nucleotide sequence in the mRNA, in turn, determines the sequence of amino acids in the protein. The sequence of amino acids in the protein determines how the protein will assemble and what its function will be.

6. *(B)* To replicate, a single-stranded DNA molecule must be synthesized from its complementary strand. A DNA molecule must be double stranded at some point for replication. Replication is facilitated when DNA molecules are maintained in their double-stranded form. On the other hand, all organisms (with the exception of some viruses) do not use RNA as the genetic material. RNA functions as the information carrier between DNA and protein, as a structural component of ribosomes, and as a carrier of amino acids. Because its functions in the cell do not require replication from an RNA template, RNA does not need to be double stranded.

7. *(B)* The three major types of RNA in the cell are: mRNA, tRNA, and rRNA.

The mRNA is a transcript of a gene that encodes a polypeptide for a protein. It carries the information transcribed from the antisense strand of the gene for assembly of amino acids.

The tRNAs are a group of small RNAs (about 80 nucleotides each) used as amino acid carrier molecules during translation of mRNA.

The rRNAs are structural components of ribosomes. Each ribosome is composed of several different rRNAs and proteins.

8. *(B)* Besides the three major classes of RNA, several other types of RNA are present in cells. These additional RNAs are generally much less abundant than the major classes of RNAs, are rather small (100–300 nucleotides), and serve a variety of functions. For example, the primers in DNA synthesis are made of RNA. Telomerase RNA is a part of the enzyme telomerase, where it serves as a template for eukaryotic DNA synthesis on chromosome ends, a mechanism for finishing synthesis of linear DNA. Small nuclear RNAs (snRNAs) assist in intron removal from pre-mRNAs. Another small RNA directs secretory proteins to receptors in the cell membrane. A few RNAs, called ribozymes, act as enzymes that catalyze biochemical reactions.

9. *(B)* The sigma (σ) factor plays an important role in initiation of transcription in prokaryotes. In prokaryotes, a single type of RNA polymerase has several polypeptide subunits, and the whole enzyme is called the holoenzyme. There is a core enzyme made up of four polypeptides. The holoenzyme consists of this core enzyme combined with the σ factor. The RNA polymerase holoenzyme binds to the promoter and initiates transcription. Once bound to the promoter, the polymerase usually makes several abortive attempts at transcription, often synthesizing a very short RNA molecule of less than 10 nucleotides before ceasing transcription and starting over. Once transcription has succeeded beyond about 10 nucleotides, the σ factor is released and the core enzyme proceeds through the elongation phase.

10. *(B)* One of several proteins that enhance chain elongation of RNA during RNA synthesis in prokaryotes is TFIIS. TFIIS comes into play when RNA polymerase II stalls for some reason as it is transcribing DNA. This usually happens when the polymerase encounters adverse configurations in the template DNA. When the polymerase stalls, TFIIS causes RNA polymerase to back up, and removes a few nucleotides from the 3′ end of the RNA, permitting RNA polymerase to attempt elongation again through the point where the stall occurred.

11. *(B)* There are several reasons why transcription and translation are not coupled in eukaryotes. First, eukaryotic mRNAs undergo extensive posttranscriptional processing before translation can occur on the finished mRNA product. Second, processed mRNAs must be transported out of the nucleus through the nuclear membrane pores to sites in the cytoplasm where translation takes place. For these major reasons, coupled transcription and translation of eukaryotic mRNA is not possible.

12. *(B)* The cell must prevent premature transcription termination when RNA polymerase transcribes through nucleotide sequences within the coding regions of genes that could signal termination. For instance, rho-dependent transcription termination involves binding of the protein rho to a rho binding site on the transcribed mRNA behind RNA polymerase, causing RNA polymerase to cease transcription. Within a single gene, there may be more than one rho binding site. These sites are called potential terminators because they have nucleotide sequences that should cause rho-dependent termination but rarely do because of coupled transcription and translation. Ribosomes follow closely behind RNA polymerase, blocking potential sites on the mRNA where rho could bind. Without rho on the RNA, RNA polymerase continues transcribing. The prokaryotic transcription system ensures that the ribosomes stay close to the RNA polymerase. Because transcription of mRNA can go faster than ribosome movement, certain regulatory proteins, such as NusA, slow the polymerase so that ribosomes stay close to it, covering the mRNA and preventing rho from binding to the RNA in the coding region. Eventually, the ribosomes arrive at the translation termination site and dissociate from the mRNA. Beyond the translation termination site, ribosomes do not bind to the mRNA, and rho is free to bind to the mRNA when a termination signal is encountered, and facilitate termination of transcription.

13. *(B)* The difference in (A+T)/(C+G) ratios between the two species will be in the genes that code for mRNA. The genes coding the tRNAs and rRNAs are highly conserved among prokaryotes because they encode molecules that are similar in structure. These genes contribute little to the difference between the

two species in (A+T)/(C+G) ratio.

14. *(A)* The promoters for genes transcribed by RNA polymerase III are located within the transcribed region of the gene, downstream from the transcription startpoint. For genes transcribed by RNA polymerases I and II, the promoters are located immediately upstream of the transcribed sequences.

15. *(B)* **(a)** RNA polymerase II. **(b)** RNA polymerase III. **(c)** RNA polymerase I. **(d)** (We will consider the sense strand as the "gene," so the 5′ end of the gene is upstream from the transcription startpoint on the antisense strand.) RNA polymerases I and II. **(e)** RNA polymerase I. **(f)** RNA polymerase II. **(g)** In most eukaryotic species it is RNA polymerase III. In some species it is RNA polymerase I, which transcribes the 5S rRNAs as part of the large precursor rRNA. **(h)** RNA polymerase III.

16. *(C)* *Initiation of transcription in prokaryotes.* The transcription startpoint is an A in most *E. coli* genes. Examination of a number of promoters in *E. coli* has revealed two important conserved sequences. The center of a six-nucleotide conserved sequence is located about 10 nucleotide pairs upstream from the transcription startpoint, although the actual distance may vary from 9 to 18 nucleotide pairs. Because of its position, this sequence is referred to as the −10 sequence, or sometimes the Pribnow box in honor of its discoverer. The consensus sequence is TATAAT. The other conserved sequence in prokaryotic promoters is located about 35 nucleotides upstream of the transcription startpoint and is called the −35 sequence. Its consensus sequence is TTGACA. The −10 sequence and the −35 sequence in *E. coli* genes each have specific roles in transcription. The −35 sequence is necessary for the initial binding of RNA polymerase holoenzyme to the promoter. The −10 sequence is the site where the two DNA strands separate in preparation for initiation of transcription by the polymerase.

In prokaryotes, a single type of RNA polymerase transcribes every gene, including genes that encode rRNAs, tRNAs, and mRNAs. This polymerase has several polypeptide subunits, and the whole enzyme is called the holoenzyme. There is a core enzyme made up of four polypeptides: two copies of the α subunit and one copy each of the β and β′ subunits. The holoenzyme consists of this core enzyme combined with a fifth polypeptide known as the sigma (σ) factor. The RNA polymerase holoenzyme binds to the promoter and initiates transcription. Once bound to the promoter, the polymerase usually makes several abortive attempts at transcription, often synthesizing a very short RNA molecule of less than 10 nucleotides before ceasing transcription and starting over. Once transcription has succeeded beyond about 10 nucleotides, the s factor is released and the core enzyme proceeds through the elongation phase.

Initiation of transcription in eukaryotes. In eukaryotic genes that encode mRNA, the transcription startpoint is typically the central A within a short conserved sequence of three nucleotides, PyAPy (where "Py" refers to either of the two pyrimidines, C or T). Because transcription begins at the A in this sequence, the first nucleotide on the 5′ end of the mRNA is usually an A followed by a pyrimidine. Most eukaryotic mRNA genes have a conserved DNA sequence at about −25 to −30 called the TATA box or Hogness box, which has the consensus sequence TATAAAA. The CAAT box, with the consensus sequence GGCCAATCT, is present in many promoters at about −75 to −80, although this position and sequence may vary significantly. Upstream of the CAAT box, most eukaryotic promoters have additional conserved sequences. Two of the most common are the GC box (GGGCGG) and the CACCC box (GCCACACCC). These sequences identify the most common features of promoters for eukaryotic genes that encode mRNAs. Some mRNA genes lack one or more of these sequences, so we cannot say that they are essential parts of every promoter.

In eukaryotes, RNA polymerase does not recognize conserved sequences in promoters on its own and bind to them. Proteins called transcription factors first bind to the conserved sequences and then assist the RNA polymerase in initiation of transcription.

Several transcription factors are required for a eukaryotic RNA polymerase to initiate transcription. As an example, consider a model for the assembly of transcription factors and RNA polymerase II to form the basal eukaryotic transcription complex. According to this model, TFIID is the first transcription factor to bind with the promoter, and it does so at the TATA box. TFIID is a complex that consists of a protein called TBP (for TATA-binding protein) and any of several additional proteins depending on the promoter. TFIIA binds to TFIID either before or after TFIID binds to the DNA. When it binds before, TFIIA appears to accelerate the binding of TFIID to the DNA. A third transcription factor, TFIIB, then binds to the DNA-bound TFIID-TFIIA complex downstream of the TATA box and sets up a conformation that allows RNA polymerase II to bind to the complex and the DNA. Two other transcription factors, TFIIE and TFIIF, then bind to the complex. One of them, TFIIF, acquires energy by hydrolyzing ATP to ADP. TFIIH and TFIIJ also bind to the complex. TFIIH is a helicase that apparently assists in unwinding the DNA into single strands for transcription to begin. Once initiation has begun, RNA polymerase II separates from the transcription initiation complex and proceeds on its own through elongation.

17. *(B)* Both sequences are high in A-T base pairs. Both sequences are used for separation of DNA strands to expose the template DNA strand to the RNA polymerase system in preparation for transcription to begin at the transcription initiation site. These sites perform that function best because A-T bases pairs, which are held together by two hydrogen bonds, require less energy to separate than G-C base pairs, which are held together by three hydrogen bonds.

18. *(B)* We described the functions of TFIIA, TFIIB, TFIID, TFIIE and TFIIF in the answer to question 16. They are transcription factors for RNA polymerase II. They assist in binding the polymerase to gene promoters and separating the DNA strands for initiation of transcription. TFIIS comes into play when RNA polymerase II stalls. Occasionally, RNA polymerase II enters into a configuration or encounters a nucleotide sequence that causes the polymerase to stall on the DNA, halting transcription with the RNA still attached. When this happens, TFIIS causes the RNA polymerase to back up, and then TFIIS removes the 3′ end of the RNA, permitting the RNA polymerase to attempt elongation again over the point where it stalled.

19. *(C)* In RNA the pyrimidine U replaces T. Because the DNA strand shown is the sense strand, the sequence should have 5′ GTTTATCA 3′ in it. Once this sequence has been identified, the −10 and −35 sequences can be identified by counting 10 and 35 nucleotides upstream from the G at the transcription startpoint, then identifying the sequences that most closely correspond to the −10 and −35 consensus sequences. The positions of these sequences are as follows:

```
             −35                                −10
5´  ATTCTCATGT(TTGACA)GCTTATCATCGATAAGC(TTTAAT)GCGGTAGTTTATCACAGT  3´
```

20. *(B) Initiation of transcription.* The holoenzyme (core enzyme plus σ factor) binds initially to the −35 sequence. The −10 sequence is where the two DNA strands first separate in preparation for transcription initiation and DNA strand separation at the Pribnow box (−10 sequence). Once bound to the promoter, the polymerase makes several abortive attempts at transcription (the transcription startpoint is an A about 10 nucleotides downstream from the −10 sequence), synthesizing a short RNA of about 10 nucleotides before ceasing and starting over. Once transcription has succeeded beyond about 10 nucleotides, the σ factor is released and the core enzyme proceeds through the elongation phase of transcription.

Termination of transcription. Transcription is terminated in two different ways: rho-dependent termination and intrinsic termination. Both kinds of transcription termination can occur only after the ribosome nearest the polymerase has disassembled from the RNA at the site for termination of translation. The absence of ribosomes in the mRNA exposes the sites for termination of transcription.

In intrinsic termination, the nucleotide sequence near the end of the transcribed RNA specifies where transcription terminates. The nucleotide sequence at the transcription termination site is called an intrinsic terminator. Intrinsic terminators contain a conserved sequence with the consensus sequence UUUU-UUA in the RNA and a hairpin structure in the RNA just upstream from the conserved sequence. The hairpin forms when complementary nucleotides in the RNA pair with each other to form a double-stranded segment. RNA polymerase pauses because of the hairpin and the RNA separates from the DNA at the UUUUUUA conserved sequence. Because this sequence is formed entirely of the weaker U-A and A-T nucleotide pairs (recall that these nucleotide pairs share only two hydrogen bonds), separation of the RNA from the DNA requires a minimum of energy.

Rho-dependent termination is the termination of transcription resulting from the interaction of a protein called rho with the mRNA and the RNA polymerase at a site called a rho-dependent terminator. A high C and low G content upstream of the terminator signals rho to bind to the mRNA. Downstream from the rho binding site is a sequence that causes RNA polymerase to pause. Rho moves along the mRNA and catches up to the RNA polymerase at the point where RNA polymerase has paused. Rho then causes RNA polymerase to separate from the DNA, terminating transcription.

21. *(B)* **(a)** Elongation does not proceed at a constant rate. *E. coli* RNA polymerase apparently elongates the RNA in periodic bursts of RNA synthesis, each followed by a brief pause. Also, certain proteins, such as NusA, affect the rate of elongation. NusA modulates the rate of transcription so that it is similar to the rate of translation, permitting the slower ribosomes to stay close to the RNA polymerase. **(b)** A major benefit of maintaining translation at the same rate as transcription is that this reduces the possibility of premature termination of transcription. Rho-dependent termination sites are often present in nucleotide sequences within the polypeptide-encoding regions of genes in *E. coli*. If rho were to bind at these sites near enough to interact with the polymerase, transcription could be prematurely terminated. NusA slows the polymerase so that the nearest translating ribosome can keep up with the polymerase, keeping the internal rho binding sites covered. The same problem is possible with sequences that resemble intrinsic terminators within the polypeptide-encoding region. The hairpins of potential intrinsic terminators cannot form when ribosomes are in close proximity to the RNA polymerase.

22. *(B)* A hairpin in newly transcribed RNA immediately behind the prokaryotic polymerase causes the RNA polymerase to pause momentarily.

23. *(B)* Rho binding to the rho-dependent binding site immediately behind the RNA polymerase is sufficient to terminate transcription; no hairpin is required.

24. *(B) Prokaryotic termination.* In prokaryotes such as *E. coli*, termination is achieved by either of two basic means: rho-dependent termination or intrinsic termination. Termination occurs after the ribosomes have ceased translation on the mRNA strand, having encountered a translation termination signal. The RNA polymerase proceeds until it passes a rho-dependent terminator site or an intrinsic terminator site. Transcription ceases at these sites, and the polymerase is released from the DNA template.

Eukaryotic termination. In eukaryotes, cleavage of the RNA may precede termination of transcription, so the 3′ end of the RNA may not represent the true termination site. Termination differs depending on the RNA polymerase that transcribes the gene. RNA polymerase I terminates transcription about 18 nucleotides upstream of a site characterized by a 17-nucleotide consensus sequence AGGTCGACCAG-(A/T)(A/T)NTCG.

The RNA molecules transcribed by RNA polymerase II are usually cleaved about 11–30 nucleotides downstream from a highly conserved sequence in the RNA with the consensus sequence AAUAAA. After cleavage, RNA polymerase II continues transcribing the gene. Many genes transcribed by this polymerase lack a specific site for termination. Transcription may terminate anywhere from a few hundred to a thousand nucleotides downstream from the cleavage site. The RNA fragment produced between the cleavage site and termination is degraded.

RNA polymerase III apparently recognizes a specific site in the genes it transcribes as a termination site.

25. *(C)* An mRNA may contain a potential intrinsic terminator (a sequence of nucleotides that can form a hairpin followed immediately by a series of U's). Ribosomes stay close enough to the RNA polymerase to completely interfere with hairpin formation within polypeptide-encoding sequences of the mRNA, preventing potential intrinsic terminators from terminating transcription.

26. *(C)* Ribosomes do not translate rRNAs. Consequently, ribosomes cannot cover potential terminators in rRNAs and prevent them from terminating transcription. Because premature termination of transcription for rRNAs is highly disadvantageous to the cell (it would interfere with ribosome formation), natural selection should readily eliminate these sites.

27. *(C)* The hairpin region contains a sequence, half of which is inversely complementary to the other half, that is found in the underlined regions below:

5´ AACGCATGAG<u>AAAGCCCCCGGAAG</u>ATCACC<u>CTTCCGGGGGCTTT</u>ATATAATTAGCGCGGTTGAT 3´

When these regions pair with one another, they form the hairpin diagrammed below:

```
              C
          T       A
          A       C
            G-C
            A-T
            A-T
            G-C
            G-C
            C-G
            C-G
            C-G
            C-G
            C-G
            G-C
            A-T
            A-T
            A-T
5´ AACGCATGAG    ATATAATTAGCGCGGTTGAT 3´
```

28. *(C)* **(a)** The A should be found between two pyrimidines (PyAPy) to serve as a startpoint for transcription. If the A is altered by mutation, RNA polymerase II must search beyond the mutation point for another sequence that meets this criterion to begin transcription. The chance that the configuration will occur is $(1/2 \times 1/4 \times 1/2) = 1/16$ nucleotides (about once every 16 nucleotides). This means that the distance between the "boxes" that signal polymerase attachment and the start signal must increase. This distance has been shown to be critical for initiation of transcription. Apparently, in this case transcription was not stopped but was reduced by the increased distance to the next available startpoint. **(b)** The first nucleotide in eukaryotic pre-mRNA is usually an A. This nucleotide plays an important role as the nucleotide to which the 5´ cap is attached during pre-mRNA processing.

29. *(C)* **(a)** The sense strand has the same sequence as the mRNA fragment, but with U replacing T in the mRNA. The sense strand is listed below with the corresponding sequence underlined:

5´ GTAAACACGGTACGATGTACCAC<u>ATGAAACGACAGTGAG</u>TCA 3´

(b) Based on the sequence of the 5′ end of the mRNA, the transcription startpoint is indicated below by the arrow. The -10 sequence is boxed.

$$\downarrow$$

5′ GTAAACACGG⏢TACGAT⏢GTACCAC<u>ATGAAACGACAGTGAG</u>TCA 3′

(c) The –10 sequence differs from its consensus sequence by two nucleotides.

30. *(C)* The position of the intron is indicated below by parentheses. Its position can be found by recognizing that its 5′ end must be a GT and its 3′ end an AG, and that the nucleotides at the ends of the intron should resemble their respective consensus sequences. The sequence on the 5′ end (GTTGGT) differs from its consensus sequence (GTAAGT) by two nucleotides. The nucleotides on the 3′ end (CCACC-CTTAG) differ from the consensus sequence (6PyNCAG) by two nucleotides. Also, a conserved sequence (TGCCTAT) that differs by one nucleotide from the consensus sequence PyNPyPyPuAPy is located 25 nucleotides upstream of the 3′ end of the intron. These conserved sequences are underlined below:

TTGGTGGTGAGGCCCTGGGCAG(<u>GTTGGT</u>ATCAAGGTTACAAGACAGGTTTAAGGAGACCAATAGAAACTG-

GCATGTGGAGACAGAGAAGACTCTTGGGTTTCTGATAGGCACTGACTCTCTC<u>TGCCTAT</u>TGGTCTATTTTC-

<u>CCACCCTTAG</u>)GCTGCTGGTGGTCTAC

Note that the intron is 129 nucleotides long, as indicated in the problem.

31. *(C)* **(a)** The intron can be identified with the same procedure used in solving the previous problem. The intron is indicated by parentheses below with the conserved sequences on the ends underlined. The conserved sequence at the 3′ end of the intron is ACCTTTTCAG which differs from its consensus sequence (6PyNCAG) by one nucleotide. Knowing the intron is 87 nucleotides long, we count 86 nucleotides upstream from the G and encounter a GT in the right position. The sequence GTTACT differs from its consensus sequence (GTAAGT) by two nucleotides.

ATACGTTGTGAAGATGGAAAATGGACAGAACCTCCAAAATGCATTG(<u>GTTACT</u>AACACCTTGAAGAAGCTTTGC-

TAAAATGAAATCTGCATGTGTAGCTAAATGGTCAGTTCTCTTTCAACTGT<u>ACCTTTTCAG</u>)AAGGACAGGAGAA-

GGTAGCCTGTGAGGACCCA

(b) The nucleotide sequence of the mRNA in this region is established by splicing the ends of the exons together and substituting U for T:

AUACGUUGUGAAGAUGGAAAAUGGACAGAACCUCCAAAAUGCAUUGAAGGACAGGAGAAGGUAGCCUGUGAGGACC-

CA

32. *(C)* **(a)** The consensus sequence is the AAUAAA sequence that signals cleavage and polyadenylation on the 3′end of the mRNA. Below we have aligned the sequences by the AAUAAA sequence and have boxed that sequence in the mRNAs:

```
     UGGUCUUUGAAUAAAGUCUGAGUGAGUGGCpoly(A)

        UGGCUAAUAAAGGAAAUUUAUUUUCAUUGCpoly(A)

     UGGUCUUUGAAUAAAGUCUGAGUGGGCGGCpoly(A)

        UGCCUAAUAAAAACAUUUAUUUUCAUUGCpoly(A)

     AAUAUUCAAUAAAGUGAGUCUUUGCACUUGpoly(A)

   CCUUUAAUCAUAAUAAAAACAUGUUUAAGCpoly(A)
```

(b) The distances between the AAUAAA consensus sequences and the polyadenylation sites vary between 13 and 19 nucleotides.

33. *(C)* **(a)** Apparently, the AUUAAA alternative sequence does not affect cleavage of the pre-mRNA. The mutant sequences AACAAA, AAUUAA, AAUACA, and AAUGAA prevent cleavage. The two studies do not contradict one another. A U can substitute for an A in the second position but not in the fourth position. And a C cannot substitute for a U in the third position, nor a C for an A in the fifth position, nor a G for an A in the fourth position. **(b)** These results suggest that most mutations within the AAUAAA site eliminate the signal for cleavage.

Chapter 4
Translation and Protein Function

1. *(B)* Before answering the questions, fill in all of the blanks in the DNA, mRNA, and polypeptide chains in the diagram by comparing the DNA, mRNA, and polypeptide sequences with one another. You can use the base-pairing rules and the genetic code to identify all of the nucleotides and amino acids.

```
            1         5          10          15          20          25
DNA   5´  C A C T G A A G A T G A G G T T G A A A A A C C T G A C  3´
      3´  G T G A C T T C T A C T C C A A C T T T T T G G A C T G  5´


mRNA  5´  C A C U G A A G A U G A G G U U G A A A A A C C U G A C  3´

polypeptide   methionine-arginine-leucine-lysine-asparagine-leucine-threonine-
```

(a) The sense strand has the same sequence as the mRNA with T replacing U. It is the upper strand in the DNA. **(b)** To answer this part of the question, be sure to identify the correct reading frame within the mRNA by verifying the correct position of each codon for each amino acid in the polypeptide chain shown. Then locate the codon corresponding to the missing amino acid and find the amino acid specified by the codon in the genetic code. The amino acid is leucine. **(c)** The key to the missing nucleotide in position 11 is the corresponding amino acid in the amino acid chain, which is methionine, encoded by AUG. Therefore, the nucleotide at position 11 is G.

2. *(B)* The genetic code is universal. This means that tRNAs, ribosomes, and proteins associated with transcription and translation interpret the same genetic information in the same way. The gene that encodes a polypeptide in one species encodes exactly the same polypeptide in cells of another species. The inserted firefly luciferase gene was reengineered to carry a promoter sequence that could be controlled in the tobacco plant cells and tissues. The tobacco cells transcribed the mRNA and their ribosomes translated the mRNA into luciferase.

3. *(B)* **(a)** Note that the sequence is near the 5´ end of insulin mRNA. Be sure you are looking for this sequence by reading the mRNA in the correct direction. **(b)** We conclude that the sequence shown here (CCUGUGGAUGCGCCU) does not begin with the proper reading frame. Using the given amino acid sequence (LeuTrpMetArgLeu) as the basis for determining the proper code sequence in the polynucleotide, we note that the codons for the amino acid leucine begin with either UU or CU. The first CU above ends with a G. According to the genetic code, CUG codes for leucine. The correct reading frame for the codon sequence must be

LeuTrpMetArgLeu
CCUGUGGAUGCGCCU

4. *(B)* That AUG codon is found within the sequence CCUUCUGCC<u>AUG</u>G, which differs by four nucleotides from the consensus sequence GCCGCCPuCC<u>AUG</u>G that is recognized by the small ribosomal subunit and complex as the initiation site for translation. The most important nucleotides, the G following the AUG codon and the purine three nucleotides before the AUG codon, are fully conserved in this sequence. Therefore, this is the initiation codon.

5. *(B)* The CCUCCU is complementary to the AGGAGG sequence in mRNA that appears about seven

nucleotides upstream from the AUG initiation codon in prokaryotic genes. This is called the Shine-Dalgarno sequence and is important for establishing the proper positioning of the ribosome to initiate translation at the AUG initiation codon.

6. *(B)* In prokaryotic initiation, the Shine-Dalgarno sequence is the site where the small subunit of the ribosome binds to the mRNA and is positioned over the AUG initiation codon. In eukaryotic initiation, the small ribosomal subunit and tRNA$_i$Met bind to the 5′ cap of the mRNA, then scan the mRNA until the initiation codon AUG is encountered. Thus, the 5′ cap, rather than a Shine-Dalgarno sequence, serves as the binding site for the small ribosomal subunit in eukaryotes.

7. *(C)* Prokaryotic mRNAs can carry more than one set of reading frames and eukaryotic mRNAs can carry only one set of reading frames because of the differences in the way translation is initiated in the two kinds of cells. Prokaryotic mRNAs can be polycistronic (carry several sets of separate reading frames) because the binding site for the small ribosomal subunit (a Shine-Dalgarno sequence) appears within the mRNA downstream from the 5′ end and can be present in several positions. For instance, the prokaryotic mRNA could be diagrammed as follows:

5′—Shine-Dalgarno—AUG———TER——Shine-Dalgarno-AUG———TER—etc.

where AUG denotes an initiation codon and TER a termination codon. Note that the Shine-Dalgarno sequence (the ribosome attachment site) occurs downstream from the 5′ end. Ribosomes begin attachment at this sequence, move to the AUG, and translate until they disassemble from the mRNA at the termination codon. Ribosomes assemble at the next Shine-Dalgarno sequence, begin translating at the second AUG, continue until they disassemble at the next termination codon, and so on. Hence prokaryotic mRNAs can be polycistronic, coding for several kinds of polypeptides. The reason why eukaryotic mRNA cannot carry information for more than one polypeptide is that the small ribosomal subunit binds at the 5′ end. The 5′ cap, placed on mRNA during posttranscriptional processing, is the signal for the small ribosomal subunit to attach to the mRNA and scan for the initiation codon. All small ribosomal subunits must attach at the 5′ end of the eukaryotic mRNA, and, therefore, they must all begin translation at the first initiation codon. There is no mechanism in eukaryotes for attachment of ribosomes downstream from the 5′ end of mRNA.

8. *(A)* The polynucleotide is UCUCUCUCUCUCUCUCUCUCUC. . . . The codons are UCU CUC UCU CUC and so forth. These codons correspond to the amino acids serine and leucine. Note that the codons are the same no matter where we put the reading frame. The polypeptide synthesized would be SerLeuSerLeu etc. Or the polypeptide could be LeuSerLeuSer etc., depending on whether the initial codon is UCU or CUC.

9. *(A)* The polynucleotide is UCAGUCAGUCAGUCAG. . . . The codons are UCA GUC AGU CAG UCA GUC AGU CAG and so forth. This forms a four-codon repeating sequence composed of UCA GUC AGU CAG. These codons specify the amino acids serine-valine-serine-glutamine-serine-valine-serine-glutamine in a repeating sequence.

10. *(B)* The polynucleotide is CUAGCUAGCUAGCUAG. . . . The codons are CUA GCU AGC UAG CUA GCU AGC UAG and so forth. This forms a four-codon repeating sequence composed of CUA GCU AGC UAG. An important feature of this sequence is that every fourth codon, UAG, is a termination codon. This sequence produces a tripeptide leucine-alanine-serine.

11. *(B)* The cell would not die if one 5.8S rRNA gene were deleted from the genome because many copies of this gene are present in the genome and are actively transcribed.

12. *(B)* You can answer this question by looking at each amino acid and the codons that encode it, then determining how many different tRNAs are required to encode that amino acid. For example, the

codons for phenylalanine are UUU and UUC. Both can pair with the anticodon 3′ AAG 5′, so a single tRNA is required for phenylalanine. Three amino acids (leucine, serine, and arginine) require three tRNAs each. Five amino acids (valine, proline, threonine, alanine, and glycine) require two tRNAs each. The 12 remaining amino acids (phenylalanine, isoleucine, methionine, tyrosine, histidine, glutamine, asparagine, lysine, aspartic acid, glutamic acid, cysteine, and tryptophan) require one tRNA each. This adds up to a total of 31 different tRNAs as the minimum requirement. However, most cells have more than the minimum number.

13. *(A)* A charged tRNA enters the P site without having previously occupied the A site only during initiation of translation. The only tRNA that may do this is the initiator tRNA.

14. *(C)* For this particular nucleotide sequence in the mRNA,

The AAG lysine codon can pair with the anticodons 3′ UUU 5′ and 3′ UUC 5′.
The AUG methionine codon can pair only with the anticodon 3′ UAC 5′.
The UUU phenylalanine codon can pair with the anticodons 3′ AAA 5′ and 3′ AAG 5′.
The CUA leucine codon can pair with the anticodons 3′ GAU 5′ and 3′ GAI 5′.
The GUU valine codon can pair with the anticodons 3′ CAA 5′, 3′ CAG 5′, and 3′ CAI 5′.
The CAG glutamine codon can pair with the anticodons 3′ GUU 5′ and 3′ GUC 5′.

Notice that according to the wobble rules, the anticodon 3′ UAU 5′ should pair with a methionine codon. However, the anticodon 3′ UAU 5′ cannot exist because it could also pair with the AUA isoleucine codon, according to the wobble rules, which would be a violation of the genetic code. Several other anticodons, such as 3′ AAI 5′ and 3′ GUI 5′, also cannot exist because they likewise would violate the genetic code.

15. *(B)* The anticodon 3′ ACI 5′ would pair with the cysteine codons UGU and UGC, and it would also pair with the termination codon UGA. A 3′ ACI 5′ anticodon tRNA would allow the UGA codon to encode cysteine instead of termination of transcription.

16. *(B)* The two codons for tyrosine are UAU and UAC. There are two possible anticodons, 3′ AUA 5′ and 3′ AUG 5′. However the anticodon 3′ AUG 5′ can pair with both tyrosine codons and is therefore the only anticodon required in a tRNA that carries tyrosine.

17. *(B)* Polypeptide synthesis proceeds in the amino → carboxyl direction. Each amino acid (with the exception of the first methionine on the amino end) is added by the formation of a peptide bond between its amino group and the carboxyl group of the amino acid on the carboxyl end of the growing chain. The reaction could not proceed if the amino group were tied up by the tRNA.

18. *(C) Initiation.* The intact ribosome consisting of the large (50S) and small (30S) ribosomal subunits is the structure that is positioned over the initiation codon and receives the charged initiator tRNA.

IF-1 is a protein initiation factor that separates the large and small ribosomal subunits of a free intact ribosome prior to initiation of transcription.

IF-3 is a protein initiation factor that binds to the 30S (small) ribosomal subunit before initiation of translation. This complex then binds to an initiation sequence (the Shine-Dalgarno sequence and the initiation codon) near the 5′ end of mRNA.

N-formyl-methionyl-tRNA is a specialized initiator tRNA that carries N-formyl-methionine and pairs only with the initiation codon.

GTP is a source of energy for combining the 30S and 50S ribosomal subunits.

Elongation. The intact ribosome consisting of the large (50S) and small (30S) ribosomal subunits is the structure that moves along mRNA at three-nucleotide intervals. It carries the A and P sites for activated tRNAs and provides the structure for alignment of tRNA anticodons with mRNA codons.

EF-Tu and GTP are molecules that attach to the activated tRNA and assist it in entering the A site.

Peptidyl transferase is the enzyme that catalyzes formation of a peptide bond between the carboxyl group of the amino acid in the P site with the amino group of the amino acid in the A site.

Ef-G and GTP are molecules that assist the ribosome in translocation from one codon to the next.

19. *(B)* There is no known way for the sequence of amino acids in a protein to be copied directly into another protein molecule. Amino acids cannot pair with one another as nucleotides can. Also, it is not possible to reverse-translate the amino acid sequence of a protein into a series of codons in a nucleic acid because the ribosome cannot synthesize RNA using a polypeptide template. The biochemical system of most cells (DNA replication, transcription, and translation) is set up to transfer information in only one direction: DNA → RNA → protein. Replication is DNA → DNA. Transcription is DNA → RNA. Enzymes called reverse transcriptases can synthesize DNA from an RNA template (RNA → DNA), so the first step (transcription) is reversible. However, translation is exclusively RNA → protein.

20. *(B)* Yanofsky observed that each mutation that substituted a single nucleotide within a gene substituted a single amino acid in the protein specified by that gene. If the code were overlapping, a single nucleotide substitution within the gene would affect three adjacent amino acids in the protein. In no case did a single base substitution affect more than one amino acid. Thus, his experiments led to two major conclusions: (1) the nucleotide sequence in DNA is colinear with the amino acid sequence in a protein, and (2) the genetic code is nonoverlapping.

21. *(C)* The sequence CACCATG includes the gene's initiation codon (ATG). The initiation codon must be embedded within a conserved sequence (with the consensus sequence GCCGCCPuCC<u>AUG</u>G) that identifies it as the initiation codon. The two most important nucleotides that must be conserved within this sequence (aside from the initiation codon itself) are the G that follows the AUG codon and the purine that is three nucleotides upstream from the AUG codon. This mutation changes a purine at that position (A) to a pyrimidine (C). Thus, the mutation prevents initiation of transcription at the correct initiation codon.

22. *(C)* Poly UC produces two codons, UCU and CUC, which code for serine and leucine, respectively. Two kinds of charged tRNAs are needed. With only one amino acid added to the cell-free translation system, only one of the needed charged tRNAs can be formed. Without both kinds of charged tRNAs, the ribosome cannot translate the synthetic mRNA.

23. *(C)* The results of this study indicate that it is the anticodon in the tRNA, not the amino acid attached to the tRNA, that determines whether or not the amino acid is incorporated. Once an amino acid is bound to a tRNA, that amino acid will be incorporated into the polypeptide chain wherever the corresponding codon is located in the mRNA even if the amino acid is modified chemically before incorporation.

24. *(C)* **(a)** The 3′ ACU 5′ mutant anticodon is complementary to the UGA termination codon. When this mutant tRNA is present, the ribosome incorporates tryptophan wherever it encounters a UGA termination codon and continues to translate beyond the termination codon. **(b)** According to the wobble rules, the 3′ ACU 5′ mutant anticodon can also pair with a UGG tryptophan codon, so it will place tryptophan in the polypeptide when it pairs with a UGG codon. **(c)** The mutant tRNAs are called suppressor tRNAs because they suppress (overcome) the premature termination effect of a TGG → TGA mutation.

25. (D) (a) The six leucine codons are UUA, UUG, CUU, CUC, CUA, and CUG. The codons CUU and CUC should be present in the synthetic mRNAs made from the U/C mixture. The codon UUG should be found in the synthetic mRNAs made from the U/G mixture. One of the leucine tRNAs recognized CUU and/or CUC but not UUG. The anticodon of this leucine tRNA should have 3′ GA in the first two positions. In the wobble position it could carry either a G or an I, so the anticodon could be either 3′ GAG 5′ or 3′ GAI 5′. The leucine tRNA that recognized the UUG codon in the U/G synthetic mRNA should have 3′ AA in the first two positions. The nucleotide at the wobble position must be able to pair with G and must, therefore, be C or U. This leucine tRNA could have the anticodons 3′ AAC 5′ or 3′ AAU 5′. (b) Both UUA and UUG codons pair with the anticodon 3′ AAU 5′. Codons CUU and CUC pair with the anticodon 3′ GAG 5′, and codons CUA and CUG pair with the anticodon 3′ GAU 5′. Thus, a minimum of three kinds of leucine tRNAs are required to pair with all six leucine codons. Alternatively, codons CUU, CUC, and CUA pair with the anticodon 3′ GAI 5′, and the codon CUG pairs with 3′ GAC 5′. This alternative also requires a minimum of three kinds of leucine tRNAs. (c) and (d) The U/C mixture would make codons UUU, UUC, CCC, CCU, UCC, and UCU in addition to the leucine codons CUU and CUC.

UUU is a phenylalanine codon that pairs with the anticodons 3′ AAA 5′ and 3′ AAG 5′.
UUC is a phenylalanine codon that pairs with the anticodons 3′ AAG 5′ and 3′ AAI 5′.
(Note that the anticodon 3′ AAI 5′ cannot exist because it would violate the genetic code.)
CCC is a proline codon that pairs with the anticodons 3′ GGG 5′ and 3′ GGI 5′.
CCU is a proline codon that pairs with the anticodons 3′ GGA 5′, 3′ GGG 5′, and 3′ GGI 5′.
UCC is a serine codon that pairs with the anticodons 3′ AGG 5′ and 3′ AGI 5′.
UCU is a serine codon that pairs with the anticodons 3′ AGA 5′, 3′ AGG 5′, and 3′ AGI 5′.

The U/G mix would make codons UUU, UGG, GGG, GGU, UGU, GUU, and GUG in addition to UUG, which is a leucine codon.

UUU is a phenylalanine codon that pairs with the anticodon 3′ AAG 5′.
(Note that the anticodon 3′ AAI 5′ cannot exist because it would violate the genetic code.)
UGG is a tryptophan codon that pairs with the anticodon 3′ ACC 5′.
(Note that the anticodon 3′ ACU 5′ cannot exist because it would violate the genetic code.)
GGG is a glycine codon that pairs with the anticodons 3′ CCU 5′ and 3′ CCC 5′.
GGU is a glycine codon that pairs with the anticodons 3′ CCA 5′, 3′ CCG 5′, and 3′ CCI 5′.
UGU is a cysteine codon that pairs with the anticodons 3′ CCA 5′ and 3′ CCG 5′.
(Note that the anticodon 3′ CCI 5′ cannot exist because it would violate the genetic code.)
GUU is a valine codon that pairs with the anticodons 3′ CAA 5′, 3′ CAG 5′, and 3′ CAI 5′.
GUG is a valine codon that pairs with the anticodons 3′ CAC 5′ and 3′ CAU 5′.

26. (B) The nucleotide pairs should be purine-pyrimidine pairs. Purine-purine or pyrimidine-pyrimidine pairs are unstable and cannot form at the wobble position.

27. (C) Inosine and adenine are both purines. Typically two purines do not pair with one another. However, the positions in the inosine molecule that carry slight positive charges and slight negative charges are such that inosine and adenine are capable of forming two hydrogen bonds between one another. According to the wobble rules, inosine can pair with adenine. Thus, poly-A and poly-I molecules should form a series of A-I pairs with one another to form a double helix. Because the pairs are all purine-purine pairs, the molecule should be of uniform width throughout.

28. *(D)*

Position in Polypeptide	Original Amino Acid	Original Codon	Mutant Amino Acid	Mutant Codon	Nucleotide Substitution in DNA
11	Val	GUG	Met	AUG	G → A
20	Pro	CCN	Thr	ACN	C → A
20	Pro	CCN	Leu	CUN	C → T
21	Ile	AU(Py,A)	Thr	AC(Py,A)	U → C
21	Ile	AU(Py,A)	Val	GU(Py,A)	A → G
25	Asn	AAPy	Ser	AGPy	A → G
33	Asn	AAPy	Ser	AGPy	A → G
46	Arg	AGPu	Lys	AAPu	G → A
61	Arg	AGPu	Gly	GGPu	A → G
65	Gly	GGPy	Ser	AGPy	G → A
81	Thr	ACN	Ala	GCN	A → G
97	Glu	GAPu	Gly	GGPu	A → G
99	Glu	GAPu	Arg	CAPu	G → C
122	Arg	AGPu	Gly	GGPu	A → G
126	Asn	AAPy	Ser	AGPy	A → G
129	Ile	AU(Py,A)	Val	GU(Py,A)	A → G
134	Arg	AGPu	Gly	GGPu	A → G
138	Ser	UCPy	Phe	UUPy	C → T
148	Ser	UCPy	Phe	UUPy	C → T
156	Pro	CCN	Leu	CUN	C → T

29. *(C)* **(a)** The mutant site is at position 156. **(b)** It is the Ser at position 148 which in Table 4.4 is a Ser → Phe substitution. **(c)** This confirms that the genetic code is nonoverlapping. If the code were overlapping, the C → T nucleotide substitution in codon 156 would affect the codons for at least two and perhaps three adjacent amino acids.

30. *(D)* **(a)**

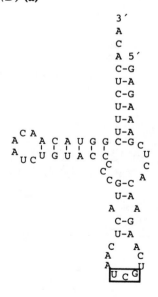

(b) This structure does not have a D arm as most tRNAs do. It does have a TψC arm and an anticodon arm. **(c)** The anticodon is 3´ UCG 5´.

31. *(C)* The pre-mRNA sequence for this fragment is

GAGAUU<u>CGU</u>GGAACUAAUCAUGCCUUUACGCCUAUC

This sequence codes for all amino acids except for the edited CGU codon (underlined). CGU codes for arginine, not cysteine. RNA editing changes the C in CGU to a U to make a UGU codon, which codes for cysteine:

```
GluIleCysGlyThrAsnHisAlaPheThrProIle
GAGAUUUGUGGAACUAAUCAUGCCUUUACGCCUAUC
```

Chapter 5
Mutation

1. *(C)* There are several types of DNA damage that result in transitions. In general, the damage chemically alters the base so that it pairs with the wrong nucleotide during DNA replication. Usually, purines that are damaged still pair with a pyrimidine, and pyrimidines that are damaged still pair with a purine. Thus, most mutations caused by DNA damage are transitions. Here are some examples: (1) Cytosine deamination, in which the amino group on the number 2 carbon of cytosine is replaced by a double-bonded oxygen, converts C to U. When the DNA replicates, an A is paired with the U, causing a G → U transition. (2) Cytosine methylation followed by deamination creates a C → T transition. (3) When base analogs, such as 5-bromouracil or 2-amino purine, are incorporated into a DNA strand during replication, they are lesions that tend to undergo tautomeric shifts more frequently than the nucleotides they replaced. Tautomeric shifts result in transitions, so transitions are more frequent when base analog lesions are present in the DNA. (4) Deaminating agents cause deamination of C to U and A to hypoxanthine, both of which result in transitions when the DNA replicates. (5) Hydroxylating agents add hydroxyl groups to bases and may cause transitions during replication. For example, hydroxylation of C changes C to hydroxyaminocytosine, which pairs with A instead of G, a transition. (6) Alkylating agents add alkyl groups to bases, which causes transitions and transversions, although transitions are more common.

2. *(B)* A loss-of-function mutation is a mutation that causes a decrease or complete loss of functional product encoded by the mutant gene. A mutation that causes an alteration in the amino acid sequence of a polypeptide usually causes the polypeptide to lose its function, hence the term *loss-of-function mutation*. Mutations that alter promoter sequences usually eliminate or reduce transcription, also a loss-of-function mutation. Also, mutations that alter intron removal usually eliminate a gene's function. More rarely, a mutation may cause a gene to produce more functional product when compared to the gene's previous state. These are called *gain-of-function mutations*. Gain-of-function mutations usually alter regulatory regions upstream from a gene that are responsible for reducing transcription. Although gain-of-function mutations are more rare than loss-of-function mutations, they are quite important. Many of the mutations that contribute to the development of cancer are gain-of-function mutations.

3. *(B)* A forward mutation is a change from the original sequence of a gene to a mutant sequence. Most forward mutations are loss-of-function mutations. A reversion is a change from the mutant function of a gene back to its original function. Reversions often consist of a change from a mutant DNA sequence back to the original DNA sequence, restoring the original form of the gene and its product. A transition is more likely to revert to its original form than a transversion. Transitions are also more common than transversions. Thus, a mutation, regardless of how it arose, is more likely to be altered by a transition than a transversion. A mutation that arose by transition reverts back to its original form when it undergoes a second transition. However, a transversion does not revert back to its original form when it undergoes a transition.

4. *(A)* Insertion and deletion mutations in the reading frame for a polypeptide that are not multiples of three nucleotides shift the reading frame for all codons downstream from the mutation, altering most of the amino acids translated from that point on. Most single-nucleotide substitutions, if they have an effect, alter only one amino acid in the polypeptide. Because insertions and deletions affect a larger proportion of the amino acids, they tend to have a greater deleterious effect than substitutions.

5. *(B)* Reversion of a substitution usually requires restoration of the mutant nucleotide to its original form. The probability of such a second mutation is low. A single-nucleotide deletion alters the reading frame by one nucleotide. A single-nucleotide insertion elsewhere in the reading frame can restore the

reading frame and often the gene's function. Because the insertion that restores the reading frame can occur at a number of different sites, it is more probable than reversion of a substitution.

6. *(B)* Cytosine deamination results in a transition. The deamination reaction replaces an amino group in cytosine with a double-bonded oxygen, which converts C to U. The U pairs with A during DNA replication, causing a G → A transition.

7. *(D)* The DNA sequence aligns with the amino acids as follows:

```
SerAlaArgLeuArgLeuAlaGlyTrpHisLys
TCGGCGCGTCTGCGTCTGGCTGGCTGGCATAAA
```

Within the DNA sequence are three copies of the tetranucleotide repeat CTGG:

```
TCGGCGCGTCTGCGTCTGGCTGGCTGGCATAAA
```

A slippage mutation during DNA replication that *adds* one copy of the CTGG repeat creates a mutant sequence that encodes the first mutant polypeptide and brings a TAA termination codon into frame:

```
SerAlaArgLeuArgLeuAlaGlyTrpLeuAlaTer
TCGGCGCGTCTGCGTCTGGCTGGCTGGCTGGCATAAA
```

A slippage mutation during DNA replication that *deletes* one copy of the CTGG repeat creates a mutant sequence that encodes the second mutant polypeptide:

```
SerAlaArgLeuArgLeuAlaGlyIleLys-(9 amino acids)-COOH
TCGGCGCGTCTGCGTCTGGCTGGCATAAA
```

The premature termination codon is nine codons downstream from the end of the sequence given. This is a mutation hotspot because it is a repeated sequence that is prone to slippage mutations.

8. *(D)* **(a)** This question is solved by comparing the appropriate genetic code for the mutational change:

UGG (transition) (Trp) → UGA
CAG (transition) (Gln) → UAG
CGA (transition) (Arg) → UGA
UGG (transition) (Trp) → UAG
UCA (transversion) (Ser) → UGA

GGA (transversion) (Gly) → UGA
UAU or UAC (both transversions) (Tyr) → UAG
CAA (transition) (Gln) → UAA
UAU or UAC (both transversions) (Tyr) → UAA

(b) Codons that could be converted to termination codons by single-nucleotide substitutions are:

UAU → UAA
UAC → UAA
CAA → UAA
GAA → UAA
AAA → UAA
UUA → UAA
UCA → UAA

UAU → UAG
UAC → UAG
UUG → UAG
UCG → UAG
UGG → UAG
CAG → UAG
AAG → UAG
GAG → UAG

UGU → UGA
UGC → UGA
UGG → UGA
CGA → UGA
AGA → UGA
GGA → UGA
UUA → UGA
UCA → UGA

(c) GAA, AAA, UUA, UUG, UCG, AAG, GAG, UGU, UGC, and AGA. **(d)** Each codon listed in the answer to part c requires a transversion to change it into a termination codon.

9. *(B)* Transitions are the most common type of single-nucleotide substitution. Transitions in the first nucleotide of CAA and CAG glutamine codons, the second or third nucleotide of a UGG tryptophan codon, and the first nucleotide of a CGA arginine codon create termination codons.

10. *(C)* All mutagenic agents listed in this question promote transitions during DNA replication. Each causes specific transitions. However, it is important to remember that a transition in one strand results in a transition in the other strand when the mutant DNA strand serves as a template during replication. For example, deamination of C to hydroxyaminocytosine when hydroxylamine is present causes a G → A transition in the newly synthesized strand during replication. When the strand with the mutant A is used as a template during the next round of replication, it causes a T to be placed where a C should be. Thus, for every purine → purine transition in one strand, there is a pyrimidine → pyrimidine transition in the other strand after replication, and vice versa. If hydroxyaminocytosine is in the antisense strand of a gene, it causes a G → A transition in the sense strand. If hydroxyaminocytosine is in the sense strand, it indirectly causes a C → T transition in the sense strand after two rounds of replication. With this in mind, let's look at the specific transitions caused by the listed mutagens. **(a)** Nitrous acid causes all possible transitions (C → T, T → C, G → A, A → G). **(b)** and **(c)** 5-BU and 2-AP both cause A → G and T → C transitions. **(d)** and **(e)** Bisulfite compounds and hydroxylamine both cause G → A and C → T transitions.

Now let's look at the amino acid substitutions in the question. Of those listed, only three result from transitions: Val → Ile, Ala → Thr, and Trp → Ter all arise from a G → A mutation in the sense strand (which corresponds to a C → T mutation in the antisense strand). All of the other amino acid substitutions listed require at least one transversion, and therefore are not likely to arise from any of the mutagens listed. Of the mutagens listed, nitrous acid, bisulfite compounds, and hydroxylamine can cause G → A and C → T transitions.

11. *(B)* Intercalating agents tend to cause insertion or deletion mutations, usually of a single nucleotide. If such a mutation occurs in the reading frame for translation, it causes a frameshift mutation. An insertion of a single nucleotide can restore the reading frame that was shifted by deletion of a single nucleotide; or a deletion of a single nucleotide can restore the reading frame that was shifted by insertion of a single nucleotide. Thus, mutagens that are most likely to cause reversions of a frameshift mutation are those that cause single-nucleotide insertions and deletions. Of the mutagens listed in the question, only proflavin (an acridine dye) causes single-nucleotide insertions or deletions.

12. *(A)* Ionizing radiation causes free radicals to form, which, in turn, damage DNA. The two enzyme system of superoxide dismutase and catalase eliminates free radicals before they can damage DNA.

13. *(B)* Several mechanisms can repair pyrimidine dimers. They include:

(1) Photoreactivating enzyme (PRE), an enzyme that repairs lesions in DNA when in the presence of blue light.

(2) Excision repair, a mechanism that excises a lesion and some surrounding nucleotides from double-stranded DNA, then uses the other strand as a template to fill in the gap with new nucleotides.

(3) Recombination repair, a mechanism that recognizes a lesion after the DNA strands have separated for replication, pairs a segment of DNA from the complementary strand with the DNA that contains the lesion, then uses excision repair to remove the lesion.

(4) Error-prone repair, a mechanism that allows insertion of an incorrect nucleotide opposite a lesion, followed by repair of the lesion using the incorrect nucleotide as a template.

(5) Transcription-repair coupling, a mechansim that is activated when RNA polymerase encounters a lesion in the antisense strand during transcription and ceases transcription. The lesion is then repaired and transcription can proceed.

14. *(B)* (1) AP endonucleases are part of excision repair mechanisms that specifically recognize AP sites and remove them along with surrounding nucleotides. DNA polymerases then fill in the gaps. (2) Recombination repair can repair AP sites, as illustrated in Figure 5.20. (3) An AP site can also be repaired through error-prone repair or transcription-repair coupling.

15. *(B)* Postreplication DNA repair would be affected. There would be a failure to recognize errors in the newly synthesized strand and repair them because the newly synthesized strand could not be distinguished from the template strand by the postreplication repair system.

16. *(A)* Photoreactivating enzyme (PRE) repairs pyrimidine dimers caused by nonionizing radiation. PRE can only function in the presence of light in the blue range of the spectrum. Hence, PRE can function in the cells treated with the full-spectrum visible light but not in the cells treated with just UV light. Thus, more mutations should accumulate in the cells treated with UV light only.

17. *(C)* **(a)** All of the mutations listed arise from transitions except Pro $\rightarrow$ Thr, which arises from a C $\rightarrow$ A transversion in the sense strand. **(b)** Of the 32 mutations observed, 31 (96.875%) were transitions. **(c)** Transitions are much more frequent than transversions in RNA treated with nitrous acid.

18. *(C)* **(a)** To be a frameshift mutation, the deletion must be within the reading frame. Because the deletion is outside of the reading frame, it is not a frameshift mutation. **(b)** The deletion is within the recognition sequence for initiation of translation. As discussed in section 4.6, the small ribosomal subunit and initiator tRNA scan the mRNA until they encounter a conserved sequence that is close to the consensus sequence GCCGCCPuCCAUGG (where the underlined AUG is the initiation codon). The most important nucleotides in this sequence (aside from the AUG codon) are the purine that is three nucleotides upstream from the AUG codon, and the G following the AUG codon. The deletion mutation eliminates an A, which is the purine three nucleotides upstream from the AUG codon. After the deletion, the nucleotide in this position is a C, which is a pyrimidine. Thus, although correctly spliced mRNA is produced, the ribosomes cannot correctly translate the mRNA because they fail to recognize the correct initiation codon.

19. *(C)* **(a)** The mutation is a T $\rightarrow$ A transversion:

AAGCTGA**T**TCAGGAG (normal)

AAGCTGA**A**TCAGGAG (mutant)

The following boldfaced terms from sections 5.1 and 5.2 apply to this mutation:

point mutation (Only a single nucleotide position was affected.)

substitution mutation (The substitution was T $\rightarrow$ A.)

missense mutation (The mutation altered the amino acid sequence.)

loss-of-function mutation (Fragile X syndrome is caused by a loss of FMRP function. Apparently, the mutation eliminated the function of FMRP.)

forward mutation (The mutation changed the functional protein to a mutant form.)

transversion (The mutation was pyrimidine → purine substitution.)

(b) The mutation affects the third codon in the sequence given. The mutation is a T → A transversion in the second nucleotide of the codon (ATT → AAT), which causes the amino acid substitution Ile → Asn. **(c)** The number of trinucleotide repeats in the mutant sequence is normal and, therefore, is not the cause of fragile X syndrome in this case. Instead, the substitution caused fragile X syndrome by eliminating FMRP activity. **(d)** Males inherit their X chromosome from their mothers. The observation that his mother did not have the mutation indicates that the mutation is a new one that probably occurred in the cells of his mother's germline.

20. *(B)* These mutations are all loss-of-function mutations that eliminate the normal function of FMRP by altering the amino acid sequence of the translated protein or by eliminating transcription of the mRNA, thereby eliminating the protein. When FMRP function is lost, fragile X syndrome develops.

21. *(C)* The presence of AGG's within the CGG repeats breaks up the long CGG repeat sequences into smaller groups of repeats. If the portion of the DNA strand that contains an AGG cryptic triplet slips during replication, the A mispairs with a C, and the mispairing encourages the strands to reassume their proper pairing. Thus, slippage mutations are less likely when cryptic triplets are present.

22. *(C)* Transitions are the most common type of substitution. Transitions at the third nucleotide are same-sense mutations in 60 of the 64 codons in the genetic code. Many transitions at other positions in the codons substitute an amino acid that has similar properties to the original amino acid. For example, valine and alanine are both nonpolar. A GTA → GCA transition causes a valine → alanine substitution, which has little adverse effect on protein function because valine and alanine have similar chemical properties.

23. *(C)* **(a)** As shown in the following table, 63.24% of the observed mutations are transitions:

Transitions		Transversions	
T → C	26	T → A	3
C → T	44	A → T	5
A → G	13	T → G	11
G → A	46	G → T	14
		C → A	13
		A → C	5
		C → G	10
		G → C	14
Totals:	129		75

(b) These results indicate that naturally occurring transitions are observed about twice as often as transversions in this gene. **(c)** Transitions occur spontaneously due to tautomeric shifts in the molecular structure of nucleotides. Spontaneous transversions are much less likely. **(d)** As noted in the answer to the previous question, many transitions are silent or do not adversely affect protein function, and thus are not detected.

24. *(C)* **(a)** CAA, CAG, and CGA. **(b)** The most probable mechanism for mutation at these hotspots is deamination of methylated cytosine to create thymine. **(c)** Cytosine deamination may happen spontaneously or in response to deaminating agents. Unmethylated cytosine is deaminated to uracil, which repair mechanisms may recognize as a lesion that they then repair. However, when methylated cytosine is deaminated, it becomes thymine, which is one of the standard nucleotides, so repair mechanisms are less likely to correct the change, and the mutation is more likely to persist.

25. *(C)* **(a)** It would cause a T → A transversion during replication in the strand paired with the alkylated adenine. A T → A transversion in one strand causes an A → T transversion in the other strand after another round of replication. **(b)** Among the mutations that Takeshima et al. observed were A → T transversions in the sense strand. This model shows how PAHs could cause such mutations.

26. *(D)* **(a)** This is a C → T transition. **(b)** Comparison of the mRNA sequence to the DNA sequence reveals that the startpoint for transcription is 35 nucleotides downstream from the mutation, so the mutation is not in the reading frame and, therefore, does not alter the polypeptide. **(c)** The location of the mutation 35 nucleotides upstream from the transcription startpoint indicates that the mutation probably lies within the –35 sequence of the promoter. The –35 sequence of the original version of the gene is GGCGCA, which differs by four nucleotides from the TTGACA consensus sequence (see section 3.3). The mutation changes the –35 sequence of this gene so that it more closely resembles the consensus sequence. Such a change should increase binding of RNA polymerase and cause increased transcription and, therefore, a gain of function.

27. *(C)* The function of the *lacI* gene product is to inhibit transcription of the *lacZ* gene. Thus, a mutation that increases the function of the *lacI* gene product is a gain-of-function mutation for the *lacI* gene, even though the result is a reduction in the *lacZ* gene product.

28. *(B)* Slippage of mononucleotide, dinucleotide, or tetranucleotide repeats can cause insertions or deletions that are not multiples of three nucleotides, resulting in frameshift mutations. Slippage of trinucleotide repeats causes insertions or deletions that are multiples of three, and they do not shift the reading frame.

29. *(E)* From the genetic code, it is possible to reconstruct the original sequence in the mRNA as follows:

Ala	Glu	Lys	Leu	Phe	Asn
GCN	GAPu	AAPu	UUPu CUN	UUPy	AApy

(where Py signifies a pyrimidine, Pu a purine, and N any of the four nucleotides). The mutant sequence is

Ala	Glu	Lys	Thr	Leu	Ter
GCN	GAPu	AAPu	ACN	CUN UUPu	UAPu UGA

The mutation is a frameshift mutation. The observation that it is at a mutation hotspot suggests that there is a repeated sequence that slips during replication to cause the mutation. When the two sequences are compared, it is clear that the mutant sequence contains a single-nucleotide insertion mutation:

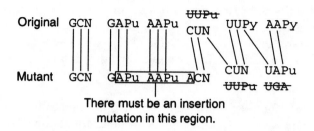

Original   GCN   GAPu   AAPu   ~~UUPu~~   UUPy   AAPy
                                    CUN
Mutant   GCN   GAPu   AAPu   ACN   CUN   UAPu
                                    ~~UUPu~~   ~~UGA~~

There must be an insertion
mutation in this region.

The mutation is probably an insertion of an A in the original sequence of five A's to make a string of six A's in the mutant sequence:

Original   GCNGAAAAACUCUUUAAPy

Mutant   GCNGAAAAAACUCUUUAA

30. *(D)* The first three mutations listed were upstream from the transcribed region and were not within any of the known conserved sequences of promoters. The fourth mutation listed is within an intron in a region whose sequence is not important for intron removal. The intron is removed normally, so the mutation is not present in the mature mRNA. The fifth, sixth, seventh, and eighth mutations are all same-sense mutations; they cause no change in the amino acid chain even though they are within the reading frame.

Chapter 6
An Integrated View of Gene Expression

1. *(B)* Gene expression is the process through which the nucleotide sequence of a gene ultimately manifests its effects in the phenotype of an organism. It includes transcription, RNA processing, translation, protein assembly and modification, protein function, and the effect of protein function on the phenotype. Mutations alter the nucleotide sequence of a gene, which may alter the function of the protein encoded by that gene. When protein function is altered, a phenotype affected by the protein may likewise be altered.

2. *(B)* The R groups of amino acids are classified as hydrophilic (polar, acidic, and basic amino acids) or hydrophobic (nonpolar amino acids). The positions of the various amino acids in the polypeptide chain determine the protein's final three-dimensional structure and its function. Mutations that alter the sequence of amino acids located in the active site of a protein, or mutations that alter the tertiary or quaternary structure of a protein, can change the protein's ability to carry out its function. In the case of hemoglobin, the heme group (which is hydrophobic) is located in a pocket that consists of hydrophobic amino acids that prevent water molecules in the surrounding aqueous fluid from entering the pocket. Oxygen, which is hydrophobic, can enter the pocket, and the hemoglobin molecule can then carry the oxygen. Hemoglobin must also be soluble in the aqueous solution, so the amino acids found on the external surface of hemoglobin are hydrophilic. Mutations that may exchange hydrophilic and hydrophobic amino acids in critical positions within the polypeptide chains can alter either the solubility of hemoglobin or its oxygen-carrying capacity.

3. *(C)* Glutamic acid is acidic and hydrophilic, whereas valine is nonpolar and hydrophobic. The sixth amino acid in each of the two β subunits of hemoglobin is not part of the active site (the heme pocket). Instead, it is located on the external surface of the hemoglobin molecule, where it interacts with the aqueous environment. When a mutation substitutes valine for glutamic acid at this site, the water solubility of the molecule is decreased and the hydrophobic valine seeks a hydrophobic region with which it can interact. A valine on the surface of one molecule may insert itself into the hydrophobic pocket of another molecule, which may likewise insert a valine on its surface into the hydrophobic pocket of a third molecule. The process repeats itself to form a long chain of mutant hemoglobin molecules. Because the hydrophobic pockets are occupied by valine, oxygen molecules cannot enter the pockets, and the hemoglobin loses its oxygen carrying ability. The long chains cause the erythrocytes to assume a sickle shape, which prevents them from passing through capillaries. The lost oxygen-carrying function and sickled cells cause the symptoms of sickle-cell anemia.

4. *(B)* Hemoglobin is not transported in the endoplasmic reticulum but remains outside of cell organelles dissolved in the aqueous solution of the cytoplasm.

5. *(C)* **(a)** There are six codons that encode serine: UCU, UCC, UCA, UCG, AGU, and AGC, and four codons that encode proline: CCU, CCC, CCA, and CCG. The most likely mutation to cause a Ser → Pro substitution is a T → C transition in the DNA that changes the first nucleotide of a UCU, UCC, UCA, or UCG codon to a C. **(b)** Proline cannot participate in the a helix so its presence eliminates an a helix and alters the protein's secondary and tertiary structures, which, in turn, eliminates the activity of the enzyme.

6. *(B)* The word *step* is defined by the method that Srb and Horowitz used to screen for mutants in *Neurospora*. They supplemented minimal medium with arginine and two intermediates, ornithine and citrulline, which allowed them to detect only three "steps" in the pathway. In reality there are more biochemical steps in the pathway because there are more intermediates than the two they tested. Their results showed that the mutations *arg 4, arg 5, arg 6,* and *arg 7* affect steps before the synthesis of ornithine, which is the first intermediate of the two they tested. There may be other intermediates that

precede ornithine in the pathway, and other biochemical steps to synthesize these intermediates, each requiring a different enzyme encoded by a different gene. A mutation in any gene encoding an enzyme that catalyzes a step preceding the synthesis of ornithine would appear at the same step (just before ornithine) in an analysis of the experiments. Thus, the mutations *arg 4, arg 5, arg 6,* and *arg 7* may encode as many as four different enzymes, all of which precede ornithine synthesis in the pathway. Also, many enzymes consist of two or more different subunits, each different subunit encoded by a different gene. Thus, more than one gene may encode a single enzyme that catalyzes a single step in the pathway.

7. *(C)* Chain-terminator mutations create a premature termination codon, so the reading frame ends earlier than it should. The result is an abnormally shortened β-globin polypeptide that is completely non-functional, which renders the hemoglobin nonfunctional as well. The absence of functional hemoglobin causes β^0-thalassemia. Defective promoter mutations reduce transcription but do not alter the product produced by the reduced transcription. Reduced transcription, therefore, produces functional hemoglobin, but less of it, which causes β^+-thalassemia. Some defective mRNA processing mutations affect intron removal and eliminate protein activity, which, in turn, causes β^0-thalassemia. Other defective mRNA processing mutations affect poly (A) tail addition or capping on the 5′ end. These mutations do not alter the reading frame but reduce translation so that less functional hemoglobin is produced. The lower amount of functional hemoglobin causes β^+-thalassemia.

8. *(B)* A major source of metabolic tyrosine is the conversion of phenylalanine to tyrosine. Tyrosine is a precursor for the synthesis of melanins. Even though tyrosine is present in dietary proteins, it is not usually present in amounts sufficient to supply all metabolic requirements for tyrosine. People with PKU, therefore, have a reduced amount of tyrosine available for synthesis of melanins.

9. *(B)* As noted above, tyrosine, the essential precursor for melanin synthesis, is present in reduced amounts in people with PKU because dietary phenylalanine cannot be converted to tyrosine. But tyrosine is not eliminated entirely because it is present in dietary proteins. Thus, in people with PKU, the production of melanin is restricted but not eliminated.

10. *(B)* No. The absence of functional phenylalanine hydroxylase has no effect on the production of homogentisic acid oxidase, even though the two enzymes are part of the same biochemical pathway. Therefore, homogentisic acid oxidase converts homogentisic acid to 4-maleylacetoacetic acid, and homogentisic acid does not accumulate.

11. *(C)* Normally, *Neurospora* has very simple nutritional requirements. This is because the organism has the biochemical capacity to make almost every organic molecule it needs, including all of the amino acids. Consequently, the food requirements for this organism can be reduced to certain inorganic salts, sugar, and biotin. Mutant strains of *Neurospora* that require the amino acid tryptophan as a dietary supplement cannot make tryptophan because one of several enzymes that are part of the biosynthetic pathway for tryptophan has been disabled by the mutation. Normally, we would expect that all other enzymes in the biosynthetic pathway for tryptophan are intact and fully functional in the mutant strain. Supplemen-tation of the medium with the intermediate that is the product of the mutant enzyme, or any intermediate at any step after the one affected by the mutant enzyme, restores the pathway and permits synthesis of tryptophan. Supplementation of the medium with an intermediate that precedes the step affected by the mutant enzyme leaves the pathway blocked. Because one strain could not grow in the presence of anthranilic acid but could grow in the presence of indole or tryptophan, anthranilic acid must precede indole and tryptophan in the pathway. The other strain could not grow when either anthranilic acid or indole was supplied, so both anthranilic acid and indole must precede tryptophan in the pathway. In summary, the pathway is anthranilic acid → indole → tryptophan.

12. *(C)* This problem can be solved by applying the same logic used in the previous question. The mutant *me-1* strain cannot grow when any of the substances except methionine is added. The mutant *me-1* enzyme must affect a step that follows synthesis of all of the substances except methionine, an

observation that places methionine at the end of the pathway. The mutant *me-2* strain cannot grow when cysteine or cystathionine is added but can grow when methionine or homocysteine is added. The mutant *me-2* enzyme must affect a step that precedes synthesis of homocysteine and methionine, and follows synthesis of cysteine and cystathionine. The mutant *me-3* strain cannot grow when cysteine is added but can grow when all other substances are added. The mutant *me-3* enzyme must affect a step that follows synthesis of cysteine and precedes synthesis of all other substances tested. The mutant *me-4* strain can grow when any of the substances tested is added. The mutant *me-4* enzyme must therefore affect a step that precedes synthesis of all the substances tested. In summary, the pathway is as follows:

$$\xrightarrow{\textit{me-4}} \text{cysteine} \xrightarrow{\textit{me-3}} \text{cystathionine} \xrightarrow{\textit{me-2}} \text{homocysteine} \xrightarrow{\textit{me-1}} \text{methionine}$$

13. *(D)* This result contradicts the one gene–one enzyme hypothesis because a mutation in a single gene may affect more than one enzyme. Notice that the four mutant strains mentioned all lack activities for the same three enzymes, anthranilate synthetase, PRA isomerase, and InGP synthetase. Hütter and de Moss explained this observation by proposing a model in which these three enzymes form an aggregate enzyme that then functions to catalyze several steps in the pathway. They tested this hypothesis by isolating the enzymes and determining whether or not they were aggregated. They discovered that the three enzymes were indeed aggregated and functioned as a single unit.

14. *(D)* The substitution is at position 21, which is the amino-terminal end of the translated protein and is probably the site where the signal peptide is cleaved. The mutant codon (GUG) encodes valine rather than alanine. Both amino acids are nonpolar and hydrophobic; therefore, this change should not drastically change the chemical properties of the polypeptide. However, because this amino acid is at the site that signal peptidase recognizes as the site for signal peptide cleavage, it prevents cleavage of the signal peptide and the polypeptide is longer than it should be. The polypeptide, thus remains attached to the endoplasmic reticulum and cannot be transported to its normal site in the cell.

15. *(D)* **(a)** To have a phenotypic effect, a mutation must alter the activity of the enzyme. Mutations can do this in two ways: (1) They can alter the enzyme's active site directly so that the active site no longer functions, or (2) they can alter the overall enzyme structure in such a way that the alteration disables the enzyme. Those mutations in exons 5–12 probably directly alter the active site, and single amino acid substitutions within the active site should have an appreciable effect on enzyme activity. Most of the mutations outside of exons 5–12 are the types that should alter overall enzyme structure. Most substitution mutations outside of exons 5–12 probably do not have an appreciable effect on enzyme activity and are thus not detected. **(b)** These observations suggest that exons 5–12 encode the active site of the enzyme.

Chapter 7
Bacterial Genetics

1. *(A)* **(a)** Growth media are autoclaved to kill contaminating organisms so that when the researcher introduces the desired bacteria to the growth media, a pure culture of the bacteria can be assured. **(b)** Some substances, such as certain antibiotics, that a researcher may need to add to the sterile growth media may be chemically altered by the high temperatures in an autoclave. These substances are not autoclaved but are filtered to remove any contaminating bacterial cells and are then added to the sterilized medium.

2. *(B)* *arg⁻* (cannot grow in the absence of arginine): This is an auxotrophic allele. Bacteria with this allele cannot make arginine. For survival, arginine must be added to the growth medium.
gal⁻ (cannot grow when galactose is the only sugar present): This allele is a carbon source mutation. Bacteria with this allele cannot utilize galactose as a source of carbon.
kanˢ (cannot grow in the presence of kanamycin): Kanamycin is an antibiotic. Bacteria with this allele are susceptible to kanamycin, so they either die or cease to grow in its presence.
bio⁻ (cannot grow in the absence of biotin): This is an auxotrophic allele. Bacteria with this allele cannot make biotin, a vitamin that is essential for growth, and therefore must have biotin supplied in the growth medium.
lac⁺ (can grow when lactose is the only sugar present): Bacteria with this allele can utilize lactose as a carbon source.
ampʳ (can grow in the presence of ampicillin): This allele is an antibiotic resistance allele. Bacteria with this allele can grow and divide in the presence of ampicillin.
thr⁺ (can grow in the absence of threonine): This is a prototrophic allele because bacteria with this allele can make threonine in minimal medium.

3. *(C)* **(a)** The time-of-entry map: based upon average time of entry for each gene is as follows:

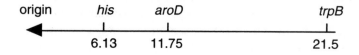

(b) Approximately 21.5 minutes are represented by this map.

4. *(B)* **(a)** *arg⁻* strains require replica plating for identification and recovery. *arg⁻* is an auxotrophic mutation, so cells that carry it require arginine in the medium to grow and divide. Colonies must first be grown on a master plate with minimal medium plus arginine. The *arg⁺* and *arg⁻* colonies grow equally well on this plate and cannot be distinguished from one another. Then the colonies are transferred to a replica plate with minimal medium. The *arg⁺* colonies grow on this plate, but the *arg⁻* colonies do not. The researcher then compares the replica plate with the master plate and isolates from the master plate those colonies that failed to grow on the replica plate. The bacteria from those colonies can then be cultured in a medium that contains arginine. **(b)** *met⁻* strains require replica plating for identification and recovery. *met⁻* is an auxotrophic mutation, and the procedure for identifying and isolating colonies that carry it is the same as that described in the answer to part a, with methionine substituted for arginine. **(c)** *ampʳ* (ampicillin-resistant) strains can be distinguished from *ampˢ* (ampicillin-susceptible) strains by growing *ampʳ* and *ampˢ* cells on plates containing ampicillin. Only the *ampʳ* cells survive, and they can be isolated directly from the medium. No replica plating is required. **(d)** *ampˢ* strains are distinguished from *ampʳ* strains and recovered by replica plating. They are plated on minimal medium (nonselective medium in this case) then replica-plated to selective medium containing ampicillin. The *ampˢ* colonies growing on the nonselective medium are identified by lack of survival on the selective ampicillin plate. **(e)**

lac⁻ strains carry a carbon source mutation and require replica plating for identification and recovery. They cannot grow on medium with lactose as the sole carbon source. The researcher first plates colonies on a master plate with non selective minimal medium that has glucose as the carbon source. Both *lac⁺* and *lac⁻* colonies grow equally well on this medium and cannot be distinguished from each other. Then the researcher transfers the colonies to a replica plate with lactose as the sole carbon source. Colonies that fail to grow on this medium carry a *lac⁻* mutation, and those colonies can be recovered from the master plate. **(f)** *gal⁻* strains carry a carbon source mutation and must be identified and recovered with replica plating. The procedure is the same as that described in the answer to part e, with galactose substituted for lactose. **(g)** Temperature-sensitive strains that die at 40°C require replica plating for identification and recovery. Colonies are first grown on a master plate with minimal medium at 37°C and are then transferred to a replica plate with minimal medium, which is immediately incubated at 40°C. Those colonies that fail to grow at 40°C are identified and recovered from the master plate.

5. *(A)* The two strains of bacteria used for this study were each auxotrophic for three substances (Y-10 was auxotrophic for threonine, leucine, and thiamin; Y-24 was auxotrophic for biotin, phenylalanine, and cysteine). In the control experiments, in which each strain was cultured alone, single gene reversions to prototrophy appeared, albeit rarely. For example, Y-10 colonies might rarely become prototrophic for threonine but remain auxotrophic for leucine and thiamin. Lederberg and Tatum expected such reversions and correctly explained them as mutations. However, they neither expected nor observed reversions for two or three genes in pure culture. The probability of reversion mutations in two or more genes is the product of the probabilities of a reversion mutation in each of the individual genes. For example, if the probability of a reversion mutation in one gene is one per million colonies (10^{-6}), then the probability of a reversion in two genes is one per trillion colonies ($10^{-6} \times 10^{-6} = 10^{-12}$). Thus, the probability of reversion mutations in multiple genes decreases exponentially with the number of genes.

6. *(B)* The cross was Y-10 (*thr⁻ leu⁻ thi⁻ bio⁺ phe⁺ cys⁺*) × Y-24 (*thr⁺ leu⁺ thi⁺ bio⁻ phe⁻ cys⁻*). They selected for cells that were fully prototrophic: *thr⁺ leu⁺ thi⁺ bio⁺ phe⁺ cys⁺*. They were able to determine the reversion mutation rates for individual genes from the control experiments, and from these rates estimate the reversion rates for multiple genes. Prototrophy appeared in the colonies derived from mixed culture at a frequency that was orders of magnitude higher than the expected mutation reversion rate. Because they observed prototrophy only in mixed culture (Y-10 plus Y-24) and never in the pure culture control experiments (Y-10 alone and Y-24 alone), they concluded that the cells in mixed culture must be exchanging and recombining genes.

7. *(B)* One bacterial strain can acquire genes from another through transformation or conjugation. In transformation, DNA released into the culture environment from cell rupture can be taken up by intact cells, and the introduced DNA may recombine with the bacterial cell's chromosomal DNA, causing reversion to prototrophy for those genes that recombined. A bacterial strain may also acquire genes from another through conjugation provided one of the strains is an Hfr strain or carries an F′ plasmid and transfers its genes via a conjugation bridge to the other bacterial cell. The introduced DNA may then recombine with the recipient bacterial cell's chromosomal DNA, causing a reversion to prototrophy for those genes that were transferred and recombined.

8. *(B)* The U-tube experiments conducted by Davis (1950. *Journal of Bacteriology* 60:507–508) highlighted in Example 7.4 showed that cell contact was required for recombination. Transformation does not require cell contact. DNA can pass across the filter in a U tube, and Davis should have observed recombination in the U-tube experiments had transformation been the mechanism of recombination. However, conjugation requires cell contact, so the observation that cell contact was required suggests that conjugation, rather than transformation, explains the recombination observed by Lederberg and Tatum.

9. *(B)* An Hfr cell encounters an F⁻ cell and initiates a conjugation bridge between the two. Then the Hfr cell initiates rolling circle replication of its chromosome at the site of the integrated F factor. Part of the

Hfr cell's chromosome enters the F- cell. Before transfer of the entire chromosome is complete, the conjugation bridge is broken and part of the Hfr chromosome remains in the F- cell. Any alleles that are on the introduced fragment of the Hfr chromosome may recombine with corresponding alleles on the F- cell's chromosome. After recombination is complete, the recombinant cell can express any new alleles it has acquired through recombination.

10. (C) We will select for gal+ and bio+ phenotypes in *E. coli* because the genes that confer these phenotypes are close to the λ attachment site in the *E. coli* chromosome. The strain we select that is lysogenic for λ should be gal+ bio+. The strain that does not contain λ should be gal- bio-. We expose the lysogenic cells to UV light, which induces λ and causes lysis and release of phage particles. We separate the phage particles from the bacterial cells by filtration. We add the filtrate that carries the phage particles to the gal- bio- strain growing in a liquid medium that contains glucose and biotin. We allow the culture to incubate so that the phage particles can infect the cells and enter lysogeny. We then plate the infected cells on a master plate with solid medium that contains glucose and biotin so that colonies arising from single cells can be isolated. We make one replica plate on medium with galactose as the sole carbon source and biotin to identify recombinant cells that are gal+. We make a second replica plate on solid minimal medium with glucose and no biotin to identify cells that are bio+. We select the gal+ and bio+ colonies from the master plate and test them to determine which are gal- bio+ or gal+ bio-, the genotypes that are recombinant. Once the recombinant colonies are identified, we culture them in liquid medium that contains glucose and biotin to grow large quantities of the selected cells. The recombinant cells contain the transducing phage.

11. (B) Conjugation between Hfr and F- cells is used for chromosome mapping studies. After conjugation, DNA transfer, and interruption of conjugation, we must work only with the F- cells to detect recombination because the Hfr cells still contain the genes we are interested in detecting in the recombinant F- cells. Thus, we need a way to eliminate the Hfr cells and leave only the F- cells in the medium. If the Hfr cells are susceptible and the F- cells are resistant to an antibiotic, then transfer of the cells to a medium that contains the antibiotic will eliminate all of the Hfr cells but allow the F- cells to grow and divide. Then we can detect recombinant colonies among the F- cells without interference from colonies derived from Hfr cells.

12. (B) By selecting an antibiotic resistance gene that is distant from the leading gene in the region being mapped, the researcher can terminate conjugation after the region being mapped enters the F- cell but before the allele that causes susceptibility enters. Thus the worker can eliminate the Hfr cells from the mixed culture by antibiotic treatment without affecting the resistant F- cells. If the allele that causes susceptibility were within the region being mapped, it would enter the F- cell, where it could recombine with the allele that causes resistance and make the F- cell susceptible to the antibiotic.

13. (B) The objective of Wollman, Jacob, and Hayes was to map four genes: *azi, tonA, lac,* and *galB*. The *thr, leu,* and *str* genes allowed them to eliminate the parental cells by growing the cells in medium that contained streptomycin and lacked threonine and leucine. This left only recombinant cells in the medium, so they could focus on mapping the genes in question.

14. (B) When answering this question, keep in mind that all of these strains of bacteria can use glucose as a carbon source. For instance, lac+ and lac- cells will utilize glucose as the sole carbon source in the growth medium. The completed table follows on the next page:

Genotype				
$lac^+leu^-str^s$	$lac^-leu^-str^s$	$lac^-leu^-str^r$	$lac^+leu^+str^r$	$lac^-leu^-str^r$

	$lac^+leu^-str^s$	$lac^-leu^-str^s$	$lac^-leu^-str^r$	$lac^+leu^+str^r$	$lac^-leu^-str^r$
Minimal	S	S	N	N	S
Minimal + leucine	N	N	N	N	N
Minimal − glucose + lactose	S	S	S	N	S
Minimal + streptomycin	N	N	N	S	N
Minimal + leucine +streptomycin	N	N	N	S	S
Minimal + lactose − glucose + streptomycin	N	N	N	S	N
Minimal + leucine + lactose − glucose + streptomycin	N	N	N	S	N

15. *(D)* Note that the two donor strains used (AB261 and AB259) have two loci in common (*proA* and *thr*). The times of entry for each of these markers provides the information to determine the direction of entry and the positions of the origins of replication. From strain AB261, *proA* enters the F⁻ cells at 5.5 minutes and *thr* enters the F⁻ cells at 12 minutes. From strain AB259, these genes enter in reverse order, with *proA* at 15 minutes and *thr* at 7.25 minutes. The differences in time of entry between the markers are similar (15 − 7.25 = 7.75 minutes; 12 − 5.5 = 6.5 minutes). These observations allow us to place these genes on the map relative to the origins of replication. We can now determine the positions of the remaining genes by comparing them with genes already on the map. In summary, the map is as follows:

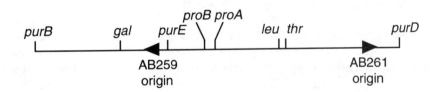

(b) Because of differences in position of origin and direction of insertion, time of entry will be different for common genes in Hfr strains AB261 and AB259. Yet relative positions and directions should be consistent within the map. The total distance represented by the map is approximately 34.5 minutes.

16. *(D)* So far we have assembled three conjugation maps, two in questions 3 and 15 and one in Example 7.6 in the text. From the information given in the question, we know that *purD* and *metB* are close

together (separated by 1 minute of distance). This joins the left end of the map developed in Example 7.6 (Figure 7.21) with the right end of the map from question 3. Notice that *his* (the right end of the map in Example 7.6) is close to *aroD* in the map assembled in the solution to question 3. From the information given in question 16, we know that the right marker of the map in question 3 (*trpB*) is close to *gal*. This information links the map in question 3 with the combined map at the *gal* position. The map is thus closed into a full circle as shown below:

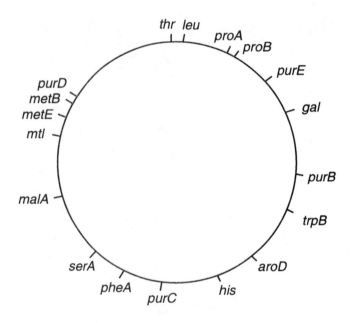

17. *(C)* **(a)** The experiment was designed to determine if phage particles can transfer genetic information from one bacterial cell to another. In this case the workers wanted to determine if λ phage from a *gal⁺* strain could transfer the *gal⁺* gene to *gal⁻* bacteria. A petri dish with galactose as the sole carbon source was inoculated with *gal⁻* bacteria, which could not utilize galactose and could not grow on this plate. If the λ phage from lysed *gal⁺* bacteria carried the *gal⁺* gene into the *gal⁻* bacteria, the infected cells carrying the introduced gene should begin to grow, utilizing galactose for energy and as a carbon source. Because only half the culture plate was inoculated with the λ phage from the *gal⁺* strain, only very few of the uninoculated bacteria are expected to grow (due to natural reversion mutations in the *gal* gene), whereas many more colonies should appear in the inoculated cells due to phage transfer of the *gal⁺* gene. **(b)** There was no cell contact between the two strains, so conjugation (which requires cell contact) is excluded. Only phage particles, not chromosomal DNA, were used to inoculate the plate, so transformation is also excluded. The best explanation of the results is transduction.

18. *(C)* Zinder and Lederberg observed transduction for many different genes. This can best be explained as generalized transduction in *S. typhimurium* in which the phage particles incorporated chromosomal DNA from various parts of the chromosome. Morse, Lederberg, and Lederberg observed transduction only for the *gal* gene when they inoculated cells with λ. The integration site for lysogenic λ in *E. coli* is near the *gal* gene, so λ is likely to transfer this gene through specialized transduction. Morse, Lederberg, and Lederberg observed specialized transduction in *E. coli*.

19. *(D)* A few of the *gal⁻* cells that were inoculated with λ phage particles may have become *gal⁺* because of a reversion mutation rather than transduction. They could then be infected with normal λ, rather than a transducing λ, and still grow on the galactose medium. They would produce normal λ phages when induced. The cells that were *gal⁺* because of transduction would produce transducing phages when induced.

20. *(D)* Several of the genes in this section encode products that perform functions we have discussed in previous chapters, Chapters 2 and 5 in particular. The product of the *dnaA* gene participates in initiation of replication. The *gyrA* and *gyrB* genes encode subunits of DNA gyrase, a topoisomerase that relieves tension from unwinding the DNA strands during replication. The *mutB1* gene encodes a DNA helicase that unwinds the DNA strands. The *lig* gene encodes DNA ligase that seals nicks after the primers have been replaced. The *polI* gene encodes DNA polymerase I, the DNA polymerase that removes primers and fills in the gap left by primer removal with DNA. The *polC, dnaE, dnaN*, and *dnaH* genes encode subunits of DNA polymerase III, the DNA polymerase that carries out most of the DNA synthesis. The *dnaE* genes encode primase, the enzyme that synthesizes primers. The *topA, parC*, and *parE* genes encode topoisomerases that relieve tension and tangling in DNA. The genes *addA, nfo, uvrA, uvrB, uvrC, ruvA, ruvB, recA, dnaB*, and *ung* encode products that participate in DNA repair and recombination.

21. *(C)* The color coding in the figure shows the general functions of genes. The genes are not randomly distributed. Genes with similar functions are grouped into several different clusters throughout the genome, with as few as two and as many as 20 genes in a cluster.

22. *(C)* **(a)** Three lines of evidence led the authors to conclude that *pcsA* and *rfaG* are the same gene: (1) The two genes were mapped to the same position, (2) the phenotypes associated with known mutations in these genes were similar, and (3) there were no other unassigned genes in the region, so there were no other options than to conclude that the two were the same gene. **(b)** A complementation test should confirm that the two are indeed the same gene. If mutant forms of the two genes are placed together in a merozygote, the merozygote should have the mutant phenotype if they are indeed the same gene. If they are not the same gene, then the merozygote should not have the mutant phenotype.

Chapter 8
Regulation of Gene Expression

1. *(A)* Most genes are regulated initially at the transcriptional level, with further regulation of expression at levels beyond transcription. In most cases, regulation at levels beyond transcription can be thought of as fine-tuning the expression of a gene. Transcriptional controls determine whether or not the gene is transcribed and, if so, at what level. Posttranscriptional controls determine the final level at which the product functions.

2. *(B)* There are three major mechanisms that regulate expression of the *trp* operon, two that operate at the level of transcription and a third that operates posttranslationally. The first mechanism is a repressor system. It includes a constitutively expressed repressor gene that encodes a repressor protein that has the ability to bind at the *trp* operator and block transcription of the operon. For the repressor to bind to the operator, the corepressor, tryptophan, must first be bound to an allosteric site on the repressor protein. In the absence of tryptophan or when tryptophan is in short supply, the allosteric site is vacant and the repressor protein does not bind to the operator and does not block transcription of the operon. As the concentration of tryptophan increases in the cell, tryptophan binds to the allosteric site on the repressor protein and increases the binding affinity of the tryptophan-repressor complex to the operator. When bound to the operator, the tyrptophan-repressor complex blocks transcription of the *trp* operon.

The second mechanism is attenuation. Near the 5´ end of the operon is a region that contains a small reading frame for translation that encodes a polypeptide that is 14 amino acids long. The region also contains sequences that can potentially form base pairs to create hairpins in the nascent mRNA. One of the hairpins is an intrinsic terminator of transcription. Two adjacent tryptophan codons are present near the end of the reading frame. When tryptophan is abundant, ribosomes translate the entire reading frame. Under these conditions, the terminator hairpin forms and terminates transcription before any of the genes of the *trp* operon are transcribed. When tryptophan is in short supply, the ribosomes stall at the tryptophan codons (because there is insufficient tryptophan for them to place tryptophan in the reading frame). With the ribosomes stalled, a hairpin that is not a transcription terminator forms, and it blocks formation of the termination hairpin. Transcription does not terminate at the terminator, and RNA polymerase transcribes the genes of the *trp* operon.

The third regulation mechanism operates at the posttranslational level through feedback inhibition of the biosynthetic pathway for tryptophan. The first enzyme of the pathway is inhibited by the product of the pathway, tryptophan. When tryptophan becomes increasingly abundant by the activity of the pathway, it increasingly inhibits the first enzyme of the pathway, reducing the synthesis of tryptophan.

3. *(B)* **(a)** Normally, the *lacI* gene is constitutively transcribed at a low rate. Translation maintains a small number of *lac* repressor molecules within the cell at all times. Presence of the repressor protein, which binds to the DNA at the *lac* operator locus, keeps transcription of the *lac* operon repressed in the absence of lactose. Transcription of the *lacI* gene only in the presence of lactose would be a wasteful process. In the absence of lactose, the repressor would not be present and the *lac* operon would be transcribed, producing enzymes for lactose metabolism when no lactose is available to be metabolized. **(b)** If the *lacI* gene were transcribed only in the absence of lactose, the *lac* operon would be efficiently regulated because the repressor would be produced only when there is no lactose to metabolize. However, repression of the operon could be delayed when lactose is consumed. Synthesis of the repressor will begin due to absence of inhibition of transcription of the *lacI* locus. But meanwhile the *lac* operon will continue to make the lactose-metabolizing enzymes that are no longer needed. Eventually, however, the *lac* operon will be repressed when the newly formed repressor molecules reach sufficient concentration to bind to the *lac* operators.

4. *(C)* The premature termination codon within the *lacZ* gene shortens the polypeptide and destroys the

activity of β-galactosidase. This enzyme is necessary for the conversion of lactose to allolactose, which is the inducer of the *lac* operon. In the absence of allolactose, the *lac* operon cannot be induced and none of the other genes can be transcribed. Such a frameshift mutation in the first gene of other operons would not necessarily be polar because the enzymes encoded by those genes are usually not needed to produce the inducer.

5. *(C)*

Carbohydrate Concentration

Mutation	Lactose High Glucose High	Lactose High Glucose Low	Lactose Absent Glucose High	Lactose Absent Glucose Low
1	–	+	–	–
2	–	–	–	–
3	–	–	–	–
4	–	–	–	–
5	–	+	–	–
6	–	+	–	–
7	–	+	–	+
8	–	–	–	–
9	–	+	–	–
10	–	+	–	+
11	–	+	–	+

6. *(B)* Yes. The I^+ allele in the F′ factor is trans acting and will therefore regulate the O^+ operator in the bacterial genome and in the F′ plasmid genome. β-galactosidase, encoded by the Z^+ allele in the chromosome, and β-galactoside permease, encoded by the Y^+ allele in the F′ factor, will be regulated normally and the merozygote will metabolize lactose when lactose is present and glucose levels are low.

7. *(B)* Yes, for two reasons. First, because both the *I* genes (the one in the F′ factor and the one in the chromosome) are mutant, neither produces functional repressor protein. In the absence of functional repressor protein, the operon is transcribed when glucose concentrations are low. Second, the operator in the chromosome is a constitutive operator, so the *Z* and *Y* genes that it regulates (remember that it is a cis-acting element) will be transcribed constantly regardless of whether or not functional repressor is present. Thus, the *lac* operons in both the F′ factor and the chromosome will be constantly transcribed regardless of the concentrations of lactose and glucose.

8. *(B)* Yes. Both *I* genes are mutant, so no repressor protein is produced. In the absence of the repressor, both *lac* operons are transcribed when glucose is low. The *lac* operon in the chromosome has a functional Z^+ gene and the *lac* operon in the F′ factor has a functional Y^+ gene, so functional β-galactosidase and β-galactoside permease are produced.

9. *(B)* Attenuation relies on the concentration of an amino acid encoded in the reading frame of the leader peptide. Amino acids are encoded by a leader peptide, so the absence of an amino acid encoded in the leader peptide causes ribosomes to stall. Substances other than amino acids are not encoded by the leader peptide, so their absence cannot cause the ribosome to stall at a particular codon in the leader peptide. Because attenuation relies on leader peptides, it is an effective regulation mechanism only for operons that encode the enzymes in an amino acid biosynthesis pathway.

10. *(B)* Yes. The repressor protein would not be present and thus would not repress the *trp* operon.

However, the absence of the repressor protein should have no effect on attenuation. Attenuation would still reduce transcription when tryptophan concentrations were high.

11. *(C)* **(a)** The mutation causes a frameshift in the leader peptide, so the ribosomes will translate in a different reading frame downstream from the site of the mutation and will continue translating until they encounter a termination codon. The first termination codon in the mutant reading frame is a UAA codon at position 123, which results in a polypeptide with the sequence MetLysAlaIlePheValLeuLysArgLeu-ValAlaHisPheLeuLysArgAlaValTyrSerProCysValLysGlnSerValThrGlnProAla. **(b)** There are no tryptophan codons in the mutant leader peptide, so translation will continue to the first termination codon, regardless of the level of tryptophan. The termination codon is within the sequence for hairpin #3, which is the terminator. Thus, ribosomes will block formation of hairpin #3 and transcription of the operon will continue regardless of the level of tryptophan.

12. *(C)* **(a)** The mutations changes the G in the AUG initiation codon into an A, so the codon is now AUA. It can no longer function as an initiation codon, so ribosomes do not initiate translation of the leader peptide and no leader peptide is produced. **(b)** Without translation of the leader peptide, the situation is equivalent to that in Figure 8.18c, in which hairpins #1 and #3 form. Because hairpin #3 forms, transcription is terminated regardless of the concentration of tryptophan.

13. *(B)* Many cells that contain methylated genes have differentiated into specific tissue types. The cells within a given tissue carry out the same function and thus should utilize methylation to inactivate the same genes. The daughter cells that arise from a parent cell in a differentiated tissue should both carry out the same function as their parent cell, which is possible if their genes are regulated in the same way as those in the parent cell. Retention of the parental cell's methylation pattern in the daughter cells ensures that the same genes that were inactivated in the parent cell are inactivated in the daughter cells.

14. *(B)* Many steroid receptor proteins are eukaryotic transcription factors that recognize specific sequence elements near promoter regions in DNA. When the steroid molecule binds to the steroid receptor, it changes the conformation of the receptor in such a way that the steroid receptor can bind to its sequence element in the DNA. A single receptor may bind to several different genes, regulating all of them simultaneously. A mutation in the gene that encodes a receptor protein may eliminate the function of the receptor protein so that it cannot bind to its sequence element whether or not the steroid molecule is present. Under these circumstances, all of the genes that are under the regulation of the mutant receptor protein's sequence are insensitive to the presence of the steroid hormone.

15. *(C)* GAL4 and GAL80 are two interacting protein transcription factors found in yeast. They control transcription of genes that encode enzymes for galactose metabolism. GAL4 binds to DNA sequence elements that enhance transcription of several genes encoding the enzymes for galactose metabolism. In the absence of galactose, GAL80 binds to GAL4 and prevents it from binding to DNA, thus reducing transcription of the genes it influences. In the presence of galactose, GAL80 does not bind to GAL4, and GAL4 binds to its sequence elements and stimulates transcription. A mutation in the *GAL80* gene that prevents the GAL80 protein from binding to GAL4 leaves GAL4 free to bind to the DNA regardless of the level of galactose. Thus, this mutation causes transcription of the genes under the regulation of GAL4 in both **(a)** the presence and **(b)** the absence of galactose.

16. *(B)* The DNA that contains an enhancer can be located thousands of nucleotides upstream or downstream from the promoter because the DNA bends and brings the enhancer and the proteins bound to it into contact with the basal transcription apparatus, which is bound to the promoter.

17. *(C)* Because neolactose, a derivative of lactose, can be utilized only by constitutive mutants of the *lac* operon, we must assume that β-galactosidase can cleave neolactose into monosaccharides that can then be metabolized. However, because neolactose does not induce the *lac* operon, we can assume that β-galactosidase cannot convert neolactose to allolactose, the inducer for the operon. A constitutive opera-

tor prevents repressor binding and thus allows transcription of the lactose operon whether or not the inducer is present. Thus, when the operon contains a constitutive promoter, no inducer is required for transcription in the presence of neolactose.

18. *(C)* Four of the genotypes contain an O^c mutation in the F′ factor. In all four cases, when the inducer is absent, β-galatosidase is produced only if there is a Z^+ gene in the F′ factor. The O^c mutation has no effect on the Z gene in the chromosome. These observations indicate that the O^c mutation is cis acting and not trans acting.

19. *(D)* The data for mutation 1 indicate that phosphatase, transaminase, dehydrogenase, and pyrophosphorylase are active and that cyclase and isomerase are not active. Mutation 1 must be in the gene that encodes cyclase, isomerase, or amido transferase. (We must include the gene that encodes amido transferase as a possibility because the lack of data for the enzyme it encodes prevents us from excluding it.) From the data for mutation 1, we can draw the biochemical pathway as follows:

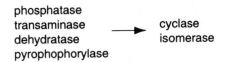

(Note that we cannot include amido transferase in the pathway derived from the information for mutation 1 because the data for this enzyme are missing.) Because phosphatase was active in the presence of mutation 1, but was inactive in mutation 2, while transaminase, dehydrogenase, and pyrophophorylase were active in the presence of mutations 1 and 2, mutation 2 must be in the gene that encodes phosphorylase. From this information, we can refine the biochemical pathway to

Using the same logic as in the analysis of mutation 2, we can conclude that mutation 3 is in the gene that encodes transanimase. We can refine that biochemical pathway to

Mutation 4 must be in the gene that encodes dehydrogenase. We can refine the biochemical pathway to

This pathway is refined as much as possible given the data in this question. We cannot determine the relative orders of isomerase, cyclase, and amido transferase from these data. The data for mutations 5, 6, and 7 indicate that these three mutations must be in the gene that encodes pyrophosphorylase.

20. *(D)* **(a)** To determine the consensus sequence, identify which nucleotide is most frequent at each position. In these operators, a particular nucleotide predominates at each position except the seventh. In the seventh position, three of the operators have a C and three have a T, so we label that position as a pyrimidine (Py) in the consensus sequence. The consensus sequence of the upper strand in Figure 8.32 is TACCACPyGGCGGTGATA. **(b)** The 2nd, 4th, 12th, 14th, and 16th nucleotides are fully conserved. **(c)** The consensus sequence of the lower strand is TATCACCGCCPuGTGGTA. The two consensus sequences match exactly at 12 of 17 positions, and at 16 of 17 positions when matched by purines and pyrimidines.

Thus, the consensus sequence is an imperfect palindrome. **(d)** Each of the two subunits of the dimer binds to the same general sequence in the operators. **(e)** The only position at which O_R1 and O_R2 are the same but differ from O_R3 is at the 13th nucleotide in the upper strand, which is a T in O_R1 and O_R2 and a G in O_R3.

21. *(C)* The two strands of the principal operator, compared in the $5' \rightarrow 3'$ direction are:

sense strand:	AATTGTGAGCGGATAACAATT
antisense strand:	AATTGTTATCCGCTCACAATT

The two strands differ at only five positions, indicative of significant symmetry, as depicted in Figure 8.6. Identical subunits in the repressor protein bind to similar sequences in the operator.

22. *(C)* When mutations that profoundly affect the function of a protein cluster in certain codons within a gene, one can rightly assume that these codons encode important functional domain in the protein encoded by the gene. In this case, codons 1–60 probably encode the DNA-binding domains of the repressor protein.

23. *(D)* The observation that the *lacI⁻* mutations clustered in codons 1–60 have a dominant effect when combined with a *lacI⁺* allele in a merozygote indicates that the DNA binding domain is encoded by this region. In a merozygote with one *lacI⁻ᵈ* allele and one *lacI⁺* allele, about half of the protein subunits will be mutant and half will be functional. If the mutation affects the DNA binding domain, but does not affect the ability of the mutant proteins to assemble in the tetramers, then most of the tetramers (about 15 out of 16) will have at least one mutant subunit and will not be able to effectively bind to DNA. Thus, even though about half of the subunits are functional, only a small proportion (1 of 16) tetramers should be functional—hence, the dominant effect of the mutation. If the codons downstream from codon 60 participate in tetramer formation, then the *lacI⁻* mutations in this region will produce mutant subunits that cannot assemble into tetramers. In a merozyote with such a mutation in one of its *lacI* genes, only the subunits encoded by the *lacI⁺* allele will assemble into tetramers, and all such tetramers will be fully functional. Thus, these mutations do not have a dominant effect.

24. *(C)* The *lacIˢ* mutations prevent the inducer, allolactose, from binding to the repressor. The sites of the mutation clusters are probably the portions of the polypeptide that constitute the inducer binding site. The regular spacing of these nine mutation clusters suggests that the inducer binding site is formed by a repeated folding of the protein that brings the distant components of the binding site together.

25. *(C)* These results suggest that for the λ repressor to remain bound to the DNA, it must be in its dimeric form. Even though RecA cleavage leaves the DNA-binding domains intact, when the dimer is disrupted, the subunits are no longer able to bind to the DNA. With the repressor no longer bound to the DNA, λ cannot remain in lysogeny, and lysis is induced.

26. *(D)* If we assume that this mutant form of the repressor functions to repress lysis, then a lysogenic host cell containing this mutant phage would remain permanently lysogenic and would probably be permanently immune to lysis by other infecting λ phage particles. Recall that the repressor keeps the λ phage in a lysogenic state. Conversion of the lysogenic state to the lytic state is achieved by cleavage of the dimer-binding domain from the DNA-binding domain of the λ repressor by RecA. If the repressor cannot be cleaved, it will remain bound to the operator and lysogeny will be maintained.

27. *(D)* The observation that mouse embryos with defective DNA methyltransferase were stunted and poorly developed suggests that the decreased methylation adversely affected genes that regulate development. We can speculate that methylation of appropriate genes in the developing mouse embryo is essential to prevent their untimely expression. Why then are genomic DNAs not methylated in such

eukaryotic organisms as *Drosophila* and yeast? We know methylation is only one of several mechanisms for gene regulation. Evidently, some eukaryotic organisms do not require methylation but instead utilize other mechanisms for regulation of gene expression.

28. *(D)* Mammalian genomes are much larger and contain many more genes than those of *Drosophila* and yeast. The large and complex genome of mammals may account for the addition of methylation as a mechanism of gene regulation. Methylation is a comparatively simpler mechanism than protein-DNA interactions and could more easily regulate large groupings of genes. This simplicity in control could provide an important selective advantage, which could outweigh any disadvantage due to slightly increased mutational tendencies of mC $\rightarrow$ T mutations.

29. *(D)* If threonine is not included in the medium, it is not possible to fully inhibit aspartate kinase; the form of aspartate kinase that is inhibited only by threonine will remain active. However, if both lysine and threonine are included in the medium, all three forms of the enzyme will be inhibited. Under these conditions, only those cells that contain feedback-insensitive mutant forms of aspartate kinase can survive.

Chapter 9
Recombinant DNA and Molecular Analysis

1. *(A)* Recombinant DNA is a DNA molecule made in vitro by connecting DNA from two or more individuals or species into a single DNA molecule. In most cases, recombinant DNA consists of foreign DNA inserted into a cloning vector such as a plasmid, phage particle, cosmid, bacterial artificial chromosome (BAC), or yeast artificial chromosome (YAC).

2. *(B)* **(a)** Bacterial cells use restriction endonucleases to destroy foreign DNA that enters the cells. The host cell protects its own DNA through specific methylation patterns that render the DNA insensitive to the restriction endonucleases. **(b)** In the laboratory, scientists use restriction endonucleases to cut DNA into specific fragments to reduce very large DNA molecules to manageable size and to specifically recombine DNA molecules.

3. *(B)* Type II restriction endonucleases cleave at specific recognition sites, which allows researchers to know the nucleotide sequences on the ends of the fragments, and to use the DNA fragments easily in recombinant DNA research. Also, type II restriction endonucleases do not require ATP to cleave DNA, which simplifies procedures when compared to reactions that require ATP. Type I and type II enzymes do not cleave DNA at their recognition sites, and they require ATP. Thus, they are not as useful to scientists as type II enzymes.

4. *(B)* As shown in Figure 9.21, the polymerase chain reaction functions by using DNA synthesized in one cycle as a template for DNA synthesis in subsequent cycles. The primer binding sites determine where DNA synthesis begins, so each synthesized fragment has a primer on its 5′ end. When a fragment synthesized in a previous cycle is used as a template, the template ends at the primer, and the DNA polymerase must terminate synthesis when it reaches the end of the template. Thus, as shown in Figure 9.21, constant-length fragments (fragments of amplified DNA that are bordered on both ends by primers and their binding sites) eventually become the predominant molecules in the reaction.

5. *(B)* Constant-length fragments bordered by primer binding sites increase in number exponentially with each cycle because each new strand synthesized during a cycle becomes a template for the next cycle, and the template from which it was synthesized is also a template in the next cycle. Thus, the number of constant-length fragments doubles with each cycle. Variable-length fragments are synthesized only from the original template DNA added to the reaction before the first cycle. The original DNA functions as a template in each cycle, but its numbers do not increase with each cycle. Thus, for every copy of original template DNA, one variable-length fragment is synthesized per cycle. The variable-length fragments increase by one per original template in each cycle. The exponential increase of constant-length fragments eventually renders the proportion of variable-length fragments in the reaction insignificant.

6. *(C)* Only one strand of the double-stranded DNA is provided in Figure 9.38, and it is written in the 5′ → 3′ direction. The sequence of the other strand can be deduced from the base-pairing rules. One primer must have the same sequence as the strand given in the figure, and the other must have the complementary sequence. The primer with the sequence 5′ CTAGCGCCTTCGAGCAGTGG 3′ matches the sequence in Figure 9.38 beginning at nucleotide 557 and ending at nucleotide 576. Thus, the complementary sequence of the other primer should be found at another position in the sequence. Written in the 5′ → 3′ direction, the complementary sequence of the other primer is 5′ GACGACTGACGAGTGTTGAT 3′. This sequence matches the sequence in Figure 9.38 beginning at nucleotide 1708 and ending at nucleotide 1727. The primers become part of the amplified sequence, so the total number of nucleotide pairs in the sequence can be determined by counting the number of nucleotides between the distal ends of the two primer sequences in Figure 9.38, which is 1171 nucleotide pairs. Another way to calculate the number of nucleotide pairs in the amplified fragment is to subtract the number of nucleotides in Figure

9.38 that precede the first nucleotide of the first primer from the number of nucleotides that ends with the last nucleotide of the second primer: 1727 − 556 = 1171 nucleotide pairs.

7. *(C)* **(a)** With properly chosen concentrations of each primer, the more highly concentrated primer will be more efficient in finding its complementary binding site on the template DNA. The number of strands initiated from it will exceed those initiated from the other primer, so there will be an excess of single-stranded copies of the DNA synthesized from the more highly concentrated primer. **(b)** To produce many single-stranded copies of the target DNA strand, the template strand must also be present in multiple copies. The other primer initiates synthesis of those template strands. After the amplification reaction has proceeded for an adequate number of cycles, there will be an excess of single-stranded copies of one strand of the target DNA sequence, along with double-stranded copies of the target sequence.

8. *(B)* A cloning vector is a segment of DNA, usually a modified plasmid or phage, that will replicate in host bacterial cells with a segment of foreign DNA inserted into it. By itself, foreign DNA usually cannot be replicated in a bacterial cell. However, a cloning vector carries an origin of replication, so it, along with any foreign DNA it contains, can replicate in a bacterial cell. To replicate the DNA in the vector, researchers simply grow bacterial cultures that contain the recombinant vector. The purpose of the vector is simply to provide a means of replicating the foreign DNA.

Most cloning vectors do not allow the foreign DNA to be transcribed or translated. An expression vector is a cloning vector that has been modified so that the foreign DNA can be transcribed and translated in the bacterial host cell. It usually contains a promoter that the bacterial cell recognizes and a means for turning transcription on or off by altering the composition of the growth medium. The foreign gene must also be structured in such a way that the bacterial cell will properly translate the mRNA. If the gene is eukaryotic, it must have its introns removed and have an appropriate bacterial translation signal in the correct position relative to the initiation codon.

9. *(B)* **(a)** The *Pst*I site is located within the *amp^r* gene in the pBR322 plasmid. Insertion of a DNA fragment at the *Pst*I site causes an insertion mutation that renders the *amp^r* gene nonfunctional. Therefore, when the *Pst*I site is used for cloning, the *amp^r* gene can be used to distinguish bacterial colonies that carry a recombinant plasmid from those that carry a nonrecombinant plasmid. **(b)** Insertion of DNA at the *Pst*I site leaves the *tet^r* gene unaffected and functional. When using the *Pst*I site for cloning, researchers can use the *tet^r* gene to distinguish cells that contain a plasmid (either recombinant or nonrecombinant) from those cells that do not. **(c)** The *ori* segment contains a bacterial origin of replication that causes the plasmid (whether recombinant or nonrecombinant) to replicate in the bacterial cell. Without an origin of replication, the plasmid could not replicate and would be lost. **(d)** The *Bam*HI site can be used as the site for cloning DNA fragments that disrupt the *tet^r* gene. Under these circumstances, the *amp^r* gene is used to distinguish cells that contain a plasmid from those that do not, and the *tet^r* gene is used to distinguish colonies that contain a recombinant plasmid from those that contain a nonrecombinant plasmid.

10. *(B)* **(a)** Reverse transcriptase is an enzyme encoded by genes in certain RNA viruses called retroviruses. In nature, when a retrovirus infects a cell, the cell's ribosomes translate reverse transcriptase from a gene in the viral RNA, and the enzyme transcribes a DNA strand from the viral RNA. The DNA can then serve as a template for transcription of many copies of the RNA virus. **(b)** To make a cDNA library, researchers isolate mRNAs from a tissue, then synthesize single-stranded cDNA strands from the mRNAs. They use a DNA polymerase to make the single-stranded DNAs double stranded, then clone the double-stranded cDNAs into vectors that they maintain in bacterial cells as a cDNA library. A cDNA library contains the cDNA clones from a particular tissue and thus represents the genes that are expressed in that tissue.

11. *(B)* The size of DNA fragments that can be cloned in plasmids is limited by the inability of most plasmids to efficiently transform cells and replicate beyond a certain size. Phage cloning vectors also have a size limitation that affects packaging of the recombinant phage DNA into a capsid. A nonrecombinant cosmid vector is much smaller than most plasmid and phage vectors, and utilizes aspects of both phage and plasmid vectors during the cloning process. A nonrecombinant cosmid replicates as a plasmid in bacteria. However, a cosmid contains cos sites, sequences that are located at the ends of a linear λ DNA molecule. When a fragment of DNA is cloned in a cosmid vector, the recombinant cosmid is made linear with cos sites on both ends of the linear molecule. When the inserted DNA is the appropriate size (up to 46 kb in some cosmid vectors), the recombinant cosmid resembles λ DNA and can be packaged in λ capsids. The recombinant phage particles efficiently insert the large DNA into the bacterium, avoiding the need for transformation. Once inside the cell, the recombinant cosmid assumes a circular conformation by joining at the cos sites, and replicates in the cell as a plasmid.

12. *(D)* In the first printing of the text, this question contained two errors. First, the sequence contains six rather than 12 amino acids. Second, the last sentence of the question should read: "Determine how many degenerate DNA probes are required to represent this amino acid sequence."

The number of probes required in a complete degenerate set for this sequence can be determined by multiplying the number of codons that specify each amino acid in the sequence. In this instance, asparagine and glutamic acid are each specified by two codons, threonine and proline each by four codons, and serine and arginine each by six codons, so $4 \times 4 \times 6 \times 2 \times 6 \times 2 = 2304$. This number of probes is too long to list here, but we can take a shortcut by listing purines as Pu, pyrimidines as Py, and any nucleotide as N at the positions that vary in the probes. The 2304 probes must all have the sequences ACNCCNUCNAAPyCGNGAPu, ACNCCNAGPyAAPyCGNGAPu, ACNCCNUCNAAPyA-GPuGAPu, or ACNCCNAGPyAAPyAGPuGAPu. This amino acid sequence is not a good choice for creation of a degenerate set of probes because it contains two amino acids that are each specified by six codons (serine and arginine). Choice of a sequence that contains serine or arginine greatly increases the number of probes in a degenerate set.

13. *(A)* DNA recognition sites for restriction endonucleases are palindromic. In a double-stranded palindromic sequence, the sequence of both strands is the same when read in the 5′ → 3′ direction. Most restriction endonucleases cut within a palindromic recognition sequence and cut at the same site in both strands. Thus, all ends of a linear DNA molecule that arose from a cut by the same enzyme have the same sequence. Notice in Table 9.1 that all of the enzymes listed produce ends that have identical DNA sequences when read in the 5′ → 3′ direction. For example, *Eco*RI cleaves DNA to produce the following cohesive ends:

```
5´ G           AATTC 3´
3´ CTTAA           G 5´
```

That both ends are identical becomes obvious if we flip one of the ends around so that its orientation is the same as the other's:

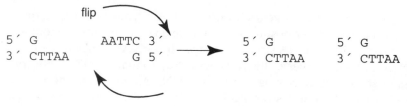

14. *(A)* The *Bam*HI site is located within the *tet*r gene, so insertion of a DNA segment into that site causes a large insertion mutation that disrupts the gene and prevents it from encoding a functional product.

15. *(B)* pUC19 is a cloning vector and does not carry the necessary sequences for expression of a gene inserted into the cloning site. To be expressed, the cDNA for insulin must be cloned in an expression vector.

16. *(B)* **(a)** The *amp^r* gene confers resistance to ampicillin. It can be used to distinguish colonies that contain a recombinant plasmid from those that do not if the cloned DNA fragment is inserted into the *PstI* site. **(b)** The *kan^r* gene confers resistance to kanamycin. It is used to distinguish cells that contain a plasmid (recombinant or nonrecombinant) from those that do not. **(c)** The *ori* segment is a bacterial origin of replication that initiates plasmid replication. **(d)** The *EcoRI* site is where the gene to be expressed can be inserted. **(e)** The *PstI* is also a site where the gene to be expressed can be inserted. It is potentially of greater value than the *EcoRI* site because insertion of DNA into it disrupts the *amp^r* gene and permits distinction of cells that contain a recombinant plasmid from those that contain a nonrecombinant plasmid. **(f)** The P_L segment is a promoter that can be activated by incubating the cells at 42°C to express the inserted gene.

17. *(B)* **(a)** Because DNA has a net negative charge, it is attracted to the positive pole in a direct current electrical field. Gels composed of agarose or polyacrylamide contain a matrix of microscopic pores through which DNA molecules can migrate. The rate at which DNA fragments migrate through the gel matrix is inversely proportional to their sizes: Large molecules pass through fewer pores than the smaller molecules and thus move more slowly than small molecules. DNA molecules of the same size migrate together. Thus, gel electrophoresis separates DNA molecules on the basis of their sizes. **(b)** DNA carries a net negative charge because the hydrogens on the phosphate groups of the sugar-phosphate backbone ionize and break away as hydrogen ions in aqueous solutions, leaving all of the phosphate groups in the DNA sugar phosphate backbone with a net negative charge:

18. *(B)* A dideoxynucleotide triphosphate (ddNTP) lacks hydroxyl groups on both the 2′ and the 3′ carbons (see Figure 9.35). When a DNA polymerase adds nucleotides to the growing chain, it can place a ddNTP in the chain just as easily as it can place a normal dNTP. However, once a dideoxynucleotide is in place, another nucleotide cannot be added to the chain. To attach the next nucleotide, DNA polymerase must use the 3′ hydroxyl group. Because there is no hydroxyl group on the 3′ carbon of the dideoxynucleotide, chain elongation terminates at this point.

19. *(B)* In automated DNA sequencing, each ddNTP is labeled with a different fluorescent dye. Because these dyes cause the labeled nucleotides to fluoresce differently, each nucleotide can be distinguished from the others. Incorporation of the four labeled ddNTPs is done in the same reaction tube, instead of in four separate tubes. The sample is then electrophoresed through a gel to separate the fragments by length. Each fragment reaches the end of the gel in order of its size, starting with the smallest fragment and ending with the largest. As the fragments come off the gel, they pass through a laser beam, and the DNA sequencing machine measures the fluorescence of the fragment. The machine can then identify both the terminal nucleotide and its position in the chain, and from this information compile the DNA sequence. Sanger dideoxy sequencing requires four reactions because the radioactive labels on the four dNTPs are identical and the different nucleotides cannot be distinguished from one another in the same reaction.

20. *(E)* **(a)** Digestion with *EcoRI* alone produces six fragments and digestion with *Hind*III alone produces

eight fragments. Digestion with both enzymes should yield 14 fragments if the molecule is circular and 13 fragments if the molecule is linear. The double digestion yields 13 fragments, so the molecule is linear. **(b)** There are two *Eco*RI fragments (21226 and 3530) and three *Hind*III fragments (2027, 564, and 125) in the double digestion. The remaining fragments must have an *Eco*RI site on one end and a *Hind*III site on the other end. 23130 – 21226 = 1904, so the 1904 and 21226 fragments must be contiguous:

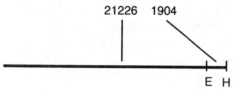

We'll let E represent an *Eco*RI site and H a *Hind*III site. The left end in our diagram must be one of the ends of the linear λ molecule because that site cannot simultaneously be an *Eco*RI site and a *Hind*III site. 1904 + 2027 + 947 = 4878, so the 2027 *Hind*III fragment must be within the 4878 *Eco*RI fragment, and the 1904 fragment is part of the 4878 *Eco*RI fragment, so the left border of the 4878 *Eco*RI fragment must be the *Eco*RI site in the diagram above. Therefore,

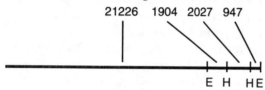

We now can begin adding fragments to the right end by taking the right-most fragment and adding it with other fragments until the sum equals the size of another fragment. To continue, 947 + 1375 = 2322:

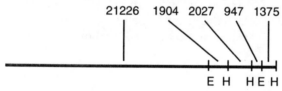

1375 + 4268 = 5643:

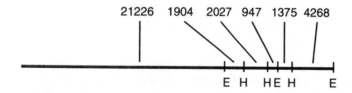

4268 + 5148 = 9416:

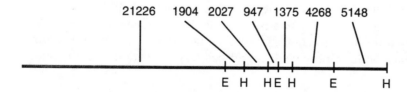

Now we face a bit of a problem. In the last several steps, *Eco*RI and *Hind*III sites alternated, making the task of adding fragments to the map relatively easy. The 5148 fragment does not add up with any of the other remaining fragments in the double digestion to yield an *Eco*RI fragment, so one of the two remaining *Hind*III fragments from the double digestion (564 or 125) must be on the right end. If we add all possible combinations of the 5148 fragment, another fragment from the double digestion, and one of the two *Hind*III fragments, we still do not arrive at the size of one of the two remaining *Eco*RI fragments (7421 or 5804). Therefore, the two remaining *Hind*III fragments from the double digestion (564 and 125) must be adjacent to one another, and we cannot determine their order in relation to the other fragments from these data. So we draw the map as follows:

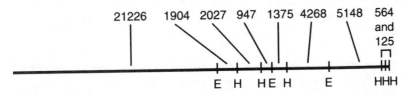

Now, 5148 + 564 + 125 + 1584 = 7421, so the 564 and 125 *Hind*III fragments are within the 7421 *Eco*RI fragment, and the 1584 fragment must be located immediately to the right of the 564 and 125 *Hind*III fragments:

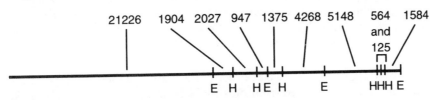

1584 + 4973 = 6557:

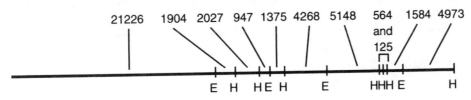

4973 + 831 = 5804:

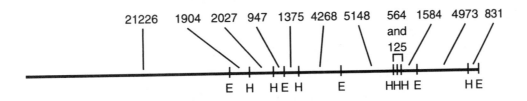

Now, there is only one fragment remaining in the double digestion, the 3530 fragment, which must be the other end. Notice that 831 + 3530 = 4361, which is the only remaining *Hind*III fragment, confirming that the 3530 fragment is the end fragment because it cannot have a *Hind*III and an *Eco*RI site on the same end. Therefore, the entire map is as follows:

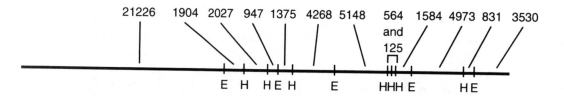

21. *(B)* The fragments' sizes are approximately 600, 430, and 220 nucleotide pairs.

22. *(D)* The first five amino acids, PheValAsnGlnHis, yields the smallest set of degenerate probes. Four of the five amino acids in this sequence are each specified by two codons (phenylalanine, asparagine, glutamine, and histidine). Valine is specified by four codons. The total number of probes required is therefore $2 \times 4 \times 2 \times 2 \times 2 = 64$. All other five-amino acid sequences in the given amino acid sequence require more than 64 probes.

23. *(E)* The answer to this question is not an easy one and requires information from Chapters 5 and 8. As explained in section 8.5, the C's in CG doublets tend to be methylated in eukaryotes. Spontaneous deamination of methylated cytosine substitutes a T for C in the DNA (see section 5.2). Because T is one of the four standard nucleotides in DNA, DNA repair mechanisms don't recognize the T as a damaged nucleotide. Therefore, methylated cytosines in CG doublets are more prone to mutations than most other nucleotides. For this reason (according to Lathe. 1985. *Journal of Molecular Biology* 183:1–12), natural selection disfavors CG doublets, so they appear much less frequently than expected in most eukaryotes, especially within the reading frames of genes. Where possible, most eukaryotes tend to utilize codons that do not have a CG doublet. Thus, probes with CG doublets are less likely to encounter their complementary sequences in DNA than alternative probes that do not contain CG doublets.

24. *(C)* This procedure placed the Shine-Dalgarno sequence at exactly the same distance from the initiation codon as in the *lacZ* gene of the *lac* operon. Thus, translation should be initiated in this engineered recombinant plasmid just as it is for the *lacZ* gene in the *lac* operon.

25. *(D)* Assuming that the left-to-right order of the nucleotides is T, C, A, G (as in Figure 9.34), we can read the sequence from the bottom to the top as

CTGTTGAGTTAGTATCTACTAGTAGTCATGTCGCTATTCAGATCGTGTGCTATCTATCTGACTGCCT-
TACGTCCTCGATTATTATAGGACTCAGGGGTCATA

Chapter 10
Eukaryotic Genome Organization

1. *(B)* To determine the complexity of the DNA, add the number of nucleotides in each unique sequence and the number of nucleotides of one repeat in all repetitive sequences. **(a)** 1,000,000 nucleotide pairs; **(b)** 2,100,005 nucleotide pairs; **(c)** 2,000,000 nucleotide pairs.

2. *(B)* The C-value paradox is the observation that the amount of DNA in most eukaryotic genomes is much greater than required to accommodate the number of genes in the genome. It is related to DNA complexity in that the complexity of a genome exceeds the number of nucleotides required to accommodate all of the genes much less than the entire genome does because of repetitive DNA. Most repetitive DNA sequences are not part of genes and contribute little to the complexity of the genome.

3. *(A)* A-T pairs are held together by two hydrogen bonds, whereas G-C pairs are held together by three, so a DNA molecules that consists mostly of G-C pairs requires more energy to dissociate into single strands than does a molecule that consists mostly of A-T pairs. **(a)** A molecule that consists predominantly of A-T pairs has a T_m that is lower than the T_m of a molecule with an equal number of A-T and G-C pairs because there are fewer hydrogen bonds to break. **(b)** A molecule that consists predominantly of G-C pairs has a T_m that is higher than the T_m of a molecule with an equal number of A-T and G-C pairs because there are more hydrogen bonds to break.

4. *(B)* The unique DNA renatures in an S-shaped curve and is the last DNA to renature. Therefore, the S-shaped part of the curve that is on the right side of the graph is the unique DNA. The upper limit of that part of the curve corresponds to a fraction of single-stranded DNA of about 0.8, so the proportion of unique DNA is about 80%.

5. *(B)* rRNA genes and tRNA genes fall into the moderately repetitive class. They encode rRNAs and tRNAs, which are essential for translation. Transposable elements fall into the moderately repetitive or highly repetitive classes of DNA. They may cause mutations and, in so doing, contribute to genetic variation, but they perform no essential function in the cell. Some genes that encode mRNA are repeated several times. In some cases, these genes are repeated so that they can produce abundant quantities of their products. In other cases, genes that encode mRNAs may be repeated in a family of genes that are differentially expressed in different tissues or at different times of development. Pseudogenes also represent repeated DNA. They perform no essential function in the cell.

6. *(C)* **(a)** According to this information, on average, there is one nucleosome per 230 nucleotide pairs. So, in a molecule of 1 million nucleotide pairs, there should be $1,000,000 \div 230 = 4348$ nucleosomes. **(b)** According to information from Chapter 2, the distance between each nucleotide pair is 3.4 Å, so a linear DNA molecule with no nucleosomes that is 1 million nucleotide pairs long should be 3,400,000 Å long. The length of a 10 nm fiber is reduced to about 1/6 to 1/7 the length of the original linear DNA molecule, so the range is $3,400,000 \text{ Å} \div 7 = 485,714 \text{ Å}$ to $3,400,000 \text{ Å} \div 6 = 566,667 \text{ Å}$. The length of a 30 nm fiber is reduced to about 1/40 the original length, which is $3,400,000 \text{ Å} \div 40 = 85,000 \text{ Å}$.

7. *(B)* Linker histones are not part of the central core of histones in a nucleosome and are, therefore, not as important in the formation of nucleosome structure. Mutations in the genes that encode the histones in the central core can alter nucleosome structure in the entire genome, which could have serious consequences. Thus, we expect natural selection to conserve nucleosome structure and, in so doing, conserve the DNA sequences of those genes that encode the histones in the central core. Linker histones apparently tie the nucleosomes together in the solenoid, and the ways that they do this may vary. Thus, greater variation is possible in linker histones, and natural selection probably does not conserve the nucleotide sequences of genes that encode linker histones as highly as it does the sequences of genes that encode the core histones.

8. *(C)* According to the Standing Committee on Human Cytogenetic Nomenclature (1995. *An International System for Human Cytogenetic Nomenclature.* Basel, Switzerland: Karger), human chromosomes are divided into six groups based on size and structure. Chromosomes 1–3 are metacentric, 4 and 5 are submetacentric, 6–12 and X are metacentric or submetacentric, 13–15 are acrocentric with satellites, 16–18 are metacentric or submetacentric, 19 and 20 are metacentric, and 21, 22, and Y are acrocentric with satellites. In the photograph, chromosomes 13–15 appear submetacentric, but the short arm appears longer because there are chromosome satellites on the short arms of these chromosomes. These designations have been obtained from examinations of many different karyotypes. Individual karyotypes and karyotypes prepared with different methods can yield varied results. Therefore, your results may vary somewhat from these.

9. *(B)* The system for plants has four classifications. Because there are no telocentric human chromosomes, the human system has only three classifications: metacentric, submetacentric, and acrocentric. The acrocentric classification in humans and the subtelocentric classification in plants are essentially the same.

10. *(B)* Each of the chromosomes in the photograph is duplicated and contains two sister chromatids, each of which contains one DNA molecule. Therefore, **(a)** the number of chromosomes in the photograph is 46, **(b)** the number of chromatids is 92, twice the number of chromosomes, and **(c)** the number of DNA molecules equals the number of chromatids, which is 92.

11. *(A)* Euchromatin is the portion of the chromatin that contains the genes; it consists mostly of unique DNA sequences. Repetitive DNA is found mostly within heterochromatin.

12. *(B)* **(a)** Constitutive heterochromatin is found predominantly in the centromeres and telomeres, **(b)** because these regions contain large quantities of repetitive DNA.

13. *(B)* **(a)** The observations that the pseudogene contains introns and that it is located near its functional counterparts in a gene cluster, suggest that it (along with the other genes in the cluster) arose through duplication of an original gene, followed by mutation that rendered the pseudogene nonfunctional. **(b)** The observation that this pseudogene does not contain introns suggests that it arose from reverse transcription of an mRNA followed by insertion of the reverse-transcribed DNA into a chromosome that is different from the one that contains the gene from which the mRNA was transcribed.

14. *(B)* Presumably, a single mutation rendered the gene nonfunctional and made it a pseudogene. In the meantime, because a copy of the gene continued to carry out its function, natural selection did not disfavor the mutant pseudogene. After becoming nonfunctional, further mutations in the pseudogene have no effect on expression of its functional counterpart, so natural selection has no effect on the accumulation of new mutations in the pseudogene. Over a period of many generations, we expect mutations to accumulate in pseudogenes. In the functional genes of a gene family, however, we do not expect as many mutations to accumulate because natural selection would disfavor many of them.

15. *(C)* **(a)** Thalassemia caused by a mutation in the ζ gene would be expressed only during early fetal development and could result in the inability of fetal blood to carry oxygen to the developing fetus. **(b)** Thalassemia for the α_2 gene would begin during late fetal development and would continue through birth and throughout the remainder of the person's life. **(c)** Because the θ gene is not expressed, a mutation in it should have no effect. **(d)** Thalassemia caused by a mutation for the $\gamma\beta$ gene would be expressed during late fetal development and should disappear shortly after birth. **(e)** A mutation in the δ gene should have a negligible effect throughout the person's because the gene supplies only about 2% of the β globin. **(f)** Thalassemia caused by a mutation in the ε gene would be expressed only during embryonic development.

16. *(B)* Most genes that encode mRNA are not transcribed at very high levels, so their nucleosomes may reassemble immediately after RNA polymerase II has passed. On the other hand, cells require tremendous amounts of rRNA, which is supplied by very high levels of transcription of rRNA genes. Because rRNA genes are so highly transcribed, they are devoid of nucleosomes because nucleosomes could interfere with the large numbers of RNA polymerase I molecules that are transcribing each gene.

17. *(B)* DNase attacks DNA that is not protected by proteins such as histones. DNase-hypersensitive sites are those regions of DNA that do not have any histones bound to them. The promoters of actively transcribed genes do not have histones because the basal transcription apparatus and transcription factors must bind to the DNA at this site. Thus, the promoter regions of actively transcribed genes are DNase hypersensitive sites.

18. *(B)* These genes (rRNA and tRNA genes) are repeated many times because their products are required in abundance. Loss of function in a single gene because of a mutation is not of serious consequence to the cell because the remaining functional copies of the gene can continue to carry out its function. Thus, natural selection probably does not effectively eliminate these pseudogenes.

19. *(B)* It is very unlikely that an *Alu* element would independently insert itself at exactly the same site independently in two different species. Thus, the *Alu* element insertion mutation that created the ψα-globin pseudogene probably arose before divergence of the ancestors of modern humans and chimpanzees.

20. *(C)* Unprocessed pseudogenes arise from duplication of the DNA that contains the gene. Such duplication appears due to phenomena associated with replication and recombination, so the duplicated genes are close to one another in the DNA molecule. A processed pseudogene, on the other hand, arises from a fully processed mRNA molecule. The mRNA is freed from the DNA before processing begins, so it does not remain near the site of the gene from which it is transcribed. The site of the original gene has no influence over the position at which the reverse-transcribed DNA is inserted into the genome.

21. *(B)* The pseudogene has a mutant promoter and contains a 31-nucleotide pair insertion mutation. Because of its promoter mutation, the mutant gene cannot be transcribed and is, therefore, a pseudogene.

22. *(C)* **(a)** These positively charged sites probably bind to the negatively charged phosphate groups of DNA. **(b)** This histone binds to DNA at two places and thus links different parts of the DNA molecule together. A mutation in any one site prevents that site from binding to the DNA and causes that part of the DNA molecule to be DNase hypersensitive because the histone no longer protects it from DNase.

23. *(C)* **(a)** The third position of 32 of the 64 codons may vary without altering the amino acid encoded. Because the coding region of many genes developed in GC-rich regions, we expect that the third codon will be a G or a C in most cases when any of the nucleotides will function in that position. **(b)** Constitutive heterochromatin tends to be AT-rich.

24. *(B)* AT-rich regions are located mostly in centromeres and telomeres.

25. *(B)* **(a)** In CDEI, 7 of the 8 nucleotides, or 87.5%, match the consensus sequence. In CDEIII, 23 of the 26 nucleotides, or 88.5%, match the consensus sequence. **(b)** In CDEII, 73 of the 77 nucleotides, or 94.8%, are A's or T's.

26. *(B)* Because the genes are similar in organisms that are so different from one another, we can expect to find genes more quickly in the large genomes of complex eukaryotes (such as humans) by identifying those genes first in a model organism with a relatively small genome, such as yeast. Researchers have identified the DNA sequences of several important human genes by taking human nucleotide sequences

obtained through massive sequencing and comparing them to the nucleotide sequences of known genes from *S. cerevisiae* and other model organisms.

27. *(C)* All of the genes listed encode products that are important in replicating DNA or protecting it from damage. Such functions are essential in all organisms, so we expect conservation of these genes among all species.

28. *(C)* The drawing in Figure 10.29 reveals some similarity in terms of gene size and gene organization. For example, proximal to both W′ regions is a relatively large gene followed by a large space that contains no genes, and distal to both W′ regions is a pseudogene. When Bussey et al. (1995. *Proceedings of the National Academy of Sciences*, USA 92:3809–3813) compared the DNA sequences of these regions, they discovered that the two large genes are similar and that the two pseudogenes are similar, indicating that more than the W′ region is duplicated.

29. *(C)* This chromosome segment has duplicated at some point during the evolution of the yeast genome. The duplicated segments have then diverged. This pattern of duplication followed by divergence is apparent at several locations in the yeast genome.

30. *(C)* There are several types of DNA that are not included within the coding sequences of genes. These include introns, regulatory regions of genes, DNA that intervenes between genes and their regulatory elements, transposable elements, DNA that constitutes chromosomal structural elements such as centromeres and telomeres, and repetitive DNA that is dispersed throughout the chromosomes. All of these types of DNA help explain the C-value paradox. The large and complex genomes of many multicellular eukaryotes contain relatively large proportions of repetitive DNA that is not part of the coding sequences of genes.

31. *(C)* **(a)** The large blocks of duplicated DNA consist of thousands to tens of thousands of nucleotide pairs and often contain functional genes. Highly repetitive DNA consists of very short DNA sequences (often shorter than 10 nucleotide pairs) that are repeated millions of times. The highly repetitive DNA contains no genes. **(b)** The genes within duplicated DNA may continue to carry out the same function (such as the duplicated α_1- and α_2-globin genes in humans), they may diverge to carry out different but similar functions (such as the α and β clusters of globin genes in humans), or some of the duplicated genes may mutate to become pseudogenes. **(c)** Gene duplication can be an advantage to the organism in that duplicated genes can compensate for mutant genes, allowing the organism to retain gene function even when a mutation disables one of the genes.

Chapter 11
Mitosis, Meiosis, and Life Cycles

1. *(B)* The asexual reproduction is advantageous in that it allows the aphids to produce large numbers of individuals, permitting survival of populations under heavy predation. The annual sexual reproduction is advantageous in that it permits genes to be shuffled to produce a high degree of genetic variation in the population.

2. *(B)* The asexual reproduction provides an advantage to these weed species because the underground stems and roots allow the weeds to regrow after the upper part of the plant is removed mechanically (such as by mowing, hoeing, or cultivation). These weeds are also well adapted to areas treated with herbicides. Systemic herbicides applied to the plants can kill entire plants, including the underground stems and roots. However, these herbicides have no effect on the dormant seeds in the soil, which may germinate to produce new weeds when the herbicides have degraded and are no longer effective. Some of the dormant seeds may germinate years after herbicide treatment. Thus, efforts to eradicate such weeds are often unsuccessful.

3. *(B)* **(a)** In meiosis I, duplicated homologous chromosomes pair with and then separate from one another. In mitosis, homologous chromosomes do not pair, and sister chromatids separate from one another. **(b)** In meiosis II, the chromatids are not identical (because of crossing over) as they are in mitosis. Also, there is no duplication of chromosomes immediately before meiosis II as there is just before mitosis.

4. *(B)* Mitosis does not reduce the chromosome number as meiosis does, so mitosis can operate at any ploidy level. Meiosis halves the chromosome number. Haploid and triploid cells have odd chromosome numbers, so it is not possible for the cell to halve the chromosome number and maintain full sets of chromosomes in the cell.

5. *(B)* Meiosis in a triploid plant cannot halve the chromosome numbers. Because meiosis cannot proceed normally, it aborts and gametes cannot form. In the absence of functional gametes, fertilization cannot take place and seeds cannot develop.

6. *(B)* Each gamete would have the same number of chromosomes as do the somatic cells. In a diploid individual, the gametes that arise from such an event would be diploid.

7. *(B)* The endosperm arises when two maternal polar nuclei fuse with one paternal sperm nucleus. Therefore, the proportion of maternal chromosomes in the endosperm is 2/3.

8. *(C)* **(b)** Primary oocyte. Primary oocytes form during gestation in human females, then remain arrested in prophase I until just before ovulation. The period during which they are arrested may last for decades.

9. *(B)* Prophase I is an extended phase of the cell cycle characterized by a series of stages. The first stage is leptonema, during which chromosomes begin to condense and sister chromatids associate tightly with each other. The chromatids attach to the nuclear envelope at their telomeres. The next stage is zygonema, during which homologous chromosomes pair, synapsis begins, and chromosomes condense further. At pachynema, synapsis is complete throughout the entire chromosome, and nonsister chromatids of paired homologous chromosomes initiate crossing-over. During diplonema, the paired chromosomes decondense somewhat and separate, except at the chiasmata. Some genes are transcribed during diplonema. At diakinesis, the chromosomes recondense and the chiasmata terminalize.

10. *(C)* During leptonema, the chromosomes take on a thin, threadlike appearance as the sister chro-

matids adhere to one another. During zygonema, the homologous chromosomes begin to pair with one another as if they were yoked (a yoke is a device that connects draft animals to one another). During diplonema, the chromosomes decondense to the point that the sister chromatids become apparent and appear as double threads of a chromosome. During diakinesis, the chiasmata move through the chromosome toward the telomeres.

11. *(B)* No. Crossing-over produces chromatids that consist of maternal and paternal segments.

12. *(B)* The number of possible combinations is 2 raised to a power equal to the number of tetrads. In this case, $2^{10} = 1024$.

13. *(B)* Paired chromosomes are not connected at the centromeres as are sister chromatids. However, the paired homologous chromosomes must be held together. The terminalized chiasmata hold the homologous chromosomes together until anaphase I.

14. *(C)* Cells that fail to form synaptonemal complexes because of the *zip1* mutation still undergo chromosome untangling. Therefore, even though synaptonemal complex formation and chromosome untangling occur at about the same time, chromosome untangling is not dependent on formation of the synaptonemal complex.

15. *(D)* The observation that crossing-over is reduced but not eliminated by failure to form a synaptonemal complex suggests that the synaptonemal complex affects, but is not essential for, crossing-over. The observation that failure of the synaptonemal complex is associated with migration of the two homologues to the same pole suggests that the synaptonemal complex has an important role in orienting the paired homologous chromosomes so that they segregate to opposite poles.

16. *(D)* **(a)** Migration of sister chromatids to opposite poles during meiosis I leaves cells with unduplicated chromosomes as they enter meiosis II. Depending on what happens to the homologue of the unduplicated chromosome, cells may end up with either no copies or two copies of a chromosome after meiosis II is complete, and may thus have aberrant chromosome numbers in the cells. **(b)** These results suggest that sister chromatid adhesion holds the sister chromatids together throughout meiosis I.

17. *(C)* Telomerase is not active in most human somatic cells, so the chromosomes will shorten with each cell division.

18. *(B)* The nucleolus is a structure that contains newly transcribed rRNAs. It is attached to chromosome 6 because the nucleolus organizer region (NOR), which contains the rRNA genes, is located on chromosome 6 at the site to which the nucleolus is attached.

Chapter 12
Mendelian Genetics

1. *(C)* **(a)** The *AABB* genotype produces only one type of gamete: *AB*. The *AaBb* genotype produces four types of gametes: *AB*, *Ab*, *aB*, and *ab*. Thus, there are four types of genotypes in the progeny, all in equal frequencies: *AABB*, *AABb*, *AaBB*, and *AaBb*. **(b)** The *AaBb* genotype produces four types of gametes: *AB*, *Ab*, *aB*, and *ab*; and the *aaBb* genotype produces two types of gametes: *aB* and *ab*. In the progeny, the *Aa* and *aa* genotypes appear in a 1:1 ratio, and the *BB*, *Bb*, and *bb* genotypes appear in a 1:2:1 ratio, respectively. Because the *A* and *B* loci assort independently, the progeny appear in the ratio 1 *AaBB*:1 *aaBB*:2 *AaBb*:2 *aaBb*:1 *Aabb*:1 *aabb*. **(c)** The *Aabb* genotype produces two types of gametes: *Ab*, and *ab*. The *aaBb* genotype produces two types of gametes: *aB*, and *ab*. These gametes unite to produce the genotypes *AaBb*, *Aabb*, *aaBb*, and *aabb*, all in equal frequencies. **(d)** The *AaBbCc* genotype produces eight types of gametes: *ABC*, *AbC*, *aBC*, *abC*, *ABc*, *Abc*, *aBc*, and *abc*. The *aaBbcc* genotype produces two types of gametes: *aBc* and *abc*. In the progeny, the *Aa* and *aa* genotypes and the *Cc* and *cc* genotypes appear in 1:1 ratios, and the *BB*, *Bb*, and *bb* genotypes appear in a 1:2:1 ratio, respectively. Because the *A*, *B*, and *C* loci assort independently, the progeny appear in the ratio 1 *AaBBCc*:2 *AaBbCc*: 1 *AabbCc*:1 *AaBBcc*:2 *AaBbcc*:1 *Aabbcc*:1 *aaBBCc*:2 *aaBbCc*: 1 *aabbCc*: 1 *aaBBcc*:2 *aaBbcc*:1 *aabbcc*.

2. *(B)* **(a)** 2^{15} = 32,768. **(b)** 3^{15} = 14,348,907. **(c)** 2^{15} = 32,768.

3. *(C)* The expected numbers are 12 "homozygous" heads, 24 "heterozygous", and 12 "homozygous" tails. The chi-square test will have 2 degrees of freedom, and its outcome will vary depending on the results of your particular experiment. Let's work through one example to see how it's done. Suppose the outcome is 16 "homozygous" heads, 21 "heterozygous," and 11 "homozygous" tails. The chi-square calculation is $[(16 - 12)^2 \div 12] + [(21 - 24)^2 \div 24] + [(11 - 12)^2 \div 12] = 1.79$ with 2 degrees of freedom, which is less than the critical value of 5.99 at $P = 0.05$. There is no evidence to reject the hypothesis that these results conform to a 1:2:1 ratio.

4. *(A)* The degrees of freedom are usually one less than the number of possible classes. Because there are three possible classes ("homozygous" heads, "heterozygous", and "homozygous" tails), there are 2 degrees of freedom.

5. *(C)* The chi-square values for the experiments in the order listed in Table 12.1 are as follows: 0.2629, 0.0150, 0.3907, 0.0635, 0.4506, 0.3497, and 0.6065, each with 1 degree of freedom. All but the last one (0.6065) have associated probabilities that are greater than 0.5. In a set of independent experiments, we expect about half of the probabilities to exceed 0.5. In this set of Mendel's experiments, 6 of 7 experiments have probabilities that exceed 0.5, so the results are indeed close to expected values.

6. *(B)* Because the individual is heterozygous at only two of the four loci, there are $2^2 = 4$ possible gametes: *ABCd*, *AbCd*, *ABcd*, and *Abcd*.

7. *(B)* Mutations that reduce or eliminate the functional product encoded by a gene usually create recessive alleles. If the gene encodes an enzyme in a biochemical pathway, then the pathway can proceed beyond the step catalyzed by the enzyme as long as there is functional enzyme present. When a single mutation in one gene eliminates the functional product encoded by that gene, then the corresponding gene on the homologous chromosome may still encode the functional enzyme and the pathway can proceed. Thus, the mutant allele is recessive because the allele on the homologous chromosome that encodes the functional enzyme compensates for the absence of functional product from the mutant allele. Only when mutant alleles are present at the same locus on both homologous chromosomes is no enzyme produced and the pathway is therefore blocked.

8. *(C)* The *su* allele is a mutant allele that fails to encode a functional enzyme in the pathway for starch

synthesis. In an *Susu* heterozygote, the *Su* allele encodes functional enzyme, so starch is produced. Only in the *susu* homozygote is there no functional enzyme.

9. *(C)* There are several ways; in this answer we'll discuss two. Suppose that a gene has a regulatory element to which a repressor protein binds. When the repressor protein is bound, the gene is inactivated. Suppose a mutation in the regulatory element prevents the repressor protein from binding. Under these conditions, one allele of that gene is expressed when it should not be, and the presence of the gene's product produces a particular phenotype. The product is produced and the phenotype is present whether the individual is homozygous or heterozygous for the allele.

A second type of dominant mutant allele is one that affects an enzyme that functions as a tetramer of four identical subunits, all encoded by the same gene. Suppose that a mutant allele encodes a product that cannot function but can participate in tetramer formation. Suppose further that if at least one of the subunits in the tetramer is mutant, the tetramer cannot function; it functions only when all four subunits are nonmutant. In a cell that is heterozygous for such a mutant allele, half of the subunits should be mutant and half nonmutant. If the subunits associate at random, then the probability that all four subunits of the tetramer will be nonmutant is $(1/4)4 = 1/16$. Thus, 15/16 of the tetramers will be nonfunctional, and the enzyme activity in the heterozygote is reduced to 1/16 the activity of a homozygote. The mutant allele has a dominant effect by drastically reducing enzyme activity in heterozygotes.

10. *(B)* Same-sense mutations do not alter the gene's polypeptide product, so they cause no phenotypic alteration. Because they cannot be detected phenotypically, most same-sense mutations are not detected. To be detected, they must be identified by examination of the DNA using a method that detects the difference in DNA sequence.

11. *(B)* **(a)** Yes. There can be many dominant alleles for a locus. Mutations that do not alter the function of a gene's product, or those that increase the function of a gene's product, typically create new dominant alleles. Such mutations can occur at many different sites within a gene. **(b)** Yes. There can be many recessive alleles at a single locus. Most mutations that reduce or eliminate the function of the gene's product create recessive alleles. Such mutations can occur throughout the gene.

12. *(A)* The observation of a dwarf, white-flowered pea plant indicates both the phenotype and the genotype. Because both characteristics (dwarf stature and white flowers) are recessive phenotypes, the plant must be homozygous for the recessive alleles.

13. *(B)* The allele for cystic fibrosis is recessive. Many of the people who carry the recessive allele are heterozygous and do not have the disorder.

14. *(B)* The allele is recessive because it contains a mutation that prevents it from encoding a functional enzyme that is part of the melanin synthesis pathway. Rabbits that are homozygous for the recessive allele lack the functional enzyme and cannot synthesize melanins.

15. *(B)* The individual will have neither of the disorders. There is a dominant allele at each of the two loci. The dominant alleles both encode functional enzymes, so the pathway is not blocked at either step.

16. *(B)* **(a)** Because both are heterozygous for the allele that causes albinism, the probability is 25% for each child. **(b)** Because both are heterozygous for the allele that causes phenylketonuria, the probability is 25% for each child. **(c)** Assuming that the alleles responsible for inheritance of albinism and phenylketonuria assort independently, we can determine the probability that a child will inherit both albinism and phenylketonuria as the product of the individual probabilities, which is $0.25 \times 0.25 = 0.0625$.

17. *(D)* **(a)** The purple-flowered, tall parent must have at least one dominant allele at each locus. Because it had progeny with the recessive phenotypes (white-flowered and dwarf), it must be heterozygous at

300

both loci. Its genotype is *Aa Bb*. The purple-flowered, dwarf parent must be *bb* because it is dwarf, and it must have at least one *A* allele because it has purple flowers. It has white-flowered progeny, so it must be heterozygous at the *A* locus. Its genotype must be *Aa bb*. **(b)** Given the genotypes of the parents, we expect half of the progeny to be tall and half to be dwarf. We also expect three-fourths of the progeny to be purple-flowered and one-fourth to be white-flowered. Because the two traits are inherited independently, we expect 3/8 of the progeny to be purple-flowered, tall; 3/8 to be purple-flowered, dwarf; 1/8 to be white-flowered, tall; and 1/8 to be white-flowered, dwarf. The observed and expected values are as follows:

Phenotype	Observed	Expected
Purple flowers, tall	58	59.25
Purple flowers, dwarf	64	59.25
White flowers, tall	15	19.75
White flowers, dwarf	21	19.75

The chi-square value is $[(58 - 59.25)^2 \div 59.25] + [(64 - 59.25)^2 \div 59.25] + [(15 - 19.75)^2 \div 19.75] + [(21 - 19.75)^2 \div 19.75] = 1.63$ with 3 degrees of freedom, which is not significant at the 0.05 probability level. There is no evidence to reject the hypothesis that the genotypes are correct.

18. *(C)*

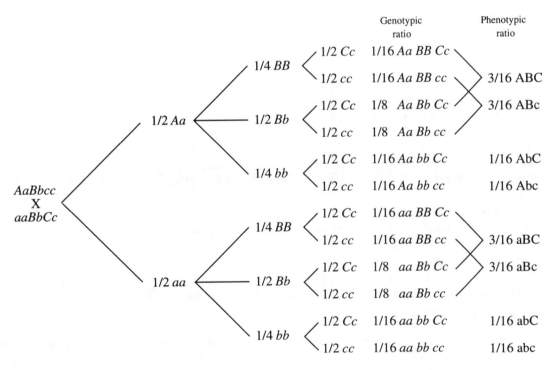

19. *(C)* Because neither parent has phenylketonuria (PKU) but their first child does, both parents must be heterozygous for the recessive allele that causes PKU. Thus, the probability that any one child will have PKU is 0.25, and the probability that any one child will not have PKU is 0.75. The probability that none of the three additional children will have PKU is $0.75^3 = 0.421875$. So, the probability that at least one of the three children will have PKU is $1 - 0.421875 = 0.578125$.

20. *(C)* Use the binomial distribution to solve this problem. Let $x = 3$ and $y = 5$, then $p = 0.5$, $q = 0.5$, and $n = 8$

$$P = \frac{8!}{3!5!} 0.5^8 = 0.21875$$

21. *(C)* In this instance, "at least five" refers to four combinations: 5 white, 3 black; 6 white, 2 black; 7 white, 1 black; and 8 white, 0 black. We use the binomial distribution to calculate the probability of each outcome, then sum the probabilities:

$$P = \frac{8!}{3!5!} 0.5^8 = 0.21875$$

$$P = \frac{8!}{2!6!} 0.5^8 = 0.109375$$

$$P = \frac{8!}{1!7!} 0.5^8 = 0.03125$$

$$\underline{P = \qquad 0.5^8 = 0.00390625}$$

Sum   0.36328125

22. *(C)* Had the *A* locus encoded chalcone synthase, then the activities of chalcone synthase should have differed between the *AA* and *aa* genotypes. The observation that there was no difference indicates that the *A* locus does not encode chalcone synthase.

23. *(C)* The *A* locus must encode an enzyme that catalyzes a step that follows synthesis of *p*-coumaric acid. Had the *A* locus encoded an enzyme that catalyzes a step that precedes synthesis of *p*-coumaric acid, *p*-coumaric acid would not have been synthesized and would not have been detected.

24. *(C)* In this example, anthocyanin, the purple pigment in pea flowers, is synthesized through a biochemical pathway that consists of a series of steps, each step ending with an intermediate that is the substrate for the next step. Each step is catalyzed by an enzyme that is composed of one or more proteins, each encoded by a different gene. Homozygosity for mutant alleles in any one of the several genes that encode the enzymes that participate in the pathway can reduce or eliminate anthocyanin synthesis. Because all of the genes that encode enzymes for the anthocyanin synthesis pathway govern flower color, mutations in any of those genes affect the same trait.

25. *(E)* **(a)** The forked-line diagram is on the next page. **(b)** For the *A* locus, the observed number of *AA* plants is $8 + 14 + 9 + 11 + 22 + 17 + 15 + 18 + 45 = 159$, and the expected number is $639 \div 4 = 159.75$; the observed number of *Aa* plants is $14 + 18 + 20 + 16 + 38 + 40 + 49 + 48 + 78 = 321$, and the expected number is $639 \div 2 = 319.5$; and the observed number of *aa* plants is $8 + 10 + 10 + 7 + 25 + 20 + 19 + 24 + 36 = 159$ and the expected number is 159.75. The chi-square value is $[(159 - 159.75)^2 \div 159.75] + [(321 - 319.5)^2 \div 319.5] + [(159 - 159.75)^2 \div 159.75] = 0.01$, which is below the critical value of 5.99 at $P = 0.05$ for 2 degrees of freedom. There is no evidence to reject the hypothesis that the observed data conform to a 1:2:1 ratio.

For the *B* locus, the observed number of *BB* plants is $8 + 14 + 8 + 10 + 22 + 25 + 14 + 18 + 38 = 157$, and

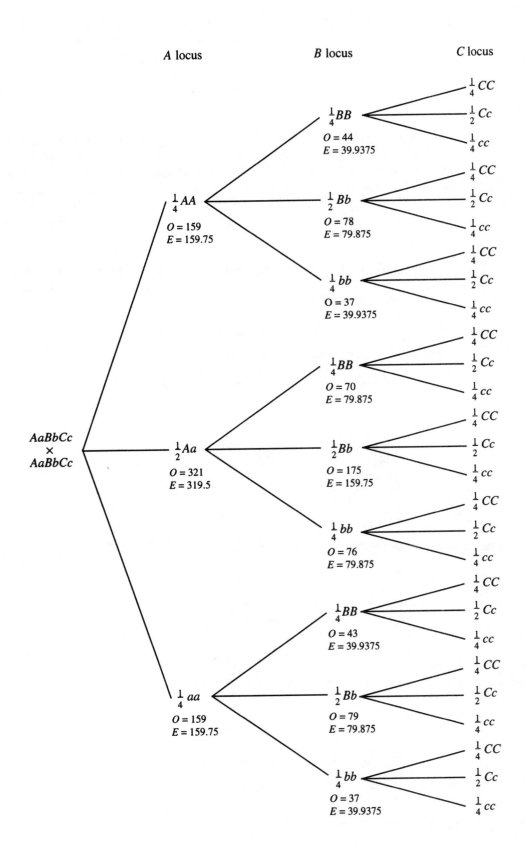

303

the expected number is $639 \div 4 = 159.75$; the observed number of Bb plants is $15 + 18 + 19 + 24 + 45 + 36 + 49 + 48 + 78 = 332$, and the expected number is $639 \div 2 = 319.5$; and the observed number of bb plants is $9 + 11 + 10 + 7 + 17 + 20 + 20 + 16 + 40 = 150$ and the expected number is 159.75. The chi-square value is $[(157 - 159.75)^2 \div 159.75] + [(332 - 319.5)^2 \div 319.5] + [(150 - 159.75)^2 \div 159.75] = 1.13$, which is below the critical value of 5.99 at $P = 0.05$ for 2 degrees of freedom. There is no evidence to reject the hypothesis that the observed data conform to a 1:2:1 ratio.

For the C locus, the observed number of CC plants is $8 + 9 + 10 + 10 + 15 + 19 + 14 + 20 + 49 = 154$, and the expected number is $639 \div 4 = 159.75$; the observed number of Cc plants is $22 + 17 + 25 + 20 + 45 + 36 + 38 + 40 + 78 = 321$, and the expected number is $639 \div 2 = 319.5$; and the observed number of cc plants is $14 + 11 + 8 + 7 + 18 + 24 + 18 + 16 + 48 = 164$, and the expected number is 159.75. The chi-square value is $[(154 - 159.75)^2 \div 159.75] + [(321 - 319.5)^2 \div 319.5] + [(164 - 159.75)^2 \div 159.75] = 0.33$, which is below the critical value of 5.99 at $P = 0.05$ for 2 degrees of freedom. There is no evidence to reject the hypothesis that the observed data conform to a 1:2:1 ratio.

(c) We'll represent the chi-square analysis in tabular form. We have written chi-square rounded to four decimal places but have conducted all calculations with unrounded values. Your answer may vary slightly if you use rounded values in the calculations.

Genotype	Observed	Expected	Chi-Square Value $[(O - E)^2 \div E]$
$AA\,BB\,CC$	8	9.984375	0.3944
$AA\,BB\,cc$	14	9.984375	1.6150
$AA\,bb\,CC$	9	9.984375	0.0971
$AA\,bb\,cc$	11	9.984375	0.1033
$aa\,BB\,cc$	8	9.984375	0.3944
$aa\,BB\,CC$	10	9.984375	0.0000
$aa\,bb\,CC$	10	9.984375	0.0000
$aa\,bb\,cc$	7	9.984375	0.8920
$AA\,BB\,Cc$	22	19.96875	0.2066
$AA\,bb\,Cc$	17	19.96875	0.4414
$aa\,BB\,Cc$	25	19.96875	1.2677
$aa\,bb\,Cc$	20	19.96875	0.0000
$AA\,Bb\,CC$	15	19.96875	1.2364
$AA\,Bb\,cc$	18	19.96875	0.1941
$aa\,Bb\,CC$	19	19.96875	0.0470
$aa\,Bb\,cc$	24	19.96875	0.8138
$Aa\,BB\,CC$	14	19.96875	1.7841
$Aa\,BB\,cc$	18	19.96875	0.1941
$Aa\,bb\,CC$	20	19.96875	0.0000
$Aa\,bb\,cc$	16	19.96875	0.7888
$AA\,Bb\,Cc$	45	39.9375	0.6417
$aa\,Bb\,Cc$	36	39.9375	0.3882
$Aa\,BB\,Cc$	38	39.9375	0.0940
$Aa\,bb\,Cc$	40	39.9375	0.0001
$Aa\,Bb\,CC$	49	39.9375	2.0564
$Aa\,Bb\,cc$	48	39.9375	1.6276
$AaBbCc$	78	79.875	0.0440
Sum			15.3224

The sum of 15.3224 is less than the critical chi-square value of 38.88 at $P = 0.05$ for 26 degrees of freedom. There is no evidence to reject the hypothesis that these results conform to the principle of independent assortment.

(d) All of the chi-square tests provide no evidence to reject the hypotheses that the results of this experiment conform to the principles of segregation and independent assortment.

26. *(C)* The genotypes are as follows: purple-flowered, tall parent: *Aa Bb*; white-flowered, dwarf parent: *aa bb*; purple-flowered, tall progeny: *Aa Bb*; white-flowered, tall progeny: *aa Bb*; purple-flowered, dwarf progeny: *Aa bb*; white-flowered, dwarf progeny: *aa bb*.

27. *(D)* **(a)** The dark-axil and male-fertile phenotypes are dominant, and the light-axil and male-sterile phenotypes are recessive. **(b)** If the inheritance of axil color conforms to the principle of segregation, then the phenotypic ratio of plants with dark axils to plants with light axils should not differ significantly from a 3:1 ratio according to a chi-square test. The observed number of plants with dark axils is 627 + 27 = 654, and the expected number is 663.75. The observed number of plants with light axils is 17 + 214 = 231, and the expected number is 221.25. The chi-square value is $[(654 - 663.75)^2 \div 663.75] + [(231 - 221.25)^2 \div 221.25] = 0.57$, with 1 degree of freedom, which is not significant at the 0.05 probability level. There is no evidence to reject the hypothesis that the inheritance of axil color conforms to the principle of segregation. **(c)** If the inheritance of male fertility and sterility conforms to the principle of segregation, then the phenotypic ratio of male-fertile plants to male-sterile plants should not differ significantly from a 3:1 ratio according to a chi-square test. The observed number of plants that are male-fertile is 627 + 17 = 644, and the expected number is 663.75. The observed number of plants that are male sterile is 27 + 214 = 241, and the expected number is 221.25. The chi-square value is $[(644 - 663.75)^2 \div 663.75] + [(241 - 221.25)^2 \div 221.25] = 2.35$, with 1 degree of freedom, which is not significant at the 0.05 probability level. There is no evidence to reject the hypothesis that the inheritance of male fertility and sterility conforms to the principle of segregation.

28. *(D)* **(a)** The colored and erect phenotypes are dominant, and the white and hooded phenotypes are recessive. **(b)** If the inheritance of flower color conforms to the principle of segregation, then the phenotypic ratio of plants with colored flowers:plants with white flowers should not differ significantly from a 3:1 ratio according to a chi-square test. The observed number of plants with colored flowers is 108 + 36 = 144, and the expected number is 192. The observed number of plants with white flowers is 84 + 28 = 112, and the expected number is 64. The chi-square value is $[(144 - 192)^2 \div 192] + [(112 - 64)^2 \div 64] = 48$ with 1 degree of freedom, which is highly significant. We reject the hypothesis that the inheritance of flower color in this experiment conforms to the principle of segregation. **(c)** If the inheritance of flower shape conforms to the principle of segregation, then the phenotypic ratio of plants with erect flowers:plants with hooded flowers should not differ significantly from a 3:1 ratio according to a chi-square test. The observed number of plants that have erect flowers is 108 + 84 = 192, and the expected number is 192. The observed number of plants that have hooded flowers is 36 + 28 = 64, and the expected number is 64. Because the observed and expected values match each other exactly, the chi-square value is zero with 1 degree of freedom, which is not significant at the 0.05 probability level. There is no evidence to reject the hypothesis that the inheritance of male flower shape conforms to the principle of segregation.

29. *(D)* **(a)** The chi-square value for the hypothesis that these results are not in excess of expectation is 33.73 with 1 degree of freedom, which has an associated probability of <0.01. Bateson's conclusion is justified statistically. **(b)** Bateson did not collect the data directly, so the data may not be reliable. Those who gave Bateson the pedigrees may not have counted or been aware of all the children in the families.

30. *(C)* Use the binomial distribution to solve this problem. Let $x = 1$ and $y = 7$, then $p = 0.75$, $q = 0.25$, and $n = 8$:

$$P = \frac{8!}{1!7!}(0.75^1)(0.25^7) = 0.000366211$$

31. *(B)* Parents who are close relatives may inherit the same recessive allele from a common ancestor. Thus, parents who are first cousins are more likely to be heterozygous for the same recessive allele than parents who are unrelated.

32. *(C)* If the inheritance of seed color conforms to the principle of segregation, then the phenotypic ratio of yellow seeds to green seeds should not differ significantly from a 3:1 ratio according to a chi-square test. The observed number of yellow seeds is 619, and the expected number is 618.75. The observed number of green seeds is 206, and the expected number is 206.25. The observed and expected numbers differ from one another by only 0.25 seeds, so we expect a chi-square value that is very close to zero. The chi-square value is $[(619 - 618.75)^2 \div 618.75] + [(206 - 206.25)^2 \div 206.25] = 0.0004$, with 1 degree of freedom, which is not significant at the 0.05 probability level. There is no evidence to reject the hypothesis that the inheritance of seed color conforms to the principle of segregation.

33. *(C)* **(a)** In the case of two pairs of alleles, nine different genotypic classes may occur. However, only four phenotypic classes may be distinguished externally; the number of individuals in the phenotypic classes must occur in a ratio of 9:3:3:1. **(b)** In a Punnett square for the F_2 generation in a dihybrid experiment, the 16 squares depict the 16 possible unions of gametes. Some different gametic unions create the same genotype in the zygote. For example, in the progeny of the dihybrid cross *Aa Bb* × *Aa Bb*, the genotype *Aa Bb* can arise in four different ways: female *AB* gamete unites with male *ab* gamete, female *Ab* gamete unites with male *aB* gamete, female *aB* gamete unites with male *Ab* gamete, and female *ab* gamete unites with male *AB* gamete. Although there are 16 possible gametic unions, there are only nine possible genotypes.

34. *(D)* **(a)** Mendel expected a 2:1 ratio, which out of 100 plants is 66.7:33.3. The observed ratio was 60:40. The chi-square test is $[(60 - 66.7)^2 \div 66.7] + [(40 - 33.3)^2 \div 33.3] = 2.02$, with 1 degree of freedom, which is not significant at the 0.05 probability level. There is no evidence to reject the hypothesis that these results conform to a 2:1 ratio. **(b)** According to a chi-square analysis, there is no statistical evidence to conclude that the results were too far from the expected ratio, and no statistically valid reason for Mendel to repeat the experiment. However, we cannot fault Mendel for his conclusion. Chi-square analysis had not yet been developed when he interpreted the results of his experiments, so he relied on his own intuition, rather than a statistical test, to conclude that the results were too far from the expected ratio. This example is a good illustration of why scientists should apply statistical tests instead of relying entirely on intuition for interpretation of experimental results.

35. *(E)* **(a)** Mendel clearly described the principle of parental equivalence in his paper; however, he attributed the principle to Gärtner, as is evident in the following passage from his paper:

> It was furthermore shown by the whole of the experiments that it is perfectly immaterial whether the dominant character belongs to the seed plant or to the pollen plant; the form of the hybrid remains identical in both cases. This interesting fact was also emphasized by Gärtner, with the remark that even the most practiced expert is not in a position to determine in a hybrid which of the two parental species was the seed or the pollen plant.

Whether or not it is appropriate to attribute the principles of segregation and independent assortment to Mendel has been debated substantially in scientific literature. Mendel did not state these principles by name in his paper, nor did he build his discussion around them, as textbook presentations lead many students to believe. Nonetheless, there are two passages in which Mendel clearly describes the principles of segregation and independent assortment.

The passage in which Mendel best describes the principle of segregation appears in his concluding remarks embedded within a discussion in which he attempts to reconcile his experimental results with conflicting results of other researchers who worked with species other than pea:

> With regard to those hybrids whose progeny is variable we may perhaps assume that between the differentiating elements of the egg and pollen cells there also occurs a compromise, in so far that the formation of a cell as the foundation of the hybrid becomes possible; but, nevertheless, the arrangement between the conflicting elements is only temporary and does not endure throughout the life of the hybrid plant. Since in the habit of the plant no changes are perceptible during the whole period of vegetation, we must further assume that it is only possible for the differentiating elements to liberate themselves from the enforced union when the fertilizing cells are developed. In the formation of these cells all existing elements participate in an entirely free and equal arrangement, by which it is only the differentiating ones which mutually separate themselves. In this way the production would be rendered possible of as many sorts of egg and pollen cells as there are combinations possible of the formative elements.

In this passage, Mendel perceives different alleles ("differentiating elements") of a locus to come together in a heterozygote in what he calls an "enforced union." He then states that the differing elements "mutually separate themselves" during the formation of the egg and pollen cells (meiosis), a phenomenon that we now call *segregation*.

The best passage on independent assortment appears immediately after his discussion of dihybrid and trihybrid experiments. In his interpretation of the results of those experiments, he stated:

> There is therefore no doubt that for the whole of the characters involved in the experiments the principle applies that the offspring of the hybrids in which several essentially different characters are combined exhibit the terms of a series of combinations, in which the developmental series for each pair of differentiating characters are united. It is demonstrated at the same time that the relation of each pair of different characters in hybrid union is independent of the other differences in the two original parental stocks.

In this passage, Mendel makes it clear that the inheritance of different characteristics is independent, a good summary of the principle of independent assortment.

(b) It is not entirely clear that Mendel perceived characters as paired, particularly in homozygotes. He represented homozygotes as *A* or *a*, instead of *AA* or *aa*, which has led some researchers to conclude that he did not perceive the alleles as paired. However, in the passage cited above relative to the principle of segregation, Mendel clearly perceives different alleles in a heterozygote as being held together in an "enforced union" that is not broken until the formation of pollen and egg cells. This passage seems to indicate that Mendel perceived alleles as paired, at least in heterozygotes.

36. (E) Of the experiments for which Mendel reported numerical results, the following demonstrate independent assortment: the dihybrid experiments for seed shape and seed color, the trihybrid experiment for seed shape, seed color, and color of the seed coat (flower color), the dihybrid testcross experiments for seed shape and seed color, and the dihybrid testcross experiments for plant stature and flower color. Mendel stated that he conducted dihybrid experiments for all possible combinations of the seven characteristics that he studied and that all experiments yielded results that were consistent with his hypothesis. However, he reported data for only the dihybrid experiments with seed shape and seed color and a dihybrid testcross experiment with plant stature and flower color.

37. *(C)* The "first generation" is the F_1 generation, and the first of the "succeeding generations" is the F_2 generation. Mendel observed that the F_1 progeny of true-breeding parents were all uniform and had the dominant phenotypes of the parents. He further observed that variability was present in predictable ratios in the F_2 and subsequent generations. Mendel certainly gave considerable attention to what Darwin called "a curious fact [that] deserves attention."

38. *(D)* Darwin's explanation suggests that the "conditions of life," which we may interpret as environmental conditions, cause considerable changes in the reproductive organs of the hybrids, and that the changes wrought in the reproductive organs cause the variability. In other words, Darwin supposes that the environment is responsible for the variability. Mendel's results indicate that predictable inheritance of variable genetic determinants is responsible for the variation, not any effect that the environment has on the reproductive organs.

39. *(D)* The 3:1 ratio appears in the first-generation progeny of two heterozygous parents. In natural populations, all genotypes may exist among the individuals in the population, so many matings may be between genotypes that are not both heterozygous for a particular Mendelian trait. Thus, there will be many different inheritance patterns lumped together in the population.

40. *(E)* In this instance, $a = 0.95$, $b = 0.05$. The desired type is a white-flowered, dwarf plant, and p = the probability that any one individual will be the desired type. In this example, $p = 0.0625$. Therefore, q is the probability that any one individual will not be the desired type, which is $q = 1 - p = 0.9375$. Substituting these values into the equation, we obtain

$$n = \frac{\log 0.05}{\log 0.9375} = 46.42$$

Forty-six plants provide slightly less than 95% certainty of obtaining at least one white-flowered, dwarf plant, so it is best to grow 47 plants to be slightly more than 95% certain of obtaining at least one white-flowered, dwarf plant.

Chapter 13
Variations on Mendel's Theme

1. *(C)* The direct product of the *TP53* locus is a subunit that must assemble into a tetramer of four identical subunits to form the functional protein. Dominant loss-of-function mutant alleles eliminate the function of the subunit but do not eliminate its ability to participate in tetramer formation. Such mutant alleles are dominant because their product participates in tetramer formation and eliminates the function of any tetramer of which it is a part. Recessive loss-of-function mutant alleles eliminate both the function of the subunit and its ability to participate in tetramer formation. The alleles are recessive because their products have no effect on the formation of functional tetramers from the functional subunits encoded by the other allele.

2. *(B)* The Bombay phenotype is an example of nonpenetrance for ABO blood types. Homozygosity for a mutant allele at the *FUT1* locus prevents formation of the H substance and causes the Bombay phenotype. The H substance is the substrate for enzymes encoded by the *ABO* locus. When functional H substance is absent, there is no substrate for the enzymes encoded by the *ABO* locus, so the phenotypes associated with the different alleles at the ABO locus cannot be expressed.

3. *(C)* **(a)** The wild-type allele w^+ is dominant over w^{bf} which is dominant over w^1. **(b)** The w^+ allele encodes a functional enzyme in the biosynthesis pathway for eye pigments that, when heterozygous with either the w^{bf} or w^1 allele, produces wild-type pigmentation. The w^{bf} allele is a leaky recessive mutant allele that encodes a partially functional enzyme that produces reduced amounts of pigment in w^{bf}/w^{bf} homozygotes or w^{bf}/w^1 heterozygotes. The w^1 allele is a mutant recessive allele that fails to encode a functional product. In the absence of functional product in w^1/w^1 homozygotes, the eyes have no pigment and are white.

4. *(C)* The mutant *PAH* alleles that do not cause PKU when homozygous probably encode a mutant form of phenylalanine hydroxylase (PAH) that has slightly reduced function when compared to the form encoded by the normal allele. Individuals who are homozygous for these alleles probably have enough PAH function to have a normal phenotype. However, when one of these alleles is heterozygous with a mutant allele that fails to encode functional PAH, the level of functional enzyme is reduced to the point that the non-PKU HPA phenotype appears.

5. *(D)* **(a)** *PAH*R243X*: The mutation created a premature termination codon (indicated by X) from an arginine codon in codon 243. The mutation was probably CGA → UGA. *PAH*P281L*: The mutation created a leucine codon from a phenylalanine codon in codon 281. The mutation was probably UUPy → CUPy. *PAH*R408W*: The mutation created a tryptophan codon from an arginine codon in codon 408. The mutation was probably CGG → UGG. *PAH*IVS-12*: A mutation in intron 12 eliminated proper removal of the intron. *PAH*E280K*: The mutation created a lysine codon from a glutamic acid codon in codon 280. The mutation was probably GAPu → AAPu. *PAH*R158Q*: The mutation created a glutamine codon from an arginine codon in codon 158. The mutation was probably CGPu → CAPu. *PAH*R261Q*: The mutation created a glutamine codon from an arginine codon in codon 261. The mutation was probably CGPu → CAPu. *PAH*Y414C*: The mutation created a cysteine codon from a tyrosine codon in codon 414. The mutation was probably UAPy → UGPy.

(b) An individual's predicted PAH activity is the average of the activities of the two alleles that each individual carries. We'll present the predicted levels for all possible homozygous and compound heterozygous combinations in the table below. For the sake of brevity, we've deleted the "*PAH*" designation for each allele:

Predicted PAH Activities for Homozygotes and Compound Heterozygotes Expressed as Percent of Normal PAH Activity

	Allele on one chromosome							
	R243X	*P281L*	*R408W*	*IVS-12*	*E280K*	*R158Q*	*R261Q*	*Y414C*
R243X	< 1							
P281L	< 1	< 1						
R408W	< 1	< 1	< 1					
IVS-12	< 1	< 1	< 1	< 1				
E280K	< 2	< 2	< 2	< 2	< 3			
R158Q	5	5	5	5	5-6.5	10		
R261Q	15	15	15	15	15-16.5	20	30	
Y414C	25	25	25	25	25-26.5	30	40	50

(Row labels under "Allele on other chromosome")

(c) Mild PKU is associated with reduced PAH activity, and classic PKU is associated with substantially reduced enzyme activity. The critical level of enzyme activity that distinguishes between classic PKU and mild PKU can be estimated from the clinical phenotypes given in the problem and the enzyme activities given in the table above and Table 13.3 in the book. *PAH*R158Q/*R158Q* homozygotes had 10% PAH activity and had classic PKU. Compound heterozygotes between *PAH*Y414C* and any of the first four alleles had about 25% enzyme activity [(50% + < 1%) ÷ 2 ≈ 25%] and had mild PKU. Therefore, individuals with 25% or greater enzyme activity have mild PKU (or no PKU) whereas those with 10% or less enzyme activity have classic PKU. The critical level of PAH activity that distinguishes between mild and classic PKU is somewhere between 10% and 25% of normal activity.

6. *(B)* **(a)** Two lines of evidence suggest that pleiotropy may not explain the association that Correns observed. First, the fact that stocks with purple flowers and smooth leaves as well as stocks with white flowers and hoary leaves were known, indicates that the association between purple flowers and hoary leaves and the association between white flowers and smooth leaves that Correns observed are not always maintained. Second, because the phenotypic manifestations of pleiotropy are usually due to the expression of the same gene in different tissues, we expect some biochemical relationship between the two traits. However, there is no easily identifiable biochemical relationship between flower color and leaf texture. **(b)** The most probable explanation for the associations that Correns observed is linkage. The loci that govern flower color and leaf texture that Correns studied are probably located very close to one another on the same chromosome, so alleles of these loci on the same chromosome tend to be inherited together.

7. *(A)* **(a)** Because the phenotypes of both alleles are simultaneously present in heterozygotes, the phenotypes in Figure 13.30 are codominant. **(b)** The same is true for the phenotypes in Figure 13.31; they are codominant. **(c)** In Figure 13.32, the phenotypes of the *AA* and *Aa* genotypes are indistinguishable from one another, but both can be distinguished from the phenotype of the *aa* genotype. Therefore, the markers display complete dominance.

8. *(A)* **(a)** The polymorphic marker is indicated by an arrow in the photograph below:

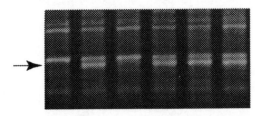

(b) The first and third individuals (from left to right) display the recessive phenotype; the second, fourth, fifth, and sixth individuals display the dominant phenotype.

9. *(B)* The *A* locus probably encodes an enzyme that functions early in the pathway for pigment synthesis. The intermediate that arises from the reaction catalyzed by the enzyme is produced in the leaf axils, seed coat, and flower petals. Another enzyme encoded by the *Am* locus is produced only in the flower petals and catalyzes one of the later steps for flower pigment synthesis. Enzymes encoded by other loci catalyze the later steps for pigment synthesis in seed coats and leaf axils.

10. *(D)* **(a)** RAPD markers display complete dominance, so segregation ratios in F_2 progeny should approximate a 3:1 ratio, and segregation ratios in testcross progeny should approximate a 1:1 ratio. The segregation ratios are as follows: 32+:35− for the 729s435 marker, 34+:33− for the E10s469 marker, and 37+:30− for the 362s244 marker. All three segregation ratios approximate a 1:1 ratio, so the progeny are testcross progeny, not F_2 progeny. **(b)** There are eight possible phenotypes, each of which is equally likely under the assumption of independent assortment. The total number of individuals is 67, so the expected number for each phenotype is $67 \div 8 = 8.375$. The possible phenotypes, the observed and expected numbers of individuals with each phenotype, and the chi-square calculation are tabulated below. We have written chi-square rounded to four decimal places but have conducted all calculations with unrounded values. Your answer may vary slightly if you use rounded values in the calculations.

Phenotype	Observed	Expected	$(O - E)^2 \div E$
+ + +	9	8.375	0.0466
− − −	5	8.375	1.3601
+ + −	7	8.375	0.2257
− − +	12	8.375	1.569
+ − +	8	8.375	0.0168
− + −	10	8.375	0.3153
− + +	8	8.375	0.0168
+ − −	8	8.375	0.0168
Totals	67	67.000	3.5672

The chi-square value of 3.5672 with 7 degrees of freedom is not significant at the 0.05 probability level. There is no evidence to reject the hypothesis that these loci assort independently.

11. *(B)* Any one diploid individual carries only two alleles for a particular locus. However, the number of alleles that are possible at a single locus in a population of individuals is many. Researchers can study many different alleles by studying different individuals that carry the alleles.

12. *(C)* The A^y allele causes lethality when homozygous because the mutation that created the allele deleted a gene close to the A locus that is essential for survival. Homozygous individuals lack that gene and thus cannot survive. Most mutations at the A locus are probably not large deletions that affect this adjacent gene but are instead restricted entirely to the A locus. The product of the A locus is not essential for survival, so most mutant alleles should not cause lethality when homozygous.

13. *(C)* **(a)** At the level of phenotypic inheritance, the coat-color and lethality phenotypes associated with the A^y allele could be considered pleiotropic. **(b)** At the molecular level, however, these phenotypes are clearly not pleiotropic. The coat-color phenotype is associated with the A locus, and the lethality phenotype is associated with the *Merc* locus. The mutation affects both loci and, therefore, both phenotypes. However, because the phenotypes are associated with different genes, they are not pleiotropic.

14. *(D)* **(a)** The ratios of progeny of the first two crosses approximate a 9:3:3:1 ratio, indicating that two loci interact to produce the phenotypes. **(b)** Let's call the two loci A and B. Then $A\_ B\_$ is black, $A\_ bb$ is chocolate, $aa B\_$ is blue, and $aa bb$ is silver-faun. **(c)** In the first cross, the expected ratio is 9:3:3:1, and the chi-square value is $[(44 - 53.4375)^2 \div 53.4375] + [(17 - 17.8125)^2 \div 17.8125] + [(17 - 17.8125)^2 \div 17.8125] + [(17 - 5.9375)^2 \div 5.9375] = 22.3520$, with 3 degrees of freedom. In the second cross, the expected ratio is 9:3:3:1, and the chi-square value is $[(67 - 63.5625)^2 \div 63.5625] + [(21 - 21.1875)^2 \div 21.1875] + [(20 - 21.1875)^2 \div 21.1875] + [(5 - 7.0625)^2 \div 7.0625] = 0.8564$, with 3 degrees of freedom. In the third cross, the expected ratio is 3:1 and the chi-square value is $[(46 - 47.25)^2 \div 47.25] + [(17 - 15.75)^2 \div 15.75] = 0.1323$, with 1 degree of freedom. The deviation from expected values is significant only in the first cross. There is evidence from the first cross to reject the hypothesis that the observed values conform to the expected ratios for independent assortment at two loci, but the other two crosses provide no evidence to reject the hypothesis. We expect about one of every 20 crosses to show a significant deviation at the 0.05 probability level when the hypothesis is correct. The first cross is probably one of these situations, and the hypothesis is probably correct, even though there is statistical evidence to reject it from one experiment.

15. *(D)* **(a)** Three loci interact in these crosses, as indicated by the results of the third cross. **(b)** Two of the loci are the same as those studied in the previous question. The third locus is one for which a recessive allele causes the albino phenotype when homozygous, regardless of alleles at the other two loci, and for which the dominant allele permits expression of the coat colors governed by alleles at the other two loci. If this model is correct, then in the progeny of the third cross, we expect one-fourth of the progeny to be albino, and among the remaining three-fourths, we expect 9/16 to be black, 3/16 to be blue, 3/16 to be chocolate, and 1/16 to be silver-faun, which is close to the ratio observed. **(c)** In the first cross, the expected ratio is 9:3:4, and the chi-square value is $[(19 - 16.3125)^2 \div 16.3125] + [(4 - 5.4375)^2 \div 5.4375] + [(6 - 7.25)^2 \div 7.25] = 1.0383$ with 2 degrees of freedom. In the second cross, the expected ratio is 9:3:4 and the chi-square value is $[(76 - 71.4375)^2 \div 71.4375] + [(24 - 23.8125)^2 \div 23.8125] + [(27 - 31.75)^2 \div 31.75] = 1.035$ with 2 degrees of freedom. In the third cross, the expected ratio is 27:9:9:3:16, and the chi-square value is $[(33 - 27.421875)^2 \div 27.421875] + [(10 - 9.140625)^2 \div 9.140625] + [(8 - 9.140625)^2 \div 9.140625] + [(2 - 3.046875)^2 \div 3.046875] + [(12 - 16.25)^2 \div 16.25] = 2.8291$, with 4 degrees of freedom. The deviation from expected values is not significant in any of the three crosses. There is no evidence to reject the hypothesis that the observed values conform to the expected ratios for independent assortment at three loci.

16. *(D)* Incomplete dominance: For a phenotype to be fully expressed, a particular amount of gene product must be produced. At some loci, a single dominant allele produces sufficient product for full expression of the phenotype, so the presence of a second dominant allele does not add to the expression of the phenotype and complete dominance is observed. However, at other loci, a single allele may not produce sufficient product for full expression of the phenotype; full phenotypic expression requires two alleles that both encode functional product. Such alleles display incomplete dominance.

Codominance: If an allele encodes a product that results in production of a particular substance, and another allele at the same locus encodes a product that results in production of another substance, then individuals who are heterozygous for the two alleles simultaneously produce both substances, and both phenotypes appear. The alleles are codominant.

The Bombay phenotype: This phenotype is type O blood without the H antigen. Typically, people with type O blood have the H antigen but lack the A and B antigens. People with the Bombay phenotype are homozygous for a mutant allele at the *FUT1* locus, which encodes the enzyme that synthesizes the H antigen. The H antigen is the substrate for synthesis of the A and B antigens, so people who have the Bombay phenotype cannot produce A and B antigens because the substrate for their synthesis is absent.

Leaky recessive alleles: Many mutations completely eliminate the function of a gene's product. However, some mutations reduce, rather than eliminate, the function. The product of such a mutant allele still carries out the gene's function, albeit at reduced levels. If this causes a reduction in the phenotypic expression of the gene in an individual who is homozygous for the mutant allele, the allele is called a leaky recessive allele.

Recessive lethal genes: Some genes encode products that are essential for survival. A mutation may eliminate the function of such a gene's product and be a recessive allele if the functional allele in a heterozygote produces enough product to compensate for the mutant allele's loss of function. Homozygosity for the mutant allele causes lethality because there is no functional product.

Pleiotropy: A particular gene may encode an enzyme that is required in more than one tissue. If so, the phenotype associated with the enzyme (or its absence) may be expressed in the several tissues in which the enzyme normally functions.

Epistasis: A 9:3:3:1 epistatic ratio appears in F_2 progeny when two genes that are inherited independently encode enzymes that affect the same trait in different ways. The combination of effects produces a 9:3:3:1 ratio. A 9:3:4 ratio appears in F_2 progeny when a recessive allele, *a*, at one locus eliminates the function of an enzyme and causes a recessive phenotype when homozygous *aa* regardless of the genotype at the other locus, which we'll call *B*. In the presence of a dominant *A* allele, products encoded at the *B* locus can be expressed. If there is a leaky recessive allele at the *B* locus, then *A_ bb* genotypes have a different phenotype than *A_ B_* or *aa _ _* genotypes, and a 9:3:4 ratio appears in F_2 progeny. A 9:7 epistatic ratio appears when the products of two genes complement one another. If two dominant alleles, *A* and *B*, encode enzymes that participate in the same pathway, then the enzymes are present, the pathway is complete, and the dominant phenotype appears in *A_ B_* genotypes, which constitute 9/16 of the F_2 progeny. Homozygosity for a recessive loss-of-function allele at either locus blocks the pathway and causes the recessive phenotype. A 12:3:1 ratio appears when a recessive phenotype is due to the absence of functional products encoded by two loci, *A* and *B*. The recessive phenotype appears only in the *aa bb* genotype, which is homozygous for loss-of-function alleles at both loci. This genotype constitutes 1/16 of the F_2 progeny. Individuals with the *aa B_* genotype have a functional enzyme encoded by the *B* locus but lack functional enzyme encoded at the *A* locus. Their phenotype differs from all others, and they constitute 3/16 of the F_2 progeny. The product encoded by the *A* locus overrides the effect of alleles at the *B* locus, so all individuals with at least one *A* allele (12/16 = 3/4 of the F_2 progeny) have the same phenotype. A 15:1 ratio in F_2 progeny appears when two genes encode the same product (or different products that perform the same function). Under these circumstances, functional product is absent only when the individual is homozygous for recessive loss-of-function alleles at both loci, *aa bb*. Only 1/16 of the F_2 progeny have the *aa bb* genotype.

Variable expressivity: Variable expressivity, the differential expression of a phenotype in individuals who have the same genotype at a particular locus, may be due to differences in modifier alleles at other loci among the individuals in the population. The different genotypes at the modifier loci cause slight differences in the expression of a phenotype associated with alleles at a major locus. Alternatively, differences in the environment may alter the expression of an allele at a major locus and cause variable expressivity.

Incomplete penetrance: An allele may fail to be expressed for a number of reasons and thus cause incomplete penetrance. The genotype at another locus may have an epistatic effect on an allele and prevent its expression, causing incomplete penetrance. Alternatively, an environmental effect may prevent an allele from being expressed, also causing incomplete penetrance.

17. *(C)* **(a)** 1 colored:3 white. **(b)** 3 colored:5 white. **(c)** 1 colored:3 white. **(d)** 9 colored:7 white.

18. *(B)* To be true-breeding for the colored-flower phenotype, the genotype must be *CC PP*. All other genotypes with colored flowers are *Cc P_* or *C_ Pp* and will produce some white-flowered offspring when self-fertilized. All white-flowered genotypes (*CC pp, Cc pp, cc PP, cc Pp,* and *cc pp*) breed true for white flowers when self-fertilized. Thus, 1/16 of the F_2 progeny (*CC PP*) breed true for colored flowers, and 7/16 (*CC pp, Cc pp, cc PP, cc Pp,* and *cc pp*) breed true for white flowers, for a total of 1/2 of the F_2 progeny that breed true for their respective flower colors when self-fertilized.

19. *(D)* The genotypes of two lines can be determined without examining the results of the experiments. The genotype of line 1 is given as *cc PP*, and because line 4 has colored flowers, its genotype must be *CC PP*. Line 2 has white flowers, so its genotype must be *cc PP, CC pp,* or *cc pp*. When hybridized with line 1, all of the F_1 offspring have colored flowers. Had the genotype of line 2 been *cc PP* or *cc pp*, line 2 should have produced white-flowered offspring when hybridized with line 1. The genotype of line 2 must be *CC pp*. The 9:7 ratio in the F_2 progeny of line 1 × line 2 indicates that the genotype of the F_1 progeny must be *Cc Pp*, which confirms that the genotype of line 2 must therefore be *CC pp*. Line 3 has white flowers, so its genotype must be *cc PP, CC pp,* or *cc pp*. The F_2 progeny of the line 3 × line 4 cross appear in a 9:7 ratio, which indicates that the genotype of the F_1 progeny must be *Cc Pp*. To produce this genotype in the F_1 progeny, the genotype of line 3 must be *cc pp*. The results of all experiments are consistent with these conclusions. In summary, the genotypes are as follows: line 1: *cc PP*, line 2: *CC pp*, line 3: *cc pp*, line 4: *CC PP*.

20. *(A)* Although the phenotype is determined predominantly by alleles at a single locus, alleles at other loci probably cause variable expressivity for the phenotype. Also, there is a possibility that multiple alleles at a locus can cause variable expressivity of a phenotype, as illustrated in problems 4 and 5.

21. *(B)* **(a)** If we examine only the fat-color phenotype, the situation is one of complete dominance. However, when we examine enzyme activity, the situation is one of incomplete dominance. **(b)** Because the *y* allele fails to encode functional enzyme, it arose from a loss-of-function mutation. **(c)** No, the *y* allele cannot be considered an example of a dominant mutant allele because both the enzyme-activity and fat-color phenotypes associated with it are not dominant.

22. *(C)* **(a)** The cross is *RR pp* (rose) × *rr PP* (pea). All of the progeny are *Rr Pp* and are walnut. **(b)** The cross is *rr Pp* (pea) × *Rr pp* (rose). The progeny are 1/4 *Rr Pp* (walnut), 1/4 *Rr pp* (rose), 1/4 *rr Pp* (pea), and 1/4 *rr pp* (single). **(c)** The cross is *Rr Pp* (walnut) × *Rr pp* (rose). The progeny are 3/8 *RR Pp* or *Rr Pp* (walnut), 3/8 *RR pp* or *Rr pp* (rose), 1/8 *rr Pp* (pea), and 1/8 *rr pp* (single). **(d)** The cross is *Rr Pp* (walnut) × *rr Pp* (pea). The progeny are 3/8 *Rr PP* or *Rr Pp* (walnut), 1/8 *Rr pp* (rose), 3/8 *rr PP* or *rr Pp* (pea), and 1/8 *rr pp* (single).

23. *(C)* This case, in which homozygosity for alleles at any one locus causes the same recessive phenotype, is an example of complementary gene action. **(a)** In the first cross, *ChsAChsA ChsJchsJ C^1c^1* × *ChsAChsA ChsJchsJ C^1c^1*, both parents have the same genotype and are heterozygous at two of the three loci. The phenotypic ratio should be 9 colored:7 green. **(b)** In the second cross, *ChsAchsA ChsJchsJ C^1C^1* × *ChsAchsA ChsJchsJ C^1C^1*, both parents have the same genotype and are heterozygous at two of the three loci. The phenotypic ratio should be 9 colored:7 green. **(c)** In the third cross, *ChsAchsA ChsJchsJ C^1c^1* × *chsAchsA chsJchsJ c^1c^1*, one parent is heterozygous at all three loci, and the other parent is homozygous

for the recessive alleles at all three loci. The progeny consist of eight possible genotypes, each of which is equally likely. Only one of the eight genotypes will be colored, *ChsAchsA ChsJchsJ C¹c¹*, and all others will be green. The phenotypic ratio should be 1 colored:7 green.

24. *(D)* When dominant alleles are present at all three loci, the inducer encoded by the C^1 locus induces transcription of the *ChsA* and *ChsJ* loci, and their products act as enzymes in the pathway. The pathway is complete and pigment is produced:

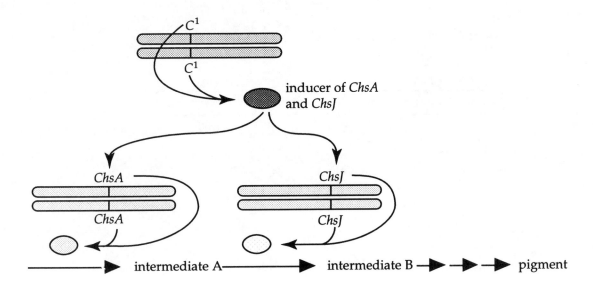

When homozygous for the *chsA* mutant allele, the *ChsA* locus fails to produce a functional enzyme and the pathway is blocked. No pigment is produced:

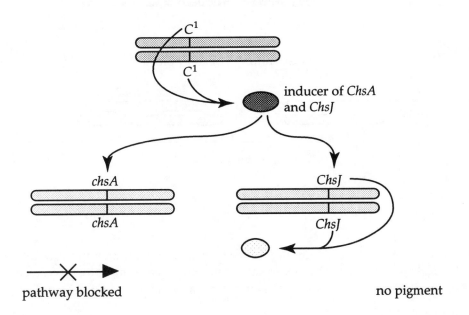

When homozygous for the *chsJ* mutant allele, the *ChsJ* locus fails to produce a functional enzyme and the pathway is blocked. No pigment is produced:

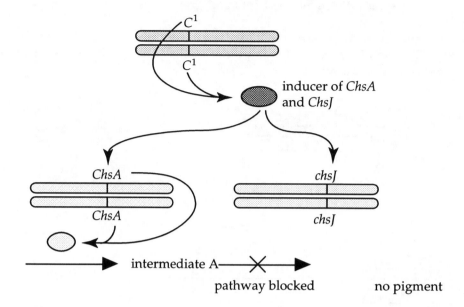

When homozygous for the *c¹* mutant allele, the *C¹* locus fails to produce a functional inducer and neither the *ChsA* nor the *ChsJ* loci are transcribed. In the absence of the enzymes encoded by these loci, the pathway is blocked and no pigment is produced:

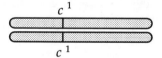

No inducer is produced.

No transcription of *ChsA* or *ChsJ*

No pigment is produced.

25. *(C)* **(a)**, **(b)**, and **(c)** All three biochemical models proposed in this question produce inheritance patterns that are identical and typical of complementary gene action. In all three instances, the F_2 dihybrid ratio is 9 purple:7 green. The genotype of the F_1 is $A^1a^1 A^ma^m$ and the phenotype is purple.

26. *(B)* The cross in this question is *CC II* × *cc ii* and the cross illustrated in Figure 13.21 is *CC ii* × *cc II*. However, both of these crosses produce F$_1$ progeny with the genotype *Cc Ii*. Because the F$_1$ genotypes are identical, the F$_2$ progeny ratios are identical for both crosses. Thus, the F$_2$ phenotypes and expected proportions from the cross *CC II* × *cc ii* are identical to those illustrated in Figure 13.21, 13 white:3 colored.

27. *(B)*

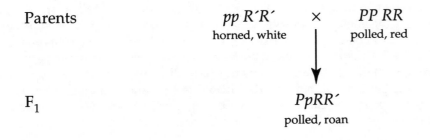

Parents   *pp R′R′*   ×   *PP RR*
           horned, white   polled, red

F$_1$ *PpRR′*
                  polled, roan

F$_2$

	PR	PR′	pR	pR′
PR	*PP RR* polled, red	*PP RR′* polled, roan	*Pp RR* polled, red	*Pp RR′* polled, roan
PR′	*PP RR′* polled, roan	*PP R′R′* polled, white	*Pp RR′* polled, roan	*Pp R′R′* polled, white
pR	*Pp RR* polled, red	*Pp RR′* polled, roan	*pp RR* horned, red	*pp RR′* horned, roan
pR′	*Pp RR′* polled, roan	*Pp R′R′* polled, white	*pp RR′* horned, roan	*pp R′R′* horned, white

28. *(C)* **(a)** All of the F$_1$ progeny are e^+e; b^+b and are wild type. The F$_2$ progeny are 9/16 wild type, 7/16 black, in accordance with a pattern of complementary gene action. **(b)** In both crosses, half the progeny should be wild type and half black.

29. *(D)* There is an error in this question in the first printing and we have reworded the question on the webpage for this chapter. (Links to the webpage can be found at http://www.brookscole.com/biology). *H* and *Su H* are both homozygous lethal alleles, so it is not possible to maintain homozygous true-breeding strains as indicated in the question; all hairless flies and all flies that carry *Su H* must be heterozygous. The question is reworded to read as follows: In *Drosophila melanogaster*, the hairless phenotype, discovered by Calvin Bridges, causes missing bristles on the abdomen and is caused by a mutant allele *H* that is dominant over the wild-type allele (H^+). The *H* locus is on chromosome 3. A dominant suppres-

sor allele *Su H* at a locus on chromosome 2 was also discovered by Calvin Bridges. In the presence of *Su H*, the effect of the *H* allele is completely suppressed and the phenotype is indistinguishable from the wild-type phenotype. The *H* and the *Su H* alleles are homozygous lethal. A hairless female is crossed with a wild-type male that may carry the *Su H* allele. Among the offspring, 1/4 of the flies are hairless and 3/4 are wild type. **(a)** What is the critical evidence that indicates the suppressor gene is present in this cross? **(b)** What are the genotypes and their expected ratios in the progeny?

Answer: The phenotype of the hairless parent indicates that it is heterozygous for the *H* allele. (It cannot be homozygous for the allele because the allele is homozygous lethal.) The ratio of 1 hairless:3 wild type indicates that the wild-type parent was a heterozygous carrier of the *Su H* allele. Had the wild-type parent not carried the *Su H* allele, half of the offspring would have been hairless. Half of the progeny carry the *H* allele, but half of the progeny with the *H* allele also carry the *Su H* allele and have a wild-type phenotype. Therefore, only 1/4 of the progeny are hairless. **(b)** The hairless parent's genotype is *H/+*; *+/+* and the wild-type parent's genotype is *+/+*; *Su H/+*. Among the progeny, 1/4 are *H/+*; *+/+* and are hairless, 1/4 are *H/+*; *Su H/+* and are wild type, 1/4 are *+/+*; *Su H/+* and are wild type, and 1/4 are *+/+*; *+/+* and are wild type.

30. *(D)* This question also requires some rewording from how it appears in the first printing, and has been corrected on the webpage. The question should read as follows: Devise a set of experiments to determine the genotypes of the wild-type progeny from the previous question.

Answer: There are three genotypes among the wild-type progeny. All three genotypes can be distinguished if each of the wild-type progeny flies is mated to a fly with the genotype *H/+*; *+/+*. Flies that are *H/+*; *Su H/+* should produce 1/3 hairless and 2/3 wild-type progeny. (The ratio of 1:2 is due to the fact that 1/4 of the progeny die because they are homozygous *H/H*.) Flies that are *+/+*; *Su H/+* produce 1/4 hairless and 3/4 wild-type progeny. Flies that are *+/+*; *+/+* produce 1/2 hairless and 1/2 wild-type progeny.

31. *(D)* Part c of this question as it appears in the first printing is not relevant because of the corrections in question 29, so only parts a and b should be answered. This question too has been corrected on the webpage. **(a)** The ratio in the F_2 progeny approximates 13 wild-type eyes:3 purple eyes. The genotype of the purple-eyed parent strain is *pr/pr*; *+/+*, and the genotype of the wild-type strain is *+/+*; *su pr/su pr*. All of the F_1 flies have the genotype *pr/+*; *su pr/+* and are wild type. Among the F_2 progeny, only those flies with the genotypes *pr/pr*; *+/+* and *pr/pr*; *su pr/+* have purple eyes. The genotype *pr/pr*; *+/+* appears in 1/16 of the F_2 flies, and the genotype *pr/pr*; *su pr/+* appears in 2/16 of the F_2 flies, for a total of 3/16 F_2 flies with purple eyes. **(b)** There are many plausible biochemical explanations for this type of epistasis. However, molecular examination of a *pr* mutant allele has revealed a possible mechanism. The article that describes this mechanism is Kim et al. 1996. *Genetics* 142:1157–1168. This article indicates that the mutation in the mutant *pr* allele is an insertion mutation within the first intron. The functional product of the suppressor gene participates in removal of the intron. When both copies of the gene contain the insertion in *pr/pr* homozygotes, the product of the suppressor gene cannot function properly. The intron is not removed, and the mutant phenotype appears. In flies that are homozygous *pr/pr*; *su pr/su pr*, the mutation in the suppressor gene eliminates the protein, and the intron with the insertion mutation is removed normally, restoring the function of the *pr* gene's product and conferring the wild-type phenotype.

32. *(C)* There were both black and yellow pups in the litter. In order to produce both black (*aa R_*) and yellow (*A_ rr*) pups, both gray parents must be *Aa Rr*. Even though no cream (*aa rr*) pups were observed in the litter, these two parents can produce cream pups, although the cream phenotype is the least likely, with a probability of 1/16.

33. *(C)* The genotype of line 3 can be determined from the phenotype as *aa rr C_*. Because none of the

progeny were albino, line 3 is probably *aa rr CC*. Lines 1 and 2 are both homozygous *cc* because they are albino. When crossed with line 3, line 1 produces all black (*aa Rr Cc*) progeny. Its genotype must be *aa RR cc*. When crossed with line 3, line 2 produces all gray (*Aa Rr Cc*) progeny. Its genotype must be *AA RR cc*.

34. *(D)* **(a)** The *W* allele is lethal when homozygous. Two white horses who mate with each other are both *Ww*: 1/4 of their progeny are *ww* and are colored, 1/2 are *Ww* and are white, and 1/4 are *WW* and do not survive gestation. The result is a 2 white:1 colored ratio. The *R* allele is also lethal when homozygous, resulting in a 2 roan:1 nonroan ratio. **(b)** Of the progeny, 7/16 are *WW _ _* or *_ _ RR* and do not survive gestation, 6/16 are *Ww _ r* and are white, 2/16 are *ww Rr* and are roan, and 1/16 are *ww rr* and are nonroan and not white. Thus, the phenotypic ratio among the surviving progeny is 6 white:2 roan:1 nonroan, not white.

35. *(E)* **(a)** The F_1 horses are all *Aa Bb Cc Ee*. Their phenotype is buckskin or palomino. **(b)** We can use the product and sum rules to determine the expected phenotypic ratios. Let's look first at the *C* locus. Horses that are *cc* are cremello, a phenotype that eliminates all of the other colors. The proportion of *cc* horses is 1/4, so 1/4 are cremello regardless of alleles at the other loci. The *Cc* genotype causes intermediate colors (buckskin and palomino), and half of the horses are *Cc* and have these phenotypes. The remaining 1/4 of the horses have the *CC* phenotype and can express the other colors governed by the *B*, *E*, and *A* loci. Of these horses, 3/4 are *AA* or *Aa* and have dark colors only on the mane, tail, and lower legs. Of these, 1/4 are *ee* and the dark color is chestnut, and 3/4 are *EE* or *Ee* and have either black or brown as the dark color. Of those that are *EE* or *Ee*, 3/4 have black as the dark color and 1/4 have brown as the dark color. Among the *aa* horses, 1/4 are chestnut (*ee*), $3/4 \times 3/4 = 9/16$ are black, and $3/4 \times 1/4 = 3/16$ are brown. In summary, 1/4 of the horses are cremello, 1/2 are buckskin or palomino, $1/4 \times 3/4 \times 1/4 = 3/64$ have chestnut on the mane, tail, and lower legs, $1/4 \times 3/4 \times 3/4 \times 3/4 = 27/256$ have black on the mane, tail, and lower legs, $1/4 \times 3/4 \times 3/4 \times 1/4 = 9/256$ have brown on the mane, tail, and lower legs, $1/4 \times 1/4 \times 1/4 = 1/64$ are solid chestnut, $1/4 \times 1/4 \times 3/4 \times 3/4 = 9/256$ are solid black, and $1/4 \times 1/4 \times 3/4 \times 1/4 = 3/256$ are solid brown.

36. *(C)* The subcloned DNA is a better choice as a probe because it reveals only those fragments that are informative with respect to sickle-cell anemia. The other probe reveals at least five fragments, four of which are uninformative with respect to sickle-cell anemia and may interfere with accurate determination of the genotype.

Chapter 14
Sex Determination and Sex-Related Inheritance

1. *(A)* Dioecious plants have separate sexes (each plant is either male or female) and consequently cannot self-fertilize. Plants that are self-incompatible are hermaphroditic (each plant has both male and female reproductive structures) but cannot self-fertilize.

2. *(C)* Heteromorphic chromosomes are typically distinguishable by their different sizes and centromere locations, and they differ between males and females. The authors detected no differences between male and female karyotypes for chromosome size or structure, so there was no karyotypic evidence for heteromorphic chromosomes. Had there been a pair of heteromorphic chromosomes, the authors should have found more than a single male-specific marker if the markers were sampled at random. The lack of any additional male-specific markers from the 158 primers tested also supports the conclusion that there are no heteromorphic chromosomes. Their results suggest that a small heteromorphic region on otherwise homologous chromosomes, perhaps just a single gene, is responsible for sex determination.

3. *(B)* Because dioecy is spread among many species and because there are many different sex determination mechanisms, it has probably arisen independently many times.

4. *(B)* Among mammals, the sex determination mechanism probably arose only once in the common ancestor of mammals. Evidence to support this conclusion comes from the observation that in all mammals, the same gene (*SRY*) on the Y chromosome is responsible for development of the male phenotype.

5. *(C)* In *Drosophila*, sex is determined by the ratio of X chromosomes to autosomes, and the Y chromosome has no effect on sex determination (although it does have an effect on male fertility). The ratio of X chromosomes to autosomes in an XXY individual is 1.0, which is the same ratio as in normal XX females. Therefore, XXY individuals are females. In humans, the presence of the *SRY* gene on the Y chromosome determines the male phenotype. In its absence, a female phenotype develops. Because an XXY individual has a Y chromosome with a functional *SRY* gene, he is male.

6. *(B)* **(a)** No. We cannot truly say that sex determination in *Drosophila melanogaster* is due to heteromorphic chromosomes because the Y chromosome, which is a heteromorphic chromosome, has nothing to do with sex determination. **(b)** No again. We also cannot truly say that sex determination in humans is due to heteromorphic chromosomes. It is due to a single gene (*SRY*) on the Y chromosome, and it is the gene, not the chromosome, that determines sex.

7. *(C)* In most insects, sex phenotype is determined at the level of individual cells. For this reason, an individual that has both XX and XO or XY somatic cells has a female phenotype in the XX cells and a male phenotype in the XO or XY cells (the O indicates that the cells had one X chromosome and no corresponding X or Y chromosome). In mammals, sex phenotype is determined in the entire body by hormones that circulate throughout the body, rather than at the level of individual cells.

8. *(B)* **(a)** The evidence against the *ZFY* and *H-Y antigen* genes as the testis-determining factor was discovered in sex-reversed humans. XY females lacked a short region on the short arm of the Y chromosome, and XX males had this region. Because the *H-Y antigen* gene is on the long arm of the Y chromosome, it was excluded as a candidate for the testis-determining factor. Further observations indicated that the *ZFY* gene was not within the region of the Y chromosome that was associated with the male phenotype. **(b)** The only gene in this region is *SRY*, and it is associated with the male phenotype. Thus, *SRY* is the best candidate for the testis-determining factor.

9. *(B)* The association of altered sex phenotype with a new mutation in *SRY* is strong evidence that *SRY* is the testis-determining factor. There is very little chance that the mutation and the sex-reversed pheno-

type are unrelated when considered in light of the observations of a strong association of *SRY* with the male phenotype in sex-reversed individuals.

10. *(B)* This is yet another example of an association of altered sex phenotype with a mutation in *SRY* in an XY female, providing further evidence that *SRY* is the testis-determining factor.

11. *(C)* An individual who inherits a mutant *SRY* allele that fails to encode a functional product does not have a male phenotype. For a father to transmit a mutant *SRY* allele to offspring, a functional *SRY* gene must mutate in his germ line; he cannot inherit the mutant allele and have a male phenotype.

12. *(B)* Recessive X-linked disorders are expressed in males who are hemizygous carriers of the allele. There is no dominant allele on a homologous chromosome to mask the effect of a recessive X-linked allele in males, so all males who inherit the allele express it. Recessive alleles on autosomes often remain phenotypically hidden in heterozygotes in both males and females. Thus, recessive X-linked genetic disorders are expressed in the phenotype of males more frequently than recessive autosomal disorders.

13. *(B)* The observation that a trait appears exclusively in males is not good evidence that it is due exclusively to a Y-linked allele. Many male-specific traits are determined by genes on autosomes that are expressed exclusively in males. In mammals, these traits are indirectly related to the presence of the *SRY* gene because it ultimately determines whether or not the genes that govern the trait will be expressed, but the relationship between the traits and the *SRY* gene is not direct.

14. *(C)* The correct choice is b. A trait due to a dominant X-linked allele should be more frequent in females than in males because females can inherit the allele from both parents. Males can inherit it only from their mothers.

15. *(C)* **(a)** Females who are heterozygous for a mutant *F8C* allele have half the normal level of factor VIII in their blood. A test for the concentration of factor VIII in the blood can determine whether or not a woman is heterozygous for the allele. **(b)** The underlying genetic principle that allows this test to be effective in identifying heterozygotes is the inactivation of an X chromosome in the somatic cells of mammalian females. Typically, about half of the cells that produce factor VII have the paternal X chromosome inactivated while half have the maternal X chromosome inactivated. In a heterozygote, only half of the cells produce functional factor VIII.

16. *(C)* Queen Elizabeth's lineage to Queen Victoria is through her father, George VI, who did not have hemophilia. Therefore, Queen Elizabeth did not inherit the allele from her father and is not likely to be a heterozygous carrier. Prince Philip did not have hemophilia, so he did not inherit the allele. Thus, none of their children inherited the allele.

17. *(C)* Yes, it is possible for this woman to have a child with both hemophilia and deuteranopia. On her paternal X chromosome, she carries the recessive allele for hemophilia. On her maternal X chromosome, she carries the recessive allele for deuteranopia. A crossover between the two loci during meiosis could generate an X chromosome that has both the allele for hemophilia and the allele for deuteranopia. If a son inherits this chromosome, he will have both hemophilia and deuteranopia.

18. *(C)* **(a)** The boy's maternal uncles must have inherited the allele for protanopia from their mother, who is the boy's maternal grandmother. **(b)** Because she had some sons with protanopia and some with normal color perception, the boy's maternal grandmother must have been heterozygous for the allele for protanopia and thus did not have protanopia herself. The information in the question does not allow us to determine with certainty whether or not the maternal grandfather had protanopia. However, there is no evidence that the members of his family who had protanopia inherited the allele from him, and given the fact that protanopia is rare, it is not likely that he had protanopia.

19. *(C)* The observation that individuals with more than one allele of the *GCP* gene had only one type of mRNA indicates that although several copies of the *GCP* gene may be present, only one copy is expressed.

20. *(B)* **(a)** Assuming that the woman does not have ocular albinism, we conclude that she must be heterozygous for the allele because she inherited it from her father. Her husband is hemizygous for the allele, and he will transmit it to all of his daughters. There is a 50% chance that a daughter will inherit the allele from her mother and a 100% chance that she will inherit it from her father, so the chance of a daughter inheriting ocular albinism is 50%. There is a 50% chance that a son will inherit the allele from his mother, so the chance of any son inheriting ocular albinism is also 50%. Thus, the chance of any child inheriting ocular albinism is 50%. **(b)** As explained in part a, the probability does not differ between males and females in this situation.

21. *(B)* **(a)** G6PD deficiency is caused by a recessive X-linked allele. **(b)** The mother is probably a heterozygous carrier of the allele; the father's G6PD deficiency phenotype is coincidental and unrelated to the child's phenotype.

22. *(C)* The allele for testicular feminization is a recessive X-linked allele inherited from a mother who is heterozygous for the allele. The father cannot be a hemizygous carrier of the allele because the allele causes an external female phenotype in the hemizygous condition. When the mother is heterozygous, half of her XY offspring inherit the allele and are phenotypically female, and all of her XX offspring are female, so for any one child the phenotypic probabilities are 3/4 for female and 1/4 for male.

23. *(C)* The gold phenotype is caused by a recessive Z-linked allele, which we'll call *g*, and the silver phenotype is caused by a dominant Z-linked allele, which we'll call *G*, at the same locus. Remember that chickens have a ZZ-ZW form of sex determination. The silver female parent is hemizygous *G*. The gold male parent is homozygous *gg*. All the male F₁ offspring are heterozygous *Gg* and are silver because of dominance. All the female F₁ offspring are hemizygous *g* and are gold because they inherited the *g* allele from their male parent. In the F₂ offspring, half of the females inherit the *g* allele and half inherit the *G* allele from their heterozygous male parents. Thus, half are gold and half are silver because they are hemizygous for the allele they inherit. All of the male F₂ offspring inherit the *g* allele from their hemizygous female parent. Half of them are silver because they inherit the dominant *G* allele from their heterozygous paternal parents, which makes them heterozygous *Gg*. The other half are gold because they inherit the recessive *g* allele from their heterozygous paternal parents, which makes them homozygous *gg*.

24. *(C)* As shown in the Punnett square below, all F₁ flies are wild-type, but both the males and the females are carriers of the mutant *bb* allele:

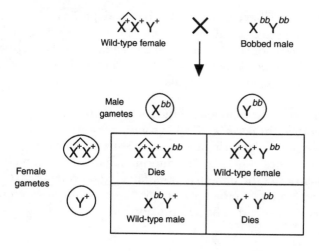

In the F$_2$ generation, all the males are bobbed and all the females are wild-type:

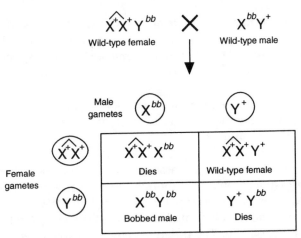

25. *(B)* As shown in Figure 14.16b, a cross between a bobbed female and a wild-type male produces wild-type females with the genotype X$^+$X^{bb} and wild-type males with the genotype X^{bb}Y$^+$. When the F$_1$ females are mated with a bobbed male (X^{bb}Y^{bb}), half of the female progeny have the genotype X$^+$X^{bb} and are wild type, and half have the genotype X^{bb}X^{bb} and are bobbed. Half of the male progeny have the genotype X$^+$Y^{bb} and are wild type, and half have the genotype X^{bb}Y^{bb} and are bobbed.

26. *(B)* Genetic anticipation is defined as an increase in the frequency and/or severity of a phenotype over generations of inheritance. Fragile X syndrome displays genetic anticipation because it is caused by expansion of a trinucleotide repeat. The allele may expand to a premutation size, in which case it does not cause the disorder but is more likely to expand to full mutation size in subsequent generations. The premutation allele may be transmitted to offspring then expand in subsequent generations, causing the disorder to appear.

27. *(A)* The number of Barr bodies is one less than the number of X chromosomes in a somatic cell. Because an XXXY male has three X chromosomes, each of his somatic cells should have two Barr bodies.

28. *(A)* No, there should be no Barr bodies. The mechanism of dosage compensation in *Drosophila* does not utilize X chromosome inactivation, so there are no Barr bodies in *Drosophila* under any conditions.

29. *(C)* **(a)** In the table below, the genotypes are given in parentheses after the phenotypes of each parent and the numbers of progeny:

Parents (female listed first)	Number of Offspring					
	Females			Males		
	Orange	Black	Tortoiseshell	Orange	Black	Tortoiseshell
1. Black (*oo*) X black (*o*)	0	8 (*oo*)	0	0	5 (*o*)	0
2. Orange (*OO*) X black (*o*)	0	0	3 (*Oo*)	3 (*O*)	0	0
3. Tortoiseshell (*Oo*) X black (*o*)	0	9 (*oo*)	8 (*Oo*)	8 (*O*)	11 (*o*)	0
4. Orange (*OO*) X orange (*O*)	3 (*OO*)	0	0	3 (*O*)	0	0
5. Black (*oo*) X orange (*O*)	0	0	2 (*Oo*)	0	7 (*o*)	0
6. Tortoiseshell (*Oo*) X orange (*O*)	5 (*OO*)	0	1 (*Oo*)	5 (*O*)	1 (*o*)	0

(b) There are no cases of unexpected genotypes or phenotypes in the offspring.

30. *(D)* **(a)** The black females and the tortoiseshell male are the unexpected phenotypes. **(b)** The tortoiseshell male probably had an XXY genotype. The black females were probably mosaics, or may have had XO genotypes (the O indicates that they had one X chromosome and no corresponding X or Y chromosome).

31. *(C)* Because the X chromosome that carries the mutant *IP* allele is preferentially (rather than randomly) inactivated, the paternal X chromosome that carried the mutant *F8C* allele was active in most or all of this female's somatic cells, causing hemophilia A.

32. *(D)* **(a)** We will answer this question based on the assumption that the allele that causes pattern baldness is dominant in males and recessive in females, although there is some recent evidence that contradicts this assumption (see the OMIM entry for male pattern baldness, OMIM 109200). Because the man's father did not have pattern baldness, the man inherited the dominant allele from his heterozygous mother, and he is, therefore, heterozygous. **(b)** The putative gene that causes pattern baldness is designated *MPB* (for "male pattern baldness") but no alleles have been named. We'll represent the allele that does not cause pattern baldness as *MPB*B1* and the allele that causes pattern baldness as *MPB*B2*. For simplicity in the pedigree below, we'll abbreviate the allele designations as *B1* and *B2*:

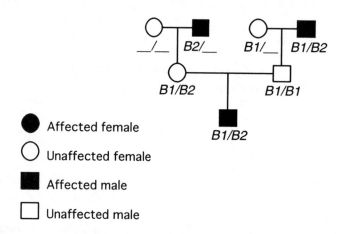

33. *(D)* **(a)** Red-spotting is a sex-influenced trait because it is observed in both males and females but is more frequent in females, and its pattern of inheritance is typical of an autosomal, rather than an X-linked, allele. **(b)** The allele for red-spotting is dominant in females and recessive in males. The allele for mahogany-spotting is dominant in males and recessive in females. The alleles belong to the same locus on an autosomal chromosome.

34. *(E)* To answer this question, we need to remember that there are two types of pigments in the eyes of *Drosophila melanogaster*, brown pigments (ommochromes) and bright red pigments (drosopterins). The pattern of inheritance can best be explained if the white-eyed male fly is hemizygous for an X-linked allele that causes white eyes, and the white-eyed female fly is homozygous at two autosomal loci for a mutant allele that blocks brown-pigment synthesis and a mutant allele that blocks red-pigment synthesis. The allele on the X chromosome is probably *w*. Let's suppose that the allele that blocks brown-pigment synthesis is *ry* (*rosy*) on chromosome 3, and the allele that blocks red-pigment synthesis is *bw* (brown) on chromosome 2. Then the female's genotype is +/+; *bw/bw*; *ry/ry*, and the male's genotype is *w*/Y; +/+; +/+. All the F_1 females have the genotype *w*/+; *bw*/+; *ry*/+ and are wild type. All the F_1 males have the genotype +/Y; *bw*/+; *ry*/+ and are wild type. The F_2 generation is diagrammed in the Punnett squares on the next page. We have separated the male and female progeny into two Punnett

324

Information for Problem 34

F₁ generation

+/w;+/bw;+/ry   X   +/Y;+/bw;+/ry
females   males

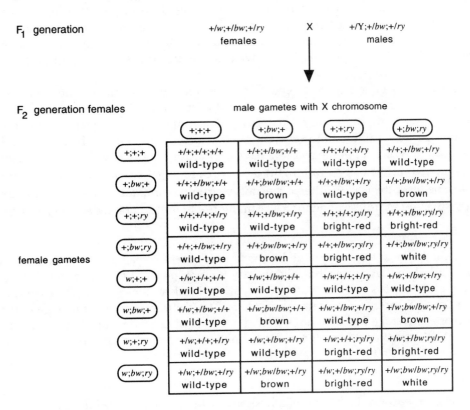

F₂ generation females

male gametes with X chromosome

female gametes	+;+;+	+;bw;+	+;+;ry	+;bw;ry
+;+;+	+/+;+/+;+/+ wild-type	+/+;+/bw;+/+ wild-type	+/+;+/+;+/ry wild-type	+/+;+/bw;+/ry wild-type
+;bw;+	+/+;+/bw;+/+ wild-type	+/+;bw/bw;+/+ brown	+/+;+/bw;+/ry wild-type	+/+;bw/bw;+/ry brown
+;+;ry	+/+;+/+;+/ry wild-type	+/+;+/bw;+/ry wild-type	+/+;+/+;ry/ry bright-red	+/+;+/bw;ry/ry bright-red
+;bw;ry	+/+;+/bw;+/ry wild-type	+/+;bw/bw;+/ry brown	+/+;+/bw;ry/ry bright-red	+/+;bw/bw;ry/ry white
w;+;+	+/w;+/+;+/+ wild-type	+/w;+/bw;+/+ wild-type	+/w;+/+;+/ry wild-type	+/w;+/bw;+/ry wild-type
w;bw;+	+/w;+/bw;+/+ wild-type	+/w;bw/bw;+/+ brown	+/w;+/bw;+/ry wild-type	+/w;bw/bw;+/ry brown
w;+;ry	+/w;+/+;+/ry wild-type	+/w;+/bw;+/ry wild-type	+/w;+/+;ry/ry bright-red	+/w;+/bw;ry/ry bright-red
w;bw;ry	+/w;+/bw;+/ry wild-type	+/w;bw/bw;+/ry brown	+/w;+/bw;ry/ry bright-red	+/w;bw/bw;ry/ry white

F₂ generation males

male gametes with Y chromosome

female gametes	Y;+;+	Y;bw;+	Y;+;ry	Y;bw;ry
+;+;+	+/Y;+/+;+/+ wild-type	+/Y;+/bw;+/+ wild-type	+/Y;+/+;+/ry wild-type	+/Y;+/bw;+/ry wild-type
+;bw;+	+/Y;+/bw;+/+ wild-type	+/Y;bw/bw;+/+ brown	+/Y;+/bw;+/ry wild-type	+/Y;bw/bw;+/ry brown
+;+;ry	+/Y;+/+;+/ry wild-type	+/Y;+/bw;+/ry wild-type	+/Y;+/+;ry/ry bright-red	+/Y;+/bw;ry/ry bright-red
+;bw;ry	+/Y;+/bw;+/ry wild-type	+/Y;bw/bw;+/ry brown	+/Y;+/bw;ry/ry bright-red	+/Y;bw/bw;ry/ry white
w;+;+	w/Y;+/+;+/+ white	w/Y;+/bw;+/+ white	w/Y;+/+;+/ry white	w/Y;+/bw;+/ry white
w;bw;+	w/Y;+/bw;+/+ white	w/Y;bw/bw;+/+ white	w/Y;+/bw;+/ry white	w/Y;bw/bw;+/ry white
w;+;ry	w/Y;+/+;+/ry white	w/Y;+/bw;+/ry white	w/Y;+/+;ry/ry white	w/Y;+/bw;ry/ry white
w;bw;ry	w/Y;+/bw;+/ry white	w/Y;bw/bw;+/ry white	w/Y;+/bw;ry/ry white	w/Y;bw/bw;ry/ry white

squares to show the ratios for each sex. Among the females, $18/32 = 9/16$ have wild-type eyes, $6/32 = 3/16$ have brown eyes, $6/32 = 3/16$ have bright-red eyes, and $2/32 = 1/16$ have white eyes. Notice that the white-eyed females are *not* homozygous for the *w* allele; instead, homozygosity for *bw* blocks red-pigment synthesis, and homozygosity for *ry* blocks brown-pigment synthesis, resulting in white eyes. Among the males, $16/32 = 1/2$ are hemizygous for *w* and have white eyes; another $1/32$ are homozygous for *bw* and *ry* and have white eyes, for a total of $16/32 + 1/32 = 17/32$ with white eyes. Among the rest of the males, $9/32$ have wild-type eyes, $3/32$ have brown eyes, and $3/32$ have bright-red eyes.

35. *(C)* **(a)** Cock feathering is governed by a gene on an autosome, but the phenotype is expressed exclusively in males. Cock feathering is, therefore, a sex-limited trait. **(b)** Let *A* represent a dominant allele that causes hen feathering in roosters, and *a* a recessive allele that causes cock feathering in roosters when homozygous. The hen-feathered rooster from the true-breeding flock has the genotype *AA*, and the hen from the flock in which all of the roosters have cock feathering is *aa*. All of the F_1 offspring are *Aa* and are hen feathered. In the F_2 generation, the genotypes segregate in a 1 *AA*:2 *Aa*:1 *aa* ratio in both females and males. Because the cock-feathered phenotype does not appear in females, all of the F_2 females are hen feathered regardless of genotype. Among the F_2 males, $1/4$ are *aa* and have cock feathering.

36. *(C)* The results can be most easily explained if the female parent has an attached X chromosome and a Y chromosome. The allele that causes the yellow-body phenotype is called *y*, and the allele that causes the vermilion-eyes phenotype is called *v*. Both are recessive X-linked alleles. Both copies of the X chromosome in the attached X chromosome carry the *y* allele. The X chromosome in the male parent carries the *v* allele. In a cross between a female who has an attached X chromosome and a Y chromosome, and a male with a normal XY genotype, the male transmits his X chromosome to all surviving male offspring, and the female transmits her attached X chromosome to all surviving female offspring, as diagrammed in Figure 14.18.

37. *(C)* The white-eyes phenotype is caused by a recessive X-linked allele called *w*. All of the wild-type females have an attached X chromosome that carries a dominant wild-type allele at the *w* locus, and they carry a Y chromosome. When these females are mated with hemizygous *w* males, all the male offspring have white eyes and all the female offspring have wild-type eyes. The vestigial wing phenotype is caused by a recessive allele on an autosome. Because the attached X chromosome has no effect on the inheritance of autosomes, the inheritance pattern for the vestigial-wing phenotype shows typical Mendelian inheritance and is independent of the inheritance of X and Y chromosomes.

Chapter 15
Chromosome Mapping

1. *(A)* The 28 chromosomes consist of 14 pairs of homologous chromosomes. Each homologous pair constitutes one linkage group, so there are 14 linkage groups.

2. *(D)* **(a)** In each of the crosses, the noncrossover types can be identified as the two classes with the greatest number of individuals. From their phenotypes, we can determine whether the alleles are in coupling or repulsion conformation in the heterozygous parent. In testcross 1, one noncrossover type has frizzled feathers and is white; the other noncrossover type has normal feathers and is black. Normal feathers and white are the dominant phenotypes, and they are not found together in a noncrossover type. Therefore, the dominant alleles are in repulsion conformation in this testcross. In testcross 2, the two dominant phenotypes (normal feathers and crested) are found together in a noncrossover type. Therefore, the dominant alleles are in coupling conformation in this testcross. In testcross 3, the two dominant phenotypes (white and crested) are not found together in a noncrossover type. Therefore, the dominant alleles are in repulsion conformation in this testcross. **(b)** To determine which allele is between the other two in the linkage map, we first determine the recombination frequencies in each of the crosses. In testcross 1, the recombination frequency between F and I is $(43 + 35) \div (168 + 172 + 43 + 35) = 0.1866$. In testcross 2, the recombination frequency between F and Cr is $(40 + 47) \div (129 + 128 + 40 + 47) = 0.2529$. In testcross 3, the recombination frequency between I and Cr is $(36 + 45) \div (321 + 330 + 36 + 45) = 0.1107$. The greatest distance is between F and Cr, so I must be between F and Cr.

(c)

| | Genes | Recombination Frequencies | | |
		No Correction	Haldane Function	Kosambi Function
Testcross 1	*F-I*	0.1866	0.2336	0.1961
Testcross 2	*F-Cr*	0.2529	0.3524	0.2785
Testcross 3	*I-Cr*	0.1107	0.1250	0.1125

(d) To determine which calculation provides the most consistent map, we add the *F-I* and *I-Cr* distances and see which of the three calculations is closest to the *F-Cr* distance. With no correction, the sum of the *F-I* and *I-Cr* distances is $0.1866 + 0.1107 = 0.2973$, which differs from the *F-Cr* distance by $0.2973 - 0.2529 = 0.0444$. After correction with the Haldane function, the sum of the *F-I* and *I-Cr* distances is $0.2336 + 0.1250 = 0.3586$, which differs from the *F-Cr* distance by $0.3586 - 0.3524 = 0.0062$. After correction with the Kosambi function, the sum of the *F-I* and *I-Cr* distances is $0.1961 + 0.1125 = 0.3086$, which differs from the *F-Cr* distance by $0.3086 - 0.2785 = 0.0301$. The lowest difference, and therefore the most consistent map, is obtained after correction with the Haldane function. This conclusion is correct for this particular set of data. In most data sets, however, the Kosambi function provides a more consistent map than the Haldane function does.

3. *(B)* Map distances are based on the actual frequency of crossing-over, not necessarily the observed frequency of recombination. A double crossover between two linked genes appears as a nonrecombinant phenotype and is often undetected. Undetected double crossovers cause researchers to underestimate the actual map distance unless they adjust the results to account for undetected crossovers.

4. *(E)* To solve this problem, we must first rearrange the Kosambi function to solve for y. Starting with the Kosambi function,

$$x = 0.25\ln \frac{1 + 2y}{1 - 2y}$$

multiply both sides by 4,

$$4x = \ln \frac{1 + 2y}{1 - 2y}$$

take the antilogarithm of both sides,

$$e^{4x} = \frac{1 + 2y}{1 - 2y}$$

and rearrange the equation to solve for y,

$$y = 0.5 \frac{e^{4x} - 1}{1 + e^{4x}}$$

The corrected recombination frequency (x) between y and v is 0.33, between y and r it is 0.545, and between v and r it is 0.545 − 0.33 = 0.215. The predicted observed recombination frequencies can be determined by substituting these values for x in the equation we derived above. The predicted observed recombination frequency for the y-v interval is

$$y = 0.5 \frac{e^{4(0.33)} - 1}{1 + e^{4(0.33)}} = 0.2892$$

and the predicted recombination frequency for the v-r interval is

$$y = 0.5 \frac{e^{4(0.215)} - 1}{1 + e^{4(0.215)}} = 0.2027$$

Assuming that the heterozygous female parent has all three recessive alleles in coupling conformation, we determine that the noncrossover phenotypes are (1) wild-type and (2) yellow, vermilion, rudimentary. The phenotypes that result from a single crossover between y and v are (1) vermilion, rudimentary and (2) yellow. The phenotypes that result from a single crossover between v and r are (1) rudimentary and (2) yellow, vermilion. The phenotypes that result from a double crossover between y and v and between v and r are (1) vermilion and yellow, rudimentary.

Let's determine the expected frequency of double crossover phenotypes first. It is the product of the frequencies for the y-v and v-r intervals, which is 0.2892 × 0.2027 = 0.0586. Because there are two double-crossover phenotypes, we divide this number by 2 to determine the frequency of each phenotype: 0.0586 ÷ 2 = 0.0293. The predicted frequency of progeny that arise from a single crossover between y and v is the predicted recombination frequency for this interval, minus the frequency of double-crossover types: 0.2892 − 0.0586 = 0.2306. Because there are two phenotypes in this class, we divide this number by 2 to determine the expected frequency for each phenotype: 0.2306 ÷ 2 = 0.1153. We determine the frequency of progeny that arise from a single crossover between v and r in the same way: 0.2027 − 0.0586 = 0.1441, which we divide by 2 to obtain the frequency of each phenotype: 0.1411 ÷ 2 = 0.0721. We determine the predicted frequency of each noncrossover phenotype by summing the frequencies of recombinant types, subtracting the sum from 1, and dividing by 2: [1 − (0.2306 + 0.1441 + 0.0586)] ÷ 2 = 0.2834. This results in the following predicted frequencies for all phenotypes:

Phenotype	Predicted Frequency
Wild type	0.2834
Yellow, vermilion, rudimentary	0.2834
Vermilion, rudimentary	0.1153
Yellow	0.1153
Rudimentary	0.0721
Yellow, vermilion	0.0721
Vermilion	0.0293
Yellow, rudimentary	0.0293
Total	1.0002

Because of rounding, the frequencies do not add up to exact unity.

5. *(D)* **(a)** Notice that among the nonrecombinant phenotypes (black, Himalayan, white fat and brown, full-colored, yellow fat) two of the dominant phenotypes (black and white fat) are in the same recombinant type as a recessive phenotype (Himalayan). Therefore, the C allele is in repulsion to the Y and B alleles in the heterozygous parent. The double-crossover phenotypes (black, Himalayan, yellow fat and brown, full-colored, white fat) indicate that the Y allele is between the C and B alleles. Therefore, the conformation of alleles in the heterozygous parent in linkage notation is as follows:
(b) The genotypes of the gametes from the heterozygous parent that were transmitted to each phenotypic class of progeny are as follows:

$$\frac{C \quad y \quad b}{c \quad Y \quad B}$$

Phenotype	Genotype of Gametes from Heterozygous Parent			Number of Progeny
black, full-colored, white fat	C	Y	B	33
black, full-colored, yellow fat	C	y	B	48
black, Himalayan, white fat	c	Y	B	151
black, Himalayan, yellow fat	c	y	B	2
brown, full-colored, white fat	C	Y	b	11
brown, full-colored, yellow fat	C	y	b	142
brown, Himalayan, white fat	c	Y	b	67
brown, Himalayan, yellow fat	c	y	b	23

(c) The total number of progeny is 477. The map distance between C and Y is $(33 + 23 + 2 + 11) \div 477 \times 100 = 14.47$ cM. The map distance between Y and B is $(48 + 67 + 2 + 11) \div 477 \times 100 = 26.83$ cM. **(d)** The observed frequency of double-crossover types is $(2 + 11) \div 477 = 0.0273$, and the expected frequency is $0.1447 \times 0.2683 = 0.0388$. The coefficient of coincidence is $0.0273 \div 0.0388 = 0.7036$, and the interference is $1 - 0.7036 = 0.2964$.

6. *(C)* **(a)** The genotype of the heterozygous parent in coupling conformation is

$$\frac{Bk \quad Wv}{bk \quad wv}$$

The genotypes of the gametes and their frequencies are

_Bk_	_Wv_ (nonrecombinant)	0.47
_bk_	_wv_ (nonrecombinant)	0.47
_Bk_	_wv_ (recombinant)	0.03
_bk_	_Wv_ (recombinant)	0.03

(b) The genotype of the heterozygous parent in repulsion conformation is

$$\frac{Bk \quad wv}{bk \quad Wv}$$

The genotypes of the gametes and their frequencies are

_Bk_	_wv_ (nonrecombinant)	0.47
_bk_	_Wv_ (nonrecombinant)	0.47
_Bk_	_Wv_ (recombinant)	0.03
_bk_	_wv_ (recombinant)	0.03

7. *(B)* **(a)** Homozygosity for an allele that reduces the frequency of crossing-over will result in fewer crossover-type gametes. **(b)** Map distances will be underestimated.

8. *(E)* The answer to part a of question 6 provides the frequencies of gametes that arise from plant 1 (a double heterozygote with alleles in coupling conformation), which are

_Bk_	_Wv_ (nonrecombinant)	0.47
_bk_	_wv_ (nonrecombinant)	0.47
_Bk_	_wv_ (recombinant)	0.03
_bk_	_Wv_ (recombinant)	0.03

When self-fertilized, these gametes will combine in 16 possible combinations, generating 9 possible genotypes and 4 possible phenotypes. The frequencies of each genotype and phenotype can be determined using the product and sum rules. Below are the genotypes, their associated phenotypes, and the calculations of their respective frequencies. Notice that some frequencies are multiplied by 2 or 4, numbers that represent the different ways that the genotype can arise. The dominant phenotypes are round fruit and green tips; the recessive phenotypes are beaked fruit and yellow-white tips.

Genotype	Phenotype	Frequency Calculation
BkBk WvWv	Round fruit, green tips	$0.47^2 = 0.2209$
BkBk Wvwv	Round fruit, green tips	$2(0.47)(0.03) = 0.0282$
Bkbk WvWv	Round fruit, green tips	$2(0.47)(0.03) = 0.0282$
Bkbk Wvwv	Round fruit, green tips	$2(0.47^2) + 2(0.03^2) = 0.4436$
BkBk wvwv	Round fruit, yellow-white tips	$0.03^2 = 0.0009$
Bkbk wvwv	Round fruit, yellow-white tips	$2(0.47)(0.03) = 0.0282$
bkbk WvWv	Beaked fruit, green tips	$0.03^2 = 0.0009$
bkbk Wvwv	Beaked fruit, green tips	$2(0.47)(0.03) = 0.0282$
bkbk wvwv	Beaked fruit, yellow-white tips	$0.47^2 = 0.2209$

The phenotypic frequencies are obtained by summing the frequencies of all genotypes with the same phenotype:

Phenotype	Frequency Calculation
Round fruit, green tips	$0.2209 + 2(0.0282) + 0.4436 = 0.7209$
Round fruit, yellow-white tips	$0.0009 + 0.0282 = 0.0291$
Beaked fruit, green tips	$0.0009 + 0.0282 = 0.0291$
Beaked fruit, yellow-white tips	0.2209

Notice that these values correspond to the values in Table 15.1a for a recombination frequency of 0.06.

The answer to part b of question 6 provides the frequencies of gametes that arise from plant 2 (a double heterozygote with alleles in repulsion conformation), which are

_Bk_ _wv_ (nonrecombinant)	0.47
_bk_ _Wv_ (nonrecombinant)	0.47
_Bk_ _Wv_ (recombinant)	0.03
_bk_ _wv_ (recombinant)	0.03

When self-fertilized, these gametes will combine in 16 possible combinations, generating the same 9 possible genotypes and 4 possible phenotypes as in the coupling situation, but in different frequencies. The frequencies of each genotype and phenotype are also determined using the product and sum rules.

Genotype	Phenotype	Frequency Calculation
BkBk WvWv	Round fruit, green tips	$0.03^2 = 0.0009$
BkBk Wvwv	Round fruit, green tips	$2(0.47)(0.03) = 0.0282$
Bkbk WvWv	Round fruit, green tips	$2(0.47)(0.03) = 0.0282$
Bkbk Wvwv	Round fruit, green tips	$2(0.47^2) + 2(0.03^2) = 0.4436$
BkBk wvwv	Round fruit, yellow-white tips	$0.47^2 = 0.2209$
Bkbk wvwv	Round fruit, yellow-white tips	$2(0.47)(0.03) = 0.0282$
bkbk WvWv	Beaked fruit, green tips	$0.47^2 = 0.2209$
bkbk Wvwv	Beaked fruit, green tips	$2(0.47)(0.03) = 0.0282$
bkbk wvwv	Beaked fruit, yellow-white tips	$0.03^2 = 0.0009$

The phenotypic frequencies are obtained by summing the frequencies of all genotypes with the same phenotype:

Phenotype	Frequency Calculation
Round fruit, green tips	$0.0009 + 2(0.0282) + 0.4436 = 0.5009$
Round fruit, yellow-white tips	$0.2209 + 0.0282 = 0.2491$
Beaked fruit, green tips	$0.2209 + 0.0282 = 0.2491$
Beaked fruit, yellow-white tips	0.0009

Notice that these values correspond to the values in Table 15.1b for a recombination frequency of 0.06.

9. (C) The greatest distance is between S15s407 and pA8s309, so these markers must be on the ends of the linkage group. The marker most closely linked to S15s407 is A12a1213, and the marker most closely linked to pA8s309 is 169s313, so the relative locations of the markers on the map must be

S15s407—A12a1213—169s313— pA8s309

The map distances may now be placed in the map:

$$S15s407—9.1—A12a1213—2.9—169s313—5.7—pA8s309$$

10. *(E)* **(a)** Under the hypothesis of independent assortment, the four phenotypes should appear in a 9:3:3:1 ratio. The observed and expected values under this hypothesis are as follows:

Phenotype	Observed	Expected	$(O - E)^2/E$
Round fruit, simple inflorescence	126	145.6875	2.6605
Elongate fruit, simple inflorescence	66	48.5625	6.2613
Round fruit, compound inflorescence	63	48.5625	4.2922
Elongate fruit, compound inflorescence	4	16.1875	9.1759
Totals	259	259.0000	22.3899

The chi-square value of 22.3899 with 3 degrees of freedom is highly significant, so we reject the hypothesis of independent assortment.

(b) Notice in the table above that the observed values for round fruit, simple inflorescence (both dominant phenotypes) and elongate fruit, compound inflorescence (both recessive phenotypes) are less than expected under the hypothesis of independent assortment. This observation suggests that the loci are linked and that the alleles are in repulsion conformation. We can attempt to determine a recombination frequency by calculating the observed phenotypic frequencies and comparing them with the values in Table 15.1b.

Phenotype	Observed Frequency	Corresponding Frequency of Recombination in Table 15.1b
Round fruit, simple inflorescence	0.4865	< 0.01
Elongate fruit, simple inflorescence	0.2548	< 0.01
Round fruit, compound inflorescence	0.2432	0.165
Elongate fruit, compound inflorescence	0.0154	0.248

This example is a good illustration of why it is not advisable to calculate map distances from F_2 data for alleles in repulsion conformation. In this example, the values in the table above do not correspond consistently to recombination frequencies in Table 15.1b. Such an outcome is not unusual for F_2 data for alleles in repulsion conformation. Notice in Table 15.1b that for the range of recombination frequencies from 0.01 to 0.25, the range of phenotypic frequencies is only 0.0156. A small difference in the number of plants for any one class can cause a large difference in the calculation of linkage. For example, in the table above we expect the plants with elongate fruit, simple inflorescence to appear in the same frequency as plants with round fruit, compound inflorescence. The respective numbers of plants were 66 and 63, a difference of only 3 plants, yet the difference in linkage calculation for those two classes is over 16 cM.

So how do we calculate linkage in such a cross? One way is to see which linkage value has the highest probability associated with the data set, a procedure known as calculation of maximum likelihood. One way for us to determine maximum likelihood is to conduct a series of chi-square tests for a range of recombination frequencies, then choose the recombination frequency that produces the lowest chi-square value. For this data set, a recombination frequency of 0.23 produces the lowest chi-square value, which is 0.8597:

Phenotype	Observed	Expected	$(O-E)^2/E$
Round fruit, simple inflorescence	126	132.9188	0.3601
Elongate fruit, simple inflorescence	66	61.3312	0.3554
Round fruit, compound inflorescence	63	61.3312	0.0454
Elongate fruit, compound inflorescence	4	3.4188	0.0988
Totals	259	259.0000	0.8597

The chi-square value for a recombination frequency of 0.22 is 0.9141 and the chi-square value for a recombination frequency of 0.24 is 0.8825. Therefore, the most likely recombination frequency is 0.23.

Because these are actual data, we can turn to the original paper to review the author's conclusion. Although he does not tell us how he calculated the frequency of crossing-over, MacArthur (1928. *Genetics* 13:410–420) stated that "the 259 F_2 progeny fell into classes showing about 20% crossing-over in both sexes" (p. 413), which is close to the value of 0.23 that we determined. MacArthur also included data from a testcross for these genes, which showed a recombination frequency of 0.20, and this may have influenced his conclusion.

11. *(C)* **(a)** The noncrossover types (those with the greatest number of individuals) have the dominant phenotype for one gene and the recessive phenotype for the other gene. Therefore, the alleles in the heterozygous parent are in repulsion conformation. **(b)** These are testcross progeny, so the recombination frequency is (12 + 12) ÷ (12 + 123 + 133 + 12) = 0.0857.

12. *(C)* **(a)** The recombination frequency is (1678 + 1718) ÷ 20785 = 0.1634. **(b)** One of the noncrossover types (those with the greatest numbers of progeny) has the dominant phenotypes for both genes. The other noncrossover type has the recessive phenotypes for both genes. Therefore, the alleles are in coupling conformation in the heterozygous female parents. **(c)** The correction with the Haldane function is

$$x = -0.5\ln[1 - 2(0.1634)] = 0.1979$$

The correction with the Kosambi function is

$$x = 0.25\ln \frac{1 + 2(0.1634)}{1 - 2(0.1634)} = 0.1696$$

(d) The distance from *sc* to *cv* in the map in Figure 15.3 is 13.7 cM, so the recombination frequency calculated in part (a) is closest to the value in the map.

13. *(B)* The genotypes of the four gametes are

A	b	c
A	B	C
a	b	c
a	B	C

14. *(D)* **(a)** To answer this question, look at the noncrossover types. One is claret; the other is ebony, rough. Therefore, the alleles at the three loci are not in coupling conformation; *ca* is in repulsion to *ro* and *e*. **(b)** Now that the coupling-repulsion conformation for the alleles has been identified, the next step is to determine which locus is between the other two. Look at the double-crossover types. One is ebony; the other is rough, claret. The only conformation that produces these double-crossover types is
The recombination frequency between *ca* and *ro* is (49 + 66 + 1 + 1) ÷ 1090 = 0.1073. The recombination

ca	+	+
+	ro	e

frequency between *ro* and *e* is $(119 + 89 + 1 + 1) \div 1090 = 0.1927$. The map is

$$ca - 10.73 - ro - 19.27 - e$$

(c) The observed frequency of double-crossovers is $(1 + 1) \div 1090 = 0.0018$ and the expected frequency is $0.1073 \times 0.1927 = 0.0207$. The coefficient of coincidence is $0.0018 \div 0.0207 = 0.0870$, and the interference is $1 - 0.0870 = 0.9130$.

15. *(D)* **(a)** Look at the noncrossover types. One is wild type; the other is sepia, spineless, rough. Therefore, the alleles at the three loci are in coupling conformation. **(b)** Look at the double-crossover types. One is spineless; the other is sepia, rough. The only conformation that produces these double-crossover types is

The recombination frequency between *se* and *ss* is $(96 + 114 + 46 + 43) \div 1336 = 0.2238$. The recombina-

$$\frac{+ \quad + \quad +}{se \quad ss \quad ro}$$

tion frequency between *ss* and *ro* is $(156 + 173 + 46 + 43) \div 1336 = 0.3129$. The map is

$$se - 22.38 - ss - 31.29 - ro$$

(c) The observed frequency of double crossovers is $(46 + 43) \div 1336 = 0.0666$ and the expected frequency is $0.2238 \times 0.3129 = 0.0700$. The coefficient of coincidence is $0.0666 \div 0.0700 = 0.9514$, and the interference is $1 - 0.9514 = 0.0486$. **(d)** The correction with the Kosambi function for the *se-ss* interval is

The correction with the Kosambi function for the *ss-ro* interval is

$$x = 0.25\ln \frac{1 + 2(0.2238)}{1 - 2(0.2238)} = 0.2408$$

After correction with the Kosambi function, the map is

$$x = 0.25\ln \frac{1 + 2(0.3129)}{1 - 2(0.3129)} = 0.3672$$

$$se - 24.08 - ss - 36.72 - ro$$

(e) The distance from *se* to *ss* in the map in Figure 15.3 is $58.5 - 26.0 = 32.5$ cM. The map distance obtained with the Kosambi function (24.08 cM) is closer to the value in the map than the map distance derived from the uncorrected recombination frequency (22.38 cM). The distance from *ss* to *ro* in the map in Figure 15.3 is $91.1 - 58.5 = 32.6$ cM. The uncorrected recombination frequency (31.29 cM) is closer to the value in the map than the map distance derived from the Kosambi function (36.72 cM).

16. *(E)* **(a)** There are two missing classes. One is spineless, the other is delta, stripe (zero individuals were observed with these phenotypes). These missing classes are the double-crossover types. No individuals with the double-crossover types were observed because the three loci are so close to one another that double-crossovers are very unlikely. **(b)** To determine the coupling-repulsion conformation, look at the noncrossover types. One is delta, the other is spineless, stripe. Therefore, *D* is in repulsion to *sp* and *sr*. **(c)** The missing double-crossover types indicate that *sr* must be between *D* and *sp* in the map, and because *D* is in repulsion to *sp* and *sr*, the genotype of the heterozygous parent must be

The recombination frequency for the *D-sr* interval is $(41 + 35) \div 1387 = 0.0548$. The recombination fre-

$$\frac{D \quad + \quad +}{+ \quad sr \quad sp}$$

quency for the *sr-sp* interval is (25 + 22) ÷ 1387 = 0.0339. Therefore, the genetic map is

$$D - 5.48 - sr - 3.39 - sp$$

(d) The observed number of double-crossover types was 0, so the interference is 1 − 0 = 1.

17. *(E)* **(a)** In cross #1, all dominant alleles are in coupling conformation, and the double-crossover types are *Ss bb Ll* and *ss Bb ll*, so *b* must be between *s* and *l* in the map. The recombination frequency for the *s-b* interval is (38 + 45 + 11 + 20) ÷ 1580 = 0.0722. The recombination frequency for the *b-l* interval is (256 + 284 + 11 + 20) ÷ 1580 = 0.3614. The map is

$$s - 7.22 - b - 36.14 - l$$

In cross #2, all dominant alleles are in coupling conformation, and the double-crossover types are *Bb gg Ll* and *bb Gg ll*, so *g* must be between *b* and *l* in the map. The recombination frequency for the *b-g* interval is (272 + 326 + 5 + 6) ÷ 1795 = 0.3393. The recombination frequency for the *g-l* interval is (28 + 25 + 5 + 6) ÷ 1795 = 0.0357. The map is

$$b - 33.93 - g - 3.57 - l$$

In cross #3, all dominant alleles are in coupling conformation, and the double-crossover types are *Ss bb Gg* and *ss Bb gg*, so *b* must be between *s* and *g* in the map. The recombination frequency for the *s-b* interval is (127 + 125 + 42 + 45) ÷ 5159 = 0.0657. The recombination frequency for the *b-g* interval is (710 + 783 + 42 + 45) ÷ 5159 = 0.3063. The map is

$$s - 6.57 - b - 30.63 - g$$

(b) By comparing the three maps, we determine that the gene order is *s—b—g—l*. To determine the map distances on the four-factor map, we should use all available data for each interval. It is not appropriate to average map distances because one cross may have more progeny than another. Instead, we take all progeny that represent a crossover within a particular interval, then divide by the total number of progeny from the crosses we utilized for the calculation. The recombination frequency for the *s-b* interval is (38 + 45 + 11 + 20 + 127 + 125 + 42 + 45) ÷ (1580 + 5159) = 0.0672. The recombination frequency for the *b-g* interval is (272 + 326 + 5 + 6 + 710 + 783 + 42 + 45) ÷ (1795 + 5159) = 0.3148. The recombination frequency for the *g-l* interval is (28 + 25 + 5 + 6) ÷ 1795 = 0.0357. The four-point linkage map is

$$s—6.72—b—31.48—g—3.57—l$$

(c) The table below shows the recombination frequency (*y*) for each interval from the three-point maps, the combined frequencies used for the four-point map, and the corresponding frequencies after correction with the Kosambi function (*x*)

Interval	y	x
s-b (cross #1)	0.0722	0.0727
s-b (cross #3)	0.0657	0.0661
s-b (crosses #1 and #3 combined)	0.0672	0.0676
b-g (cross #2)	0.3393	0.4133
b-g (cross #3)	0.3063	0.3565
b-g (crosses #2 and #3 combined)	0.3148	0.3704
b-l (cross #1)	0.3614	0.4567
g-l (cross #2)	0.0357	0.0358

Correction with the Kosambi function lengthens each interval in the map. **(e)** We can determine whether correction with the Kosambi function overcomes problems with additivity by looking at the *b-l* interval. From cross #1, the uncorrected recombination frequency for the *b-l* interval is 0.3614. The added uncorrected recombination frequencies in this interval are 0.3148 + 0.0357 = 0.3505. The difference is 0.3614 − 0.3505 = 0.0109. The corrected frequency for *b-l* from cross #1 is 0.4567 and the added corrected frequencies in this interval are 0.3704 + 0.0358 = 0.4062. The difference is 0.4567 − 0.4062 = 0.0505. In this example, correction with the Kosambi function does not overcome problems with additivity.

18. *(E)* **(a)** According to the four-point linkage map in the previous problem, the recombination frequency between *s* and *b* is 0.0672, and between *b* and *g* it is 0.3148. According to the information from the previous problem, all of the dominant alleles are in coupling conformation in the heterozygote. To calculate the gametic frequencies, let's start with the double-crossover type gametes *SbG* and *sBg*. Their combined frequency is 0.0672 × 0.3148 = 0.0212. The frequency of each gamete is half of their combined frequency: 0.0212 ÷ 2 = 0.0106. To determine the combined frequency of the single-crossover-type gametes *Sbg* and *sBG*, we take the recombination frequency between *s* and *b* and subtract the frequency of double-crossover type gametes: 0.0672 − 0.0212 = 0.0460. The frequency of each gamete is half of their combined frequency: 0.0460 ÷ 2 = 0.0230. To determine the combined frequency of the single-crossover-type gametes *SBg* and *sbG*, we take the recombination frequency between *b* and *g* and subtract the frequency of double-crossover-type gametes: 0.3148 − 0.0212 = 0.2936. The frequency of each gamete is half of their combined frequency: 0.2936 ÷ 2 = 0.1468. We determine the combined frequency of the noncrossover-type gametes *SBG* and *sbg* by substracting the combined frequency of all crossover-type gametes from unity: 1 − (0.0212 + 0.0460 + 0.2936) = 0.6392. The frequency of each gamete is half of their combined frequency: 0.6392 ÷ 2 = 0.3196. In summary, the expected frequencies of gametes are as follows:

Gamete	Frequency
SBG	0.3196
sbg	0.3196
Sbg	0.0230
sBG	0.0230
SBg	0.1468
sbG	0.1468
SbG	0.0106
sBg	0.0106
Total	1.0000

(b) To answer this question, we list all possible genotypes that could arise from self-fertilization of a plant with the genotype *Ss Bb Gg*. Then, we'll determine all gametic unions that could produce each genotype. To determine the frequency of each possible gametic union, we apply the product rule and multiply the respective frequencies of the two gametes. To determine the frequency of each phenotype, we apply the sum rule and add the frequencies of all gametic unions that cause that phenotype. The results of this exercise are summarized in the table below. For gametic unions, the female gametes are written first.

Phenoype	Genotype	Gametic Unions	Frequencies
SBG	SS BB GG	SBG + SBG	0.1021
	SS BB Gg	SBG + SBg	0.0469
		SBg + SBG	0.0469
	SS Bb GG	SBG + SbG	0.0034
		SbG + SBG	0.0034
	SS Bb Gg	SBG + Sbg	0.0074
		Sbg + SBG	0.0074
		SbG + SBg	0.0016
		SBg + SbG	0.0016
	Ss BB GG	SBG + sBG	0.0074
		sBG + SBG	0.0074
	Ss BB Gg	SBG + sBg	0.0034
		sBg + SBG	0.0034
		SBg + sBG	0.0034
		sBG + SBg	0.0034
	Ss Bb GG	SBG + sbG	0.0469
		sbG + SBG	0.0469
		SbG + sBG	0.0002
		sBG + SbG	0.0002
	Ss Bb Gg	SBG + sbg	0.1021
		sbg + SBG	0.1021
		Sbg + sBG	0.0005
		sBG + Sbg	0.0005
		SBg + sbG	0.0216
		sbG + SBg	0.0216
		SbG + sBg	0.0001
		sBg + SbG	<u>0.0001</u>
			0.5919
SBg	SS BB gg	SBg + SBg	0.0216
	SS Bb gg	SBg + Sbg	0.0034
		Sbg + SBg	0.0034
	Ss BB gg	SBg + sBg	0.0016
		sBg + SBg	0.0016
	Ss Bb gg	SBg + sbg	0.0469
		sbg + SBg	0.0469
		Sbg + sBg	0.0002
		sBg + Sbg	<u>0.0002</u>
			0.1258
SbG	SS bb GG	SbG + SbG	0.0001
	SS bb Gg	SbG + Sbg	0.0002
		Sbg + SbG	0.0002
	Ss bb GG	SbG + sbG	0.0016
		sbG + SbG	0.0016
	Ss bb Gg	SbG + sbg	0.0034
		sbg + SbG	0.0034
		Sbg + sbG	0.0034
		sbG + Sbg	<u>0.0034</u>
			0.0173

Sbg	SS bb gg	Sbg + Sbg	0.0005
	Ss bb gg	Sbg + sbg	0.0074
		sbg + Sbg	0.0074
			0.0153
sBG	ss BB GG	sBG + sBG	0.0005
	ss BB Gg	sBG + sBg	0.0002
		sBg + sBG	0.0002
	ss Bb GG	sBG + sbG	0.0034
		sbG + sBG	0.0034
	ss Bb Gg	sBG + sbg	0.0074
		sbg + sBG	0.0074
		sbG + sBg	0.0016
		sBg + sbG	0.0016
			0.0257
sBg	ss BB gg	sBg + sBg	0.0001
	ss Bb gg	sBg + sbg	0.0034
		sbg + sBg	0.0034
			0.0069
sbG	ss bb GG	sbG + sbG	0.0216
	ss bb Gg	sbG + sbg	0.0469
		sbg + sbG	0.0469
			0.1154
sbg	ss bb gg	sbg + sbg	0.1021
Total			1.0004

The sum of the frequencies of all phenotypes is slightly greater than unity due to rounding.

19. *(E)* **(a)** The map is

$$a—10—b—15—c—20—d—5—e$$

(b) The distances calculated from the observed recombination frequencies are not additive because of undetected double crossovers. **(c)** The table below shows the distances after correction with the Haldane and Kosambi functions:

Map Distances

Interval	No Correction	Haldane	Kosambi
a-b	10	11	10
b-c	15	18	15
c-d	20	26	21
d-e	5	5	5
a-c	22	29	24
b-d	31	48	36
c-e	22	29	24

(d) We can determine to what extent (if any) correction with a mapping function improves additivity of map distances by comparing the additive distance with the observed distance for a particular interval. For example, without correction, the additive distance for the *a-c* interval is 10 + 15 = 25 cM, whereas the observed distance is 22 cM, a difference of 25 − 22 = 3 cM. After correction with the Haldane function, the additive distance for the *a-c* interval is 11 + 18 = 29 cM, and the corrected observed distance is also 29 cM, a difference of 0 cM. After correction with the Kosambi function, the additive distance for the *a-c* interval is 10 + 5 = 25 cM and the corrected observed distance is 24 cM, a difference of 25 − 24 = 1 cM. The table below provides the differences between the additive and observed distances without correction and with correction by the Haldane and Kosambi functions. A difference of 0 indicates perfect additivity.

Difference (in cM) Between Additive and Observed Distances

Interval	No correction	Haldane	Kosambi
a-c	3	0	1
b-d	4	−4	0
c-e	3	2	2

Correction with the Kosambi function improves additivity for all three intervals. Correction with the Haldane function improves additivity for the *a-c* and *c-e* intervals.

20. **(C)** The difference between the observed distance between RFLP A and RFLP B in experiment 1 and the additive distance between RFLP A and RFLP B in experiment 2 is due to undetected double crossovers. The difference is 35 − 31 = 4 cM. Because centimorgans represent percentage of crossing-over, the percentage of undetected double crossovers is 4%.

21. **(E)** We'll assume that all dominant alleles are in coupling conformation. **(a)** With no interference, the combined frequency of double-crossover-type gametes, *Sh wx Gl* and *sh Wx gl*, should be the product of the recombination frequencies for the *sh-wx* and *wx-gl* intervals, in this case 0.3 × 0.1 = 0.03. We divide by 2 to determine the frequency of each double-crossover-type gamete: 0.03 ÷ 2 = 0.015. The combined frequency of the single-crossover-type gametes *Sh wx gl* and *sh Wx Gl* is 0.3 − 0.03 = 0.27, and the frequency of each gamete is 0.27 ÷ 2 = 0.135. The combined frequency of the single-crossover-type gametes *Sh Wx gl* and *sh wx Gl* is 0.1 − 0.03 = 0.07, and the frequency of each gamete is 0.07 ÷ 2 = 0.035. The combined frequency of the noncrossover-type gametes *Sh Wx Gl* and *sh wx gl* is determined by subtraction: 1 − (0.27 + 0.07 + 0.03) = 0.63, and the frequency of each gamete is 0.63 ÷ 2 = 0.315. In summary, the gametes and their respective frequencies are as follows:

Gamete	Frequency
Sh Wx Gl	0.315
sh wx gl	0.315
Sh wx gl	0.135
sh Wx Gl	0.135
Sh Wx gl	0.035
sh wx Gl	0.035
Sh wx Gl	0.015
sh Wx gl	0.015
Total	1.000

(b) An interference value of 0.6 corresponds to a coefficient of coincidence of 0.4. To calculate the combined frequency of the double-crossover-type gametes, *Sh wx Gl* and *sh Wx gl*, multiply the product of the recombination frequencies for the *sh-wx* and *wx-gl* intervals by 0.4: $0.4 \times 0.3 \times 0.1 = 0.012$. We divide by 2 to determine the frequency of each double-crossover-type gamete: $0.012 \div 2 = 0.006$. The combined frequency of the single-crossover-type gametes *Sh wx gl* and *sh Wx Gl* is $0.3 - 0.012 = 0.288$, and the frequency of each gamete is $0.288 \div 2 = 0.144$. The combined frequency of the single-crossover-type gametes *Sh Wx gl* and *sh wx Gl* is $0.1 - 0.012 = 0.088$, and the frequency of each gamete is $0.088 \div 2 = 0.044$. The combined frequency of the noncrossover-type gametes *Sh Wx Gl* and *sh wx gl* is determined by subtraction: $1 - (0.288 + 0.088 + 0.012) = 0.612$, and the frequency of each gamete is $0.612 \div 2 = 0.306$. In summary, the gametes and their respective frequencies are:

Gamete	Frequency
Sh Wx Gl	0.306
sh wx gl	0.306
Sh wx gl	0.144
sh Wx Gl	0.144
Sh Wx gl	0.044
sh wx Gl	0.044
Sh wx Gl	0.006
sh Wx gl	0.006
Total	1.000

22. *(D)* **(a)** One noncrossover type has all three dominant phenotypes (colored, full, starchy), and the other has all three recessive phenotypes (colorless, shrunken, waxy). Therefore, the dominant alleles are in coupling conformation at all three loci. **(b)** The double-crossover-type gametes are *C1 sh Wx* and *c1 Sh wx*, so *sh* is between *c1* and *wx* in the map. The recombination frequency between *c1* and *sh* is $(509 + 524 + 20 + 12) \div 45832 = 0.0232$. The recombination frequency between *sh* and *wx* is $(4455 + 4654 + 20 + 12) \div 45832 = 0.1994$. The genetic map is

$$c1—2.32—sh—19.94—wx$$

(c) The expected frequency of double-crossover types is $0.0232 \times 0.1994 = 0.0046$. The observed frequency is $(20 + 12) \div 45832 = 0.0007$. The coefficient of coincidence is $0.0007 \div 0.0046 = 0.1522$, and the interference is $1 - 0.1522 = 0.8478$. **(d)** The distance between *c1* and *sh* in this example (2.32 cM) is about 1.2 cM less than the corresponding distance calculated in Example 15.7 (3.5 cM). The distance between *sh* and *wx* in this example (19.94 cM) is about 1.5 cM greater that the corresponding distance calculated in Example 15.7 (18.4 cM). **(e)** The most probable reason for the discrepancies is sampling error.

23. *(E)* **(a)** A crossover between the knob and the *c1* locus generates the genotypes *c1c1 Wxwx* knob and *C1c1 wxwx* knobless. **(b)** We calculate the recombination frequency between the knob and the *c1* locus by summing the numbers of individuals that arose from a crossover between the knob and *c1* and dividing this number by the total number of individuals: $(5 + 5) \div 63 = 0.1587$, which equals about 15.9 cM. We calculate the recombination frequency between *c1* and *wx* by summing the numbers of individuals that arose from a crossover between *c1* and *wx* (those individuals with the genotypes *C1c1 Wxwx* knob and *c1c1 wxwx* knobless) and dividing this number by the total number of individuals: $(4 + 3) \div 63 = 0.1111$, which equals about 11.1 cM. **(c)** and **(d)** The table below provides all possible genotypes that could arise among the progeny of cross #2; it also indicates the crossover type and location of the crossover(s) that cause each genotype. The abbreviations are NCO = no crossovers, SCO = single crossover, DCO = double crossover, and TCO = triple crossover. All genotypes that were observed in the progeny are marked with an asterisk (*).

C1c1 WxWx	knobless	no translocation	DCO: knob-*c1*, *c1-wx*
C1c1 Wxwx	knobless	no translocation	DCO: knob-*c1*, *c1-wx*
			or DCO: knob-*c1*, *wx*-translocation
C1c1 wxwx	knobless	no translocation	DCO: knob-*c1*, *wx*-translocation
*c1c1 WxWx	knobless	no translocation	NCO
*c1c1 Wxwx	knobless	no translocation	NCO or DCO: *c1-wx*, *wx*-translocation
c1c1 wxwx	knobless	no translocation	DCO: *c1-wx*, *wx*-translocation
*C1c1 WxWx	knob	no translocation	SCO: *c1-wx*
*C1c1 Wxwx	knob	no translocation	SCO: *c1-wx*, or SCO: *wx*-translocation
C1c1 wxwx	knob	no translocation	SCO: *wx*-translocation
c1c1 WxWx	knob	no translocation	SCO: knob-*c1*
c1c1 Wxwx	knob	no translocation	SCO: knob-*cl*, or TCO
c1c1 wxwx	knob	no translocation	TCO
C1c1 WxWx	knobless	translocation	TCO
C1c1 Wxwx	knobless	translocation	TCO
C1c1 wxwx	knobless	translocation	SCO: knob-*c1*
*c1c1 WxWx	knobless	translocation	SCO: *wx*-translocation
*c1c1 Wxwx	knobless	translocation	SCO: *c1-wx* or SCO: *wx*-translocation
*c1c1 wxwx	knobless	translocation	SCO: *c1-wx*
C1c1 WxWx	knob	translocation	DCO: *c1-wx*, *wx*-translocation
C1c1 Wxwx	knob	translocation	NCO or DCO: *c1-wx*, *wx*-translocation
*C1c1 wxwx	knob	translocation	NCO
c1c1 WxWx	knob	translocation	DCO: knob-*c1*, *wx*-translocation
c1c1 Wxwx	knob	translocation	DCO: knob-*c1*, *c1-wx*, or
			DCO: knob-*c1*, *wx*-translocation
c1c1 wxwx	knob	translocation	DCO: knob-*c1*, *c1-wx*

Notice that all the types that Creighton and McClintock observed (those marked with an asterisk) probably arose from no crossover, or from a single crossover between *c1* and *wx*, or from a single crossover between *wx* and the translocation. The genotypes missing from the data are the double- and triple-crossover types and the single-crossover types from a crossover between the knob and *c1*.

24. *(D)* **(a)** Flies with white eyes and flies with yellow bodies are the crossover types, regardless of sex. Wild-type flies and flies with white eyes and yellow bodies are the noncrossover types, regardless of sex. The map distance is $[(17 + 12) \div 2205] \times 100 = 1.3$ cM. **(b)** F_2 progeny can be used because all F_1 females are heterozygous at both loci and all F_1 males are hemizygous for both recessive alleles. Therefore, all crossovers are in the F_1 females, and the intermating of F_1 individuals is the equivalent of a testcross.

25. *(D)* Yes, it is possible to identify with near certainty the individual in which the crossover took place. The female in the first parental generation (at the top of the pedigree) must be a heterozyous carrier of the mutant allele that causes color blindness because two of her sons have color blindness. It is highly unlikely that she is a carrier of the mutant allele that causes hemophilia because two of her sons have neither hemophilia nor color blindness and none of her daughters have hemophilia. The male in the first parental generation contributed the mutant allele that causes hemophilia to the pedigree. The female whose son had both hemophilia and color blindness must have been a heterozygous carrier of the two mutant alleles, and the two mutant alleles must have been in repulsion conformation. A crossover during meiosis in this female coupled the two alleles on the X chromosome, and the male who has both hemophilia and color blindness inherited this crossover-type chromosome.

26. *(D)* **(a)** We can determine the recombination frequencies from Sturtevant's data by taking the number of recombinant progeny for each interval and dividing by the total number of progeny for that interval. The results of this exercise are summarized below. We have rounded the recombination frequencies to three decimal places to correspond to the one-decimal place cM resolution in Sturtevant's map:

Loci	Recombination Frequency
y-w	0.010
y-v	0.322
y-r	0.355
y-m	0.375
w-v	0.297
w-r	0.337
w-m	0.452
v-r	0.030
v-m	0.269

Examination of the data reveals that Sturtevant used the lowest recombination frequencies available to him to construct his map. From his map the distance between *y* and *w* is 1.0 cM, which corresponds to the *y-w* recombination frequency of 0.010. The distance on the map between *w* and *v* is 30.7 – 1.0 = 29.7 cM, which corresponds to the *w-v* recombination frequency of 0.297. The distance on the map between *v* and *r* is 33.7 – 30.7 = 3.0 cM, which corresponds to the *v-r* recombination frequency of 0.030. The distance on the map between *r* and *m* is 57.6 – 33.7 = 23.9 cM. There are no data that directly provide the recombination frequency between *r* and *m*. Instead, the *v-m* recombination frequency is 0.269, which corresponds to the additive distance of 3.0 + 23.9 = 26.9 cM for the *v-r* and *r-m* intervals on the map. Sturtevant placed *m* on the map as its distance from *v*, rather than from *r*. **(b)** We expect an underestimation of map distances for long intervals due to undetected double crossovers. In Sturtevant's data, map distances are underestimated only for the *y-m* and *w-m* intervals, which are the two longest intervals in the data set. Deviations from additivity may also be due to sampling error.

27. *(D)* **(a)** The map distance calculated from the female progeny is [(109 + 124) ÷ 634] × 100 = 36.75 cM. The map distance calculated from the male progeny is [(114 + 123) ÷ 613] × 100 = 38.66 cM. **(b)** Both male and female progeny inherit their recombinant X chromosomes from the same female parents, so there should be no difference. The slight observed difference is due to sampling error. **(c)** F_2 progeny can be used because all F_1 females are heterozygous at both loci and all F_1 males are hemizygous for both recessive alleles. Therefore, all crossovers are in the F_1 females, and the intermating of F_1 individuals is the equivalent of a testcross.

Chapter 16
Genetic Fine Structure

1. *(B)* Only half of the spores in a second-division-segregation ascus are crossover types. Therefore, there are twice as many second-division-segregation asci as there are crossovers, so we must divide the number of second-division-segregation asci by 2 to estimate the actual number of crossovers when calculating map distances between a gene and its centromere in *Neurospora*.

2. *(D)* As shown in the diagram on the following page, two-strand and four-strand double crossovers produce first-division-segregation asci and are not detected as crossovers. A three-strand double crossover produces a second-division-segregation ascus, and a single crossover is detected. The undetected crossovers cause researchers to underestimate the map distance between the gene and the centromere.

3. *(C)* A cross can be designed to include heterozygosity for a second gene that lies between the gene being mapped and the centromere. Under these circumstances, recombination of alleles of the second gene with the gene being mapped and the centromere will reveal double crossovers.

4. *(C)* In a 5:3 segregation, two different alleles segregate from one another during the single mitotic division that takes place after meiosis is completed, so the segregation is postmeiotic. Such segregation is possible whenever there is a nucleotide mismatch within heteroduplex DNA. Heteroduplex DNA is expected in all three models of DNA recombination reviewed in Chapter 16, as shown in Figures 16.9, 16.11, and 16.12.

5. *(D)* Two lines of evidence suggest that recombination is initiated at recombination hotspots in fungi. First, recombination between two alleles of the same gene is rare in fungi. This is expected if recombination is usually initiated at the same site. If the recombination hotspot does not lie between the mutation sites of the two alleles, recombination between these sites is not likely. Second, recombination in fungi is polar, which is expected if recombination begins at the same place each time. When recombination begins at random sites within a gene, polarity is not observed. There is abundant evidence of recombination between alleles of the same gene in *Drosophila* and other multicelluar eukaryotes, suggesting that recombination is not associated with hotspots in these species.

6. *(C)* The two observations that support the existence of recombination hotspots mentioned in the previous question are expected results of the double-strand-break repair model, and therefore support the existence of double-strand breaks at recombination hotspots.

7. *(B)* Gene conversion is best detected by examining all products of a single meiotic event. It is difficult, and often impossible, to recover the products of the same meiotic event in multicellular eukaryotes, whereas in ascomycete fungi, each ascus contains all of the products of a single meiotic event.

8. *(C)* **(a)** If there is no crossover between the genes being mapped, then a parental ditype arises. A single crossover between the genes produces a tetratype. Nonparental ditypes arise only from four-strand double crossovers, as illustrated in Figure 16.7, so nonparental ditypes represent a portion of the double crossovers. **(b)** As explained in section 16.2, the number of undetected crossovers in the parental ditype class is twice the number of nonparental ditypes, and the number of undetected crossovers in the tetratype class is also twice the number of nonparental ditypes. The number of detected crossovers in the nonparental ditype class is also twice the number of nonparental ditypes. When added together, the undetected crossovers and the detected crossovers in the nonparental ditype class equal 6 times the number of nonparental ditypes. **(c)** The multiplication of the nonparental ditype asci by 6 is based on the assumption that the four ways by which double crossovers may arise (illustrated in Figure 16.7) are equally likely. If this is true, then the nonparental ditype asci represent 1/4 of all double-crossover types and can be used to estimate the total number of crossovers.

Diagram for problem 2

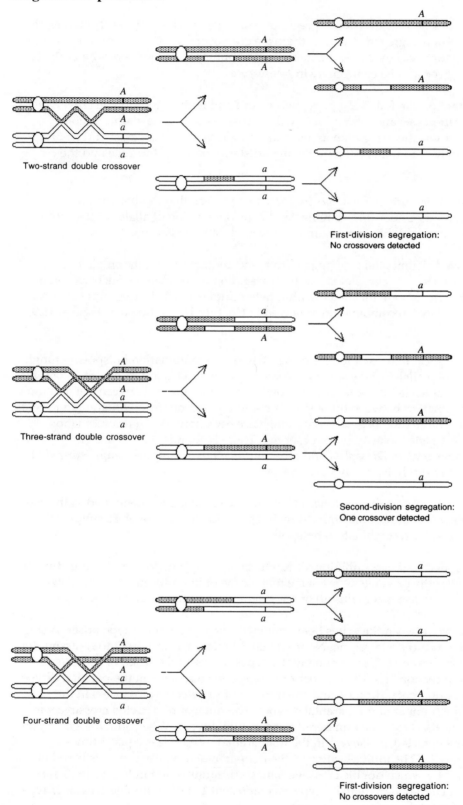

Two-strand double crossover

Three-strand double crossover

Four-strand double crossover

First-division segregation:
No crossovers detected

Second-division segregation:
One crossover detected

First-division segregation:
No crossovers detected

344

9. *(C)* Gene conversion transfers to a chromosome a strand of DNA from the homologous chromosome. If the homologous chromosome contains the wild-type sequence at the site of a mutant allele, then the mutant allele can be converted to a wild-type allele. If both homologous chromosomes contain the same mutant allele, then the mutant allele cannot be changed to a wild-type allele through gene conversion because there is no wild-type sequence available as a pattern for the conversion. Only a mutation can make such a change.

10. *(C)* We can calculate the recombination frequency by dividing the number of second-division-segregation asci by 2, then dividing the result by the total number of asci: $[(57 \div 2) \div (57 + 635)] = 0.0412$. The map distance is 4.12 cM.

11. *(C)* According to equation 16.1, to calculate the recombination frequency between a gene and its centromere, we divide the number of second-division-segregation asci by 2. For these data, we estimate the number of second-division-segregation asci by multiplying the number of symmetrical second-division-segregation asci by 2, which cancels out the division by 2. Thus, to calculate the recombination frequency, we simply divide the number of symmetrical second-division-segregation asci by the total number of asci. For the C17 × WT cross, $159 \div 2094 = 0.0759$, or 7.59 cM. For the C22 × WT cross, $278 \div 3159 = 0.0880$, or 8.80 cM. For the C29 × WT cross, $65 \div 1084 = 0.0600$, or 6.00 cM.

12. *(C)* **(a)** To determine the map distances for each of these gene intervals, we use equation 16.2. For the R83-C28 interval, the map distance is $[(6 \div 2) \div 213] \times 100 = 1.41$ cM. For the R155-C28 interval, the map distance is $[(1 \div 2) \div 213] \times 100 = 0.23$ cM. For the R83-R155 interval, the map distance is $[(5 \div 2) \div 213] \times 100 = 1.17$ cM. The R83-C28 interval is the longest, so R155 must lie between R83 and C28. The map is

R83—1.17—R155—0.23—C28

(b) Nonparental ditype asci arise from a four-strand double crossover between two genes and represent 1/4 of the double-crossover types. The map distances are so small in this example that the probability of observing a single nonparental ditype ascus among 213 progeny is very low. For example, with no interference, the expected number of nonparental ditype asci for the R83-C28 interval (the longest distance in the map) is $0.25 \times 0.0141^2 \times 213 = 0.01$. The chance of observing a single nonparental ditype ascus in an experiment with 213 progeny is only about 1%.

13. *(C)* **(a)** Take a male that is hemizygous for the new mutation and mate him with a female that is homozygous for the *w* (mutant *white*) allele. (The reciprocal cross is an equally good experiment to determine whether or not the new allele is at the *w* locus.) **(b)** If the new allele is at the *white* locus, we expect the male and female progeny to have the mutant white-eyes phenotype. **(c)** If the new allele is not at the *white* locus, we expect only the males to have the mutant white-eyes phenotype. **(d)** To determine the map distance between the two loci, we isolate the female progeny of the cross made in part a before they mate. These females are heterozygous for both alleles, and the alleles are in repulsion conformation. We mate these females with wild-type males and observe the male progeny. Half of the crossover-type male progeny will have wild-type eyes, and all other male progeny will have white eyes. To calculate the recombination frequency, we multiply the number of wild-type male progeny by 2, then divide this number by the total number of male progeny. **(e)** If the locus of the new allele is not linked (but is syntenic) to the *w* locus, we should map the new allele's locus in relation to other X-linked loci whose locations on the X chromosome are known and are at various places throughout the X chromosome. The loci most closely linked to the new locus can then be identified, and the location of the new allele's locus identified in relation to them.

14. *(C)* **(a)** To determine whether or not the allele is at the *brown* locus, we take a fly that is homozygous for the new mutant allele and mate it with a fly that is homozygous for a mutant allele at the *brown* locus. If the new allele is at the *brown* locus, the F_1 progeny of this cross should all have brown eyes. If

the new allele is not at the *brown* locus, the F_1 progeny should all have wild-type eyes. **(b)** We allow the F_1 progeny to mate among themselves to produce F_2 progeny. If the alleles at the two loci assort independently, we expect a 9 wild-type:7 brown-eyes ratio among the F_2 progeny. If the two loci are linked on chromosome 2, we expect a significant deviation from the 9:7 ratio. **(c)** We mate flies that are heterozygous $+/bw^5$ with flies that are homozygous for the mutant allele. **(d)** If the new allele is at the *brown* locus, we expect half of the progeny to have brown eyes and half to have wild-type eyes.

15. *(D)* For an aberrant 4:4 pattern to arise, the same nucleotide pair must be mismatched in both DNA molecules within heteroduplex DNA, and neither mismatch can be repaired. The heteroduplex DNA must be present in both DNA molecules at the same place. In the Holliday model (Figure 16.9), the heteroduplex DNA is in the same place in both molecules, so aberrant 4:4 patterns are expected unless mismatch repair corrects the mismatch in at least one of the molecules in each case. In the Meselson-Radding (asymmetric strand-transfer) model (Figure 16.11), part of the heteroduplex DNA is present in the same place in both molecules if there is branch migration, but one of the molecules has more heteroduplex DNA than the other. Because some of the nucleotide mismatches should be found in the heteroduplex DNA that is present in only one of the molecules, aberrant 4:4 patterns are possible but less likely in this model when compared to the Holliday model. In the double-strand-break repair model (Figure 16.12), heteroduplex DNA is present in both molecules but not at the same place. Thus, no aberrant 4:4 patterns are expected with this model. The observation that there were no aberrant 4:4 patterns best supports the double-strand-break repair model but does not exclude the other models.

16. *(E)* **(a)** If intragenic crossing-over were the cause of the wild-type *cys* recombinants, then we would expect all of the wild-type *cys* recombinants to have recombinant chromosomes, and none of them (except perhaps a few rare double-crossover types) to have parental (nonrecombinant) chromosomes. However, more than half of the wild-type *cys* recombinants have parental chromosomes, indicating that gene conversion, rather than crossing-over, is probably responsible for the wild-type *cys* recombinants. In addition, wild-type *cys* recombinants constitute about 0.1% of the spores, which is at least an order of magnitude too high for reversion mutation to be an adequate explanation. **(b)** The frequencies of gene conversion for each cross are calculated as the total number of wild-type *cys* recombinants from a cross divided by the total number of spores screened for that cross. The frequencies are listed in the table below:

Cross	Frequency of Gene Conversion
+ *cys*^{9} *ylo* × *lys cys*^{4} +	9.72×10^{-4}
+ *cys*^{4} *ylo* × *lys cys*^{9} +	10.42×10^{-4}
+ *cys*^{7} *ylo* × *lys cys*^{64} +	10.21×10^{-4}
+ *cys*^{17} *ylo* × *lys cys*^{64} +	10.71×10^{-4}
+ *cys*^{64} *ylo* × *lys cys*^{17} +	10.67×10^{-4}
+ *cys*^{9} *ylo* × *lys cys*^{17} +	11.09×10^{-4}
+ *cys*^{7} *ylo* × *lys cys*^{9} +	11.25×10^{-4}
+ *cys*^{4} *ylo* × *lys cys*^{15} +	11.96×10^{-4}
+ *cys*^{15} *ylo* × *lys cys*^{4} +	13.79×10^{-4}
+ *cys*^{7} *ylo* × *lys cys*^{15} +	12.71×10^{-4}

(c) The proportion of gene conversions associated with crossing-over is the total number of gene conversions in recombinant chromosomes divided by the total number of gene conversions: $(327 + 291) \div (443 + 421 + 327 + 291) = 0.4170 = 41.7\%$. **(d)** If the gene conversions were not polar, we would expect all the mutant alleles to convert at approximately the same rate. If we look at the data for the parental-type chromosomes, we can determine which allele converts more frequently in each of the crosses. For example, in the first cross in the table (+ *cys*^{9} *ylo* × *lys cys*^{4} +), the *cys*^{9} allele is on the same chromosome as the mutant *ylo* allele, and the *cys*^{4} allele is on the same chromosome as the mutant *lys* allele. Among the parental-type chromosomes, the 16 with the *ylo* allele represent conversion of the *cys*^{9} allele to wild type, and the 72 with the *lys* allele represent conversion of the *cys*^{4} allele to wild type. In this cross, the *cys*^{4} allele converts more readily to wild type than does the *cys*^{9} allele. When we examine all crosses, it is apparent that the *cys*^{4}, *cys*^{7}, and *cys*^{17} alleles convert more readily than the other alleles, an observation that suggests polarity. Presumably, the alleles that convert more readily are closer to a recombination hotspot than are the other alleles.

17. *(D)* **(a)** Recombination between flanking markers was detected in each fly with the wild-type for lozenge phenotype, an observation indicating that the wild-type phenotype is associated with crossing-over. Had mutation caused the reversions to wild type, we would not expect any association with crossing-over. **(b)** A crossover is not expected with all gene conversion events. In this experiment, each fly with a wild-type for lozenge or like lozenge-spectacled phenotype also had a crossover between flanking markers. This observation indicates that intragenic crossing-over, rather than gene conversion, is the best explanation of the data. **(c)** About half of the flies with crossover-type chromosomes should be female, but the like lozenge-spectacled phenotype can be detected only in males, so the females with the crossover-type chromosome are not detected. **(d)** In cross 1, all progeny with the wild-type for lozenge phenotype were singed, and all progeny with the like lozenge-spectacled phenotype were raspberry, vermilion. These results are possible only if *lz*^{BS} is to the left of *lz*^{46}. In cross 2, all progeny with the wild-type for lozenge phenotype were cut, and all progeny with the like lozenge-spectacled phenotype were vermilion. These results are possible only if *lz*^{BS} is to the left of *lz*^{g}. In cross 3, all progeny with the wild-type for lozenge phenotype were cut, and all progeny with the like lozenge-spectacled phenotype were vermilion. These results are possible only if *lz*^{46} is to the left of *lz*^{g}. In summary, the order of alleles on the chromosome is *ct—sn—lz*^{BS}*–lz*^{46}*–lz*^{g}*—ras—v*.

18. *(C)* Many scientists envisioned genes as indivisible particles, much like beads on a string, rather than divisible segments of DNA. For the different *lozenge* alleles to be part of the same locus, the locus itself must be divisible. Once the nature of the gene as a segment of DNA had been discovered, the idea of genes as indivisible units was discarded, and the results of the studies by Green and Green and by Oliver were explained by intragenic crossing-over.

19. *(D)* **(a)** In designing these crosses, remember that the *lz* locus is on the X chromosome. The cis test can be done as a cross between a + + / *lz*^{BS} *lz*^{46} female and a wild-type male. The trans test can be done as a cross between a *lz*^{BS} + / + *lz*^{46} female and a wild-type male. **(b)** The female parent in cross 1 is *lz*^{BS} + / + *lz*^{46}, which is the genotype required for the trans test, so Green and Green did have the flies needed for the trans test. The females with the + + / *lz*^{BS} *lz*^{46} genotype may have been present in the progeny of cross 1, but they could not be identified by their phenotypes. However, had Green and Green decided to conduct a cis test, they could easily recover females that are all + + / *lz*^{BS} *lz*^{46} by crossing a like lozenge-spectacled male with a homozygous wild-type female. **(c)** In the cis test, half of the male progeny should be wild type and half should be like lozenge-spectacled (except for rare intragenic-crossover types). In the trans test, all males should have a mutant lozenge phenotype (except for rare intragenic-recombinant types).

20. *(C)* **(a)** If the two homologous chromosomes have mutations in the same gene, the individual should have the mutant phenotype. If the mutations are in different genes, the individual should have the wild-type phenotype. The trans tests are summarized in the table below (the "L" stands for "lethal"):

Allele on One Chromosome	Wild type	Mutant 1	Mutant 2	Mutant 3	Mutant 4	Mutant 5
Wild type	+					
Mutant 1	+	–				
Mutant 2	+	–	–			
Mutant 3	+	+	–	–		
Mutant 4	+	–	–	+	–	
Mutant 5	+	–	–	–	–	L

(b) Half of the progeny will be compound heterozygotes for the mutant 1 and mutant 5 alleles and will have the mutant phenotype. Half of the progeny will be heterozygous for the wild-type and mutant 1 alleles and will have the wild-type phenotype.

21. *(C)* Notice that all crosses have a parent that is homozygous for mutant 2, which has mutations in both genes. Thus, the only wild-type progeny will be those that arise from a crossover between two mutations in the heterozygous parent. The frequency of wild-type progeny should be directly proportional to the distance between the mutations in the heterozygous parent. From highest to lowest expected frequency of wild-type progeny, the rankings are as follows:

Cross 8
Cross 2
Cross 5
Cross 9
Cross 3
Crosses 1, 4, 6, 7, and 10 (tied for last place because they produce no wild-type progeny)

22. *(C)* **(a)** The calculations of the genetic map distances for each cross are as follows:

NHS1 × *hom3*: {[9 + 6(1)] ÷ 2} ÷ (610 + 1 + 9) = 0.0121, or 1.21 cM
NHS1 × *his1*: {[41 + 6(2)] ÷ 2} ÷ (562 + 2 + 41) = 0.0438, or 4.38 cM
NHS1 × *trp2*: {[234 + 6(12)] ÷ 2} ÷ (158 + 12 + 234) = 0.3787, or 37.87 cM

(b) As given in the first cross, the distance between *NHS1* and *hom3* is 1.21 cM. The distance between *hom3* and *his1* is 4.38 – 1.21 = 3.17 cM. The distance between *his1* and *trp2* is 37.87 – 4.38 = 33.49 cM. The map is

NHS1—1.21—*hom3*—3.17—*his1*—33.49—*trp2*

23. *(D)* **(a)** The researchers crossed each genotype with itself, and in each case there were no black spores in the progeny. Had reversion mutation been responsible for the black spores, then some black spores should have been observed in the progeny of these crosses. **(b)** Gene conversion is the most reasonable explanation for the appearance of black spores because it tends to be more prevalent in fungi than intragenic crossing-over. However, the results observed in these experiments are consistent with either gene conversion or intragenic crossing-over. In the absence of flanking markers, gene conversion and intragenic crossing-over cannot be distinguished from one another in these types of experiments. **(c)** Mutation B is probably a deletion mutation and therefore cannot provide a pattern for gene conversion (or participate in intragenic crossing-over). **(d)** Mutation 63 probably lies outside of the region that has been deleted in mutation B, whereas the other mutations are probably within this region.

24. *(D)* **(a)** For twin spots to arise from the loss of X chromosomes, two adjacent somatic cells would each need to independently lose an X chromosome, one of them the paternal X chromosome and the other the maternal X chromosome, during the early stages of development. The probability of such events occurring independently in adjacent cells is highly unlikely. Somatic crossing-over is a much more plausible explanation. **(b)** Loss of an X chromosome in a cell in a heterozygous female makes the cell hemizygous for the alleles on the remaining X chromosome. Recessive (as well as dominant) alleles can be expressed phenotypically in cells that are hemizygous for those alleles. Notice in Figure 16.26 that twin spots arise from a mitotic crossover between the *sn* locus and the centromere. A mitotic crossover between the *sn* and *y* loci can result in a single yellow spot with no corresponding singed twin spot. A mitotic double crossover with one crossover between the *sn* locus and the centromere and the second crossover between the *sn* and *y* loci can result in a single singed spot with no corresponding yellow twin spot.

25. *(D)* Closely linked genes recombine through crossing-over but not by gene conversion because the region of heteroduplex DNA at the point of exchange is too short to include both genes. Interference of one chiasma with formation of a second chiasma in its vicinity causes high positive interference. The negative interference for alleles of the same gene is not really interference but rather the effect of gene conversion. The mutant sites of two alleles that are very close to one another in the same gene may both lie within the same region of heteroduplex DNA during recombination and may both be simultaneously converted, a phenomenon that appears phenotypically as negative interference.

Chapter 17
Alterations in Chromosome Number and Structure

1. *(B)* Human somatic cells function with only one active X chromosome. In males, there is only a single X chromosome in each somatic cell, and its genes carry out the functions of all X-linked genes. In females, each cell has two X chromosomes, but one is inactivated as a Barr body, so each cells functions with a single active X chromosome. Females who are monosomic with an XO chromosome constitution have a single X chromosome in their cells and no Barr body. The single X chromosome in an XO female functions much like the single X chromosome in XY males.

2. *(C)* **(a)** In a cell that is heterozygous for an interstitial duplication, one of the duplications loops out when the homologous chromosomes pair:

(b) In a cell that is heterozygous for an interstitial deletion, the portion of the normal chromosome that does not contain the deletion loops out when the homologous chromosomes pair:

(c) In a cell that is heterozygous for a pericentric inversion, the inverted region in one chromosome pairs with its corresponding segment in the other chromosome within a loop:

(d) In a cell that is heterozygous for a paracentric inversion, the inverted region in one chromosome pairs with its corresponding segment in the other chromosome within a loop:

(e) In a cell that is heterozygous for a reciprocal terminal translocation, chromosome segments pair to form a quadrivalent:

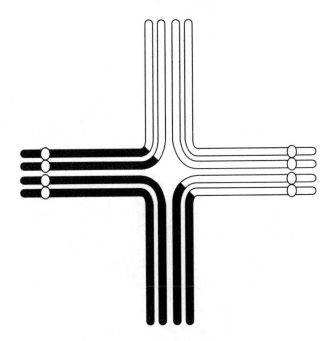

3. *(B)* In an autotetraploid, there are four copies of each homologue, any one of which may pair with another. The diploid species from which the autotetraploid arises is fertile because the homologous chromosomes in it can pair properly during meiosis. An allotetraploid, on the other hand, contains two diploid genomes, each from a separate species. There are only two copies of each homologue in an allotetraploid, so each chromosome can only pair as a bivalent with its single homologous partner. Allotetraploids arise when two related species hybridize and produce a sterile or semisterile diploid hybrid. The hybrid is sterile because the chromosomes have diverged to such an extent that they can no longer pair properly with one another during meiosis. However, if the chromosome number in the hybrid is doubled, to form an allotetraploid, each chromosome has a homologous partner with which it can pair, and fertility is restored.

4. *(D)* **(a)** Unbalanced gametes arise from crossing-over within the inversion loop of an inversion heterozygote. Because in *Drosophila* there is no crossing-over in males, none of the gametes from the male progeny will be unbalanced. **(b)** The proportion of unbalanced gametes equals the proportion of

crossover-type gametes, which can be determined from the recombination frequencies within the inversions. The female progeny are heterozygous for two inversions. The inversion in chromosome 3 spans 8 cM, so the probability of a crossover within that region is 8%, and the probability of no crossover in that region is 92%. The inversion in the X chromosome spans 14 cM, so the probability of a crossover in that region is 14%, and the probability of no crossover in that region is 86%. The two chromosomes assort independently, and any gamete that arises from a crossover in either inversion is unbalanced. There are four possible gamete types. The table below lists the four gamete types, their respective proportions, and whether the gamete type is balanced or unbalanced:

Gamete type	Proportion	Balanced or Unbalanced
No crossover in either inversion	$0.92 \times 0.86 = 0.7912$	Balanced
Crossover in chromosome 3 inversion	$0.08 \times 0.86 = 0.0688$	Unbalanced
Crossover in X chromosome inversion	$0.92 \times 0.14 = 0.1288$	Unbalanced
Crossovers in both inversions	$0.08 \times 0.14 = 0.0112$	Unbalanced

The proportion of unbalanced gametes can most easily be determined by subtracting the proportion of balanced gametes from unity: $1 - 0.7912 = 0.2088$. It can also be determined by summing the proportions of all unbalanced types: $0.0688 + 0.1288 + 0.0112 = 0.2088$ (an application of the sum rule). **(c)** Among the first-generation progeny, all of the males are hemizygous for the X chromosome without an inversion. The first generation females are all heterozygous for the X-linked inversion. When these flies intermate, half of their female progeny will be heterozygous for the X-linked inversion. Among the first generation progeny, all flies are heterozygous for the inversion on chromosome 3. When they intermate, half of their progeny will be heterozygous for the inversion on chromosome 3. Chromosome 3 and the X chromosome assort independently, so the proportion of second-generation females that should be heterozygous for both inversions is $0.5 \times 0.5 = 0.25$ (an application of the product rule).

5. *(D)* In this case, there are two ways for trisomy 21 to arise: inheritance of an extra chromosome 21 because of nondisjunction (with a probability of 0.011, from Figure 17.26), and inheritance of an extra copy of 21q on a 14q;21q translocation chromosome (with a probability of 0.02 because inheritance is from the male). Let's first determine the probability that a child will be disomic for 21q (i.e., will be balanced for 21q and thus will not have Down syndrome). The probability that a child will not inherit an extra copy of chromosome 21 from the mother is $1 - 0.011 = 0.989$. The probability that a child will not inherit an extra copy of 21q as part of a 14q;21q translocation from the father is $1 - 0.02 = 0.98$. The probability that a child will be disomic for 21q is, therefore, $0.989 \times 0.98 = 0.96922$. Initially, we can conclude that the probability of having a child with Down syndrome is $1 - 0.96922 = 0.03078$, and for practical purposes we could stop here and say that the probability is about 3%. However, for those who wish to be strictly accurate, we must consider that one possible outcome is inheritance of an extra copy of chromosome 21 from the mother and inheritance of an extra copy of 21q as part of a 14q;21q translocation from the father. The probability of this outcome is $0.011 \times 0.02 = 0.00022$. Such a zygote is tetrasomic for 21q (four copies of 21q), and the fetus that develops from it will probably not survive gestation. To obtain the actual probability of children with Down syndrome among those that survive gestation, we must adjust the probability to account for the loss of tetrasomic fetuses. The actual probability of a child with Down syndrome is $0.03078 \div (1 - 0.00022) = 0.030786773$. The difference between the adjusted probability and the unadjusted probability we calculated earlier is 0.000006773 (less than 1 per 100,000). The effect of the adjustment is negligible.

6. *(C)* Had the father of the children been heterozygous for the translocation, then the probability of all six children being heterozygous would be $0.5^6 = 0.015625$. He probably does not carry the translocation.

7. *(C)* **(a)** At least one of the parents is heterozygous for the translocation, and the other parent is homozygous or heterozygous for the translocation. **(b)** Homozygosity for a translocation causes no loss

of fertility because the two chromosomes with the translocation pair normally as a bivalent.

8. *(C)* **(a)** Look at Figure 17.30. It shows the zygotes that arise from a mating between an individual who is a Robertsonian translocation heterozygote and an individual who does not carry a translocation. Notice that of the six outcomes, only two are balanced, one with a normal karyotype and one that is a translocation heterozygote. Thus, we expect a 1:1 ratio among the balanced zygotes. The other four types of zygotes are unbalanced, and the embryos that arise from them usually do not complete gestation. **(b)** The absence of trisomic individuals is explained by the observation that most autosomal trisomies result in spontaneous abortion in humans. Although trisomic zygotes are formed from unbalanced gametes produced in translocation heterozygotes, most trisomic embryos or fetuses that arise from the zygotes do not complete gestation.

9. *(D)* **(a)** Balanced gametes arise from alternate segregations, whereas unbalanced gametes arise from adjacent segregations, as illustrated in Figure 17.21. Only those embryos or fetuses that arise from balanced gametes complete gestation. As shown in parts a and c of Figure 17.21, half of the balanced gametes carry no translocation and half carry the translocation. Thus, the theoretical frequencies are 0.5 heterozygous for a reciprocal translocation and 0.5 with a normal karyotype. **(b)** The expected number of individuals who are heterozygous for a reciprocal translocation is $95 \div 2 = 47.5$, and the expected number of individuals with a normal karyotype is also 47.5. The chi-square value is $[(49 - 47.5)^2 \div 47.5] + [(46 - 47.5)^2 \div 47.5] = 0.095$, with 1 degree of freedom. There is no evidence to reject the hypothesis that the data conform to the theoretical frequencies.

10. *(C)* In this study, based on RFLP analysis, at least 92% of the children inherited the extra copy of chromosome 21 from their mothers. Studies based on the less reliable chromosome banding technique suggested that only about 75% of children inherit the extra copy of chromosome 21 from their mothers. The studies based on RFLP analysis suggest that the frequency of inheritance of an extra chromosome from the mother is higher than the frequency indicated by studies based on chromosome banding.

11. *(D)* As diagrammed on the next page, the inversion may arise through recombination between *gene A* within the intron and copies of *gene A* that lie upstream from the *F8C* gene. The inversion may have arisen many times independently because duplicated genes can undergo recombination with one another to form the inversion. Recombination at any homologous point within the duplicated copies of *gene A* can produce an inversion that eliminates the function of the *F8C* gene.

12. *(C)* There is no homologous region between the *ABL* and *BCR* genes in which recombination could repeatedly create the same translocation. Because translocations with break points in these genes had been observed among many different people, the researchers suspected that there might be some homology between these genes that made them prone to translocation. However, the results of this study did not reveal any homology between the two genes.

13. *(C)* **(a)** Numerous species in the genus *Gossypium* have $2n = 26$ chromosomes. These species must be diploid because half of 26 is 13, which is a prime number. These species are not tetraploid, hexaploid, or octaploid because 26 divided by 4, 6, or 8 does not equal a whole number. Therefore, $x = 13$. **(b)** The species of cotton cultivated in the Old World, *G. herbacium* and *G. arboreum*, are diploids with $2n = 2x = 26$ chromosomes. The species of cotton cultivated in the New World, *G. hirsutum* and *G. barbadense*, are tetraploids with $2n = 4x = 52$ chromosomes.

14. *(C)* **(a)** The strict bivalent pairing and the resemblance of half of the chromosomes to *G. herbacium* and the other half to wild New World diploid species indicate that the New World cultivated cotton species are allotetraploids. **(b)** New World cultivated cotton probably arose from hybridization between *G. herbacium* and a wild New World diploid species. The resulting hybrid should have been sterile. However, chromosome doubling produced a fertile allotetraploid that is the ancestor of the New World species *G. hirsutum* and *G. barbadense*.

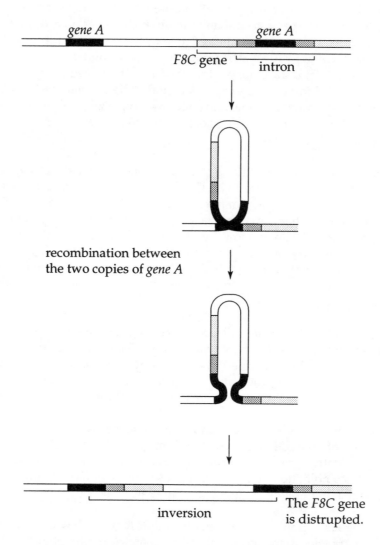

recombination between
the two copies of *gene A*

inversion   The *F8C* gene
is distrupted.

15. *(C)* Maize is diploid and bread wheat is hexaploid. Maize gametes with 9 chromosomes completely lack all of the genes on the missing chromosome; there is no complete genome in the gamete. Wheat gametes with 41 chromosomes are missing one chromosome in one of three genomes in the gamete. The genes that are missing because of the absent chromosome are present on the homeologous chromosomes in the other two genomes. The maize gametes with 9 chromosomes are missing proportionally much more genetic material than the wheat gametes with 41 chromosomes.

16. *(D)* **(a)** Sorghum and maize are both diploids with $2n = 2x = 20$. Their relationship with sugarcane is sufficiently close to permit hybridization. Therefore, it is highly likely that $x = 10$ in sugarcane, and that noble canes are octaploids ($2n = 8x = 80$). **(b)** The numbers of chromosomes are so high in sugarcane that there are at least eight copies of each chromosome and often as many as 10–12. A loss or gain of a chromosome has little effect proportionally on the amount of genetic material, and this flexibility, due to high redundancy of genetic material, probably permits fertility with various chromosome numbers.

17. *(C)* **(a)** A tetraploid arises when an unreduced triploid gamete from a triploid plant unites with a reduced monoploid gamete from a diploid plant. **(b)** A breeder can restore the triploid number by hybridizing a tetraploid plant with a diploid plant to produce all triploid offspring.

18. (C) The purpose of this question is to illustrate that one of the consequences of allopolyploidy is repetition of the same gene on homeologous chromosomes, and that gene repetition can have phenotypic consequences. We will return to the example of kernel color in wheat in Chapter 20 in a different context. For now, we can use drawings in Chapter 20 to illustrate the answer to this question. (a) The F_2 genotypic and phenotypic frequencies that arise from self-fertilization of an F_1 plant with the genotype $A^1A^2 B^1B^2 C^1C^2$ are illustrated in Figures 20.3 and 20.4 (pages 612 and 613). (b) Homeologous chromosomes in an allopolyploid are chromosomes that have a common ancestral chromosome from a common ancestral species, but the chromosomes have now diverged to the point that they no longer pair with one another when brought together in an allopolyploid. Although they have diverged from one another, homeologous chromosomes should still have many genes in common. The three genes that govern kernel color are probably copies of the same gene on three pairs of homeologous chromosomes. The inheritance patterns can be explained if each gene encodes the same product at the same level and the alleles show incomplete dominance.

19. (C) (a) and (b) The genotype of the purple-flowered plant must be $C_1c_1c_1c_1$. The four alleles may be partitioned into any two combinations of two alleles per gamete during meiosis. At the end of meiosis I, one of the cells must receive the C_1 allele and any one of the three c_1 alleles. The other cell receives the remaining two c_1 alleles. Therefore, half of the gametes will have the genotype C_1c_1, and half will have the genotype c_1c_1. When crossed with a plant that has the genotype $c_1c_1c_1c_1$, half of the progeny will have the genotype $C_1c_1c_1c_1$ and will have purple flowers, and half will have the genotype $c_1c_1c_1c_1$ and will have white flowers. (c) When a plant with the genotype $C_1c_1c_1c_1$ is self-fertilized, 1/4 of the progeny will have the genotype $C_1C_1c_1c_1$ and will have purple flowers, 1/2 will have the genotype $C_1c_1c_1c_1$ and will have purple flowers, and 1/4 will have the genotype $c_1c_1c_1c_1$ and will have white flowers. Therefore, the proportion of purple-flowered plants will be 0.75.

20. (E) The expected ratio for entry 1 is 3:1, and the chi-square calculation is $[(135 - 124.5)^2 \div 124.5] + [(31 - 41.5)^2 \div 41.5] = 3.5422$. The expected ratio for entry 2 is 3:1, and the chi-square calculation is $[(245 - 243.75)^2 \div 243.75] + [(80 - 81.25)^2 \div 81.25] = 0.0256$. For entry 3, all progeny should have purple flowers, which is exactly the observed outcome. A chi-square test is neither appropriate nor required for this entry because there is only one class into which the progeny can fall, and no degrees of freedom. The expected ratio for entry 4 is 9:7, and the chi-square calculation is $[(33 - 34.3125)^2 \div 34.3125] + [(28 - 26.6875)^2 \div 26.6875] = 0.1148$. The expected ratio for entry 5 is 35:1 (see Figure 17.11), and the chi-square calculation is $[(110 - 109.8611)^2 \div 109.8611] + [(3 - 3.1389)^2 \div 3.1389] = 0.0063$. The expected ratio for entry 6 is also 35:1, and the chi-square calculation is $[(770 - 769.0278)^2 \div 769.0278] + [(21 - 21.9722)^2 \div 21.9722] = 0.0442$. For entry 7, all progeny should have purple flowers, which is exactly the observed outcome. A chi-square test is neither appropriate nor required. The expected ratio for entry 8 could be determined with a Punnett square, which would be a rather complicated excercise. There is an easier way, however, for us to determine the expected ratio by applying the product and sum rules. Only plants that are nullisomic for c_1, nullisomic for c_2, or nullisomic for both c_1 and c_2 have white flowers. The probability that a plant will be nullisomic for c_1 but not nullisomic for c_2 is $1/36 \times 35/36 = 35/1296$. The probability that a plant will be nullisomic for c_2 but not nullisomic for c_2 is also $35/1296$. The probability that a plant will be nullisomic for both c_1 and c_2 is $(1/36)^2 = 1/1296$. Thus, the expected proportion of purple-flowered plants is $1225/1296$ and the expected proportion of white-flowered plants is $71/1296$, a ratio of 1225:71. The chi-square calculation is $[(122 - 120.9877) \div 120.9877] + [(6 - 7.0123) \div 7.0123] = 0.1546$. All of the chi-square tests have one degree of freedom and all chi-square values are below the critical value of 3.84 at the 0.05 probability level. There is no evidence to reject the hypothesis that all of the results conform to expected ratios.

21. (D) Chromosome pairing in allopolyploids is the same as in diploids, so we can answer this question as if the plant were a diploid. Among the gametes, 50% arise from alternate segregations and are bal-

anced. The probability that two balanced gametes will unite is $0.5^2 = 0.25$. Offhand, we might think that only those zygotes that arise from the union of two balanced gametes are balanced. However, notice in Figure 17.21b and c that the deletions and duplications in the unbalanced gametes that arise from adjacent segregations are reciprocal; the material deleted in half of the gametes is duplicated in the other half of the gametes. For example, the chromosomal regions that are deleted in half of the gametes that arise from adjacent-1 segregation are duplicated in the other half of the gametes that arise from adjacent-1 segregation. If reciprocal unbalanced gametes unite, the deleted and duplicated regions in the gametes compensate for one another and restore a balanced chromosome complement in the zygote. The proportion of zygotes that should arise from union of two reciprocal gametes from adjacent-1 segregation is $0.5^2 \times 0.4 = 0.1$. Thus, the proportion of zygotes that should arise from union of two reciprocal gametes from adjacent-2 segregation is $0.5^2 \times 0.1 = 0.025$. The proportion of all zygotes that are balanced is $0.25 + 0.1 + 0.025 = 0.375$, and the proportion of all zygotes that are unbalanced is $1 - 0.375 = 0.625$.

22. *(D)* **(a)**

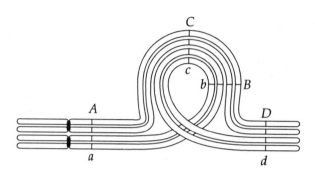

(b) To answer this question, we must remember that crossovers outside of the inverted region in an inversion heterozygote recombine the genes and do not create unbalanced gametes. All crossover-type gametes that arise from a crossover within the inverted region, however, are unbalanced and fail to produce surviving progeny. The genotypes produced from a crossover in region 1 are *Aa Bb Cc Dd* and *aa bb cc dd*. Those produced from a crossover in region 2 are *Aa bb cc dd* and *aa Bb Cc Dd*. None of the crossover-type progeny from a crossover in regions 3, 4, or 5 survive because these regions correspond to the inverted region. The genotypes produced from a crossover in region 6 are *Aa Bb Cc dd* and *aa bb cc Dd*. **(c)** The proportion of meiotic cells that are expected to have a chromatid bridge at anaphase I is twice the frequency of crossing over within the inverted region because the map distance corresponds to the frequency of crossover-type gametes and only half of the gametes that arise from a cell that undergoes a crossover in meiosis I are crossover types (see Figure 17.18e). Regions 3, 4, and 5 correspond to the inverted region, so the map distance spanned by the inverted regions is $4 + 5 + 7 = 16$ cM. We expect 32% of the meiotic cells at anaphase I to have a chromatid bridge. **(d)** All crossover-type pollen grains should abort. The proportion of crossover-type gametes equals the frequency of crossing-over within the inverted region, which equals the map distance spanned by the inverted region. Therefore, we expect 16% of the pollen grains to abort.

23. *(C)* Burnham's data indicate that the proportion of pollen abortion is about the same as the proportion of adjacent segregations (adjacent-1 and adjacent-2 segregations combined). Aborted pollen grains probably arose from adjacent segregations.

24. *(C)* Gametes with the genotypes *YY*, *Yy*, *Y*, and *y* should appear in equal frequencies.

25. *(C)* The *sr*, *e*, *ro*, and *ca* loci are within the inversion. Sturtevant's data indicate that the *st* locus is outside of the inversion. The last four classes of progeny probably arose from double crossovers within the

inversion. A single crossover within an inverted region of an inversion heterozygote causes all crossover-type gametes to be unbalanced. The phenotypic result is the near absence of crossover-type progeny for the region that corresponds to the inversion. Double crossovers within the inversion, however, do not create unbalanced crossover-type gametes, so a few double-crossover type progeny that are recombinant for genes within the inversion may appear.

Chapter 18
Extranuclear Inheritance

1. *(B)* **(a)** Human mitochondrial DNA is circular and three fragments are produced by digestion. Thus, there must be three *Eco*RI sites in human mitochondrial DNA. **(b)** The size is the sum of the sizes of the three fragments: 8050 + 7366 + 1153 = 16,569 nucleotide pairs. **(c)** The human mitochondrial genome is much smaller than plant mitochondrial genomes.

2. *(B)* There are several chloroplasts in each cell, and many copies of the chloroplastic DNA in each chloroplast, so each cell contains numerous copies of chloroplastic DNA.

3. *(B)* Each cell in a plant contains multiple plastids and mitochondria, and each cell in an animal contains multiple mitochondria, which can be thought of as populations of organelles within cells. In addition, each plastid or mitochondrion contains multiple copies of its respective genome, which can be thought of as populations of molecules within the organelles.

4. *(B)* Presumably, the large and small subunit genes were located within primitive plastids. However, at some point in the evolutionary history of plants, the small subunit gene was transferred from the plastid to the nucleus, whereas the large subunit gene remained in the plastidial genome.

5. *(B)* The mutation will probably be lost. In order for the mutation to persist into the next generation, it must be present in the germ line and ultimately be in the cytoplasm of an egg that is fertilized. There are multiple mitochondria in each cell and multiple copies of the DNA in each mitochondrion, and the mutation will be present in only a small proportion of the mitochondria. Because of somatic sorting out, the mutation is not likely to end up in the germ line.

6. *(B)* If the gene mutates in a germ-line cell, the probability of it ending up in the cytoplasm of an egg is increased when compared to a mutation in a zygote. However, many of the egg cells will probably not carry the mutation, so the probability of the mutation persisting into the next generation is low.

7. *(C)* **(a)** The seed coat is composed of maternal tissue and, therefore, displays the phenotype of the maternal parent. The cotyledons (internal parts of the seed) are composed of embryonic tissue and, therefore, display the phenotype of the embryo. **(b)** Seed coat color, seed color, and seed shape are all inherited in a Mendelian fashion and adhere to the principles of segregation, independent assortment, and parental equivalence.

8. *(D)* Several experiments can provide the information needed to determine the pattern of inheritance. Some of the small-bodied offspring should be mated with each other, some of the small-bodied female offspring should be mated with wild-type males, and some of the small-bodied male offspring should be mated with wild-type females. **(a)** If the small-body phenotype is caused by an autosomal dominant allele, then the original female must have been homozygous for the allele and all of her offspring would be heterozygous and small bodied. Her offspring that are mated with each other should produce 3/4 small-bodied and 1/4 wild-type progeny. The female offspring mated with wild-type males should produce 1/2 small-bodied and 1/2 wild-type progeny. The same should be true for the male offspring mated with wild-type females. **(b)** If the small-body phenotype is caused by an X-linked dominant allele, then the original female must have been homozygous for the allele. All of her female offspring would be heterozygous and all of her male offspring hemizygous for the allele. Her offspring that are mated with each other should produce all small-bodied female progeny and 1/2 small-bodied, 1/2 wild-type male progeny. The females mated with wild-type males should produce 1/2 small-bodied and 1/2 wild-type progeny among both males and females. The males mated with wild-type females should produce all wild-type male progeny and 1/2 small-bodied, 1/2 wild-type female progeny. **(c)** and **(d)** If the small-body phenotype is caused by a mitochondrial allele or is influenced by maternal effect, then

the offspring that are mated with each other should produce all small-bodied progeny. The females mated with wild-type males should produce all small-bodied progeny. The males mated with wild-type females should produce all wild-type progeny. Mitochondrial inheritance and maternal effect can be distinguished by allowing the progeny of each cross to intermate. If the allele is mitochondrial, the pattern of strict uniparental maternal inheritance of the small-bodied phenotype will persist into the next generation. If it is a maternal effect, then Mendelian ratios should appear in the next generation.

9. *(D)* The best way to determine the mode of inheritance of male sterility in the male-sterile plant is to pollinate it with a plant that is fully homozygous at all loci. Any male-fertile progeny should be crossed reciprocally with plants of many different nuclear genotypes. Any male-sterile progeny should be pollinated with pollen from many different types of fully homozygous plants. If all progeny of these crosses are male fertile, the plants should then be self-fertilized. The reason for using many different genotypes is to increase the probability of detecting restorer alleles should the inheritance turn out to be cytoplasmic-nuclear. If all progeny are male sterile, the inheritance of male sterility is probably cytoplasmic only. If the inheritance of male sterility is nuclear only, typical Mendelian patterns of 3:1 or 1:1 ratios should appear among the second- or third-generation progeny of the reciprocally crossed male-fertile plants, and the patterns should not differ in the progeny of reciprocal crosses. If the inheritance of male sterility is cytoplasmic-nuclear, typical Mendelian patterns of 3:1 or 1:1 ratios should appear among the second- or third-generation progeny of the reciprocally crossed male-fertile plants, and only one of a pair of reciprocal crosses should produce any male-sterile progeny.

10. *(C)* **(a)** The female (male-sterile) parent must be *rr*, and the male is *Rr*. Half the progeny will be *rr* and will be male sterile. The other half will be *Rr* and will be male fertile. **(b)** None will fail to produce seed because half of the plants will be male fertile and will produce pollen that will pollinate both the male-sterile and the male-fertile plants.

11. *(C)* Mitochondrial somatic segregation is a somewhat random process, so the relative proportions of two mitochondrial types may vary among tissues and organs. The degree of heteroplasmy varies among heteroplasmic cells, and changes from one cell generation to the next. The number of mitochondria of a particular type in a cell can determine to what degree characteristics influenced by mitochondrial genes are expressed.

12. *(C)* **(a)** The observation that the proportion of mutant mitochondrial DNA in the children of one female varied from 0% to nearly 100% suggests that mitochondria can segregate within a few cell generations in the human germ line. **(b)** People must be nearly homoplasmic for the mutant allele for the symptoms of LHON to appear. Only one sibling (the one with > 95% mutant mitochondrial DNA) was close to being homoplasmic and thus was the only one with symptoms of LHON.

13. *(C)* The proportion of mitochondria present in the cytoplasm of an ovum is determined largely by the proportion in the cytoplasm of the cells in the germ line that undergo meiosis. A mother with > 95% mutant mitochondrial DNA is nearly (or perhaps fully) homoplasmic and there is little opportunity for the proportion of mitochondria to change significantly through sorting out. Therefore, all of her children are expected to inherit a very high proportion of mutant mitochondrial DNA. In fact, in this example, it is highly likely that both the mother and her children were fully homoplasmic for the mutant mitochondrial DNA, in which case there is no opportunity for sorting out and all of her children should have LHON.

14. *(C)* Because the female parent has a sinistral phenotype itself, its maternal parent must have had the genotype *ss*, and the female parent inherited an *s* allele from this parent. Because the female parent had all dextral progeny, it must have inherited an *S* allele from its paternal parent. Its genotype is therefore *Ss*. Because the second-generation progeny segregate in a 1:1 ratio, the male parent's genotype must be *ss*.

15. *(D)* **(a)** Because the restriction fragment patterns of the regenerated plants were identical to those of the paternal parent, each of the regenerated plants must have inherited that pattern through paternal transmission of plastids. We can rule out mutation as the cause of the streptomycin resistance because there were 44 plants that produced streptomycin-resistant cells. For mutation to cause restriction fragment patterns that are identical to the pattern in the paternal parent, the same mutations must have occurred independently in the plastidial DNA of all 44 plants, an event that is extremely unlikely. **(b)** The observations that of the 6800 seedlings tested, all were susceptible to streptomycin, and that cells from only 44 of the additional 1500 seedlings produced streptomycin-resistant callus demonstrate that plastidial inheritance is biparental but almost entirely maternal. Paternal plastid transmission probably represents a very small proportion of plastidial inheritance, and most somatic cells become homoplasmic for maternal plastids through sorting out. **(c)** Had the cells been heteroplasmic, their restriction fragment patterns would have been the superimposed patterns of their two parents. The observation that each regenerated plant had only the paternal patterns indicates that the plants are homoplasmic for paternal plastidial DNA.

16. *(C)* In each of the studies, the same mutation is always associated with both phenotypes (male sterility and susceptibility to the toxin). The collective results of these studies indicate that males sterility and susceptibility to the toxin are caused by the same mutant allele, an example of mitochondrial pleiotropy.

17. *(C)* **(a)** Gymnosperms tend to inherit plastids in a uniparental-paternal fashion. Loblolly pine and coast redwood are both coniferous species and are therefore gymnosperms. **(b)** These results indicate that mitochondrial inheritance patterns may vary among species of gymnosperms.

18. *(D)* **(a)** The founder female was heteroplasmic for the two types of mitochondria. The restriction fragments patterns of the two types are superimposed when the mitochondrial DNA of a heteroplasmic individual is examined, resulting in three rather than two fragments in the mixed mitochondrial DNA. **(b)** The best explanation for the variation of the two fragments is mitochondrial sorting out. As the proportion of one mitochondrial type increases through sorting out, the other declines. If selection does not favor one type over the other, then flies with different proportions of both types should appear.

19. *(C)* A proportion of paternal mitochondrial DNA of 0.1% is equal to 1 paternal molecule per 1,000 molecules. The proportion of paternal mitochondrial DNA is mouse zygotes is about 1 per 100,000, which is two orders of magnitude less than the proportion in *Drosophila*.

20. *(C)* If paternal transmission of organellar DNA represent a very small fraction of the total transmission, then zygotes should have very small proportions of paternal DNA in them. Most of the somatic cells that arise from such a zygote will be homoplasmic for maternal mitochondrial DNA because of sorting out. Researchers typically examine DNA from a small proportion of somatic cells in each individual, and from a small number of progeny from only a few matings. Most of the somatic cells that researchers examine have already undergone sorting out and are homoplasmic, usually for maternal organelles. Unless very large samples of individuals (and large samples of cells within each individual) are examined, the probabilities of detecting low frequencies of paternal transmission of organelles are very low. The conclusion that organellar inheritance is purely uniparental-maternal in a species may not be entirely correct unless it can be demonstrated that there are no paternal organelles in zygotes.

21. *(D)* **(a)** Inheritance is predominantly maternal, but there is significant biparental inheritance in many of the crosses. **(b)** There is substantial evidence that plastidial genotype has an effect on inheritance throughout the entire data set. For example, in the first four sets of reciprocal crosses, plastidial inheritance is predominantly uniparental-maternal when the green type is the maternal parent, but significant proportions of the progeny display biparental inheritance when the mutant types are the maternal parent. **(c)** In general, maternal transmission predominates in reciprocal crosses whether or not the maternal plastids are mutant.

Chapter 19
Population Genetics

Important note: When we are conducting calculations that require us to use exponents (such as squaring), it is important to avoid rounding until we have reached the end of all calculations and have a final answer. If we use rounded values for calculations with exponents, the exponents tend to magnify rounding discrepancies substantially. In the solutions for this chapter, we have rounded the written numbers to four decimal places to avoid writing long strings of numbers beyond the decimal point, but we have conducted the calculations with the unrounded numbers. For this reason, some of our calculations will differ from yours if you use the rounded numbers in the calculation.

1. *(C)* Of the 76 rabbits in the parental generation, 60 are homozygous CC and 16 are homozygous cc. The frequency of the C allele is $p = 60 \div 76 = 0.7895$, and the frequency of the c allele is $q = 16 \div 76 = 0.2105$. With random mating, Hardy-Weinberg equilibrium is established in one generation, and the allele frequencies in the progeny are the same as in the parents. **(a)** The proportion of albino (cc) progeny is $q^2 = 0.0443$. **(b)** The proportion of agouti (gray) progeny (CC and Cc) is $p^2 + 2pq = 0.9557$. **(c)** The proportion of progeny that are heterozygous Cc is $2pq = 0.3324$.

2. *(B)* There are four times as many agouti (gray) rabbits as albino (white) rabbits, so the proportion of agouti rabbits is 0.8 and the proportion of albino rabbits is 0.2. The frequency of the c allele is $q = \sqrt{0.1} = 0.4472$.

3. *(C)* The initial frequency of the c allele is $q_0 = \sqrt{0.1} = 0.3162$. The frequency of the c allele after selection is $q_t = \sqrt{0.01} = 0.1$. The number of generations required to reduce the allele frequency from 0.1 to 0.01 is $t = (1 \div 0.1) - (1 \div 0.3162) = 6.8377$, which is about 7 generations.

4. *(D)* Initially, $q^2 = 0.1$, so the frequency of the c allele is $q_0 = \sqrt{0.1} = 0.3162$, and the frequency of the C allele is $p_0 = 1 - 0.3162 = 0.6838$. The frequency of the c allele after selection is $q_t = \sqrt{0.2} = 0.4472$, and the frequency of the C allele is $p_t = 1 - 0.4472 = 0.5528$. The selection coefficient is $s = 0.3$. To solve the problem, we use equation 19.15 to determine the change in p with each generation, and repeat the calculations for each generation until we reach $q_t = 0.4472$. In the first generation of selection, $\Delta p = [-0.3(0.6838)(0.1)] \div [1 - 0.3 + 0.3(0.1)] = -0.0281$. The frequency of the c allele after 1 generation of selection is $0.3162 + 0.0281 = 0.3443$. In the second generation of selection, $\Delta p = [-0.3(0.6557)(0.3443^2)] \div [1 - 0.3 + 0.3(0.3443^2)] = -0.0317$. The frequency of the c allele after 2 generations of selection is $0.3443 + 0.0317 = 0.3760$. In the third generation of selection, $\Delta p = [-0.3(0.6240)(0.3760^2)] \div [1 - 0.3 + 0.3(0.3760^2)] = -0.0356$. The frequency of the c allele after 3 generations of selection is $0.3760 + 0.0356 = 0.4116$. In the fourth generation of selection, $\Delta p = [-0.3 (0.5884)(0.4116^2)] \div [1 - 0.3 + 0.3(0.4116^2)] = -0.0398$. The frequency of the c allele after 4 generations of selection is $0.4116 + 0.0398 = 0.4515$, which exceeds the target frequency of $q_t = 0.4472$. A total of 4 generations of selection are required.

5. *(B)* Several generations of mating are required to attain Hardy-Weinberg equilibrium for X-linked alleles because X chromosomes are not transmitted equally to males and females. The frequencies of X-linked alleles oscillate between males and females from one generation to the next until equilibrium is reached.

6. *(C)* Selection that favors an allele with partial dominance is more effective than selection that favors an allele with complete dominance because selection acts on the phenotype. Selection distinguishes an individual that is homozygous for an allele with partial dominance from one that is heterozygous for that allele. Homozygotes and heterozygotes are phenotypically indistinguishable when an allele has

complete dominance, so selection favors the two genotypes equally, and recessive alleles are not readily eliminated by selection. This is evident when comparing equation 19.13 (which describes selection that favors fully dominant alleles) with equation 19.17 (which describes selection that favors alleles with no dominance). Suppose that $q = 0.2$, $p = 0.8$, and $s = 1$. If we substitute these values into equation 19.13, $\Delta q = -0.8(0.2^2) \div (1 - 0.2^2) = -0.0333$. If, instead, we substitute these values into equation 19.17, $\Delta q = -0.5(0.8)(0.2) \div (1 - 0.2) = -0.1000$. The change in allele frequency due to selection is greater with equation 19.17 than with equation 19.13.

7. (C) The frequency of the ABO*O allele is $r = \sqrt{0.36} = 0.6$. If we use the logic applied in Example 19.2, the frequency of the ABO*B allele can be calculated as $q = 1 - \sqrt{0.45 + 0.36} = 0.1$. We can now determine the frequency of the ABO*A allele by subtraction: $p = 1 - 0.1 - 0.6 = 0.3$. The frequency of type AB blood is $2pq = 2(0.3)(0.1) = 0.06 = 6\%$. The frequency of type B blood is $q^2 + 2qr = 0.1^2 + 2(0.1)(0.6) = 0.13 = 13\%$.

8. (C) (a) Before selection $q_0 = \sqrt{1 \div 5000} = 0.0141$. After selection, $q_t = \sqrt{1 \div 10000} = 0.01$. To solve this problem, we use Equation 19.14: $t = (1 \div 0.01) + (1 \div 0.0141) = 29.2893$. About 29 generations are required. (b) The number of years required is 29.2893 X 25 = 732.2330, more than 7 centuries. (c) In this example, the efficacy of restricted reproduction would be negligible unless it were practiced for centuries.

9. (D) The values of p and q can be determined directly from the data. Among the males, the frequency of the o allele is $99 \div (99 + 28) = 0.7795$, and the frequency of the O allele is $28 \div (99 + 28) = 0.2205$. Among the females, the frequency of the o allele is $[102 + 0.5(48)] \div (102 + 4 + 48) = 0.8182$, and the frequency of the O allele is $[4 + 0.5(48)] \div (102 + 4 + 48) = 0.1818$. To determine the frequency of an allele in the overall population, we multiply the frequency of the allele in females by the proportion of females in the population and add that to the frequency of the allele in males multiplied by the proportion of males in the population (a weighted average). The frequency of the o allele in the population is $p = [154(0.8182) \div 281] + [127(0.7795) \div 281] = 0.8007$. The frequency of the O allele in the population is $q = [154(0.1818) \div 281] + [127(0.2205) \div 281] = 0.1993$. Under the assumption of Hardy-Weinberg equilibrium, the expected number of black females is $154(0.8007^2) = 98.7355$, the expected number of orange females is $154(0.1993^2) = 6.1162$, and the expected number of tortoiseshell females is $154(2)(0.8007)(0.1993) = 49.1483$. The expected number of black males is $127(0.8007) = 101.6904$, and the expected number of orange males is $127(0.1993) = 25.3096$. There should be no tortoiseshell males, as was observed. A class in which no individuals are expected does not enter into the chi-square calculations (if it were included, it would require division by zero). The table below shows the chi-square calculation:

Phenotype	O	E	$(O - E)^2/E$
Black females	102	98.7355	0.1079
Orange females	4	6.1162	0.7322
Tortoiseshell females	48	49.1483	0.0268
Black males	99	101.6904	0.0712
Orange males	28	25.3096	0.2860
Totals	281	281.0000	1.2242

The degrees of freedom is the number of phenotypic classes minus the number of alleles, which in this case is 5 – 2 = 3. The chi-square value of 1.2242 is below the critical value of 7.82 for a probability level of 0.05 with 3 degrees of freedom. There is no evidence to reject the hypothesis that the population is in

Hardy-Weinberg equilibrium.

10. (C) The frequency of the HBB*S allele is $q = [0.5(89) + 9] \div 287 = 0.1864$, and the frequency of the HBB*A allele is $p = [0.5(89) + 189] \div 287 = 0.8136$. The expected number of individuals with the genotype HBB*A/*A is $287(0.8136^2) = 189.9730$. The expected number of individuals with the genotype HBB*A/*S is $287(2)(0.8136)(0.1864) = 87.0540$. The expected number of individuals with the genotype HBB*S/*S is $287(0.1864^2) = 9.9730$. The chi-square value is $[(189 - 189.9730)^2 \div 189.9730)] + [(89 - 87.0540)^2 \div 87.0540)] + [(9 - 9.9730)^2 \div 9.9730)] = 0.1434$ with 1 degree of freedom, which is well below the critical value of 3.84 at a probability level of 0.05. There is no evidence to reject the hypothesis that the population is in Hardy-Weinberg equilibrium.

11. (C) The frequency of the HBB*S allele is $q = [0.5(135) + 4] \div 840 = 0.0851$, and the frequency of the HBB*A allele is $p = [0.5(135) + 701] \div 840 = 0.9149$. The expected number of individuals with the genotype HBB*A/*A is $840(0.9149^2) = 703.0860$. The expected number of individuals with the genotype HBB*A/*S is $840(2)(0.9149)(0.0851) = 130.8280$. The expected number of individuals with the genotype HBB*S/*S is $840(0.0851^2) = 6.0860$. The chi-square value is $[(701 - 703.0860)^2 \div 703.0860)] + [(135 - 130.8280)^2 \div 130.8280)] + [(4 - 6.0860)^2 \div 6.0860)] = 0.8542$, with 1 degree of freedom, which is well below the critical value of 3.84 at a probability level of 0.05. There is no evidence to reject the hypothesis that the population is in Hardy-Weinberg equilibrium.

12. (C) The frequency of the HBB*S allele is $q = [0.5(114) + 2] \div 599 = 0.0985$, and the frequency of the HBB*A allele is $p = [0.5(114) + 483] \div 599 = 0.9015$. The expected number of individuals with the genotype HBB*A/*A is $599(0.9015^2) = 486.8114$. The expected number of individuals with the genotype HBB*A/*S is $599(2)(0.9015)(0.0985) = 106.3773$. The expected number of individuals with the genotype HBB*S/*S is $599(0.0985^2) = 5.8114$. The chi-square value is $[(483 - 486.8114)^2 \div 486.8114)] + [(114 - 106.3773)^2 \div 106.3773)] + [(2 - 5.8114)^2 \div 5.8114)] = 3.0757$ with 1 degree of freedom, which is below the critical value of 3.84 at a probability level of 0.05. There is no evidence to reject the hypothesis that the population is in Hardy-Weinberg equilibrium.

13. (C) With random mating, Hardy-Weinberg equilibrium is established in one generation. Thus, regardless of the allele distribution in an adult population, the infants in the next generation should be in Hardy-Weinberg equilibrium if there is random mating with respect to genotype. Among adults, however, selection may have altered the frequencies by favoring heterozygotes and disfavoring homozygotes.

14. (C) (a) The frequency of the MN*M allele is $[0.5(242) + 119] \div 500 = 0.48$, and the frequency of the MN*N allele is $[0.5(242) + 139] \div 500 = 0.52$. (b) The expected number of individuals with type M blood is $500(0.48^2) = 115.2$. The expected number of individuals with type MN blood is $500(2)(0.48)(0.52) = 249.6$. The expected number of individuals with type N blood is $500(0.52^2) = 135.2$. The chi-square value is $[(119 - 115.2)^2 \div 115.2)] + [(242 - 249.6)^2 \div 249.6)] + [(139 - 135.2)^2 \div 135.2)] = 0.4636$, with 1 degree of freedom, which is well below the critical value of 3.84 at a probability level of 0.05. There is no evidence to reject the hypothesis that the population is in Hardy-Weinberg equilibrium.

15. (C) (a) The frequency of the MN*M allele is $[0.5(1424) + 810] \div 2858 = 0.5325$, and the frequency of the MN*N allele is $[0.5(1424) + 624] \div 2858 = 0.4675$. (b) The expected number of individuals with type M blood is $2858(0.5325^2) = 810.5262$. The expected number of individuals with type MN blood is $2858(2)(0.5325)(0.4675) = 1422.9475$. The expected number of individuals with type N blood is $2858(0.4675^2) = 624.5262$. The chi-square value is $[(810 - 810.5262)^2 \div 810.5262)] + [(1424 - 1422.9475)^2 \div 1422.9475)] + [(624 - 624.5262)^2 \div 624.5262)] = 0.0016$, with 1 degree of freedom, which is well below the

critical value of 3.84 at a probability level of 0.05. There is no evidence to reject the hypothesis that the population is in Hardy-Weinberg equilibrium.

16. (D) (a) The uncorrected frequency of the ABO*A allele is $p = 1 - \sqrt{(297 + 1503) \div 3459} = 0.2786$. The uncorrected frequency of the ABO*B allele is $q = 1 - \sqrt{(1546 + 1503) \div 3459} = 0.0611$. The frequency of the ABO*O allele is $r = \sqrt{1503 \div 3459} = 0.6592$. The deviation from unity for these values is $1 - (0.2786 + 0.0611 + 0.6592) = 0.0011$. The corrected frequency of the ABO*A allele is $p_c = 0.2786[1 + 0.5(0.0011)] = 0.2788$. The corrected frequency of the ABO*B allele is $q_c = 0.0611[1 + 0.5(0.0011)] = 0.0612$. The corrected frequency of the ABO*O allele is $r_c = [0.6592 + 0.5(-0.0011)][1 + 0.5(-0.0011)] = 0.6601$. (b) The expected number of people with type A blood is $3459[0.2788^2 + 2(0.2788)(0.6601)] = 1541.7732$; with type B blood, $3459[0.0612^2 + 2(0.0612)(0.6601)] = 292.4088$; with type AB blood, $3459(2)(0.2788)(0.0612) = 118.0258$, and with type O blood, $3459(0.6601^2) = 1507.0146$. The chi-square calculation is $[(1546 - 1541.7732)^2 \div 1541.7732] + [(297 - 292.4088)^2 \div 292.4088] + [(113 - 118.0258)^2 \div 118.0258] + [(1503 - 1507.0146)^2 \div 1507.0146] = 0.3084$, with 1 degree of freedom, which is well below the critical value of 3.84 at a probability level of 0.05. There is no evidence to reject the hypothesis that the population is in Hardy-Weinberg equilibrium.

17. (C) If we assume that red-green colorblindness is due to a single X-linked allele (an assumption that is incorrect, as we will see in the answer to the next question), we can determine the allele frequency directly from the males. It is $q = 725 \div 9049 = 0.0801$. Now we can test the females for Hardy-Weinberg equilibrium. The expected number of females with red-green color blindness is $9072(0.0801^2) = 58.2342$. The expected number of females without red-green colorblindness is $9072 - 58.2342 = 9013.7658$. The chi-square value is $[(40 - 58.2342)^2 \div 58.2342] + [(9032 - 9013.7658)^2 \div 9013.7658] = 5.7463$, with 1 degree of freedom. Notice that in this case we did not derive the expected frequencies from the data being tested, so the number of degrees of freedom is calculated as one less than the number of phenotypic classes. The chi-square value exceeds the critical value of 3.84 at $P = 0.05$. The deviation is significant, so we reject the hypothesis that the population is in Hardy-Weinberg equilibrium.

18. (D) (a) For the deuteranopia allele (an X-linked recessive allele), the allele frequency can be determined directly from the males. It is $q = 551 \div 9049 = 0.0609$. The expected number of females with deuteranopia is $9072(0.0609^2) = 33.6361$. The expected number of females without deuteranopia is $9072 - 33.6361 = 9038.3639$. The chi-square value is $[(37 - 33.6361)^2 \div 33.6361] + [(9035 - 9038.3639)^2 \div 9038.3639] = 0.3377$, with 1 degree of freedom, which is substantially less than the critical value of 3.84 at $P = 0.05$. The deviation is not significant, so we do not reject the hypothesis that the population is in Hardy-Weinberg equilibrium.

For the protanopia allele (a recessive X-linked allele at a different locus than the deuteranopia allele), the allele frequency can also be determined directly from the males. It is $q = 174/9049 = 0.0192$. The expected number of females with protanopia is $9072(0.0192^2) = 3.3543$. The expected number of females without protanopia is $9072 - 3.3543 = 9068.6457$. The chi-square value is $[(3 - 3.3543)^2 \div 3.3543] + [(9069 - 9068.6457)^2 \div 9068.6457] = 0.0374$, with 1 degree of freedom, which is substantially less than the critical value of 3.84 at $P = 0.05$. The deviation is not significant, so we do not reject the hypothesis that the population is in Hardy-Weinberg equilibrium.

(b) The apparent deviation from Hardy-Weinberg equilibrium determined in the answer to the question 17 is actually due to superimposed equilibria for two X-linked alleles at different loci. When each allele is examined separately, however, it is evident that the population is in Hardy-Weinberg equilibrium for each of them.

19. *(B)* Equation 19.22 applies only when an equilibrium between mutation and selection has been reached. Because selection against a recessive allele is very ineffective when the allele is at a low frequency, we cannot always assume that an equilibrium between mutation and selection has been reached.

20. *(C)* The size of the population that became fixed for the mutant b allele was 10 mating individuals in each generation. In populations with such a small size, the change in allele frequency due to random genetic drift can be quite high. Even though selection favored the b^+ allele, its frequency changed dramatically from one generation to the next. In one of the populations of 10 mating individuals, the frequency of the b^+ allele reached zero because of drift, even though selection favored the allele. In this population, the b allele was then fixed, and no further change in allele frequency was possible.

21. *(E)* There is an error in this problem in the textbook's first printing. The allele in question is favored by selection, and equations 19.13 and 19.17, which are the two pertinent equations for solving this problem, represent the allele favored by selection as p. In every place where q is mentioned in the question, it should be changed to p. (This correction has been made in subsequent printings of the book.)

We calculate the average value of Δp per generation as $(p_t - p_0) \div t$, where p_t is the value of p after t generations, p_0 is the value of p at the beginning of the experiment, and t is the number of generations in the experiment. In this case, $t = 20$ and $p_0 = 0.5$ in all experiments. The question provides the values of p_t for each experiment. Notice that the values are all higher than 0.5, so q represents the allele favored by selection. The average values of Δp are as follows:

Experiment	Average Value of Δp
$N = 10$	0.0176
$N = 20$	0.0141
$N = 50$	0.0156
$N = 100$	0.0184

We must estimate s, rather than calculate it exactly, for each experiment because some of the information required to calculate s comes from the graphs rather than directly from numerical data given in the problem. There are several methods that estimate s, and each provides a slightly different answer, so your answer may differ somewhat from the one we have calculated here. The equation for calculating s when $h = 0$ is derived from equation 19.13. Equation 19.13 determines the value of Δq when q represents the frequency of the recessive allele disfavored by selection, which is the reason for the negative sign in the numerator. Under this circumstance, Δq will always be a negative number and Δp will always be the same value as Δq, but as a positive value. Thus, we modify equation 19.13 by dropping the negative sign, and substituting Δp for Δq:

$$\Delta p = \frac{spq^2}{1 - spq^2}$$

We then rearrange the equation to solve for s:

$$s = \frac{\Delta p}{pq^2 + \Delta pq^2}$$

The equation for calculating s when $h = 1/2$ is derived from equation 19.17. We likewise modify this equation by dropping the negative sign and substituting Δp for Δq:

$$\Delta p = \frac{\frac{1}{2}spq}{1 - sq}$$

We then rearrange the equation to solve for s:

$$s = \frac{\Delta p}{\Delta pq + \frac{1}{2}pq}$$

The value of Δp varies somewhat in each generation throughout selection experiments. As illustrated in Figures 19.8 and 19.9, it is highest at the beginning of the experiment and lowest toward the end. The response to selection illustrated in the graphs in Figure 19.12 is nearly linear, so we expect to encounter the average value of Δp about halfway through the experiment, and we expect the value of p at that point to be close to the midpoint between p_0 and p_t. (Note that we are justified in making this approximation only when the response to selection is linear or nearly linear.) Once we have estimated the value of p at generation 10, we can use the equations we derived above to calculate s. The table below shows the estimated values of s for each experiment when $h = 0$ and when $h = 1/2$:

Experiment	Value of s When $h = 0$	Value of s When $h = 1/2$
$N = 10$	0.24	0.15
$N = 20$	0.17	0.12
$N = 50$	0.20	0.13
$N = 100$	0.26	0.16

Notice that the value of s is substantially higher if $h = 0$ than if $h = 1/2$, which indicates that selection is more efficient when $h = 1/2$ than when $h = 0$. We can calculate the predicted values of p_t with these values of s using the modified versions of Equations 19.13 and 19.17 that we derived above, beginning with $p_0 = 0.5$ and carrying the calculations through 20 generations. This is a rather tedious procedure to do with a simple calculator, but can be done quickly with a computer spreadsheet or a programmable calculator. The predicted and observed values of p_t after 20 generations are as follows:

Experiment	Value of p_t When $h = 0$	Value of p_t When $h = 1/2$	Observed Value of p_t
$N = 10$	0.821	0.832	0.852
$N = 20$	0.771	0.780	0.781
$N = 50$	0.795	0.798	0.811
$N = 100$	0.832	0.847	0.867

The predicted values all slightly underestimate the observed value, because the response to selection deviates slightly from being linear. To determine which value of h most closely corresponds to the observed data, we can generate theoretical response curves on the graph and compare them with the observed responses. The $N = 100$ experiment is the best experiment with which to make such a comparison because the effect of drift is least in this experiment. The graphs below show theoretical response curves for $h = 0$, $s = 0.26$ and $h = 1/2$, $s = 0.16$ superimposed on the observed data for the $N = 100$ experiment.

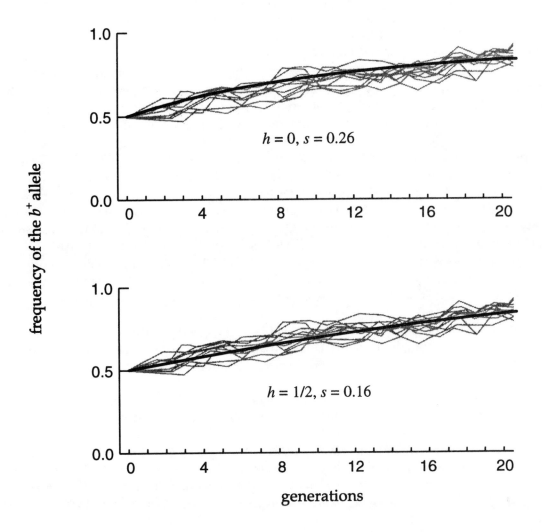

The curve for $h = 1/2$, $s = 0.16$ corresponds better with the data than the curve for $h = 0$, $s = 0.26$. The heterozygotes are phenotypically distinguishable from both homozygotes, so we do not expect h to equal zero, and comparison of the data with the theoretical response curves confirms this expectation.

22. *(D)* Because the original allele frequencies were both 0.5, we expect equal numbers of populations to become fixed for the two alleles if selection has no effect. A significant deviation from equality indicates that selection may have an effect. A total of 30 populations became fixed for the bw^1 allele and 28 became fixed for the bw^{75} allele. We can use a chi-square test to determine whether the number of populations fixed for one allele differs significantly from the number of populations fixed for the other allele. The chi-square value is $[(30 − 29)^2 ÷ 29] + [(28 − 29)^2 ÷ 29] = 0.0690$, with 1 degree of freedom, which is not significant. There is no evidence that selection had any effect in this experiment.

23. *(E)* **(a)** For experiment 22, the frequency of the ST chromosome is $[57 + 0.5(169)] ÷ 255 = 0.5549$, and the frequency of the CH chromosome is $[29 + 0.5(169)] ÷ 255 = 0.4451$. For experiment 23, the frequency of the ST chromosome is $[80 + 0.5(196)] ÷ 334 = 0.5329$, and the frequency of the CH chromosome is [58

+ 0.5(196)] ÷ 334 = 0.4671. For experiment 22, the expected number of flies with the ST/ST genotype is 255(0.5549^2) = 78.5186; with the ST/CH genotype, 255(2)(0.5549)(0.4451) = 125.9627; and with the CH/CH genotype, 255(0.4451^2) = 50.5186. For experiment 23, the expected number of flies with the ST/ST genotype is 334(0.5329^2) = 94.8623; with the ST/CH genotype, 334(2)(0.5329)(0.4671) = 166.2754; and with the CH/CH genotype, 334(0.4671^2) = 72.8623. **(b)** In the observed results, heterozygotes are more frequent and homozygotes are less frequent than expected. **(c)** For experiment 22, we divide the observed frequency of each genotype by its expected frequency. For the ST/ST genotype, 0.2235 ÷ 0.3079 = 0.7259; for the ST/CH genotype, 0.6627 ÷ 0.4940 = 1.3417; and for the CH/CH genotype, 0.1137 ÷ 0.1981 = 0.5740. For the ST/CH genotype, the relative fitness value is $w = 1$. For the ST/ST genotype, the relative fitness value is $w = 0.7259 ÷ 1.3417 = 0.5411$ and $t = 1 - 0.5411 = 0.4589$. For the CH/CH genotype, the relative fitness value is $w = 0.5740 ÷ 1.3417 = 0.4279$ and $s = 1 - 0.4279 = 0.5721$. For experiment 23, we divide the observed frequency of each genotype by its expected frequency. For the ST/ST genotype, 0.2395 ÷ 0.2840 = 0.8433; for the ST/CH genotype, 0.5868 ÷ 0.4978 = 1.1788; and for the CH/CH genotype, 0.1737 ÷ 0.2182 = 0.7960. For the ST/CH genotype, the relative fitness value is $w = 1$. For the ST/ST genotype, the relative fitness value is $w = 0.8433 ÷ 1.1788 = 0.7154$ and $t = 1 - 0.7154 = 0.2846$. For the CH/CH genotype, the relative fitness value is $w = 0.7960 ÷ 1.1788 = 0.6753$ and $s = 1 - 0.6753 = 0.3247$. **(d)** Selection favors heterozygotes over homozygotes. This observation runs against theory because an inversion heterozygote should have reduced fertility when compared to homozygotes. The higher fitness of heterozygotes is evident in these experiments but cannot be readily explained.

24. *(E)* **(a)** Graphs of the four experiments are shown on the next page. **(b)** When selection favors heterozygotes, we expect an equilibrium to be reached at a particular chromosome frequency. Once the equilibrium has been reached, the chromosome frequency should remain essentially the same from that point on. When the results of the four experiments are examined together, it appears that an equilibrium is reached at a frequency of approximately 0.8 for the ST chromosome. **(c)** Differences in the response curves among the four experiments and deviations from smooth curves are evidence of drift.

25. *(D)* **(a)** The frequency of the MN*M allele is p = [10354 + 0.5(16822)] ÷ 34309 = 0.5469, and the frequency of the MN*N allele is q = [7133 + 0.5(16822)] ÷ 34309 = 0.4531. **(b)** The expected allele frequencies are the same as the observed allele frequencies. The expected number of individuals for the MN*M/*M genotype is 34309(0.5469^2) = 10263.3485; for the MN*M/*N genotype, 34309(2)(0.5469)(0.4531) = 17003.3029; and for the MN*N/*N genotype, 34309(0.4531^2) = 7042.3485. **(c)** The chi-square value is [(10354 − 10263.3485)^2 ÷ 10263.3485] + [(16822 − 17003.3029)^2 ÷ 17003.3029] + [(7133 − 7042.3485)^2 ÷ 7042.3485] = 3.9008, with 1 degree of freedom. This value is significant at $P = 0.05$, so we reject the hypothesis that the data conform to Hardy-Weinberg equilibrium.

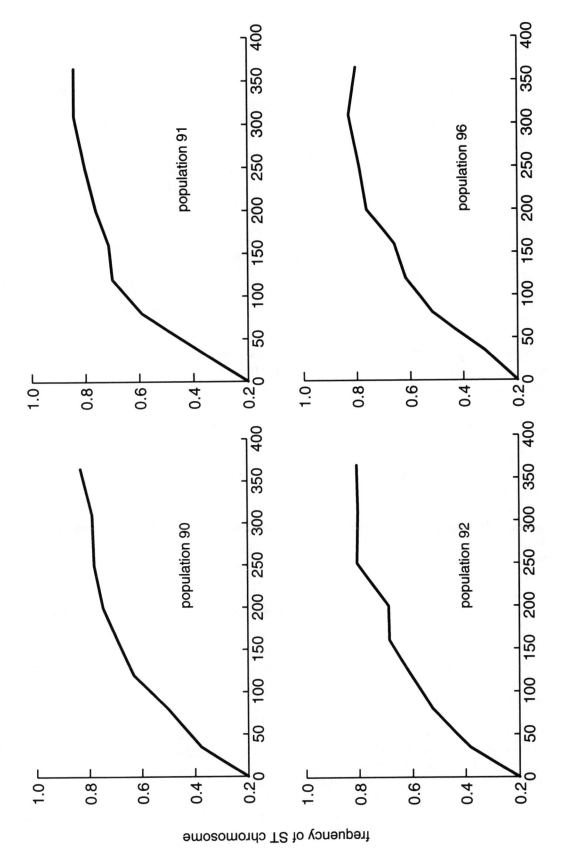

Information for problem 24

frequency of ST chromosome

days

population 90

population 91

population 92

population 96

Chapter 20
Quantitative Genetics

1. *(A)* According to your textbook, quantitative genetics "is the analysis of how genetic and environmental factors influence the inheritance and expression of quantitative traits." Quantitative genetics includes the study of genes with equal and additive effects, but it also includes the study of genes whose effects are not equal or purely additive, and the study of how the environment affects phenotypic variation.

2. *(B)* The answer to this question comes from a comparison of equations 20.6 and 20.9. These equations equal one another when $V_A = V_G$. Because $V_G = V_A + V_D + V_I$ (equation 20.8), and variances are always positive numbers (because variances are calculated from the sum of squared deviations), $V_A = V_G$ only when V_D and V_I are both zero. Thus $V_A = V_G$ when all genetic variation is additive.

3. *(B)* Broad-sense heritability is the proportion of phenotypic variance that is genetic variance (the sum of all variances that are genetic in nature). Narrow-sense heritability is the proportion of the phenotypic variance that is the variance for additive effects of genes. The variance for additive effects of genes is a component of the genetic variance, so it is usually less than the genetic variance, and narrow-sense heritability for a population is usually less than broad-sense heritability for the same population.

4. *(B)* V_P is the phenotypic variance. It is the variance for measured phenotypes for a quantitative characteristic. V_G is the genetic variance. It is a component of V_P and represents the variance for all genetic effects. V_A is the variance for additive effects of genes. It is a component of V_G and represents the variance for all additive influences that genes have on a quantitative trait. V_D is the variance for dominance deviation. It is also a component of V_G and represents the variance for deviations from additivity due to dominance. V_I is the variance for nonadditive (epistatic) interactions among genes. It is also a component of V_G. V_E is the environmental variance. It is a measure of the variation due to nongenetic influences on the phenotype. V_A, V_D, and V_I when summed equal V_G, and broad-sense heritability is the proportion of V_P that is represented by V_G. V_A is a component of V_G, and narrow-sense heritability is the proportion of V_P that is represented by V_A.

5. *(B)* All genes that influence variation for a trait contribute to V_A. A single allele may contribute to V_A, V_D, and V_I. Therefore, these terms do not refer to different types of genes but rather to a partitioning of the genetic variance into components that represent the different effects that genes can have on variation for quantitative traits.

6. *(B)* All alleles that vary contribute to V_A. If V_D is positive, the alleles that contribute to V_D must also contribute to V_A.

7. *(B)* **(a)** No, because if V_G is greater than zero, V_A must also be greater than zero. **(b)** No. If there is any genetic variation, then both V_A and V_G must be greater than zero, and both narrow- and broad-sense heritabilities must be greater than zero.

8. *(C)* Genetic loads are the deleterious recessive alleles that are not entirely removed by selection because some of them remain unaffected by selection in heterozygotes. Self-pollinated plants are so highly inbred that they are homozygous at every locus. Thus, all of the deleterious recessive alleles are in the homozygous condition and are expressed phenotypically, so selection can readily remove them from the population. However, heterozygotes are common in diploid cross-pollinated populations, and deleterious recessive alleles are unaffected by selection when in the heterozygous condition. In cross-pollinated polyploids, deleterious recessive alleles are affected by selection only when in the nulliplex condition. For example, in a tetraploid a recessive allele *a* is expressed only in the nulliplex genotype

aaaa. In all other genotypes that include the *a* allele (*Aaaa*, *AAaa*, and *AAAa*), the *a* allele is not expressed phenotypically. The frequency of nulliplex genotypes in a cross-pollinated polyploid population is much less than the frequency of homozygous recessive genotypes in a cross-pollinated diploid population when allele frequencies are the same. Consequently, polyploids tend to have higher genetic loads than diploids.

9. (B) Deleterious recessive alleles are readily removed by selection in self-pollinated species, whereas they are not as easily removed in cross-pollinated species. Recessive alleles are defined by the dominant alleles that mask them, so when recessive alleles are present in a cross-pollinated population, the dominant alleles that mask them contribute to V_D.

10. (B) (a) Because there is usually little heterosis in self-pollinated species, they are usually marketed as inbred varieties. (b) Many cross-pollinated species are marketed as hybrid varieties. Because cross-pollinated species generally have higher values of V_D than self-pollinated species, the potential for heterosis is also higher, and hybrid varieties should show a marked increase in productivity when deleterious recessive alleles are masked in the hybrid.

11. (C) According to equation 20.6, there are two ways in increase heritability: (1) increase V_G or (2) decrease V_P. A plant breeder can increase V_G by choosing genetically diverse plants as parents in a breeding program. A plant breeder can decrease V_P by growing all the progeny in an environment that is as uniform as possible, so as to minimize V_E.

12. (C) Grain yield is influenced by many environmental factors that plant breeders cannot easily control, such as rainfall, soil texture, soil fertility, temperature, and sunlight. Such factors vary substantially, even within a single field, causing consistently high values for V_E in nearly all environments, so heritabilities tend to be low. On the other hand, breeders can easily control infection with stem rust to test for resistance. The breeders grow the fungus then manually infect plants with it to determine whether the plants are susceptible or resistant. The value for V_E is consistently low, so heritabilities tend to be high.

13. (B) DNA markers are not influenced by environmental factors, so $V_E = 0$ for the DNA markers, and broad-sense heritabilities are 100%. Many DNA markers are not influenced by dominance or epistatic interactions either, so the variation is purely additive. For such markers, narrow-sense heritabilities are 100%.

14. (C) The distance from M to M^* (which equals R) is 75% of the distance from M to M^s (which equals S). Therefore $h^2 = R \div S = 0.75$.

15. (D) (a) Peas per pod is a meristic trait. (b) The mean is 4.2632, the mode is 4, the median is 4, the variance is 2.7266, and the standard deviation is 1.6512. (c) In a normal distribution, the mean equals the median and the mode, 68% of the population falls within 1 standard deviation on both sides of the mean, and 95% of the population falls within 1.96 standard deviations on both sides of the mean. The distribution in this example deviates slightly from perfect symmetry; it is skewed toward the lower values. The mean is not identical to the mode and median, but it is close. On the right side of the mean, 1 standard deviation is 4.2632 + 1.6512 = 5.1944. On the left side of the mean, 1 standard deviation is 4.2632 − 1.6512 = 2.6120. There are 114 individuals (pods) in the distribution, and 68% of them is 77.52. We expect 77.52 individuals to fall within the range of 2.6120 to 5.1944. This includes all individuals with 3, 4, and 5 peas per pod, 38.8% (1 − 0.6120 = 0.3880) of the individuals with 2 peas per pod, and 19.44% of the individuals with 6 peas per pod. (We must prorate the classes of individuals in which the cutoffs for 1 standard deviation lie.) The observed number of individuals in this range is (0.388)14 + 21 + 23 + 26 + (0.1944)17 = 78.7368, which is fairly close to the expected value of 77.52. On the right side of the mean, 1.96 standard deviations is 4.2632 + 1.96(1.6512) = 7.4996. On the left side of the mean, 1.96

standard deviations is 4.2632 − 1.96(1.6512) = 1.0268. We expect 0.95(114) = 108.3 individuals to fall within the range of 1.0268 to 7.4996. This includes all individuals with 2, 3, 4, 5, 6, and 7 peas per pod, 97.32% (1 − 0.0268 = 0.9732) of the individuals with 1 pea per pod, and 49.96% of the individuals with 8 peas per pod. The observed number of individuals in this range is (0.9732)4 + 14 + 21 + 23 + 26 + 17 + 5 + (0.4996)4 = 111.8912, which is slightly more than the expected value of 108.3. The distribution deviates slightly, but not substantially, from a normal distribution. **(d)** As mentioned in the answer to part c, the distribution is slightly skewed toward the lower values.

16. *(C)* No. Had all the genetic variation been exhausted, reverse selection should not have been effective. The observation that reverse selection was effective indicates that V_A was not zero, but that the population had reached a physiological plateau.

17. *(C)* The phenotypic variance of the F_2 progeny is V_P = 42.37. As explained in Example 20.2, V_G = 36.61. The broad-sense heritability is H^2 = 36.61 ÷ 42.37 = 0.8641.

18. *(D)* **(a)**

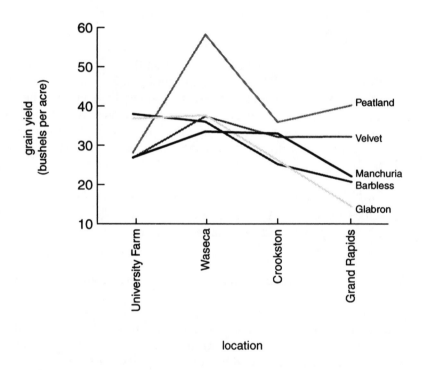

(b) Yes, there is substantial evidence of a genotype-by-environment interaction. The lines are not parallel, and several of them intersect one another. **(c)** None of the varieties yields consistently well (or consistently poorly) in all four environments. Peatland has the highest yield in three of the four environments, but its yield is close to the lowest yield in one environment (University Farm). The genotype-by-environment interaction is such that grain yields in one environment cannot be used to predict grain yields in another environment.

19. *(D)* **(a)** The phenotypic values for all three characteristics (grain yield, ear length, and daily increase

in height) are correlated with the degree of heterozygosity. The parents are inbred and are thus fully homozygous at all loci. Their phenotypic values are among the lowest. The F_1 plants have the highest degree of heterozygosity and display the highest phenotypic values. Heterozygosity decreases by half with each generation of self-fertilization. Correlated with the decrease in heterozygosity is a general decrease in phenotypic values in the F_2 to F_8 generations. **(b)** To answer this part of the question, we use equation 19.10 (page 589). The inbreeding coefficient in the F_1 plants is zero (because they have no common ancestry), so in calculating the inbreeding coefficient for the F_2 generation, $F_A = 0$. However, F_A has a positive value for all subsequent generations. The generations and their corresponding inbreeding coefficients are summarized in the table below:

Generation	Calculation of Inbreeding Coefficient
F_1	0
F_2	0.5(1 + 0) = 0.5
F_3	0.5(1 + 0.5) = 0.75
F_4	0.5(1 + 0.75) = 0.875
F_5	0.5(1 + 0.875) = 0.9375
F_6	0.5(1 + 0.9375) = 0.96875
F_7	0.5(1 + 0.96875) = 0.984375
F_8	0.5(1 + 0.984375) = 0.9921875

(c) The graphs are on the next page. **(d)** There is a general decrease in phenotypic value with an increase in the inbreeding coefficient.

20. *(C)* The average gain from selection is $R = 0.175(1.39) = 0.24325$ (equation 20.11).

21. *(C)* **(a)** Thorax length is a continuous trait. **(b)** Number of eggs laid is a meristic trait. **(c)** For the genetically uniform lines, $V_G = 0$, so $V_E = V_P = 0.186$. If we use this value as an estimate of V_E in the entire experiment, then in the genetically variable populations, $V_G = V_P - V_E = 0.366 - 0.186 = 0.180$. $H^2 = V_G \div V_P = 0.180 \div 0.366 = 0.4918$. **(d)** In the genetically uniform lines, $V_E = V_P = 16.6$. In the genetically diverse populations, $V_G = V_P - V_E = 43.4 - 16.6 = 26.8$. $H^2 = V_G \div V_P = 26.8 \div 43.4 = 0.6175$.

22. *(C)* For thorax size, $h^2 = 2.7 \div 5.72 = 0.4720$. For number of eggs laid, $h^2 = 0.108 \div 1.174 = 0.0920$.

23. *(C)* **(a)** For thorax size, the broad-sense heritability is 0.4918, and the narrow-sense heritability is 0.4720. The proportion of V_G that is represented by V_A is $0.4720 \div 0.4918 = 0.9597$. **(b)** For number of eggs laid, the broad-sense heritability is 0.6175, and the narrow-sense heritability is 0.0920. The proportion of V_G that is represented by V_A is $0.0920 \div 0.6175 = 0.1490$. **(c)** There is a higher variance for dominance for number of eggs laid because the difference between the broad- and narrow-sense heritabilities is greater for this trait.

24. *(C)* The broad-sense heritability is $(0.812 + 0.011) \div 2.460 = 0.3346$. The narrow-sense heritability is $0.812 \div 2.460 = 0.3301$.

25. *(C)* **(a)** The F_1 plants have the highest heterozygosity and therefore exhibit maximum heterosis. **(b)** Half the heterozygosity that contributed to heterosis in the F_1 generation is lost in the F_2 generation because of inbreeding. However, because they are not fully inbred, the F_2 individuals are more heterozygous than the inbred parents and therefore have a higher level of heterosis than the parents.

Information for problem 19

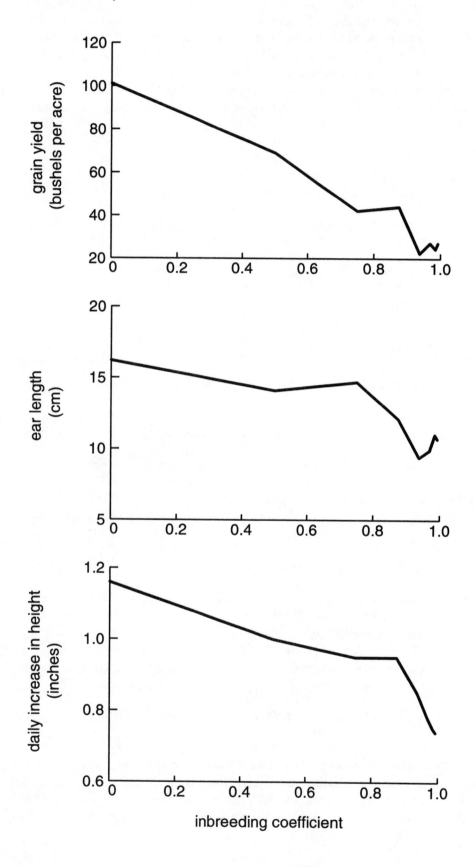

26. *(C)* **(a)** No, the distribution for the F_1 generation is not likely to be skewed. **(b)** Yes, the distribution for the F_2 generation is likely to be skewed toward the higher values. **(c)** We do not expect the distribution for the F_1 generation to be skewed because all of the F_1 individuals are genetically identical. All variation is environmental. We expect the distribution for the F_2 generation to be skewed because of dominance. The presence of heterosis implies that there is significant variation for dominance in the F_2 generation.

27. *(C)* The mean of the F_1 progeny falls outside of the range of parental means. When the mean of the F_1 progeny is less than either of the parental means, the heterosis is sometimes called negative heterosis.

28. *(C)* **(a)** Variation for at least five genes is responsible for the genetic variation observed in this study. It is important to point out that more than five genes may govern milk production in cattle, but in this particular study, at least five of those genes were responsible for most of the variation. **(b)** Researchers can use the markers to help reduce the influence of environment, dominance, and epistasis on selection efficiency. **(c)** Microsatellite markers are highly variable and permit the use of large numbers of markers at a relatively low cost. This is a very large study, requiring significant investments of time and supplies. Therefore, a PCR-based method that provides reliable results with relatively low expenditures of time and money is the best choice.

Chapter 21
Evolutionary Genetics

1. *(C)* The two products of a chromosome fission are not likely to be established as separate chromosomes because one of them usually lacks a centromere. Also, the orangutan diverged from the common ancestry of human and great apes before human, chimpanzee, and gorilla diverged from one another. If the two chromosomes are the ancestral situation, then a single fusion to form human chromosome 2 after the divergence of the human lineage from chimpanzee and gorilla easily explains the current situation. However, if the chromosomes in chimpanzee, gorilla, and orangutan are to be explained by fission, then at least two independent fissions must have occurred, events that are much less probable than a single fusion. In the case of human chromosome 2, the fusion product probably contained two centromeres (see the centromeres in the two chimpanzee chromosomes), but one of the centromeres in human chromosome 2 no longer functions as such.

2. *(B)* Seed storage proteins function as a reserve of amino acids. An alteration in one (or even many) amino acids should not drastically alter the function of the proteins. Thus, selection should not highly disfavor mutant forms of the proteins. Cytochrome *c*, on the other hand, is an enzyme, and as such its function is highly dependent on the amino acid sequence. Many alterations in the amino acid sequence (even of one amino acid) can substantially reduce or eliminate the enzyme's function. Thus, selection should disfavor many mutations and preserve much of the original protein sequence among species.

3. *(B)* The alternative explanation requires chromosome fissions, which are less likely than chromosome fusions.

4. *(C)* **(a)** Most of the nucleotides in an intron are removed from the pre-mRNA and have no effect on the structure or function of the protein. Consequently, most mutations in an intron should be selectively neutral, and are more likely to become established than mutations within the polypeptide-encoding region of a gene. The probability of finding DNA sequence variation within an intron is greater than within the exons of the gene. **(b)** These results suggest that all modern humans probably arose from a single founder population that was fixed for a single Y chromosome. The results also suggest that the founder effect for humans was more recent than any founder effects for the other primates studied.

5. *(C)* The lower diversity for human mitochondrial DNA when compared to chimpanzee mitochondrial DNA (like the lack of diversity in the Y chromosome cited in the previous question) suggests that humans arose from a founder effect that was more recent than any founder effects in chimpanzees.

6. *(C)* **(a)** The major genetic difference between the two is in the mitochondrial DNA. The gestation environment in female horses and donkeys may be quite different and have a significant effect on the hybrid offspring. **(b)** The chromosome numbers differ and chromosome imbalances arise during meiosis in a mule or hinny due to the inability of some chromosomes to pair properly.

7. *(C)* **(a)** The two types are isolated prezygotically by flowering time, a form of temporal isolation. The two types are isolated postzygotically by their different ploidies. **(b)** Hybrids are rare because there is little opportunity for cross-pollination between the species due to their different flowering periods. The rare hybrids that form are sterile because they are triploid (see section 17.2, especially page 518, for an explanation of sterility in triploids). **(c)** According to the standard definition of a species as a group of individuals that can intermate and produce fertile offspring, these two types should be classified as different species. However, most taxonomists who have studied these plants classify them as different chromosome races of the same species because they are highly similar to one another in most morphological characteristics.

8. *(D)* **(a)** The most probable scheme is one in which a common ancestral type had $2n = 2x = 22$ chromo-

somes. This type eventually developed into *Glycine wightii* with $2n = 2x = 22$ chromosomes. Chromosome doubling produced tetraploid *G. wightii* with $2n = 4x = 44$ chromosomes. At some point in the common ancestor with $2n = 2x = 22$ chromosomes, a single chromosome fusion produced a diploid type that had $2n = 2x = 20$ chromosomes. Chromosome numbers in this new type doubled to produce a species with $2n = 4x = 40$ chromosomes, and it developed into *G. soja* and perhaps other tetraploid species. *G. tabacina* and *G. tomentella* probably arose from chromosome doubling in an ancestral tetraploid species with $2n = 4x = 40$ chromosomes to produce an octaploid with $2n = 8x = 80$ chromosomes. The two species may have diverged from a common ancestral tetraploid species, or they may have arisen independently through chromosome doubling of two different tetraploid ancestral species. *G. max* is probably most closely related to *G. soja* and arose when people domesticated it from its common ancestor with *G. soja*. **(b)** Prezygotic isolating mechanisms that isolate these species are geographic and ecological isolation. Because they grow in different regions of Asia and Australia, the species are isolated geographically, although some of their geographic ranges may overlap. An example of ecological isolation is the separation of *G. max* and *G. soja*. Although their ranges overlap, *G. max* is exclusively a cultivated species, grown only on farmland, whereas *G. soja* is a wild species that is not cultivated on farmland. Postzygotic isolating mechanisms are evident in the observations sterility in some interspecific hybrids and differences in basic chromosome number ($x = 11$ for *G. wightii* and $x = 10$ for all others) and ploidy. Hybrids between species with different chromosome numbers or ploidies are likely to be sterile. Even some species with the same chromosome number and ploidy produce sterile hybrids when hybridized, such as hybrids from *G. tabacina* × *G. tomentella*. **(c)** As described in part a, *G. wightii* is the most probable ancestral type.

9. *(C) Glycine soja* is a wild species. It is selectively advantageous for a plant to produce a large number of seeds because it increases the probability that at least a few will survive to reproduce. Relatively small seeds are advantageous to a degree because production of a small seed requires fewer resources from the parent plant than does production of a large seed. It is advantageous for a wild plant to disperse its seeds before the onset of winter so that the seeds are protected within the soil, where they can germinate when spring arrives. This explains the observation that *G. soja* pods break open easily. It is also advantageous for the seeds of a wild plant to have some degree of dormancy (postponement of germination) to increase the chance that some will survive after germination. If all seeds germinated at the same time, a single spring frost, a drought, an insect infestation, or a disease could eliminate all of a plant's progeny and perhaps an entire population in a single season. If some seeds remain dormant, however, they can germinate later, perhaps in a subsequent year, when conditions are more favorable. All of these characteristics are selectively advantageous in a wild species but are not desirable in a domesticated one. Humans select plants that have larger seeds so that the seeds can be more easily harvested, processed, and consumed; that hold their seeds within the pod so that the seeds can be harvested from the plants all at the same time (rather than have many seeds fall on the ground, where they cannot be easily harvested); and that germinate readily at the same time to establish a uniform crop in a field and to maximize the proportion of seeds that can be consumed rather than planted.

10. *(C)* **(a)** The separation of the copper-resistant plants on the mine tailings from the copper-susceptible plants on the pasture soils is an example of ecological isolation. The difference between the two types for flowering time is an example of temporal isolation. **(b)** Copper resistance allows those plants that are most resistant to survive on the high copper soil and reproduce. Copper-resistant plants that flower at a different time than the copper-susceptible plants mate only with one another, so their progeny are more likely to inherit copper-resistance alleles than the progeny of plants that mate with the copper-susceptible plants. Consequently, natural selection favors the progeny of those copper-resistant plants that mate among themselves, and thus favors copper-resistant plants that flower at a different time than the copper-susceptible plants. **(c)** The populations are reproductively isolated, so genetic changes in one population are not transferred to the other population, and the two populations may change independently, eventually diverging into two different species.

11. *(C)* A founder effect can explain the presence of a trait that is not favorable for the environment in

which the population is found. If a small number of individuals that are all homozygous for an allele that is not favorable are the founders of a population, all individuals in the population will express the trait and none will have a selective advantage relative to the others for that trait. In essence, the population is uniform for the trait. Should migrants that carry a more favorable phenotype enter the population, selection should favor them, and the frequency of the favorable phenotype should increase. In the absence of diversity, however, an unfavorable trait may persist. In other environments, populations of the same species may have a favorable phenotype because at least some of the founders of those populations carried the favored alleles, or because mutation produced favored alleles, and selection then increased the frequencies of the favored alleles in the population.

12. *(C)* According to information in Chapter 20, dominance and epistasis reduce the effectiveness of selection. Alleles that exhibit no dominance or epistatic interactions can be more readily established in a population by selection than alleles that exhibit high degrees of dominance or epistatic interactions.

13. *(C)* This observation suggests that this segment includes a part of the enzyme that is essential for its function and may be at least part of the enzyme's active site.

14. *(D)* **(a)** It is not immediately obvious from the genetic code which amino acid is most ancestral, so to answer this question, we must consider the evolution of this codon in the context of other codons within the gene, and in light of the information presented in Figure 21.10. Because threonine is uniformly present in the species of two kingdoms (plants and fungi), it is probably the ancestral amino acid. Only a single C → U transition is required to change an ACG threonine codon into an AUG methionine codon. However, according to the pattern of evolution depicted in Figure 21.10, and in many of the other codons in Figure 21.8, a more complex mutation pattern must explain the arisal of the methionine codon in primates and rattlesnake. Because all animals in Figure 21.10 except primates and rattlesnake have glutamine at this position, the methionine codon was probably derived by two transversion mutations from a glutamine codon that is ancestral to all animals. **(b)** The methionine codon in rattlesnake must have been derived independently of the methionine codon in primates because, according to the pattern in Figure 21.10, snakes diverged from the ancestors of primates earlier than birds and other mammals, all of which have a glutamine codon at this position. In light of the patterns for the evolution of other amino acids in cytochrome *c*, the observation that methionine is present at the same site in primates and rattlesnake does not inidicate that rattlesnake is phylogenetically closer to primates than to other reptiles.

15. *(D)* Selection that favors heterozygotes best explains the inversion heterozygosity because the experimental results of Dobzhansky (1947. *Genetics* 32:142–160) highlighted in question 23 of Chapter 19 show a significant deviation from Hardy-Weinberg equilibrium in which heterozygotes exceed the expected frequency. Were neutrality the cause of the polymorphism, the population should have been in Hardy-Weinberg equilibrium for the genotypes. The study by Dobzhansky and Pavlovsky highlighted in question 24 of Chapter 19 (1953. *Evolution* 7:198–210) provides direct evidence of selection that favors heterozygotes.

16. *(E)* **(a)** The DNA sequence's lack of resemblance with homologous sequences from modern species suggests, but does not prove, ancient origin. The observation that the sequence was obtained from a fossilized bone and most closely matches sequences from mammals, birds, and reptiles indicates that the DNA came from the bone and not from microorganisms that contaminated the bone. The absence of DNA amplification from material that surrounded the bone also provides evidence against the possibility that the DNA came from contaminating tissue or organisms. **(b)** The criticisms of the work include (1) skepticism that DNA molecules could remain sufficiently intact over 80 million years for PCR to successfully amplify the sequence, and (2) failure of the DNA to resemble any known modern organism. For example, the DNA was obtained from large bones that several researchers speculate may have belonged to a dinosaur. However, the DNA does not resemble birds (which are thought to be the modern organisms most closely related to dinosaurs) more closely than it does reptiles or mammals, so some scientists

have argued that the DNA sequence may have come from an organism that contaminated the bone.

17. *(C)* **(a)** There are both prezygotic and postzygotic isolating mechanisms. The prezygotic isolation is geographic. The subterranean burrows that the pocket gophers occupy and the gophers' reluctance to come above ground and migrate isolate the species geographically. The postzygotic isolation is a difference in chromosome number. The chromosomes have diverged to such an extent that their numbers differ among species. Interspecific hybrids are likely to be infertile because the chromosomes should not pair properly during meiosis. **(b)** Most of the evolution in these species has probably been chromosomal, with little evolution at the DNA sequence level. Most of the genes are probably still fairly similar, although their chromosomal locations may have been altered. This conclusion suggests that the species have diverged fairly recently because insufficient time has elapsed for the DNA sequences to diverge significantly through point mutations.

18. *(B)* Transition mutations are typically more frequent than transversion mutations, so it is appropriate to apply different mutation rates to them to more accurately conduct phylogenetic analysis.

19. *(D)* The pattern for human chromosome 12 is most easily explained if the human and orangutan pattern is ancestral and the pattern in chimpanzee and gorilla resulted from a pericentric inversion that occurred *after* the divergence of the human lineage from the chimpanzee and gorilla lineage but *before* the divergence of chimpanzees and gorillas. This explanation, however, contradicts other evidence indicating that human and chimpanzee are genetically more similar to one another than either is to gorilla. If this is the case, then the inversions in gorilla and chimpanzee must have arisen separately. The results of some recent studies indicate that the inversion break points in the equivalents of chromosome 12 in chimpanzee and gorilla differ slightly in their positions, suggesting that the inversions arose from separate events and resemble one another only because their break points are close to the same locations.

20. *(D)*

Species						
Species	Chicken	Turkey	Pigeon	Pekin duck	Snapping turtle	Rattlesnake
Chicken	0	0	4	3	7	16
Turkey		0	4	3	7	16
Pigeon			0	3	8	18
Pekin duck				0	7	16
Snapping turtle					0	21
Rattlesnake						0

The lowest standard deviation is shared equally by two alternative trees. One tree groups Pekin duck first with pigeon, then with chicken and turkey; the other groups Pekin duck first with chicken and turkey, then with pigeon. All other branch points of the two trees are the same:

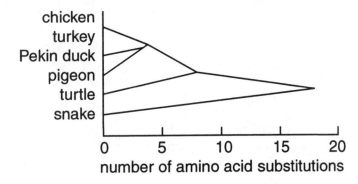

379

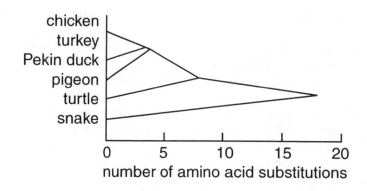

number of amino acid substitutions

Both trees place the birds (chicken, turkey, Pekin duck, and pigeon) in a group that is distinctly separated from the two reptiles (snapping turtle and rattlesnake). The two reptiles, however, are not grouped. The groupings approximate traditional taxonomic classifications but do not match them exactly in the case of the two reptiles.

21. *(E)* Powell and Moriyama (1997. *Proceedings of the National Academy of Sciences, USA* 94:7784–7790) provide three reasons why preferential mutation toward C and G cannot explain codon usage bias in *Drosophila*: (1) Warm-blooded vertebrates have blocks of AT-rich sequences and blocks of GC-rich sequences, both called isochores. Within an AT-rich isochore, codons are biased toward A and T at the third position, whereas within a GC-rich isochore codons are biased toward G and C at the third position. Mutation may be biased by the isochore in which the gene is found. Unlike the situation in warm-blooded vertebrates, there are no isochores in *Drosophila*, and genes that are very close to one another may differ greatly in codon usage bias. (2) Mutations in *Drosophila* are actually biased toward A and T, rather than C and G, even though codon usage is biased toward C and G at the third position. Therefore, codon usage bias opposes the tendency of mutation. (3) Not all amino acids display the same pattern of bias. If mutation bias were the cause of codon bias, then all codons would be expected to show similar patterns of codon bias. The authors concluded that selection for efficient translation based on the relative abundance of tRNAs and their abilities to bind to particular codons was the reason for codon bias in *Drosophila*.

22. *(E)* **(a)** The researchers recovered the bacterial cultures from ancient bees embedded in amber. The most likely source of bacteria of modern rather than ancient origin was contamination of the samples. To prevent contamination, the researchers surface-sterilized the amber before cracking it, and they conducted all experiments in a laminar flow hood, an instrument that provides a sterile environment for laboratory work (see section 7.1). Also to test for contamination, they inoculated the bacterial growth media with samples of the sterilization solutions and pieces from the exterior and interior of the amber in which the bees were embedded. To test the effectiveness of the surface-sterilization procedure, they inoculated pieces of amber with a modern isolate of bacteria, then surface-sterilized the amber pieces and placed them in culture. They simulated the recovery procedure with amber that contained no bees and tested the amber and all solutions used in the simulation for contamination. They tested for environmental contamination by maintaining three open petri plates with growth medium in the laminar flow hood during the extraction procedure. In none of these experiments did they detect contamination. They identified the culture as being similar to *Baccillus sphaericus* (a modern bacterial species that lives in bees) by examination of morphological and biochemical characteristics. They amplified DNA of the 16S rRNA gene using PCR and sequenced it. They compared the sequence with known sequences from modern bacteria and found that it was not identical with the DNA sequences of any modern species, but most closely resembled the sequence from modern *B. sphaericus*. All of these results suggest that the bacteria they recovered were of ancient rather than modern origin. **(b)** Priest (1995. *Science* 270:2015) expressed concern that there is much genetic variation in modern species of bacteria and that "until we have isolated and characterized the biodiversity of today, it is premature to claim that a bacterium is ancient by

virtue of its distinction from some strains of *B. sphaericus* selected from the rRNA sequence database." Cano (1995. *Science* 270:2016–2017) responded to this criticism by indicating that since the publication of the article the researchers had extended their DNA sequence comparisons and arrived at the same conclusion stated in their article. He also indicated that their conclusion that the bacteria were ancient in origin was based not only on the DNA sequence comparisons, but also on their experiments that provided strong evidence against the only other alternative hypothesis, that the bacteria were modern contaminants. Beckenbach (1995. *Science* 270:2015–2016) pointed out several DNA sequence anomalies in the article and stated that "if the credibility of the findings . . . rests on the DNA sequence analysis, their report fails that test." He suggested that the researchers focus their work on comparing the DNA sequence of the putative ancient strain with the modern strains they had in the laboratory. Cano responded that the first DNA sequence they reported in the article was correct, and that they had published some errors in another part of the article, but that after correction of the errors did not alter their conclusions. He also responded that they had studied modern strains only after identifying the putative ancient type and had intentionally maintained and studied all modern strains in a different laboratory to avoid possible contamination. **(c)** The research highlighted in the news releases focuses on independent methods for testing the chemical stability of proteins and DNA in ancient materials. These articles recommend that additional tests be conducted on the material to further test whether or not the DNA extracted from the material is indeed ancient.

23. *(D)* **(a)** The results of Armour et al. are similar to those of Tishkoff et al. in that both show a higher degree of allele diversity among Africans when compared to non-Africans, and that most alleles in non-African populations are also found in African populations, albeit at lower frequencies. **(b)** If the multiple-origins theory were correct, we would expect to observe a much higher degree of genetic diversity in non-African populations than was observed in both of these studies. The results of both studies support the single-origin theory, that non-African populations arose from a relatively small group of founders who migrated from Africa.

24. *(D)* The authors (Armour et al. 1996. *Nature Genetics* 13:154–160) provided two alternative scenarios that do not require a migration from Africa but instead propose multiregional development. The first is the possibility that the mutation rate of the gene they studied may be higher in African than in non-African populations. They concluded that their data did not support this hypothesis because it predicts that African populations should have recently developed diversity for alleles that are related, a pattern that is not apparent in their data. Also, there is no reason to expect that mutation rates should be different in African and non-African populations. The second is the possibility that selection somehow preserved diversity in African populations, or reduced it in non-African populations. The authors concluded that if selection were correct, it should apply to the particular locus they studied but not necessarily to other nuclear or mitochondrial genotypes. The patterns observed for other nuclear and mitochondrial genotypes are the same as those observed by these authors, and when interpreted together, they collectively indicate that non-African humans arose from a migration of a founder population from Africa.

25. *(C)* Species that are genetically closest to one another usually share the greatest number of markers. According to this study, *A. hypochondriacus* and *A. caudatus* are most closely related because they share the greatest number of markers.

26. *(C)* **(a)** Species that are genetically closest to one another usually are the most interfertile. According to this study, *A. hypochondriacus* and *A. cruentus* are most closely related because they have the highest degree of interfertility. **(b)** The conclusion derived from the study of interfertility contradicts the conclusion derived from a study of DNA markers. **(c)** The researchers placed pollen from one species on the stigmas of another species, circumventing any geographic, ecological, temporal, ethological, or mechanical isolation, several of which probably exist in nature for these species. Their recovery of only a few hybrids between *A. caudatus* and *A. cruentus*, and between *A. hypochondriacus* and *A. caudatus*, suggests that gametic isolation (a type of prezygotic isolation) is present in these hybridizations. The sterility or reduction of fertility in all hybrids indicates that all three species are postzygotically isolated in varying

degrees from one another.

27. *(D)* The presence of two species in Middle America, compared to the presence of only a single species in South America, suggests that greater genetic diversity is present in Middle America and that *A. caudatus* was perhaps derived from seeds that people carried from Middle America to South America. Although not given in the question, information from wild relatives supports this conclusion. Most wild species of *Amaranthus* are in North and Middle America, suggesting that the genus *Amaranthus* originated on the North American continent. According to the DNA marker study, *A. caudatus* is closer to *A. hypochondriacus* than it is to *A. cruentus*. According to the interfertility study, *A. caudatus* is slightly more interfertile with *A. hypochondriacus* than it is with *A. cruentus*. These observations, when interpreted in light of the geographical distribution, suggest that *A. caudatus* was probably derived from *A. hypochondriacus*.

Chapter 22
Transposable Elements

1. *(B)* Autonomous transposable elements are capable of self transposition; they do not require the presence of any other type of element to transpose. Nonautonomous transposable elements can be transposed only when an autonomous element is present. The phenotypes that are associated with excision of an element located in a particular gene are observed in every generation of a lineage that is homozygous for an autonomous transposable element, as is the case with spotted seeds in maize plants that carry the autonomous *Ac* element in the *c1* gene. A nonautonomous element located in a particular gene produces the phenotype associated with excision of the element from that gene only when an autonomous element is present. For example, a *Ds* element located in the *c1* gene fails to produce spotted seeds in the absence of an *Ac* element. However, a cross between a plant that carries the *Ds* element in the *c1* gene and a plant that carries an *Ac* element at any location produces progeny with spotted seeds. At the molecular level, an autonomous element (such as *Ac*) contains a transposase gene that encodes functional transposase. The element can be excised by the transposase that it encodes. A nonautonomous element (such as *Ds*) contains a mutant transposase gene that fails to encode functional transposase. It can only be excised by functional transposase, which is present only when an autonomous element is present.

2. *(B)* Although transposition is often more frequent than other types of mutation, it is usually not so frequent that it disrupts Mendelian ratios. Also, some species have mechanisms that inhibit transposition.

3. *(B)* Forward mutations arise from insertion of a transposable element into a gene, whereas reversion mutations arise from excision of a transposable element from a gene. The site at which a transposable element will be inserted as a forward mutation is unpredictable; the element can be inserted at any site within the entire genome. The site of a reversion mutation due to excision of a transposable element, however, is highly predictable because the location of the element is known beforehand. McClintock knew that the reversion mutations could be detected as a seed color phenotype because the elements she studied were located in a gene that governs seed color. Had she chosen to study forward mutations, she could not have predicted which genes, and which phenotypes, would be affected.

4. *(B)* **(a)** If the plant that carries the *Ac* element is homozygous *c1c1*, then all the F_1 progeny kernels are compound heterozygotes with the genotype *c1c-m1*, and the seed aleurones are colorless except in the locations where the *Ds* element has been excised. Those locations appear as colored spots on the kernel. All F_1 kernels should be spotted. **(b)** If the plant that carries the *Ac* element is homozygous *C1C1*, then all the F_1 progeny kernels are heterozygotes with the genotype *C1c-m1*, and the seed aleurones are fully colored. Excision of the *Ds* element cannot be detected because the locations in which there is a reversion mutation are already fully colored. All F_1 kernels are fully colored with no detectable spots.

5. *(D)* Let *Ac+* designate the presence of the *Ac* element and *Ac-* the absence of the *Ac* element at the site 12 cM from the *c1* locus. There are four possible genotypes in the backcross progeny: *Ac+Ac- c1c-m1*, *Ac-Ac- c1cm-1*, *Ac+Ac- c-m1c-m1*, and *Ac-Ac- c-m1c-m1*. The first two genotypes are nonrecombinant, and each should represent 44% of the progeny. The last two genotypes are recombinant, and each should represent 6% of the progeny. Any genotype with *Ac+* and *c-m1* in it should have spotted kernels. Those two genotypes and the respective proportions of the progeny that they represent are as follows: *Ac+Ac- c1c-m1* (44%) and *Ac+Ac- c-m1c-m1* (6%). A total of 44% + 6% = 50% of the backcross progeny should have spotted kernels.

6. *(C)* The footprint left behind when the element is excised may create a stable mutation that continues to disrupt the gene.

7. *(D)* Methylation is one of several mechanisms that cells use to inactivate gene transcription. Highly

methylated genes are not transcribed. An *Ac* element that is highly methylated will not produce functional transposase and cannot be excised unless another *Ac* element that is actively transcribed is present.

8. *(C)* The inactive *Ac* elements in the cultured cells may have lost their methylation during the tissue culture process. The now actively transcribed transposase genes should produce functional transposase and cause *Ac* activity in the regenerated plants.

9. *(C)* The mutant allele at the *a* locus probably contained a nonautonomous element. An autonomous element was located on another chromosome. If the two parents were heterozygous for the mutant *a* allele and the autonomous element, the pattern that Rhoades observed should appear in their progeny.

10. *(C)* When an unreplicated broken chromosome replicates, the broken end is replicated in both sister chromatids, and both contain the same terminal deletion.

11. *(C)* P elements encode a cytoplasmic repressor that prevents transposition. When a P-cytotype male is crossed with an M-cytotype female, the progeny inherit nearly all of their cytoplasm from the female, whose cells do not have the repressor. In the absence of the cytsoplamic repressor, the P elements can be transposed. A P-cytotype female, however, does carry the repressor in her cytoplasm, as do all of her progeny regardless of the male's genotype. With the repressor present in the cytoplasm of the progeny, the P elements cannot be transposed.

12. *(B)* Uniparental-maternal inheritance of the cytoplasm.

13. *(C)* The footprint that remains in the gene following excision of the transposable element is usually a multiple of three nucleotides. It does not disrupt the reading frame, but it adds one or more amino acids to the polypeptide. The enzyme encoded by the revertant allele, therefore, is not identical to the enzyme encoded by the original nonmutant allele, and the enzymatic activities of the two may differ.

14. *(C)* Electrophoretic mobility is inversely proportional to molecular weight (see section 9.7). The footprint that remained in the revertant allele added amino acids to the revertant protein product, giving it a higher molecular weight and a lower electrophoretic mobility than the protein product of the usual dominant allele.

15. *(C)* Deletions nearly always eliminate the function of the product encoded by the mutant allele. Some point mutations also eliminate the function of the product, but many either slightly reduce the activity of a protein or have no effect. A much higher proportion of deletions cause complete loss of function than do point mutations, so the probability of researchers encountering deletions in nonautonomous elements is much greater than the probability of encountering point mutations.

16. *(B)* P element insertion is not random; the elements are probably preferentially inserted at particular DNA sequences.

17. *(C)* Because it takes several generations to establish the P cytotype after a cross between an M-cytotype female and a P-cytotype male, repeated backcrosses of singed males with M-cytotype females can eventually eliminate the P elements in the progeny and establish the *sn^w* allele in an M-cytotype background, as illustrated in the diagram below:

Mate sn^w males with M-cytotype females.

$\downarrow$

The progeny have 1/2 of the P elements present in the original sn^w males.
Allow the progeny to intermate.

$\downarrow$

Select sn^w males and mate them with M-cytotype females.

$\downarrow$

The progeny have 1/4 of the P elements present in the original sn^w males.
Allow the progeny to intermate.

$\downarrow$

Select sn^w males and mate them with M-cytotype females.

$\downarrow$

The progeny have 1/8 of the P elements present in the original sn^w males.
Allow the progeny to intermate.

$\downarrow$

Continue this procedure until the proportion of P elements is so small that the P elements are essentially gone.
Then mate sn^w males with sn^w females to establish a true-breeding sn^w line.

18. *(B)* The composite transposons may replicate to produce multiple copies of the antibiotic resistance gene. The multiple copies of the gene may confer a higher level of antibiotic resistance to a cell.

19. *(C)* The antisense RNA can pair with the nucleotides in the mRNA transcribed from the transposase gene along their entire lengths to form double-stranded RNA molecules. Double-stranded RNA cannot be translated, so the antisense RNA reduces production of transposase and prevents the accumulation of too many copies of IS*10*.

20. *(D)* If a researcher has a probe that is homologous to a portion of a gene and knows that a particular mutant allele of that gene contains a transposable element, he or she can identify and isolate a clone that contains the mutant allele using the probe. The clone should contain at least part of the transposable element, which can then be used as a probe to identify and isolate a clone that contains the complete transposable element.

Chapter 23
Developmental Genetics

1. *(C)* The bicoid phenotype is a larva with posterior structures on both ends. Because the larva has no anterior structures, it dies before reaching adulthood. Thus, the bicoid phenotype is lethal in the larval stages, and it is not possible to conduct crosses with the bicoid progeny. This observation alone indicates that the trait must be nuclear rather than mitochondrial because if it were mitochondrial, it could not be maintained. Any female fly that carries a mutant mitochondrial allele that causes lethality has no surviving progeny, and the mitochondrial allele is lost in a single generation. The *bicoid* allele is a recessive nuclear allele and can be maintained from one generation to the next in homozyogus males and heterozygous females and males. Only homozygous females have no surviving progeny. Another mutant mitochondrial allele could conceivably affect development but not cause lethality or sterility. Such an allele would be transmitted entirely through the maternal lineage and could thus be distinguished from a nuclear allele, which is transmitted through both maternal and paternal lineages.

2. *(B)* Totipotency is defined as the ability of a cell to give rise to an entire organism. Most somatic cells in animals and some somatic cells in plants have differentiated to such a degree that many genes in each cell are permanently disabled and the cell cannot revert to a totipotent state.

3. *(B) Caenorhabditis elegans* has all of the characteristics of a model organism listed on page 7. With respect to development, an advantage for researchers is the limited number of somatic cells in *C. elegans*, a situation that makes the study of cellular differentiation much more simple than in an organism that may have billions to trillions of somatic cells. There is another very significant advantage that is not mentioned in your book because of its recency: the nucleotide sequence of the entire *C. elegans* genome was determined and published in December of 1998 (see the special section in the December 11, 1998 issue of *Science*, especially The *C. elegans* sequencing consortium. 1998. Genome sequence of the nematode *C. elegans*: A platform for investigating biology. *Science* 282:2012–2018; and Ruvkun, G., and O. Hobert. 1998. The taxonomy of developmental control in *Caenorhabditis elegans*. *Science* 282:2033–2041). The nucleotide sequences of all genes that affect developement, and the amino acid sequences of the proteins they encode, are now available.

4. *(B) Drosophila melanogaster* has been a model organism for genetics since 1910. Over a period of nearly 9 decades, many developmental mutations have been discovered and described. The vast body of research on this species, particularly in the area of development, has made it an excellent model organism for the study of development. It differs from *C. elegans* for the study of development in that it has a more complex pattern of development, a much larger genome, many more somatic cells, and more genes that affect development.

5. *(B)* In positional development, the cells that surround a particular cell influence its differentiation. In autonomous development, a cell differentiates according to a programmed pattern regardless of which cells surround it.

6. *(B)* The genes are regulated in an autonomous manner because transplanted eye disks developed into eye tissue in another part of the body.

7. *(C)* The chart below indicates the major classes of developmental genes in *Drosophila* and their order of expression during development. The arrows indicate the progress of development over time.

genes with maternal effects
(examples include *bicoid*, *nanos*, and *dorsal*)

↓

segmental genes
(gap genes, examples include *hunchback*, *Krüppel*, and *knirps*;
pair-rule genes, examples include *hairy*, *runt*, *fuschi tarazu*, *even-skipped*, *paired*, and *odd-skipped*;
segment polarity genes, examples include *wingless*, *engrailed*, and *gooseberry*)

↓

homeotic genes
(examples include genes of the antennapedia and bithorax complexes)

8. *(C)*

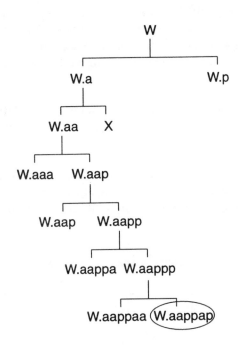

9. *(B)* Genes that are paralogous have similar DNA sequences and similar linear organizations on the same DNA molecule in two or more species. The paralogous organization may be important for development to proceed properly and is thus preserved by natural selection.

10. *(C)* As explained in Example 23.3, the *pb* gene does not need to be in its correct position in order to carry out its function. However, the maintenance of the paralogous postition of this gene (and other developmental genes) in insects and mammals suggests that there is some evolutionary advantage to that position. The advantage must be something other than the simple ability to function in another position; it may have to do instead with the coordinated regulation of all of the genes in a cluster.

11. *(C)* Homeotic mutations affect organ identity, whereas heterochronic mutations affect the timing of development. The *fusca3* mutation affects the timing of development of the embryo and is, therefore, a heterochronic mutation.

12. *(B)* The lineage that remains totipotent is the germ line. It is essential for it to remain totipotent so that new individuals can develop from zygotes.

13. *(C)* Cell differentiation initiates a genetically programmed process for cessation of cell division and eventual cell death.

14. *(C)* Mice and chickens are both vertebrates, and the *Hoxb-3* gene is one that governs development of particular regions within the vertebrate body. Its role should be very similar in both mouse and chicken.

15. *(C)* The bicoid protein initiates the expression of genes that are responsible for anterior development. Its role must be early in the pathway for development (in fact, it performs the first role).

16. *(C)* The genes that regulate muscle development probably perform similar functions in a wide range of animal species. However, their positions relative to other developmental genes are apparently not conserved among species, and are probably not essential for their function.

17. *(C)* These results do not necessarily imply different roles for the *nem* gene in muscle and nervous tissue. Similar patterns of development may exist during the early stages of development in the cells that will eventually differentiate into muscle and nervous tissue. The *nem* gene may influence the same developmental step in these early stages. When the step is disrupted by a mutation, the mutation affects both types of tissues.

18. *(D)* The two mutations are in the K domain and alter the developmental pattern of the fourth whorl only. Therefore, these results indicate that the effects of the *AG* protein on the third and fourth whorls can be separated and that the K domain governs development of the fourth whorl.

19. *(C)* Animals and plants have common evolutionary origins, and their common ancestors probably had small numbers of both homeobox and MADS box genes. In the evolutionary history of animals, homeobox genes duplicated and diverged to fulfill developmental roles. The same is true for the MADS box genes in plants.

Chapter 24
Genes and Cancer

1. *(A)* Proto-oncogenes function normally as genes that regulate the various stages of the cell cycle. They typically are genes whose products stimulate progress through the cell cycle.

2. *(B)* In this answer, we will refer only to the gene products, understanding that each product is encoded by a proto-oncogene. Cyclin D binds to CDK4 or CDK6 and transfers phosphate groups to pRB. When highly phosphorylated, pRB does not bind to certain transcription factors, leaving them free to bind to their target genes and stimulate transcription. The products of the genes stimulated by these transcription factors cause the cell to advance beyond the G_1 stage of the cell cycle. Cyclins A and E bind to specific CDKs, and these complexes activate DNA synthesis, causing the cell to proceed through the S stage of the cell cycle. The cyclin A-CDK1 complex stimulates cyclin B to bind to CDK1, and this complex stimulates the cell to progress through the G_2 stage and into mitosis.

3. *(B)* Proto-oncogenes are nonmutant genes that function as positive regulators of the cell cycle. In cells that have stopped dividing, these genes are usually not transcribed. An oncogene is a mutant proto-oncogene that, because of the mutation, is no longer subject to its normal controls and is transcribed when it should not be. It stimulates progress through the cell cycle, and in so doing contributes to the development of cancer. Tumor suppressor genes are genes whose products inhibit progress through the cell cycle. Mutations in these genes may eliminate the products and allow cells to proceed through the cell cycle when they should not, thus contributing to the development of cancer.

4. *(B)* In this answer, we'll describe the gene products only, understanding that each is encoded by a gene. p21 is a protein that inhibits cyclin-CDK complexes throughout the cell cycle. p53 is a protein that regulates the production of p21. The production of p53 is stimulated when there is something amiss in the cell; p53 causes the cell cycle to halt until the problem can be corrected. It also stimulates the cell to undergo apoptosis (programmed cell death) if the problem cannot be corrected. The product of the *APC* gene is a protein that promotes cell adhesion. The loss of cell adhesion in mutant cells contributes to metastasis in cancerous tumors.

5. *(B)* Mutations in the regulatory region of a gene can eliminate binding of proteins that inhibit transcription. In the absence of such proteins bound to the regulatory region, the genes are transcribed at abnormally high levels. Also, translocations can bring a gene under the control of a different regulatory region that causes abnormally high transcription.

6. *(B)* The *TP53* gene encodes p53, a protein that stimulates production of p21, which inhibits the cyclin-CDK complexes at several stages of the cell cycle, thus halting progress through the cell cycle. The p53 protein also stimulates apoptosis, or programmed cell death. Cells that undergo mutations in proto-oncogenes often cannot develop into cancerous cells because p53 stimulates p21 production, which halts the cell cycle, and p53 may cause the cell to undergo apoptosis, killing the cell before it can become cancerous. Mutations in the *TP53* gene eliminate these functions and allow cells with mutations in proto-oncogenes to become cancerous.

7. *(C)* The functional protein is a tetramer. Single-nucleotide substitution mutations may eliminate the activity of a subunit, but they do not eliminate the subunit's ability to participate in tetramer formation. When at least one mutant subunit is present in a tetramer, the tetramer cannot function. Thus, most tetramers (15 out of 16) in a cell that is heterozygous for a substitution mutation cannot function.

8. *(B)* Cells have redundant mechanisms that prevent cell division. For cell division to proceed to such an extent that it causes malignancy requires the elimination of several mechanisms, which can only happen when there are mutations in several genes that regulate those mechanisms.

9. *(B)* For most cancers to develop, mutations in several genes are required. Rarely does an individual inherit all the mutations required to cause cancer. Instead, the mutations occur over a period of time in somatic cells. In those individuals who inherit one of the mutations, every cell is already beyond the first step toward cancer, so accumulation of the necessary mutations for the remaining steps is more likely than in cells of an individual who did not inherit the mutation.

10. *(B)* Apoptosis is the programmed death of a cell, usually stimulated by the p53 protein. Radiation and some chemotherapy regimes cause damage to dividing cells and stimulate apoptosis. Because the treatments target dividing cells, they preferentially affect cancerous cells.

11. *(B)* Radiation and compounds used in chemotherapy damage DNA. DNA damage is one of the factors that stimulates apoptosis. Even though these substances may cause mutation, they fight cancer by preferentially targeting cancerous cells and damaging their DNA to such an extent that they die.

12. *(B)* The cells treated with radiation undergo DNA damage, and the damage stimulates the production of p53, which halts cell division and stimulates cells to undergo apoptosis.

13. *(D)* **(a)** It is a tumor suppressor gene because its product inhibits progress through the cell cycle. **(b)** As a protein kinase, it probably phosphorylates p34^{cdc2}, which then halts the G_2 to M transition. **(c)** With the cell cycle halted, the cell may initiate apoptosis if damage due to radiation is sufficient.

14. *(D)* According to the book, pRB binds to certain transcription factors, one of which is E2F. E2F is a transcription factor that stimulates transcription of several genes whose products promote progress through the cell cycle. When pRB binds to E2F, it inhibits E2F's ability to stimulate transcription. The results of the research highlighted in this question suggest that the inhibitory effect of pRB binding may lie in pRB's ability to alter the DNA-bending properties of EF2. When DNA is not bent at the proper angle by the transcription factor, transcription may not be initiated. The increased binding affinity of E2F to DNA probably does not increase transcription but leaves E2F positioned to stimulate transcription when pRB is phosphorylated and releases itself.

15. *(C)* p53 has the ability to temporarily halt the cell cycle. Its role during spermatogenesis is probably regulation of the timing of cell division, slowing the rate of meiosis to allow for development of the cells during the various stages of spermatogenesis.

16. *(C)* It can be said that all cancers are genetic in origin because all cancers require mutations in certain sets of genes. Environmental factors may influence the mutation rates of those genes, thus influencing the likelihood of cancer.

17. *(C)* Cancer becomes more likely as a person grows older because somatic cells accumulate mutations over time. Countries that have low cancer rates are also countries with high population growth rates in which a high proportion of the population consists of people in their youth. These countries also have lower life expectancies because of malnutrition and infectious disease. Those who are most susceptible to cancer are the elderly. European countries have the highest proportions of elderly people in their populations, some of the highest life expectancies in the world, and low rates of death due to malnutrition and infectious disease.

18. *(C)* **(a)** Gardner syndrome shows the inheritance pattern of a single dominant allele. **(b)** Because the mutant allele is inherited in every cell, all organs are predisposed to cancer.

19. *(C)* **(a)** After phosphorylation, CdA is a deoxynucleotide; its base is a derivative of adenine. **(b)** The diagram below shows CdA in its monophosphate form:

(c) It is incorporated into DNA in place of adenine, where it becomes a lesion.

20. *(C)* Radiation damages cells and induces apoptosis. When radiation is directed at a tumor, the tumor's cells may undergo apoptosis and die. Some tumor cells lose their ability to undergo apoptosis, often because the mutations in them eliminate production of p53. Such cells may be resistant to the effects of radiation.

21. *(C)* Telomerase is essential to prevent erosion of telomeres in the chromosomes of dividing cells. The absence of telomerase limits the number of times a cell can divide because its chromosomes shorten each time they are replicated. Tumor cells must continue to divide in an unlimited fashion, a situation that requires telomerase. If telomerase could be inhibited in tumor cells, the number of cell divisions could be limited and tumor growth halted. The research highlighted in this question is significant because an understanding of the human telomerase gene and its product could lead scientists to develop a treatment that inhibits telomerase activity in tumor cells.

22. *(C)* Because TK1 levels are correlated with the development of breast cancer, higher-than-normal TK1 levels may indicate that a cancer is in its early stages. Measurement of serum TK1 levels may be a diagnostic tool to help physicians determine whether or not further tests for detection of cancer are warranted.

23. *(C)* The results of the research highlighted in this question indicate that TK1 levels may be used diagnostically to predict which patients are most likely to suffer recurrence of breast cancer. Such a diagnosis could assist physicians as they design treatment protocols for individual patients to prevent recurrence.

Chapter 25
Genes and Immunity

1. *(B)* **(a)** At the cellular level, each rearranged antibody gene encodes one polypeptide. **(b)** At the organismal level, one individual carries many different rearrangements of each antibody gene. Thus, a single gene rearranges into many genes to encode many different but related polypeptides.

2. *(B)* The humoral immune system produces antibodies that recognize antigens that are outside of the body's cells. By attaching an antibody to an antigen, it marks for destruction those particles (such as a virus) that display the antigen. The cell-mediated immune system, on the other hand, recognizes antigen–MHC complexes on the surface of a body cell that has been infected, and destroys the cell that displays these complexes.

3. *(B)* The humoral immune system fights viruses that are in capsular form outside of the cell. It does so by recognizing antigens that are on the surface of the virus particle. The cell-mediated immune system fights viruses that have infected a cell. It does so by complexing the viral antigens with MHC markers and displaying the antigen–MHC complex on the surface of the infected cell.

4. *(B)* Antibody rearrangements are not transmitted to offspring because the rearrangements occur in the cells of the immune system, which are somatic cells, rather than germ line cells.

5. *(B)* A pathogen may have several different antigens on its surface. One individual may produce an antibody that is specific for one of the antigens, whereas another individual may produce an antibody that is specific for a different antigen on the same pathogen.

6. *(C)* An enhancer within the intron of the k light-chain gene determines which promoter will be used. When the gene is rearranged, one of its promoters is connected to the intron via a joining segment, bringing the promoter in close proximity to the enhancer within the intron. Only the promoter that is closest to the enhancer within the intron is used for transcription, and this promoter is the one that is joined via the joining segment to the intron.

7. *(C)* **(a)** The intron carries an enhancer that activates transcription of the rearranged gene. **(b)** The role of the enhancer within the intron is to stimulate transcription of the rearranged gene. Enhancers function within DNA, not RNA. The intron is not removed from the DNA of the rearranged gene; it remains within the gene, where it continues to stimulate transcription. Once in the pre-mRNA, however, the intron fulfills no function and is removed as part of mRNA processing.

8. *(C)* During gene rearrangement, some nucleotide pairs may be deleted at the point where the DNA recombines. Any deletion that is not a multiple of three nucleotide pairs is a frameshift mutation and creates a nonproductive rearrangement. Precise recombination without a deletion, or a deletion of a multiple of three nucleotide pairs, retains the correct reading frame and creates a productive rearrangement. The process that allows deletions that can result in nonproductive rearrangements is advantageous because it provides more variability among productive rearrangements than would be present without it. Each B cell rearranges one or both copies of its antibody genes until it achieves a productive rearrangement in one of the genes, so nonproductive rearrangements are of no consequence.

9. *(B)* Your textbook describes three autoimmune diseases in detail on pages 733–734. We'll briefly review them here. In insulin-dependent juvenile onset diabetes, the immune system mistakenly destroys the insulin-producing cells of the pancreas. Eventually, the pancreas can no longer produce insulin, and the patient requires insulin treatments for life. In rheumatoid arthritis, the immune system produces an antibody called rheumatoid factor that binds to the body's own IgG antibodies to form a rheumatoid factor–IgG complex. The complex is deposited on membranes in the joints, where it stimulates the com-

plement system and macrophages to attack the membranes. In hyperthyroidism, an antibody called long-acting thyroid stimulator binds to the receptors on the thyroid gland that normally accept thyroid-stimulating hormone (TSH). The antibody mimics TSH and stimulates the thyroid gland to overproduce thyroid hormone.

10. (B) All genes of the immune system are potential candidates for alleles that confer susceptibility to autoimmune disorders. A particular arrangement of an immune system gene may cause an autoimmune disease. A mutation within that gene that makes this arrangement more likely will confer inherited susceptibility to the disease.

11. (C) A bispecific antibody is a genetically engineered antibody that recognizes two different antigens. Antibodies contain two arms, each with an antigen-binding site. In natural antibodies, the antigen-binding sites in the two arms are identical. In a bispecific antibody, each antigen-binding site recognizes a different antigen. As a potential treatment for cancer, bispecific antibodies may be able to deliver a toxin bound to one antigen-binding site to tumor cells that display an antigen recognized by the other antigen-binding site.

12. (C) A monoclonal antibody is a single antibody produced in cultured cells for medical or research purposes. To acquire a cell culture that produces a monoclonal antibody, researchers inject a mouse with an antigen, isolate B cells from the spleen, and fuse the isolated B cells with mouse myeloma cells to produce hybridomas. Each hybridoma can grow and divide into a culture of identical cells that produces a monoclonal antibody.

13. (C) Natural selection has favored those HLA alleles that recognize antigens from those pathogens that are found in the immediate environment. Because pathogens may differ throughout the world, natural selection probably favors different HLA alleles in different parts of the world.

14. (B) With an increase in the number of MHC molecules, more antigen-MHC complexes can be displayed on the surface of the infected cell, increasing the ability of the cell-mediated immune system to destroy the infected cell.

15. (C) The epitopes are breakdown products of the polypeptide encoded by the *gag* gene in HIV. By producing a product that cytotoxic T cells fail to recognize, the *gag* gene enables cells that are infected by HIV to escape destruction by the cell-mediated immune system.

16. (C) The procedure described in this question is used to produce monoclonal antibodies. Monoclonal antibodies have many current applications in research and medicine. They are used in clinical tests (such as pregnancy tests and tests for rheumatoid factor) to detect the presence of specific proteins in a patient. They are also used in laboratory procedures to detect specific proteins, as in Western blotting, described on page 285 of your textbook. Among the potential applications of monoclonal antibodies is delivery of anticancer drugs directly to tumor cells.

17. (C) The products of the genes interact with one another, but they do not interact until after gene rearrangement, transcription, and translation. Therefore, rearrangements of the two genes are independent even though the gene products interact.

18. (C) This observation does not demonstrate that the product of the *RAG2* gene does not catalyze antibody gene rearrangement. However, it does suggest that the product of the *RAG2* gene is not essential for antibody gene rearrangement. Were the *RAG2* gene's product required for antibody gene rearrangement, the B cells in which both copies of the *RAG2* gene had been deleted should not have rearranged their antibody genes.

19. (C) These observations suggest that the *RAG1* gene's product alone is sufficient to catalyze rearrange-

ment of antibody genes, but that its ability to rearrange antibody genes is greatly enhanced in the presence of the *RAG2* gene's product. These observations help explain the results cited in the previous question in that the role they imply for the *RAG2* gene's product is not to directly rearrange antibody genes but to enhance their rearrangement. In the absence of the *RAG2* gene, gene rearrangement should take place, but much less efficiently than in its presence.

20. *(D)* **(a)** These results suggest that the roles of *RAG1* and *RAG2* may extend beyond antibody rearrangement to include a role in the development of B and T cells. **(b)** The studies highlighted in questions 18 and 19 did not require development of the B and T cells in an organism, so the developmental roles of *RAG1* and *RAG2* were not tested in these studies.

21. *(D)* These results suggest that the proteins have dual roles as transcription factors and as topoisomerases. The topoisomerase activity directly catalyzes rearrangement, whereas the transcription factor activity probably stimulates transcription of genes that assist in rearrangement. Mutations in the topoisomerase region eliminate the ability of the proteins to directly rearrange antibody genes, whereas mutations in the transcription factor region eliminate transcription of genes that enhance the ability of the proteins to rearrange antibody genes.

22. *(D)* **(a)** The control group provides an estimate of the expected frequency of the epitope in the absence of rheumatoid arthritis, which is 0.46. If there is no association between the epitope and rheumatoid arthritis, the frequency should be the same in the group with rheumatoid arthritis. The expected number of individuals with rheumatoid arthritis who carry the epitope is 0.46(149) = 68.54, and the expected number of individuals with rheumatoid arthritis who do not carry the epitope is 0.54(149) = 80.46. The chi-square value is $[(124 - 68.54)^2 \div 68.54] + [(25 - 80.46)^2 \div 80.46] = 83.1040$, with 1 degree of freedom. We reject the hypothesis that there is no association between the epitope and rheumatoid arthritis. **(b)** Class II MHC genes encode proteins found on the surface of B cells, T cells, and macrophages. During the development of rheumatoid arthritis, macrophages attack the joint membranes. An epitope that enhances the ability of a macrophage to attack the joint membranes should increase the susceptibility to rheumatoid arthritis. **(c)** Any alteration that allows the antigen-binding site to more effectively bind with the antigen should increase susceptibility. **(d)** These results are more consistent with the multigene theory. If a single gene were exclusively responsible for susceptibility to rheumatoid arthritis, then we would expect all people with rheumatoid arthritis to carry the epitope that is associated with rheumatoid arthritis. This study indicates that rheumatoid arthritis is associated with the epitope, but that a significant proportion of people with rheumatoid arthritis do not have the epitope. This observation implies that there are other factors, probably including other genes, that are also associated with susceptibility to rheumatoid arthritis.

23. *(C)* MHC class I proteins bind to antigens produced by pathogens that enter a host cell and display the antigens on the surface of the cell to mark it for destruction. A high degree of diversity of these proteins permits recognition of a wide range of antigens. Because MHC genes are not rearranged as are antibody genes, the diversity of MHC class I proteins is dependent on the variation for MHC genes that an individual inherits, and that diversity is directly related to the degree of heterozygosity for MHC alleles.

24. *(C)* **(a)** The usual role of the intron is to carry the enhancer that stimulates transcription of the gene. **(b)** The observation that deletion of the intron enhancer reduces rearrangement suggests that at least some of the DNA within the intron facilitates rearrangement.

Chapter 26
Genetics in Medicine and Forensics

1. *(B)* (1) The gene contains introns that the bacterial cell cannot remove. (2) The gene does not have a bacterial promoter. (3) The gene does not have the appropriate recognition sequences for translation. (4) The cell has no mechanism for creating the A and B chains and connecting them correctly.

2. *(C)* We'll start with the biological considerations. The protein should not require substantial posttranslational modifications, because such modifications may not be possible in a bacterial cell or in a laboratory after the protein has been purified. It must be possible for a physician to deliver the engineered protein to the site where it functions. This consideration excludes most enzymes as candidates for genetic pharmacology because enzymes are usually produced in the cells where they function and cannot be delivered to the cells by oral administration or injection. Notice that those products produced in genetic pharmacology are usually products that circulate in the bloodstream, such as insulin, human growth hormone, and blood clotting factors VIII and IX. There are also economic considerations. If there is a reliable and inexpensive source of the protein other than genetic pharmacology, there is little reason to produce the protein through genetic pharmacology. There must also be a sufficiently high demand for the protein to justify private investment to produce the protein with genetic pharmacology.

3. *(B)* Proteins that require substantial posttranslational modification usually cannot be effectively produced using genetic pharmacology. Even though the engineered gene may encode the correct polypeptide, the polypeptide may not assume the correct tertiary or quaternary structure in a bacterial cell.

4. *(B)* Yes, clotting factors are excellent candidates for genetic pharmacology for the following reasons: they circulate in the blood and can be delivered to the site where they function by injection, there is a high market demand for these proteins, and alternative sources of these proteins are not highly reliable. In fact, genetically engineered clotting factors VIII and IX are now produced through genetic pharmacology and are available commercially.

5. *(C)* There is a clear-cut case for PKU testing. PKU causes severe mental retardation if left untreated, but dietary treatment that begins during infancy prevents this mental retardation. The test for PKU is inexpensive and is administered routinely to virtually all newborns in the United States and many other countries. The test for sickle-cell trait is also inexpensive and could be administered to all newborns at a relatively low cost. The justification for such a test is the association of sickle-cell trait with increased susceptibility to streptococcal infection before 3 years of age. Children who are identified as having sickle-cell trait could then be monitored more closely than others for infection. However, because the allele that causes sickle-cell trait is more frequent among people of certain ethnic groups, the test has been used in ways that raised concerns about ethnic discrimination. Because the test does not clearly identify a treatable disease (only increased susceptibility to a disease), and because it has been used in a discriminatory way in the past, there is no mandatory screening for sickle-cell trait.

6. *(C)* (1) The insulin chains are so small that bacterial enzymes would destroy them, so they had to be attached to a larger polypeptide to allow them to precipitate into inclusion bodies. (2) The insulin chains are attached to the β-gal fragment with a methionine bridge because insulin does not contain methionine and CNBr cleaves polypeptide chains on the carboxyl end of methionine. This design allows scientists to remove the intact insulin chains from the β-gal fragments. (3) Insulin cDNA encodes preproinsulin, rather than the mature insulin chains. The cDNA requires some genetic engineering to eliminate the codons that encode the *pre-* and *pro-* amino acids, which are used in the two-chain method for production of recombinant human insulin. In the one-chain method, the codons that encode the *pre-* amino acids must be removed.

7. *(C)* For a product of genetic pharmacology to have an effect, it must be delivered to the site where it

normally functions. In this case, ADA is an enzyme that functions in bone marrow cells. It is normally produced in the same cells where it functions. The enzyme does not circulate in the blood, nor does it function in the digestive system. Consequently, physicians cannot deliver the enzyme to each cell in the bone marrow through oral administration or injection. There is no practical way to deliver the functional enzyme to the cells without introducing a functional gene into those cells.

8. *(C)* Protein processing in bacterial cells differs from that in human cells, so human genes cloned into bacterial cells do not always produce proteins with the same conformation as the corresponding genes in a human cell. A virus, however, relies on its host cell to transcribe and translate its genes. All of the genes in a virus that infects a human cell are transcribed and translated by that cell. Therefore, the protein products of any human genes within the virus should assume the proper conformation because they are produced within a human cell.

9. *(B)* Blood typing permits only exclusion of individuals. It cannot be used to positively identify an individual because there are a limited number of blood types, and the probability of two people chosen at random having the same blood type is relatively high. DNA fingerprints, on the other hand, are highly variable, with a vast array of phenotypes. DNA fingerprints are so variable that the probability of two people (other than identical twins) sharing the same DNA fingerprint is negligible. Thus, DNA fingerprinting can be used to identify as well as exclude individuals.

10. *(C)* The first test to conduct is an examination of the child's karyotype. The karyotype will distinguish between Down syndrome caused by trisomy 21 and Down syndrome caused by a 14q;21q translocation. If the child has translocation Down syndrome, the parents can be tested with karyotyping to determine which parent carries the translocation.

11. *(C)* About 70% of heterozygous carriers of a mutant *CF* allele carry the *CF*DF508* allele. A single test can detect this allele. The other 30% carry many different mutant alleles, which require other tests to identify them.

12. *(D)* **(a)** PCR amplification detects trinucleotide expansion mutations in the *FMR1* gene because the amplified fragments that contain the expansion mutation are much larger than the amplified fragments from a nonmutant gene. A methylation test determines the degree of methylation. Alleles that contain an expansion mutation are usually overmethylated and the gene is not transcribed. The karyotype detects the fragile site in the chromosome. **(b)** All three of these tests detect expansion mutations. None of the tests detect single-nucleotide substitution mutations.

13. *(C)* The human genome project includes determining the consensus sequence for the human genome, high-resolution mapping of human chromosomes using RFLPs and PCR-based DNA markers, cDNA cloning and sequencing, cloning large fragments of DNA in cosmids and YACs, and mapping and sequencing DNA genomes in model organisms for comparison with human gene positions and sequences.

14. *(C)* The human genome sequence must be defined as a consensus sequence that represents the most frequent sequence observed in the sequences obtained to date. The consensus sequence may change as more alleles are sequenced.

15. *(C)* Many of the highly repetitive sequences are spaced at known intervals from one another within a particular region. Overlapping regions in cloned fragments can be identified when some of the repeated sequences in each clone are spaced at the same intervals (see Figure 26.1, on page 745 in your textbook).

16. *(C)* Sequence tagged sites (STSs) are short DNA segments (200–500 nucleotide pairs) whose sequences and chromosomal locations are known. Researchers use STSs to identify overlapping clones and to assign cloned DNA to a particular chromosomal region.

17. *(D)* This problem illustrates the advantages of conducting genetic pharmacology in eukaryotic cells. The results highlighted in this problem indicate that the processing of the HBsAg protein in yeast cells is probably identical to the processing of that protein in human cells. Because the protein produced in yeast is apparently identical to the protein produced in human cells, it is no surprise that its antigenic properties are also identical.

18. *(C)* Infants who are diagnosed with PKU can be successfully treated to prevent mental retardation if the treatment is initiated in infancy. There is no medical treatment for fragile X syndrome, so early diagnosis has no effect in preventing the onset of symptoms. Also, the PKU test is inexpensive and easy to administer, whereas fragile X testing is expensive.

19. *(D)* Vectors may be chosen or redesigned so that they are capable of infecting columnar cells and are less likely to induce apoptosis of infected cells.

20. *(B)* **(a)** Thyroid hormone is an amino acid. **(b)** No, it is not advisable to attempt construction of genetically engineered bacteria to produce thyroid hormone, for two reasons. First, the best candidates for genetic pharmacology are proteins, because proteins are the direct products of genes. Thyroid hormone is not a protein but is the product of a biochemical pathway that requires several enzymes encoded by several genes. The probability of successfully introducing and expressing all of the genes required for thyroid hormone production in bacteria is quite low. Second, there is no practical reason to consider genetic pharmacology because an effective and inexpensive synthetic substitute for thyroid hormone is already available.

21. *(C)* A method such as this can be used to detect different mutant alleles of the same gene without knowing beforehand what the mutations are. It is not restricted to detection of a single mutant allele, as are some genetic tests.

22. *(D)* The IgG-binding domains provide a way to recover and purify the ZZ-proinsulin. The trypsin cleavage sites provide a way to acquire both insulin and the C peptide from the purified ZZ-proinsulin.

Chapter 27
Genetics in Agriculture and Industry

1. *(B)* Genetic erosion is most serious when modern varieties are adopted by farmers who are located in the centers of diversity for major agricultural species. The modern varieties displace the genetically diverse varieties, and unless the diverse varieties are collected and maintained, the genetic diversity they carry will be lost forever. For most agricultural species, the centers of diversity are outside the United States, as illustrated in Figure 27.2, on page 765 of your textbook. In the 1950s, modern varieties were not used in the centers of diversity to the extent that they are now.

2. *(B)* The portion of the genome that was uniform was the mitochondrial genome. It was uniform because of the widespread use of cytoplasmic-nuclear male sterility to produce hybrid maize seed. A single mitochondrial genotype was used to confer male sterility, so all mitochondrial genomes in the male-sterile female parents used to produce hybrid seed were identical. The mitochondrial genomes in the male parents were diverse, but because the mitochondrial genome in maize is inherited in a uni-parental-maternal fashion, all hybrid progeny inherited the same mitochondrial genome. The same allele that causes male sterility also confers susceptibility to southern corn leaf blight, so all plants that had a male-sterile parent were uniformly susceptible to the disease. This is an example of genetic erosion, because a single mitochondrial genotype that confers a desirable trait (male sterility) was incorporated into the vast majority of plants grown. This genotype displaced the other mitochondrial genotypes in the varieties that had previously been used.

3. *(B)* Farmers' fields in centers of diversity occupy a wide range of environments. To form gene banks, scientists collect seeds and animals from these diverse environments and bring them together into centralized facilities. The collected plants and animals are maintained and reproduce in a uniform environment where some genotypes may be better adapted than others. Unintended selection caused by the uniform maintenance conditions eliminates some alleles and genotypes, causing a loss of genetic diversity in the gene banks over time.

4. *(B)* The genetically diverse varieties and breeds have not been developed for use in modern agriculture. When used as parents in a breeding program, they introduce many characteristics that are disadvantageous in modern agricultural production.

5. *(C)* Alfalfa is highly sensitive to inbreeding depression, so it is not possible to develop inbred lines to use as parents to produce F_1 hybrid varieties. Also, alfalfa is sometimes grown in pastures where genetic diversity is desirable. A synthetic variety is the best choice under these conditions. Maize is sensitive to inbreeding depression, but its sensitivity is not sufficiently great to preclude the creation and maintenance of fully homozygous inbred lines, which can be used as parents to produce F_1 hybrid varieties. Maize is usually grown in cultivated fields where uniformity within each field is advantageous. An F_1 hybrid variety is the best choice under these conditions.

6. *(B)* The purpose of self-pollination in a maize-breeding program is to create inbred lines for use as parents in F_1 hybrid seed production.

7. *(C)* The advantage that the bulk method has over the single-seed descent method is the requirement of less labor. In a large plant-breeding program, there may be hundreds of thousands of plants in the F_2–F_5 generations. The single-seed descent method requires workers to manually harvest one seed per plant from these plants, a procedure that can be very time-consuming. With the bulk method, the seed from the plants can be harvested mechanically and a random sample of the seed saved for the next generation. The disadvantage of the bulk method when compared to the single-seed descent method is the lack of systematic sampling. Because each F_2 plant is represented equally in subsequent generations in

the single-seed descent method, a higher degree of diversity is maintained into the later generations than with the bulk method.

8. *(C)* **(a)** DNA marker alleles that are closely coupled to desirable alleles are present in one bulked sample and are usually absent from the other sample. Markers at unlinked marker loci are randomly distributed between the bulked samples and thus usually appear in both samples. **(b)** Rather than inoculate a plant with a pathogen to determine whether it is resistant or susceptible to the pathogen, breeders can indirectly identify those plants that carry a disease resistance allele by testing for a coupled DNA marker.

9. *(C)* Maize displays a high degree of heterosis and is usually sold as F_1 hybrid varieties. Breeders select inbred lines that when hybridized produce highly productive F_1 progeny. Because the progeny, rather than the parents, are sold for commercial production, the breeder is most interested in the performance of a selected plant's progeny.

10. *(C)* Production of F_1 hybrid varieties requires selection of two inbred parents. In some cases, the plant breeder chooses as one of the parents an inbred line that has already been proven in hybrid seed production, and tries to develop a new inbred line whose progeny will perform well when hybridized with the proven inbred line. Topcrossing identifies those plants that are the best candidates for the breeder to use in developing the new inbred lines.

11. *(C)* The purpose of reciprocal recurrent selection is to simultaneously develop both parental inbred lines, one from each population, that when hybridized will produce a superior F_1 hybrid variety.

12. *(D)* To achieve nearly complete homozygosity, which is required in a pure-line variety, breeders must self-pollinate plants until the F_5–F_6 generation. The procedure described in this question achieves complete homozygosity in a single generation, cutting several years from the 10–12 years usually required to develop a pure-line variety.

13. *(D)* When genetically engineering *A. tumefaciens* for use in plant breeding, scientists replace the genes in the Ti plasmid that govern crown gall development with the genes that they wish to introduce into the plant. In the absence of the genes that govern crown gall development, the infected cells cannot develop into crown galls.

14. *(C)* Most plant-breeding methods use some form of hybridization followed by self fertilization, selection, and multiplication of a uniform variety. Most animal-breeding methods rely on controlled matings of selected parents in each generation. The differences between breeding methods for plants and animals are due largely to the reproductive differences between plants and animals. Domestic animals cannot self-fertilize as can most agricultural plant species, and the generation times are generally longer in animals than in plants.

15. *(C)* **(a)** General combining ability is the ability of one parent to produce progeny that perform well regardless of which individual is the other parent. Specific combining ability is the ability of two specific parents to produce progeny that perform well. **(b)** In the past, the exploitation of specific combining ability was limited by the ability of two parents to produce only a relatively small number of offspring during their lifetimes using natural reproduction. However, reproductive technologies now allow animal breeders to substantially increase the number of genetic offspring that two parental animals can produce. Such technologies include in vitro fertilization, embryo splitting, and implantation of embryos in surrogate mothers; they may eventually include cloning of proven genotypes.

16. *(D)* **(a)** The agar rectified the damage to the zona pellucida, allowing the embryos to develop. **(b)** The two cells derived from the original embryo develop into identical twins. In this way, scientists can

increase the number of genetically desirable offspring from a single cross.

17. *(C)* The purpose of genetic development of plants used in reclamation is to establish populations of plants that will continue to reproduce naturally for many generations. There are many more environmental variables in disturbed natural lands than in agricultural farmland. A population of plants has the best chance of establishing itself if the plants in the population are highly variable. Under these circumstances, natural selection has a wide range of genotypes from which to select those individuals that will best survive and reproduce on the disturbed land.

18. *(C)* Phosphate is a common pollutant in domestic and industrial wastewater and agricultural runoff. It causes eutrophication of lakes, rivers, and streams. Bacteria that efficiently remove phosphate from water can be used in wastewater treatment to reduce the levels of this water pollutant.

19. *(B)* Animals and plants are eukaryotes, so their cells that carry a genetically engineered human gene are very likely to produce proteins that are identical in structure and function to the natural proteins produced in human cells. Bacteria are prokaryotes and are less likely to produce the same protein when genetically engineered as are human cells. Also, agricultural plants and animals are much less expensive to raise than bacteria, when considered on the basis of weight. They can potentially produce genetically engineered proteins at a much lower cost than bacteria.

20. *(B)* Agricultural biotechnology usually focuses on the improvement of single traits under laboratory conditions, whereas breeding focuses on the simultaneous improvement of all traits under field conditions. The direct products of biotechnology usually must undergo field-testing and further improvement through breeding before they are ready for commercial use.

Chapter 28
Legal and Ethical Issues in Genetics

1. *(B)* **(a)** Testing for sickle-cell trait has a tainted history involving racial discrimination. Testing for G6PD deficiency has the potential for racial and gender discrimination because of the chromosomal location of the gene (the X chromosome) and a higher frequency of mutant alleles in certain ethnic groups. The results of testing for sickle-cell trait and G6PD deficiency could potentially be used in hiring decisions if the results of the test are required for employment or are not held in confidentiality. The results of prenatal testing for Down syndrome and Tay-Sachs disease are used primarily to assist potential parents in decisions about elective abortions, a use that raises concerns among some people who are opposed to abortion. **(b)** PKU testing is mandatory for all newborns throughout much of the world and is not focused on particular ethnic groups. It detects a genetic disorder that can be effectively prevented if detected and treated early in life, and thus provides highly beneficial information to those who have the disorder. The results of the test are typically not used to discriminate for employment or health insurance, so it poses little financial or social risk.

2. *(B)* The test poses virtually no health threat to the infant, so there is no need to inform parents about the risk of an infant taking the test. Informed consent is only an issue when the test indicates that the infant may have PKU. At that point the parents are fully informed about the nature of subsequent tests that will determine whether or not the infant actually has PKU.

3. *(B)* The genotypes of pure-line and clonal plant varieties can be maintained from one generation to the next indefinitely. The patent is intended to protect the genotype. The genotype of an animal cannot be reproduced (except by cloning, which has not been developed for commercial use). Therefore, a patent on an animal's genotype has no practical purpose.

4. *(B)* Genetically engineered genes that animals carry, a cloned or sequenced gene from an animal, an inbred strain in certain species of animals (such as laboratory mice), novel genetic traits developed in animals, and techniques used in genetic improvement of animals can all be patented.

5. *(B)* Current practices that implement some form of selection in humans are usually followed for personal reasons rather than to improve humanity as a whole. The purpose of eugenics was the purported widespread improvement of humanity.

6. *(C)* Intellectual property right protection promotes progress in research by encouraging private investment in scientific research. It inhibits scientific research by inhibiting scientists' free access to patented research materials and methods.

7. *(B)* The large body of research currently available on recombinant DNA has revealed that many of the safety concerns of the past are not as serious as they were thought to be when less information was available. Also, uniform safety guidelines based on abundant research are now in place for the use of recombinant DNA in the laboratory and in the field.

8. *(C)* All individuals who consent to provide DNA must be informed of and consent to all intended uses of that DNA. Researchers who have access to the DNA must use it only for the uses to which the donors have consented. To use the DNA for any other purpose than those to which the donors have consented is prohibited unless the donors have provided their additional informed consent.

9. *(B)* This implies that regardless of what new opportunities arise, DNA can only be used for the purposes to which the donor has consented after being fully informed.

10. *(B)* Most human genetic disorders are caused by recessive alleles that are present at relatively low

frequencies. Mandatory sterilization of homozygotes has a negligible effect on reducing the frequency of these alleles. Most recessive alleles that are present at low frequencies in a population are in heterozygotes and are not expressed phenotypically. The probability of a mating between two heterozygotes in the population as a whole is low. However, the probability of a mating between two heterozygotes among close relatives is much higher. Therefore, laws that prohibit marriages between close relatives have a much greater effect on reducing the phenotypic frequency of recessive genetic disorders than do mandatory sterilization laws.

11. *(B)* From a genetic standpoint, there is little justification for such advice. Selection against a recessive allele is very ineffective in reducing the allele frequency, so following such advice has virtually no effect on the human population as a whole. A person who has any genetic disorder should be fully informed about the disorder and its inheritance from a certified genetic counselor and receive genetic testing if desired from a certified laboratory to help him or her make informed decisions about personal reproduction. In the absence of any inbreeding, the probability that a person with a rare autosomal recessive genetic disorder will have children with that disorder is very low.

12. *(C)* Individual choices about reproduction have virtually no effect on the human population as a whole, regardless of whether the allele in question is autosomal or X-linked. The probability of children having an X-linked disorder depends on whether the parent with the disorder is male or female. A certified genetic counselor can assist a patient who has an X-linked genetic disorder in making informed decisions about personal reproduction.

13. *(C)* **(a)** Genetic testing would probably increase. One reason that people may elect to not undergo a genetic test is the fear that an insurance company might raise their premiums or deny them coverage if a genetic test reveals possible susceptibility to a genetic disorder or cancer. If the guidelines are implemented, such fears should be alleviated. **(b)** A genetic predisposition for a particular disease would have no effect on insurance availability, coverage, or premiums. **(c)** Costs to the insurance industry would probably increase because insurance companies could not exclude coverage for people whose medical care could potentially be expensive.

14. *(C)* Certain genetic disorders, such as sickle-cell anemia, cystic fibrosis, or G6PD deficiency, are more frequent in particular ethnic groups when compared to others. X-linked recessive genetic disorders are more frequent among males than females. Discrimination on the basis of a genetic disorder indirectly discriminates against the group in which that disorder is more common.

15. *(B)* Public opinion can have a profound influence on the development of public policy. In the absence of appropriate education, misinformation can generate unfounded fears and lead to misguided policy. Also, people who could benefit from advances in genetics may choose to reject opportunities to benefit because they do not understand what the benefits are.

16. *(C)* Possible faulty technique and potential inaccuracy of statistical assumptions have been used to challenge DNA fingerprinting as valid evidence in court. The use of rigorous controls in DNA fingerprinting laboratories and the accumulation of large databases on DNA marker frequencies have overcome most objections to the validity of DNA fingerprinting. DNA fingerprinting is now well established as a reliable form of evidence in court.

17. *(B)* The first consideration is the value of the information to our understanding of human biology. The human genome is the most basic aspect of human biology. The completion of the human genome project will assist research in all areas of human biology. Among the most important considerations is the value of the human genome project to medicine. As part of the human genome project, researchers have identified and characterized many genes that are related to human health. An understanding of the genetic basis of human disorders and diseases is a first step toward developing appropriate preventative and therapeutic treatments. The human genome project also has benefited genetic research on organisms

other than humans. The development of new methods, such as automated DNA sequencing, is a natural outcome of the human genome project. These methods are being applied in all areas of genetic research.

18. *(B)* As the cost of research increases, governmental, university, and other nonprofit research organizations have recognized the products of research as a potential source of funding. Protection of intellectual property rights is a way to secure such funding.